MAN'S BOOK

MARK OF THE LION
The Story of Capt. Charles Upham, V.C. and Bar

Kenneth Sandford

★

THE GAUNT WOMAN

John Blackburn

★

RELIGION
AND DAVEY PEACH

Robert Holles

ODHAMS PRESS LIMITED

LONG ACRE, LONDON

S.763.RA.L.

MADE AND PRINTED IN GREAT BRITAIN BY ODHAMS (WATFORD) LTD. WATFORD, HERTS.

CONTENTS

Note

Illustrations to "Mark of the Lion" are, unless otherwise stated, from the collection in the New Zealand Government Department of Internal Affairs (War Histories Branch), to whom acknowledgment is gratefully made.

MARK OF THE LION

Kenneth Sandford

"Mark of the Lion" is published by
Hutchinson & Co. Ltd.

The Author

Kenneth Sandford lives in Hamilton, New Zealand. During World War II he was a volunteer in the New Zealand Forces overseas, serving for several years in the Pacific, where he fought against the Japanese in the Solomons, and reached the rank of Captain. In 1955, Hutchinson published his first novel, *Dead Reckoning*, which ran through a number of impressions and was widely serialized. This was followed by another thriller, *Dead Secret*, in 1957.

Mark of the Lion took over five years in preparation, the author devoting his holidays and week-ends to the gathering of the material.

MARK OF THE LION

FOR centuries the Lion has held a double place in British tradition:

★ As a hall-mark of quality, an emblem that sets a standard, against which all else may be measured. So, an Act of Parliament in 1739 provided:

> "*The Standards* (for gold and silver) *are both for the Honour and Riches of the Realm; and such shall be marked . . . with the MARK OF THE LION.*"

★ As a symbol of nobility and strength, as in the words of the Royal Warrant of 29th January 1856 instituting the Victoria Cross:

> "*. . . The Cross shall only be awarded to those officers or men who served us in the presence of the enemy, and shall have performed some signal act of valour or devotion to their country. . . . A bronze cross . . . in its centre a Royal Crown, surmounted by a LION.*"

or in the simple design of the War Medal 1939-45, awarded to all who served in the Armed Forces for twenty-eight days, the official description reading "*. . . a LION standing triumphant. . . .*"

MAB/25—A*

INTRODUCTION

CHARLES HAZLITT UPHAM, the New Zealand infantry officer who during World War II won the V.C. twice, is a man noted for his extreme modesty. It was only the intervention of his former Commanding Officer, the late Major-General Sir Howard Kippenberger, K.B.E., C.B., D.S.O. and bar, E.D., that finally extracted from Upham a reluctant consent to this biography being written.

But Charles Upham is not given to talking of his own experiences, so most of the events in this book have come from the eye-witness accounts and reminiscences of a host of independent observers, friends, and war-time comrades. They range from generals to batmen, scattered as far afield as South Africa, England, Australia, New Zealand, even Trinidad. To them, who in scores of interviews and hundreds of letters have supplied the bulk of the biographical material, I express my gratitude, and particularly to those who have critically reviewed chapters within their own intimate knowledge.

Many an incident in this story has had to be checked and re-checked a dozen times. So if some of my informants now find that the printed version differs from the way they related it, may they be consoled in the knowledge that the weight of evidence and the facts of history have had to prevail. But often truth itself has clearly emerged in a stranger and more dramatic form than many first believed.

To Charles himself and his wife Molly, my thanks for their kindness and hospitality. In many pleasant hours I have spent around his fireside Charles has revealed (perhaps unconsciously at times) some of the thoughts and feelings that accompanied the deeds of which he is so disinclined to speak. But in the end he has been kind enough to read the manuscript and to point out some errors of fact that escaped an otherwise exhaustive checking. And after much prompting, and with his characteristic reticence, he has supplied the true version of what had been little more than legend concerning several episodes in his war-time career: notably the grisly death-cellar at Mersa Matruh; his escape attempts from Weinsberg prison camp, and his twelve hours of hard-won freedom en route to Colditz Castle.

I acknowledge very gratefully the help of the editors-in-chief of the official New Zealand War Histories; first the late Sir Howard Kippenberger, and then his successor Brigadier M. C. Fairbrother, C.B.E., D.S.O., E.D. They have kindly given me permission to quote some passages from the Official Histories and to reprint certain photos.

Any war biography inevitably creates the impression that every battle was fought by only one man or by only one unit. But there is simply not room to tell of the others. Charles Upham hopes, however, that this book can be read, not as a tribute to him, but to all those others—the men with whom he served.

I would be more than pleased if the story can be read that way, if there can emerge an appreciation of the qualities of the ordinary New Zealand soldier, to be read alongside the exploits of this remarkable man.

K.S.

CHAPTER ONE

ADVANCE COPY

He flings himself over ... gropes to his feet, staggers to the bank at the side of the road, climbs up it ... then seems to pause a moment on the summit of the ridge. He has chosen the very spot, the very instant. And now he throws himself forward, loses his footing, goes sprawling, rolling over and over down the slope. His withered arm gives him an awful twinge. Near the foot of the embankment he scrambles to his feet, sets off running towards the trees....

He seems to have gone only a few yards before the bullets come. The S.S. men, well-trained marksmen, are into action in seconds. Leaping from their truck, they line the top of the bank, have a clear view of him as he races across the fields below.

With sub-machine-guns and rifles the fusillade starts, fire pouring towards the hapless man as he sprints desperately for cover.

And the word spreads from truck to truck, like a silent, sympathetic flame: *"It's Charlie Upham...."*

He had a rifle again. But with his arm in a sling it was a heavy, almost useless, weapon for a one-armed man. In the fork of the tree, though ...

Two of them to get. Only one hand to hold the rifle, to pull the trigger, then work the bolt after the first shot and bring the second round into the chamber. Would he have time for the second shot?

They came closer ... carefully ... for they could see the clearing ahead, and they were looking for his body in the grass.

He lay dead still, hardly breathing the barrel of his rifle resting snugly in the fork of the branches. Close enough ...

He squeezed the trigger. The crack of the gun seemed to shout back from the trees. He saw his man pitch forward.

Like lightning he shifted his one good hand to the bolt ... a moment's fumbling would be fatal ... seized it, drew it back, pushed it home again ... with the other man looming over him.

When he fired the second shot the man's body fell against the muzzle of his rifle ... close enough.

And now he is at the main wire. He seizes the strands, begins climbing steadily. It is easy. In no time he is at the top.

All around there are dozens now watching. Others are catching sight of him for the first time and are staring in amazement. A wire-break in broad daylight! What maniac is trying that!

Some who recognize his small wiry figure call out softly to those near: *"It's Charlie Upham,"* and there are some who remember those same words, passed from mouth to mouth, when he ran from the trucks alongside the river. There is a sudden aching sympathy for a man who will dare such fearful odds. They wait for the volley of fire any moment, wait to see his body crumple up and fall from the wire to the ground, like a sack of old clothes.

But those who wait for that haven't counted the guards today.

It is a long dash down the hillside. There can be no reconnaissance, no flanking movement. It has to be an assault into the very muzzle of the guns, straight down the lines of tracer, straight towards the German armour.

And as Upham runs, and he sees his boys all running with him, unhesitating and unflinching, a deep, savage pride possesses him. What men they are! But they are not thinking of themselves. They are looking at the fury ahead, and they are watching Upham as he races out in front of them, and they are saying . . .

". . . Australia? Well, if you're going all that way, you'd better take your own cutlery . . . and take a bath-tub, too." Johnny Upham did so.

It was about the beginning of the century when the vastness of Australia summoned him. After studying medicine at Edinburgh, then serving as a book-keeper to a tea firm in London, young Johnny Upham told his parents that he was off "down under".

He turned up on a sugar plantation in Queensland at a time when the Boer War was the talk of the Empire. He met a friend on the plantations, and in no time found himself in the swing of the independent, rugged life of the pioneers. His friend was deep in a political intrigue with quite amazing objectives. The principal scheme was for the northern half of Queensland to sever itself from the rest of the state, secede from the Commonwealth, and declare itself an independent, sovereign nation under a newly constituted monarchy.

Upham's good friend was to be no other than the King of this new domain; and lo! in tribute to his advanced education,

Johnny Upham was named as the proposed Prime Minister!

Startled by these crackpot ideas, Upham extricated himself from his friend's ambitious clutches and made his way back to London, and then promptly decided that this blow to his self-esteem would best be solved by making another sea voyage, this time to New Zealand, where he would visit his brother in Lyttelton, near Christchurch. From Christchurch Johnny Upham never returned to his homeland. There he studied law, married, and lived his days as a prominent barrister and solicitor. His wife was the daughter of a widely respected clergyman in the district. The Uphams had four children—three daughters and a son. They were all born and bred in a comfortable two-storeyed home in Gloucester Street, Christchurch; reared in the English manner, with a nurse, a housemaid, and a gardener making up a satisfactory domestic establishment. For such a family, the future might well have appeared safe, assured, and comfortable. Their son, Charles Hazlitt Upham, was born on 21st September 1908. He grew up a quiet, rather shy little boy, very gentlemanly and courteous. But from the very start there was something about him. As a child it was obstinacy: as he grew older it was called perseverance. In the light of history it was at all times nothing less than rigid single-mindedness.

He didn't like fish as a boy. Requiring him to eat it one day, Miss Turtill took him for his daily walk in the park some two hours after the fish luncheon, wondering why he remained so silent. She questioned him about it, receiving only grunted replies. At last he suddenly smiled and said: "It's gone," and triumphantly explained to her that he couldn't be bothered holding the fish in his mouth any longer. Nanny had once or twice held a fish-bone in her mouth for a few minutes, so as to observe common decencies, but it startled her to think of a mouthful of fish being obstinately held for over two hours.

He was not a strong child physically, and his parents' concern over his health was accentuated when he developed a pronounced limp, which lasted several months. The doctor's report that one leg was shorter than the other caused them to wonder if some feverish attack had really cloaked a mild bout of polio—then known as "infantile paralysis".

When Charles was nine he was sent to Waihi, a boys' preparatory boarding school near Timaru. "Puggie" was the nickname he earned at Waihi, sometimes shortened to "Pug". There was no suggestion of his being a bully—that was the very opposite of his character—but his face was cast in an aggressive line for a boy of his age, and he was already displaying a spirit of mild belligerence towards things he did not believe in.

He accepted authority only if he could be shown that it was right. At prep time this characteristic often appeared. Advancing to the master in charge, Charles would stand alongside the table and ask a question. The answer would be given. Charles would shake his head (either in genuine or simulated ignorance) and say: "But I don't understand why it should be, sir." Another explanation, a very clear one, would follow, and then: "Now go back to your seat, Upham."

Shaking his head, Upham would retreat a yard, declaring that he still did not understand. Shorter, more pithy, explanations would be flung at him. He would retreat further: and then a step-by-step argument would finally see him driven back to his seat, still muttering vaguely about the injustice of it and how the book must be wrong.

Peace would reign for five minutes, then out of the silence the voice of Upham would be raised: "But, sir, you told us yesterday . . ."

The rest of prep would see the master becoming shorter and shorter of temper, and young Upham becoming more and more deliberately obtuse. The trouble was that he would have developed a theory of his own from which he was not prepared to depart, no matter what the master or the books said. To the delight of his form-mates, this kind of running war occupied many an evening's prep.

Charles Upham was more liberally whacked than many of the others at Waihi. He could be quite exasperating, with his constant inquests into the rightness of the conclusions reached by the writers of the school-books. "A Boy-Proof watch, is it?" he said enquiringly, as a relative generously presented him with a pocket watch for his eleventh birthday. He offered the appropriate thanks, being well trained in the drill of acknowledging presents from relatives.

But immediately they were gone he stole upstairs. "Boy-Proof", eh? That's what it said on the face of the watch. But he would have to see to that for himself, make his own tests. Leaning out over the balcony, he cast the watch out into the air, watched it crash on the gravel drive beneath. As he picked up the shattered remains, he nodded wisely, saying to his friends: "That shows it wasn't boy-proof."

From 1923 to 1927 Charles Upham was a boarder at Christ's

College, Christchurch, one of the oldest of New Zealand's colleges.

Although he won prizes he was not regarded as a scholar of any note. His successes were those of the determined plodder and his intellectual attainments suggested that his place in life would not likely to be found amongst the professions, but in the more practical sciences. That was just as well, for he had already set his heart on being a farmer.

His deeper feelings seemed to be reserved for occasions when he saw injustice being done, when the weak were oppressed by the strong. Schoolboys rarely show their emotions, but it was kindness that Charles showed more than anything else. He inherited that from both his mother and father. His resolution came from them, too.

When, as a mere new boy at Christ's, he intervened between three louts who were teasing a little fat boy, shouting at them: "Leave him alone, you pigs!" he drove them back, not with the threat of his fists—for they would have availed him nothing—but with a passion that flowed from his icy-blue eyes. It was something that indicated a force of personality lying deep within him. They desisted, worried and frightened by the look that blazed from him.

That characteristic—the hatred of wrong—appeared only briefly during his early years. But as he grew to manhood the intensity of that quality set him out from his fellow-men.

Mr. Upham was a disappointed man when his only son elected not to study law and join his father's practice. But Charles said: "I'd always be jealous of my friends on farms." So Mr. Upham did the next best thing. He enrolled Charles at Canterbury Agricultural College ("Lincoln College"), where the practical and theoretical sciences of farming are taught at university level.

Going from Christ's to Lincoln in 1928, Charles rapidly found himself enthralled with the work. He plunged into the farm and study courses with an enthusiasm that convinced his parents that, after all, it was the right choice. For two years he was first in agriculture, and gained firsts also in veterinary science and economics.

Life at Lincoln brought out more of the lightness of his character, and when some years later he returned there for a further course, he was famous as a raconteur. The atmosphere of the land, and the men who worked it, appealed to him more than the stricter channels of civilian life. He was more gregarious, less the serious lone ranger.

But he was already displaying a kind of ruggedness, both of

speech and mind, that seemed at variance with his educated and respectable upbringing. He was already a critic of sham. Flash clothes were sham.

The College Principal met him on the path to the dining-hall one morning and stopped, looking mildly surprised.

"Good morning, sir," Upham said politely.

"Good morning, Upham. By the way, got a match?"

"Yes, sir . . . here."

"Then put a match to those clothes you're wearing!"

And in language he was developing a free vocabulary suitable to most occasions, like the day he and John Sandall were returning to Lincoln on a motor-bike. As they passed a stationary bus an old man suddenly stepped out into the road, right into their path. They crashed into him violently, all three went flying over the road, the bike careering to a stop on the far side. Upham and Sandall picked themselves up, found they were intact, and shook the gravel from their clothes.

"Now where's that silly old bastard?" Upham asked.

They found him lying hunched up on the roadway, dead still, his eyes closed.

"The bloody old fool's dead," Upham announced unsympathetically.

Sandall bent over more closely. "No, not yet. But the bloody old fool's drunk." Then the "corpse" stirred, and a bleary eye opened and surveyed them painfully. The old man spoke. "You're both wrong. I'm neither dead nor drunk. But you've bloody well broken every bloody bone in my bloody body." Charles looked down in mute admiration.

The college was heated with coal. Students trundled the sacks from the railway station to the college bunkers, and nothing was said when they occasionally dropped off a sack or two for use in the studies. But one shipment was so heavily raided that barely one sack finally reached the bunkers. The Principal addressed the students. "About this coal, gentlemen," he said. "Although it is forbidden for students to use coal in their studies, I have known for some time that you have occasionally helped yourselves to a sack or two. I've turned a blind eye to that—but this has gone *too* far." He continued for a while in that vein.

When he had finished, Charles got to his feet, eyed the Principal seriously, and said: "Sir, on behalf of the students, I wish to lodge a protest. The quality of the coal in this last shipment is much below standard and . . ." The delighted hoots and laughter of his fellow-students drowned the rest of his words. The Principal joined in.

With the Diploma of Agriculture, Charles Upham left Lincoln in 1930 to begin life on the land.

For the next six years he learnt his craft in the hills, gullies, and plains of Canterbury. He acted as shepherd, musterer, farm manager—in fact in every capacity; four years of this time being in the high country where men have to match the ruggedness of nature with their own ruggedness of physique and temperament.

Island Hills, Glen Wye, Rafa Downs, St. Helens—sheep stations whose names were known to all the graziers of Canterbury—Charles lived through their hot dry summers with the parching north-westerlies; and the snows of winter came down from the Alps, and the rivers rose, and the men on the stations rode the tracks and waded through the floods, living often alone in remote musterers' huts.

It was a life for men of only the tough variety. It built Upham into a man of wiry strength, of great physical endurance. He gained an eye for country, a complete indifference to personal comfort, and he came to judge men by what they did and not by the clothes they wore or the titles they carried.

Now and then he appeared back home. His hair unkempt, clothes scruffy, he cared not for the comparison with the well-dressed young bloods walking out from Christ's College a few yards down the road from home. He revelled in the rugged life, scorned social graces, and appalled his mother with the unconscious array of oaths that he learnt from his years in the out-back.

Perseverance marked this stage of his career. If a dog were slow to learn he would spend weary hours coaching and cajoling it, even though other musterers might be kept waiting. Breaking in a horse would never beat him—he would persevere to the end. Rivers, mountain slopes, outrageous weather—he never surrendered to the elements.

Charles attended the local dances that were held in his neighbourhood, but he was one of those who preferred standing in the corner. Nevertheless, he never wasted an evening, for he soon found someone with whom he could argue solidly and intently. As an arguer, he was the same as when breasting a mountainside. The more difficult the argument, the more determined he became not to give in to the other man's point of view. The weaker the case he had, the more hotly did he contest it. The girls made little progress with this rather shy, but rugged, product of the out-back.

He seemed so little interested in small talk, so contemptuous of the fripperies, so intent on more serious subjects.

"But, Charles," they cooed, "what do you do when you are living all alone? Who washes your socks?" And they tittered at the thought of the solemn young man bending over a washtub.

"My socks?" he queried. "Well, it isn't necessary. When they're dirty you throw 'em in a corner. They freshen up again in three weeks!"

It was at the races one Saturday in 1935 when he first met Molly McTamney. She was a dietitian on the staff of the Christchurch Hospital, after a period of four years hospital nursing. Molly was brunette, pretty, and gay. They danced together that evening; and next day Charles was waiting as she came off duty. He had an armful of red roses for her. It was Molly from then on.

In from the hills he came whenever he could. She liked red roses, so there he would be waiting outside the nurses' home, bouquet in hand, perhaps some attempt made to control the unruliness of his ragged hair.

Charles began to think that life ahead required something more secure. Perhaps Molly helped him towards that conclusion, for she had a more practical approach to some problems that Charles never recognized.

So in March 1937 he joined the Valuation Department. First under supervision, then alone, Upham quickly assimilated the techniques of land valuation. He was aided by the scientific knowledge gained at Lincoln College, but much more by his extensive experience of Canterbury land during his six years' work in the province. Very soon his superior officer reported on him: "He is very conscientious, very obliging, and anxious to get on. I find that he is inclined to be easy in his values, but every month seems to be increasing his efficiency."

Then around came the Valuer-General in person, visiting his branches and meeting the staff. Charles stood in the ante-room, waiting his turn for interview.

The man acting as usher drew him aside, pointed disapprovingly to a rent in Upham's coat, mildly suggested that it would be politic to change. "But it's only a hole," said Charles. "What's wrong with that?"

The usher had no chance to say any more because it was now Upham's turn, but he listened outside the door.

Upham was being asked his opinions. He gave them freely, embellished with some of his more ebullient phrases gleaned from the high country. It went on vividly for some time.

At the end the Valuer-General shook hands cordially, a little surprised at his new recruit. And as Upham turned to leave, he said rather sadly: "Upham—you'll never make a civil servant."

And Charles couldn't understand why.

To his fellow-valuers, Charles's physical toughness was a byword. If they returned late from the country their thoughts turned to a hot meal, a bath, a warm bed. But as often as not, they found that Upham was interested only in going to sleep, and he did precisely that, curling up on the large table in the Timaru Valuation Office.

In 1938 Charles and Molly became engaged. They had only a few happy months before she left New Zealand to visit her sister in Singapore.

From there, early in 1939, Molly went on to England. By that time the situation in Europe was darkening, Charles was beseeching her to return home, and he himself was planning seriously for his future career.

Granted leave from the Valuation Department, Charles returned to Lincoln College in February 1939 to take a course in valuation and farm management. Now somewhat of an elder statesman, by virtue of his earlier days at the college and his wide farming experience, he became a popular favourite of his fellow-students.

The course he took was restricted to men of wide practical background and was designed primarily to train men for managerial posts in Government departments. At the end of the year Charles had no trouble with the necessary exams, obtaining his Diploma in Valuation and Farm Management.

But the darkening months of 1939 saw Upham thinking more and more deeply about events on the other side of the world. With the call for volunteers in September 1939, he lost no time in putting his name on the lists. He enlisted out of conviction that the Nazis had to be stopped.

He marched into Burnham Camp, near Christchurch, with the first draft of New Zealand's First Echelon. He stood in the queues, found his slat bed in the hut, chafed impatiently at the slow gearing of the Army system that took so long, he thought, to get down to the business of learning to fight. He found he was in A Company of an infantry battalion. He was Private Upham now, a soldier with no special qualifications, no influence, nothing that appeared to differentiate him from the hundreds of others.

He was not to know, and does not recognize to this day, that already there lurked within him some qualities which seemed to be waiting for warfare to nourish. The needle-sharp courageous brain of his father, intent on fighting legal points; the gentle, but unyielding determination of his mother; the traditions of his schools; the toughening experiences of his years on the stations; the eye for country—either scanning it for the best track or assessing its value; the hatred of oppression; all these influences had made their mark on him.

The Principal of Lincoln College in 1939 was Professor Eric Hudson, a man of notable appearance and reputation, who had served overseas in 1914-18. He believed that the way men behave under fire is almost always unpredictable. The timid counter-salesman who dislikes killing a chicken might well be the coolest man under a barrage. The tough champion boxer, abrim with self-confidence, could be the one man of an infantry platoon who won't go over the top.

Hudson saw the men march out from Lincoln College during the war, men who were studying farming and the land, men who were more likely to be solid than flash. Hundreds of them went from Lincoln into the training camps during the six years of war. Hudson was tempted to write commendations for many of them, knowing that his position and name would command respect.

But conscious of the fallibility of his own judgment and the judgment of other men as to whether a man would make good in uniform, he refrained throughout the whole war from writing to the military authorities about his students. Only *one* exception did he make in all those years, the only student he ever wrote about. Early in October 1939 he wrote his only letter. It was:

"The Commanding Officer,
Burnham Military Camp, Burnham.

Dear Sir,

A young man by the name of Upham has left the College to join your unit. I commend him to your notice, as, unless I am greatly mistaken, he should be an outstanding soldier.

Yours faithfully,
E. Hudson."

CHAPTER TWO

MEN MARCHING

In the three mobilization camps at Hopuhopu, Trentham, and Burnham there were skeleton staffs of former Territorial officers and N.C.O.s and a smattering of Permanent Staff instructors. But from the miscellaneous ranks of those who had just arrived a number had to be chosen to act as temporary N.C.O.s. Choosing men in those circumstances depended on very undependable factors—a man's apparent enthusiasm, his appearance, his "air" of leadership, his tone of voice. If these were false indications of a man's real worth his true measure would soon become apparent. There were other criteria, too.

Captain Frank Davis, Adjutant of the infantry battalion at Burnham, went through the list of names with the C.O., Colonel H. Kippenberger. "Let's sort out a few who went to boarding school," he suggested. "Most of them have cadet training and annual camps. We could look that lot over." "Good idea," Kippenberger agreed. "The other lads will make just as good N.C.O.s in time, but it takes longer to pick them out. Here—you take this lot, I'll go through these others."

The cards were flicked through in silence, every now and then one being put aside. Kippenberger paused, card in hand. "Upham," he mused. "Christ's College boy. Farm valuer. Lincoln College." He turned to Davis. "Here's one we could try. Have a look at him anyway. I know his father—Johnny Upham, a lawyer in Christchurch. Well-known good family. And I've had a note about this chap from Eric Hudson at Lincoln College."

They put that card aside, went on working through the others.

Just as they finished Steele, the R.S.M., put his head inside. "Come in, Sergeant-Major," Kippenberger nodded. "And before you leave we've got a list of men here we'd like to have a look at for temporary stripes. Now what's the matter?"

Steele said: "The men know there's no leave this first weekend. But there's a chap here wants to make a special application for leave. Personal grounds, he says. I told him no show, but he has asked to see you. Determined sort of beggar."

"All right," the Colonel said. "The sooner I get to know them the better. Send him in. Who is he, anyway?"

"His name's Upham. In A Company. I'll get him."

Charles Upham was brought in, uneasy at the formality of his intrusion.

"All right, stand at ease, Upham," Kippenberger said. "The R.S.M. tells me you are asking for leave. There's no leave being granted, you know, except in special circumstances. What's your trouble?"

"Well," Upham replied hesitantly, "it's not exactly trouble. I just want to get leave for personal reasons." And he looked straight ahead at the wall behind Kippenberger's head. Adjutant Davis studied the man as he stood there. Rather an unkempt individual, he thought. Hardly the usual product of Christ's College. A rugged-looking face. He noticed the eyes too—intense, rather chilling eyes.

The C.O. said: "Well, I'm sorry, Upham, but you'll have to tell me the personal reasons before I can consider it. What's the matter?"

Upham hesitated again; then spoke suddenly: "I want to give a chap a hiding; that's all." There was a short, rather surprised pause.

Kippenberger found it necessary to adopt a more than usually solemn tone to control his startled amusement. "I think that's the first time I've heard that one," he said. "But go on, Upham. Tell me more about it."

Upham turned his eyes on the Colonel. "I sold a man a car," he said. "He owes me £12 10s. on it and he says he's not going to pay it. If I don't get my money I'm going to take it out of his hide."

The Colonel looked interested. "Do you know where he is?"

"Yes, at the Grosvenor Hotel in Timaru."

Kippenberger looked hard at Upham. Then he decided. "Yes, Upham," he said, "you can have your leave. There'll be only one tag to it—when you get back I want you to report personally to me. Understand?"

Upham nodded shortly. "Yes, sir. And thank you, sir."

R.S.M. Steele marched him out.

Kippenberger chuckled, then thumbed through the cards again till he found Upham's. He re-read the details on it.

"You know," he said to Davis, "that chap's got something. But he's not a bit like his father. Old Johnny Upham is a very respectable sort of family lawyer. This chap looks as if he'd be happier in the mountains than a lawyer's office."

The week-end came. Upham walked out of camp in company with a very favoured few.

Monday morning he reported again at Battalion Headquarters.

"You told me to report to you, sir, after I came back from leave."

"Oh yes, Upham," the Colonel said. "Tell me—did you find your man?" "Yes, sir." "Did you get your money?"

"I did not," Upham replied tersely.

"M-m, bad luck." A pause. "Well, then—did you give him his hiding?"

"Yes, sir, I did," came the answer, and a look of satisfaction showed momentarily on Upham's face. He had barely returned to his hut when the Orderly Sergeant came after him, telling him he was wanted again at Battalion H.Q., this time by Captain Davis, the Adjutant. He walked back obediently.

"You're a graduate of Lincoln College, aren't you?" the Adjutant enquired. "Diplomas and all that? . . ." Upham nodded.

"That means you've studied soils, laying out of crops, grass-land cultivation, and all that sort of thing, doesn't it?"

"Yes, that's right, sir."

"Well, just come back inside. There's someone here you know."

Inside the Adjutant's room Upham came face to face with R. H. Bevin, who had been his tutor at Lincoln College a few days before.

Davis said: "You know Mr. Bevin, don't you, Upham? He's over here to help us. You see, they've decided to lay down a lawn around Camp Headquarters. We asked Lincoln College if they would send someone to advise us. Mr. Bevin came over. But he's a pretty busy man, and he says if anybody ought to know how to lay down the lawn it's you. So you've been detailed for the job."

Upham stared blankly at him. Then Bevin came over and said briskly: "I've brought all the stuff over, Charlie. . . ."

And Upham stood there silently while Bevin handed over the goods and then made his departure. When he had gone Upham looked at Captain Davis stonily. He said: "Is that right—you're going to get me to lay down a bloody lawn?"

"That's right," Davis said. "You're just the man. And mind your language when you're in here."

Upham gulped. "What happens to my training while I'm doing that? We're on Lewis gun and bayonet today and I don't want to miss it."

"Plenty of time," Davis said soothingly.

"Well, I don't know that there is," Upham blurted out. "The war's not going to be won by laying down ruddy lawns. Is it an order?"

"Yes, it is. And, you know, Upham, you can't win the war today."

Upham looked at him without speaking. No, he couldn't win the war today, he knew, but he'd have a mighty good crack at it if he had the chance. So that afternoon he laid the lawn.

And that night a torrential downpour washed out all his seed and he had to sow it all afresh the following morning. And there is great doubt if any lawn in the world has been laid to the accompaniment of such profanity and discontent. Because lawns don't win battles.

Towards the end of October the training camps were told that men would have to be chosen from the ranks to train for commissions. Nominations were called for. In Burnham, where the infantry now bore the title of 20th Battalion, Colonel Kippenberger went through the lists again with his Adjutant, Davis.

Upham's name came up once more. He was getting himself noticed now by the almost ferocious intensity he was bringing to bear on his training. He gave the impression that he regarded his competence as a soldier as of tremendous importance. And to the little section of men, over whom his new one stripe gave him command, he conveyed an air of dedication and urgency. Kippenberger said: "What about him?"

"He's got a good background," Davis agreed. "Doing a good job as a lance-jack, too; he's older and got more savvy than most of them. But I wonder if he knows enough about it yet?"

"Hear about him at Tai Tapu?" Kippenberger queried, referring to manœuvres from which the battalion had just returned. "Held up the whole advance half an hour. I was chewing him up, but then I found out the reason. He'd been out scouting on his own. He came upon an 'enemy' section, rushed in on them, and demanded they surrender. Trouble was, they *wouldn't* surrender. Reckoned the battle hadn't started. Upham was late getting back because he stayed to argue with them."

Davis nodded. "And I heard more about that today. The stream was running four or five feet deep, and the 'enemy' reckoned it would be all right to post men only on the bridges. But I'm told Upham took it more seriously. He didn't have a go at the bridges; said that was crazy. He made his men wade the stream—up to their armpits. Won his little battle, all right, but it didn't make him too popular. A bit too realistic, they said."

Kippenberger listened with interest. "Yes . . . and Archie MacDuff told me he did a camouflage job that was pretty good." He sat silently for a little while. Then he continued: "A determined man. Probably get himself shot the first day we're in action. Yes . . . I'll have him. Put his name on the list. Then we'll parade these lads and have a talk to them."

The fifty men were lined up on the parade ground. Twenty of them had to be chosen for the Trentham Officer Cadet Training Unit. Frank Davis looked them over before the Colonel arrived.

He said to them bluntly: "You blokes have been sorted out

for the chance of going for commissions. The C.O.'s going to pick out twenty of you. They'll go up to Trentham this Friday night. But if any of you aren't interested, better fall out now."

One or two shuffled their feet uncomfortably. Ross Westenra, standing alongside Upham, said: "I've got a racehorse I want to see run at Ashburton this week-end. Suppose I'd better drop out."

Davis said: "Please yourself. . . . Any others?"

Charles Upham looked hesitant. Then he said to the Adjutant: "I don't want to be mucking about in New Zealand. What happens if I go to this school? Do I get away?"

"Don't ask me," Davis replied. "Try the C.O. He's coming now." Kippenberger walked over from the orderly room. He spoke to them in his quiet, sincere voice. "This is an opportunity for you men. We are badly in need of good officers. Every one of you could earn a commission if you worked reasonably hard. But don't be under any illusions about it. You'd go overseas as second lieutenants, and I think I can fairly warn you that the prospects of a one-pipper at the beginning of a war aren't particularly bright. Now, are there any questions?"

He looked along the ranks. . . . Silence.

Then he noticed an arm held up, rather like a boy in school. "Well, Upham, what do you want to say?"

"If I went up to Trentham, sir, would I still get overseas with this battalion?"

Kippenberger looked at him straight. "I couldn't give you any guarantee about that."

"In that case, sir, I'd like my name taken off the list."

Kippenberger was all the more certain then that Charles Upham was the kind of man who would put his head in the road of a bullet in a comparatively short time. But he didn't realize then, as he did later, that behind Lance-Corporal Upham's anxiety to close with the enemy lay a brain that was very quickly mopping up the fundamentals of military skill. The men who survived battles were often found to be those who could calculate the risks a soldier could fairly take; who could distinguish, in the heat of conflict, between futile risks on the one hand and, on the other, risks which were reasonably worth taking for the objective in view. In his later military career Upham was sometimes branded as a foolhardy, reckless, and lucky soldier. That was not a fair appraisal. He took fearful risks, agreed. But examination of them shows that they were all "on". And every one, if successful, stood to gain some worthwhile advantage. To be brave and foolish can be heroic. But heroism takes on a higher quality if bravery and judgment go hand in hand.

It was as the battalion returned from a long route-march after midday on 4th December that the word passed rapidly around the lines: a small advance party was about to leave for overseas, the men had been chosen, and any minute the lucky names were to be announced. Final leave for them right away. Here was the hour for those who were most anxious to be away to the wars. They were lined up in the mess queue when the R.S.M. bustled along, sheet of paper in one hand.

"Where's Corporal Upham? Ah . . . there you are, Charlie. You're in the advance party, Charlie. Get your gear together straight after mess, and report to Battalion Headquarters 1400 hours. You're going on final leave right away—lucky beggar."

For a moment Upham looked incredulous. Then an excited grin spread over his features. "Where're we going, Sar'-Major?" he shouted.

"You'll know before I do. . . . Better get on with your lunch."

But this was too wonderful to absorb right on mess time. Face alight, he went around his friends, telling them of his good fortune, leaving his lunch plates untouched. There were ten others chosen from the battalion to form part of the advance party. The others seemed to enjoy their lunch. Charles was too excited to care.

From all the training camps in the country fifty-two men were selected for the advance party. It may have been significant that Upham was singled out for special duties. Perhaps his commanders already suspected that, despite a civilian career that had been promising but unspectacular, Charles Upham had certain qualities which fitted him well for the exceptional demands of war.

He was promoted to sergeant six days before they sailed.

CHAPTER THREE

THE IMPATIENT SERGEANT

EARLY 1940 was the time of the shadow war. Some called it the "phoney" war, though it wasn't phoney for the comparatively few who saw the bullets and bombs. There were the troopships churning overseas, the factories almost reluctantly switching to war materials, the psychological change that was necessary to make a nation ready to meet fancied threats ahead. And some wondered if the threats were real. Then suddenly, with a violence that shook the world, there came the panther springs of Hitler's Germany, swallowing up the little countries of Europe. The success of it was awe-inspiring. As April turned to May, France, totally bewildered, began to crumble.

During that time, while the New Zealand Division trained in Egypt, Charles Upham worked as a sergeant. He did not become renowned as a particularly smart sergeant. Intent on learning the essentials of fighting, and nothing else, he showed no affection for parade-ground niceties, little respect for the conventions of Army life and rank.

Indeed, it is a wonder he escaped arraignment for plain insubordination. He would speak bluntly to everyone, whatever their rank. He became quickly outspoken against anything that did not immediately appear to help the business of fighting and winning a war. All else was sham, unwanted. If he thought an officer was wrong, he would tell him so to his face—not out of insolence, but from sheer honesty, from the burning sense that men had to be trained right, the war fought right, the right orders given, and the right men appointed to give them.

Late in February he was demonstrating the Bren gun to a squad of men. He told them clearly what had to be done and he gave his own practical demonstration of it.

An infantry captain came up behind him as the lesson progressed.

"Just a minute, Sergeant," he interrupted. "That's not the right way to clear that stoppage." And he proceeded to expound to the squad what he claimed was the proper method to follow. Upham looked on silently, his brow darkening, a rather ominous glint in his eye.

"There, Sergeant," the Captain concluded. "Teach it the way I've just shown you." Upham held his heels at attention. But all the stripes in the world were not worth being told he was wrong when he *knew* he was right. He had just passed out of a weapons course at Tel Aviv, and he knew his Bren completely. He snapped out: "I'm sorry, sir, but you're wrong. I was showing them the *right* way."

The Captain eyed him. "You'll teach it the way I've just shown you."

Upham's eyes flared. There was a moment of silence, then he could not contain himself. He blurted out: "Who's supposed to be giving this lecture? Me or you? If you reckon I'm wrong, well go ahead—there's the gun, there's the squad; teach 'em yourself!" And he looked his defiance as he saw his three stripes melting into thin air.

The Captain turned and walked away. Upham glared after him, then turned and eyed the squad stonily. It was a few moments before he spoke. Then he said: "Forget what he told you. He doesn't know what he's talking about. Right . . . we'll have a smoke."

And his men grinned at one another; and they rather thought their sergeant was the sort of bloke they wouldn't mind going into action with; that is, if he didn't end up in the ranks himself. But Upham kept his three stripes, for the Captain was a well-liked officer who was wise enough to recognize his own mistake and to count his blessings for an N.C.O. who had the spirit to stand up for himself.

It was the right and duty of every soldier, Charles thought, to speak his own mind if it would help win the battle. As a sergeant and later an officer, he was on familiar terms with all his men, calling them by their first names, or merely swearing at them affectionately. They called him "boss" to his face, "Charlie" behind his back. He asked for their opinions, considered them soberly; dismissed them brusquely if he thought fit; adopted them with enthusiasm if they were good.

Likewise, it was natural for him to disagree flatly with a superior officer and to tell him so bluntly, with no embarrassment on either side. Of course the officer needed to know his Upham, to know that no disrespect was intended, that it was just the mental honesty and straightforwardness of the man that accounted for it.

The 20th Battalion went out into the desert on training manœuvres. One company would establish a defensive position, another would reconnoitre and attack it. Colonel Kippenberger himself would watch and later give comments.

It was on such an occasion that Upham's forthrightness went almost as far as it safely could. Out into the desert went A Company to establish a defensive position and hold it against attack. They also had to employ the newly issued anti-tank rifle, and this required a little more thought than the usual dispositions for a company in defence. Sergeant Upham was given command of his platoon, and soon had his sections well disposed. A supervising officer arrived, looked searchingly over the sergeant's plan, and roundly condemned it. This section should be further this way, that section closer to the ridge, etc. He told Upham to move his men accordingly. This was learning warfare, Upham reasoned. Rank did not enter into the discussion. His men's lives would depend on his own decisions in months to come. So he said: "No, sir. I'm not moving them."

"Why not? I've told you you're wrong."

Upham gave his reasons, carefully thought-out reasons. To others within earshot they sounded convincing. "It would be bloody stupid to move those sections up there," he concluded brassily. "Just plumb crazy."

The officer had had enough. "All right, Sergeant," he said, "I make it an order." Upham shook his head stubbornly. "Those positions are right," he maintained. "I take my orders as to where the whole platoon goes. But it's my job to place my sections. That's my responsibility. I'm sorry, I'm not shifting them."

"Then if you don't do what you're told, Upham, I could have you placed under arrest and removed."

There was a rather long silence. Upham let his eye range over his section posts again. He knew he was right. The officer was wrong. Orders might be orders, but men's lives were more important than that. Arrest, eh? But his mind was inflexible. He always was inflexible, once he had carefully mapped out a course of action and embarked upon it. No deviation. No side issues.

But there was a hint of a smile in his eyes as he replied. "Have me arrested? I don't think you could do it, sir. We're out in the desert here, and I'd have a right to insist on two N.C.O.s of equal rank to escort me—and there aren't two other sergeants within three miles."

The two men looked at each other. Then the officer said: "I'd escort you myself, Upham, if I felt about it seriously enough. Lucky for you I don't. Say we get on with the war, then—and we'll see how your positions stand up to it. You'll find out you are wrong. Then perhaps you'll learn your lesson." So the exercise continued, but history does not record whether Charles's positions were proved right or wrong. All the story shows is that this rather brash sergeant was determined to lead his men according to his own ideas, and he wasn't mealy-mouthed over telling other people what he thought of theirs.

It was just a few days after this incident that the Battalion Adjutant, looking over his lists of N.C.O.s with a critical eye, said to Colonel Kippenberger: "This Upham ought to go to O.C.T.U. some time. His O.C. says he knows platoon tactics backwards, and he's a tiger with the bayonet and the Bren. Though I doubt if he'd make a good officer. Rough as guts. And on the parade ground he's about the world's worst. He's the scruffiest we've got, but he's a hell of a good soldier."

Kippenberger didn't need to be told. He already had Upham on his list. "Pity he couldn't smarten up his drill," the Colonel said.

"Could be smart if he tried, I think," the Adjutant replied. "But he's got no sense of time, no rhythm; and I think he reckons it's all a waste of time. He wants to be killing Germans. He's out there now taking his platoon on drill. Like to look?"

They strolled out of the orderly room and walked over towards the platoon. It had just faced round in a rather straggly left-form, and now was marching off towards the edge of the training area. Sergeant Upham strode along at the side, concentrating deeply, his stride a shade out of step with the leaders of the front rank. They came closer to the edge of the square. One or two of the front rank glanced sideways at the sergeant to make sure he hadn't forgotten them, and that he would soon give the required order to face them round and march them back towards the centre again.

But the order didn't come. Farther and farther they went. Upham had an intense, furious expression on his face as he strove vainly to remember the right command. It was something absurdly simple, he knew full well; but his mind had been preoccupied with a thought he had had about firing a Bren gun from the hip.

Kippenberger gazed in perplexity.

The Adjutant said: "There's an example of it. He's forgotten what foot to give the about-turn on."

"He won't have any platoon left if he doesn't do something," the C.O. murmured. "If he doesn't call 'Halt' pretty soon I'll call it myself."

But Upham lifted his head and yelled: "Whoa!" Like well-trained horses from the hill country of Canterbury, the platoon came to a sudden halt, and permitted themselves a friendly grin at the sergeant.

Upham swallowed hard, pushed down his web belt, and addressed his men: "You beauts. I suppose if I hadn't said anything you'd have walked right into the bloody wadi. That was one of the roughest halts you fellows have ever done. Remember, it's—halt, one, one-two. Now we'll turn round and do a proper job of it in front of Kip. Right—turn round. . . . I mean—about . . . turn!"

So they swung back across the sand determined to put on a

good show while the Colonel and the Adjutant were watching.

Upham judged his time, ordered: "Platoon . . . *halt!*"

They came to a staggering stop, one after another, and looked with mild reproof at the sergeant who had failed them.

But the sergeant was too busy with the officers.

The C.O. said: "Your men can do better than that, Sergeant. You gave them the 'Halt' on the wrong foot."

Upham nodded, cursing himself silently. Then he said hopefully: "Well, sir, even if I did, *they knew what I bloody well meant.*" Kippenberger found that unanswerable. He said to the Adjutant as they retreated to Battalion Headquarters: "Does he often swear like that?"

"Most of the time, I'm told. Must have picked up all his profanity when he was mustering. Now it just pours out of him naturally. Funny thing, though, it's not offensive. He's even sworn at me. Anyone else I'd have on the mat, but he doesn't mean anything by it."

"What about his men? Does he swear at them too?"

"They tell me he'll swear at anybody, no matter who. I expect his men swear back at him. But they're all *for* him. He looks after them so well. A real fighter for his own platoon."

Kippenberger paused, stood outside in the sun for a few minutes.

Then he said: "I'll send him to O.C.T.U. later on. But those English instructors will give him hell. What I'm thinking about is this, though—when he's commissioned would we want him back in the battalion?"

The Adjutant considered. "Depends what we are going to do. If the div is going to stooge around in Egypt much longer, doing routine stuff, Upham wouldn't be any special gain to us. He's a very thoughtful, intelligent chap, but he's too impatient."

"But what if we went into action?"

"Here in Africa? Can't see that happening."

"Well, I can tell you this—Italy will be in the war in the next few weeks."

"The Ities! My word, that's great. . . . And Charlie Upham? I can picture him now—walking in with a hundred prisoners, holding 'em up at the point of his pipe. Capture by will-power!"

Kippenberger said: "That's it exactly. And that's why I'll try to get him posted back here after he's commissioned. We want to win our battles!"

On 10th June 1940 Italy declared war on Britain. It seemed to

Mussolini that the pickings of Europe were there for the taking.

All it did to Charles Upham was to make him the more impatient to get down to business. He already comprehended that the man who could do the enemy most damage, and at the same time have the best chance of survival, was the man who made himself expert with his own weapons. So he became an expert with the Bren. He tried to train his men to be experts also. At an early stage in training, when there was only one Bren gun for the whole company, Upham utilized every second of the time the Bren was allotted to his platoon. Every man had to know the Bren better than his own hand. He drilled them on gun stoppages without respite.

Likewise he became an expert with the grenade—not merely proficient, but expert; in distance; in direction; judging how long it could be held before throwing, to make sure the enemy could not throw it back; what damage it could do both to men and morale; how many he could possibly drape around his body before going into action.

Later, when his exploits made legends throughout the British forces, the stories were always garnished with details of how many grenades Upham carried about with him. Some said he carried a sugar-sack of them as he waded through the circle of fire during the amazing break-out at Minqar Qaim; others claimed that he wore a special bandolier of them as he earned his first V.C. on Crete; that on Ruweisat Ridge there was a grave shortage of grenades in his company because Upham had corralled them all. Whatever the truth, it was common ground that Upham cherished the grenade as his favourite attacking weapon, and he went into every action carrying as great a load of them as he could bear.

But in some of the formal aspects of military life he was lost: parade-ground drill continued to be an unpleasant effort.

On several occasions he had to act as Battalion Orderly Sergeant, whose job at Battalion Parade was to dress the companies in proper line. This is accomplished by the sergeant looking down the line of each rank, moving men up or back; then, when satisfied, repeating the process with the next rank. Upham was well known for making a bungle of it more often than not. The other N.C.O.s laughed at him and the men squirmed silently. Upham hated the whole thing and realized he was hopeless at it.

Then there was the occasion when he was Guard Sergeant.

Impatient with the routine, he waited for the Orderly Officer to arrive. He checked his men again, thought they looked reasonably well turned out, and shifted his weight from one foot to the

other as the minutes ticked by. It was hot. Damn the ceremonial!
Word came that the Orderly Officer was delayed, would not be
long.

Patience exhausted, Sergeant Upham took up his station in
front of the guard, brought it to attention, inspected it meticulously, and forthwith proceeded to change the guard himself.
The Orderly Officer arrived, boots shining, Sam Browne belt
immaculate, to find that he was too late, his functions usurped,
the parade ground deserted, the new guard safely installed.

The men of his platoon were the salt of the earth. Their welfare
became his first thought. Swear at them as he did, drive them
mercilessly to become expert soldiers, show them a poor example
of military precision, yet they came to regard him as a man who
would risk a lot for their sakes.

They marched back from a long desert manœuvre that gave
them a good taste of sand in their mouths. The march back was
dry, hot, and gruelling. But as the men staggered to a halt for
lunch on the long way home, the word came down the line:
"No tea—just hard rations."

That wasn't good enough, Upham argued. He went straight to
his Company Headquarters. On the way he seized the handle of
a pick-axe, took it with him.

"My men are just about all in," he complained. "If the ration
blokes can't turn on tea pretty smartly, then I'll take this bloody
pick-axe to them!" And he shook it angrily under their noses.

"Calm down, Sergeant," the officer told him. "And put that
thing down! Don't behave like a savage. I'll see that your men
get some tea."

Often intolerant of the Army system, impatient with its slow
gearing, he was also quick to criticize any apparent abuse of the
powers of rank. One day in Cairo three Military Police were
sauntering along the footpath. They were big, powerful men,
capable of handling trouble. Trouble came. First it was three
soldiers, badly, abusively drunk. They swaggered past the M.P.s,
swayed across the footpath, threatening and obscene.

Upham was standing nearby with a group of fellow Kiwis. They
watched in amazement as the hefty M.P.s looked casually over
the lurching soldiers, then let them go past unmolested.

One of the watching men muttered: "Scared of them. Frightened
it would be too tough."

Upham had almost a pathological dislike of M.P.s as a class.
No logic about it—just one of his prejudices. Nor did he pause

to consider that these M.P.s might not be authorized to arrest soldiers of *all* Allied nationalities.

In less than a minute another drunk appeared, this time an enormous, belligerent man. Everyone visibly quailed as he set sail down the street, bent on trouble. The M.P.s pretended not to notice. Until five minutes later, when a half-pickled little Tommy came waltzing timidly along, cheerful, peaceful, happily tipsy. The three M.P.s pounced on him, roughing him up as they hurried him to the kerb.

"Are we going to stand for that?" one of the New Zealanders asked his mates. They muttered darkly, began edging slowly towards the M.P.s, circling around them, doing nothing wrong, but helping the other pedestrians crowd in on the little group. Jostling began.

Upham had seen it all, was seething with resentment.

A taxi was stopped. Into it the M.P.s bustled their diminutive prisoner. Then the men acted. Ostensibly to beat the M.P.s for the taxi, they rushed forward, elbowing and shoving. Into the taxi hustled the Kiwis. Out sprawled the M.P.s, shouting and threatening. With a roar the taxi started up. But one M.P. hung on desperately, grasping the handle of the door, feet on the running-board. Then from amongst the bystanders there appeared a soldier's boot, firmly and swiftly kicking the hand away, sending the M.P. back on to the road. Off went the victorious Kiwis with their rescued Tommy. Into the crowd disappeared the owner of the boot, losing himself rapidly in the throng that had gathered. Just as well he disappeared fast. A man like that would never have been sent up for a commission if that exploit had come to light. It is still a secret, hard to prise out from those who were there.

CHAPTER FOUR

LEGGY MEETS HIS LIEUTENANT

THE handful of New Zealanders who entered the officers' training unit in August 1940 contained Sergeant Upham. He was a reluctant candidate. He dreaded lest the war should come to the New Zealand Division while he was detached in some backwater at Base.

Like most officer-cadet courses, it was a solid test of all-round ability. Men worked hard night and day. The instructors knew their subjects, according to the standard of military knowledge believed adequate up to that time. Tactical training was based on the lessons of the Great War of 1914-18. The German lesson of Poland and France, just a few months old, had not yet filtered down.

But somehow Upham thought the tactics were wrong. He was born with an enquiring mind, and he was tremendously worried by what they taught him. Bert Steele, the 20th's R.S.M., was in the course with him. Steele readily absorbed the tactical lessons, knowing they were the product of experience and had stood the test of time.

But after one such lesson Charles spoke to him as they came out into the sun. "Bert, I dunno—but I just can't understand these tactics."

"Don't worry, Charlie. It's just common sense."

"Common sense, Bert?" Upham queried, looking at him in a puzzled way. "Well, if it is, I just can't get it. . . . I can't get it."

That night in the mess, over a pot of beer, he raised the subject again. One or two of the other New Zealanders were around him, and the talk turned to the tactical lessons of the day.

"They don't say anything about surprise," Upham complained. "Surely that's the most important thing. These fellows don't mention it. But that's how the Huns wiped up the Frogs."

"You might be right, Charlie," one of them said. "But these Tommy officers know their stuff. You can't expect to get anywhere with them if you just stand up and say 'I think that's a lot of rot'. You'll get fired from the school if you say that again. And what did you go and tell the Commandant, Charlie? Come on . . . what did you say to him? He looked a bit surprised."

"The Commandant? Oh, nothing much. I just told him I thought his ideas were *obsolete*. What's wrong with that?"

Upham couldn't understand why they laughed so loudly.

But Upham learnt the tactics they taught him, studying every word with a grim intensity, as if his life would depend on being word-perfect. Perhaps it would. And on top of the "set-piece" stuff they gave him he was quietly and earnestly fashioning some ideas of his own. The course went on. Charles mastered his map-reading, desert navigation, military law, Army administration, intelligence, drill, tactics, weapon firing, hints on command, vehicles, street fighting, aircraft recognition, gas, and the rest.

And at the end the Commandant said to the New Zealand Military Secretary: "Upham's got through all right. But you'll never make an officer out of him. They pass out tomorrow. Here's the grading list of the men from your division."

Sure enough, the Commandant's opinion of Upham was reflected in the results. It never pays to argue with the boss, does it?

Down the list of successful cadets the Military Secretary ran his eye until he came to the very last name. The name at the *very bottom* of the list read—*"Charles Hazlitt Upham"*.[1]

The same Charles Hazlitt Upham who later won two V.C.s, whose leadership was an inspiration, whose skill and whose exploits made his name a legend; of whom the London *Times* said: "Mr. Upham's courage was superhuman...."

On passing out of the school the new subalterns were posted temporarily to a Base depot, waiting there for appointments to the battalions and regiments. On the first night in the new mess Upham found himself in a corner alongside a New Zealand artilleryman named Atchley.

"You sound English," Upham said to him. "Been in New Zealand long?" Atchley told him.

"Listen," Upham said. "I've just come from O.C.T.U. They had instructors teaching us infantry tactics. Now you're a gunner —just listen to this stuff they taught us and you tell me if it makes sense to you. I don't know—it's still got me beat. . . ."

"Don't ask me about infantry tactics," Atchley protested. "I just fire the guns."

"Never mind—just listen. You're English—perhaps you'll understand it better than I do. Now take the case of a company making a night attack...."

Atchley resigned himself to listening to infantry tactics that evening—all phases of company and platoon tactics, by day and night, in attack and in defence, with and without tanks, machine-guns and artillery. And he listened to Upham's exposition of his own views, contrasted with the official view taught at the school.

The second night in the mess, Upham opened up the subject again. And again a night later.

It can be said that Trevor Atchley, after three nights of listening, knew a lot more about infantry tactics than he ever expected to. He knew, too, that the character who cornered him every

[1] To this day Upham still manfully protests that he did not pass out bottom of his O.C.T.U. class. He admits that he was amongst the C grade passes but that, as the names in that grade were published alphabetically, it thus happened that his name appeared at the bottom. However, the late Major-General Kippenberger, whose knowledge of Upham was complete, did not support Upham's contention.

evening had a curious mind—a determination to grasp the whole of a subject, to match his own reasoning against the reasoning of others, and to adhere like a limpet to the final decision he came to.

When N.C.O.s from a unit were sent to O.C.T.U. for commissions it was not the practice to post them back to their old unit.

Colonel Kippenberger of the 20th had sent in some of his best N.C.O.s. He knew they would make cracking officers. He wanted them back to the 20th. He went to see the Military Secretary about it.

But there was no change of policy. The Military Secretary went through the names of Kippenberger's men, all of whom had passed successfully out of the school and were waiting at Base for their appointments. No. The rule had to be followed—no posting back to their former units. Kippenberger pressed hard for all his men, including his former Sergeant Upham.

The Military Secretary said: "Oh well, he's at the bottom of the list. I don't suppose it'll matter much with him. All right, you take him back if you like; but I can't do it with any of the others."

Kippenberger closed the deal quickly and eagerly. Without further ado, he left instructions for Second Lieutenant Upham to report to the battalion in the Western Desert. Number 15 Platoon of C Company would have him.

The New Zealand Division was at Baggush at the time Upham was required to report back to the 20th, so, to make use of his services en route, he was put in charge of a draft of reinforce-ments travelling out to Baggush by train. The reinforcements had known more comfortable travelling in their day. Some of them were from the 3rd Echelon not long arrived from New Zealand. Others were seasoned men of the desert, returning to the division after spells in hospital, at courses of instruction, or at Base.

Packed in the train amongst his larger fellows was a rather small man whose topic of conversation centred around race-horses and their mysteries. He was voluble in his condemnation of the present travelling arrangements. He was listened to with respect by those around him, for he was not a newcomer. He had been with the division some time, had served as a batman to a Lieuten-ant Fountaine of the 20th Battalion. But he and Fountaine had parted.

The officer-in-charge wedged his way into the carriage. The little man noticed that the officer was a brand-new one-pipper, albeit with a rugged-looking face. He stuck his small chin upwards and launched into a general complaint. The new officer listened sympathetically. "What's your name?" he asked.

"Le Gros," the ex-batman answered. "What's yours?"

"Upham," the officer replied mildly.

"Well, look here, Second Lootenant Upham, these carriages aren't good enough for pigs. I bet old Kip wouldn't allow it if he knew. What are you going to do about it?"

Upham was amused by the perky confidence of the small man. He said: "I suppose if you think she's too crowded you could jump off and walk. Take longer, though."

Le Gros shrugged his shoulders. "O.K., boss. She'll do. Typical Army. I expect you officers have got an air-conditioned carriage, with a case of grog, nurses, red tabs everywhere, eh?"

Upham smiled at him. "I haven't found a seat for myself yet. You're the lucky one." The train ground on. The officer went on his way. Le Gros resumed his discussion of the 1939 Grand National.

When finally the train halted and everyone gratefully clambered out, Upham saw Le Gros again. The small man had little to carry. Upham had more than his own gear. He walked over.

"How about helping me with my pack, Le Gros? I've got a job to do here and I've got other stuff to carry. What about it?"

Le Gros stared at him incredulously. "Christ!" he said. "We're all soldiers, aren't we? What's wrong with you?"

"Never mind, never mind," Upham quickly replied. "Forget it. . . ."

The look of shocked surprise on Le Gros's face suddenly changed and was replaced with an air of benevolent tolerance.

"Aw relax, boss, relax. I'll take it. Here—give it to me. . . . Feels like a bottle of whisky in here. You'd better not be too long getting after me."

And, with a cheery, but slightly evil grin, Le Gros heaved Upham's pack on to his shoulders and marched off.

It was two hours later when Le Gros received a summons to attend before the new officer of Number 15 Platoon. . . .

"How would you like to be my batman, Le Gros?"

"Well . . . I dunno. But I suppose—seeing as I carried your pack about ten ruddy miles—all right, I'll take it on if you like. *But on one condition, though.*"

"What's that?" Upham enquired dubiously.

"I don't do any guards, eh?" Upham nodded humbly.

Major Wilson of C Company warned Charles about 15 Platoon.

They were mainly from the West Coast of the South Island, he said. Men from the West Coast were rugged. They needed an officer who could talk their language, who could be more rugged than they.

They were lined up for Upham's first inspection. They muttered between themselves, wondering if they could "have this fellow on". They had known of him as a sergeant in A Company, a rather short, wiry man, hopeless at drill, a bit grim as an instructor. He turned up smoking his pipe, a knobbly stick, like a musterer's, in his hand. He stood silently in front of the platoon, letting them look at him. He knew they were summing him up, trying to judge how far they could go with him.

He looked from one man's face to the next. What he saw pleased him. They were tough, they were individualistic, they were a little scruffy, but they looked completely dependable; they looked the sort of men one would like to have around when the going was difficult.

Finally he slowly took his pipe from his mouth and lowered his head. They saw the curious cold glint of his eyes. He said: "I'm your new officer. My name's Upham. You look a pretty tough mob to me. But you don't look fit. In fact you look like a lot of boozers. . . ."

Charles Upham was a forceful platoon commander in those days late in 1940. But that was no greater a quality than others possessed. His tactical ideas were thoughtful and sound, his training of his men painstaking, based on a determination that they must know their job thoroughly. His personal attitude to his men was more casual than military tradition preferred. "This having to salute you chaps is a damned nuisance," he complained.

He held independent views on the value of different kinds of training. "War is fighting," he argued. "Why bother with anything that doesn't help you to fight?"

As his knowledge of his men grew, so grew his concern for their well-being. To the Company Quartermaster he became a constant thorn—enquiring, demanding, making sure his men got the best of food and supplies. But in those early days, as 1940 turned into 1941, no one claimed that Upham shone above his fellow-officers in any way other than in his violent and unremitting attention to the comfort and safety of his platoon. Men like Kippenberger guessed it would only be the demands of action that would really plumb the depths of Upham's character.

Kippenberger watched him develop. A curious mixture, this

young man. A rugged exterior, a rough bluntness that would be downright rudeness in another man, superimposed on a modest, shy fellow whose bellicose intensity contrasted strangely with his intelligence and retiring nature. Kippenberger knew now how stubborn he was—he heard the stories—and yet the man was soft-hearted and easily led. "That's a hard-working platoon you've got there, Upham," he remarked to Charles one day. "They were a pretty tough lot—how do you think they'll do in action—enough discipline?"

"Discipline?" Upham queried, looking puzzled. "I don't really know, sir. I get on all right with them, I think. They know their stuff really well. They'll loaf if I let them; but they'll spring to it if I tell them to. No serious crime amongst them. . . . I suppose you could say their discipline was all right, sir."

"Yes, I expect so. One thing, Charlie—do you think it's a good thing to swear at your men? You do it a lot, you know. I don't believe in it. I'd like you to cut it out."

"Swear at them, sir? I never thought . . . I mean . . . I didn't think I swore at them much." He looked concerned.

"You probably don't know you're doing it," Kippenberger observed.

The C.O. moved on, while Upham turned thoughtfully back to his men working a few yards away. Yes, he'd have to cut out swearing if it was bad enough for Kip to notice. He watched what his platoon were doing, noticed the mess they were making of a camouflaged dug-out they were trying to construct.

"You lazy bloody loafers!" he shouted at them. "With Kip standing right in front of you you put up a ruddy shambles of a thing like that. You . . . !"

They grinned shamefacedly. They knew they'd done a poor job.

A chain away Kip paused as he heard his subaltern's tirade. He thought of turning back, of giving Upham a real dressing-down this time; but he thought better of it and walked quickly away out of earshot. He muttered to himself: "It *was* a ruddy shambles, too."

CHAPTER FIVE

KNIGHT WITHOUT ARMOUR

MUSSOLINI's entry into World War II was unimpressive, to say the least. There was Graziani's rout in North Africa in December

1940; then, when the Italians invaded Greece, they found themselves counter-attacked to such effect that 7000 Italians were
prisoners within a few weeks. To protect his Balkan flank Hitler
had to take over.

In February 1941 the United Kingdom Cabinet cabled the New
Zealand Prime Minister:

". . . We have taken full cognizance of the risks involved in
the despatch to Greece . . . of so large a proportion of the troops
available in the Middle East . . . [But] our failure to help this
small nation putting up a gallant fight against one aggressor,
and willing to defy another, would have a grave effect on public
opinion throughout the world."

"Public opinion" certainly; but military opinion should have
convinced the Allies that an expedition to Greece could only be
an honourable, possibly disastrous, gesture. For it was no more
than a gesture. The German attack had been in progress only
six days before the Greek Commander-in-Chief suggested that the
Allied forces evacuate.

Nevertheless, the New Zealand Government promised support,
though not without forebodings. Prime Minister Fraser said to
Whitehall that the operation was "a formidable and hazardous
one".

Before it even started the situation deteriorated. The Greeks
were unable to conform to the defence plan that had been jointly
arranged. "We found a changed and disturbing situation on our
arrival here, and an atmosphere quite different from our last
visit"—cabled the British Mission. And in New Zealand Fraser
cabled London:

"The operation, which had always been regarded as highly
dangerous and speculative, is now obviously much more
hazardous. . . . Pressure by the Germans might perhaps lead
to a rapid collapse of the Greeks, which would leave the British
force in the air. . . ."

Fraser's prophecy was proved exactly true.

Churchill himself sensed the inevitable. He said to Eden, who
was leading the British delegation in talks with the Greeks: "Do
not consider yourself obligated to a Greek enterprise if in your
hearts you feel it will only be another Norwegian fiasco. . . ."

That is what it turned out to be.

Yet, somehow, in the face of all this advice, the politicians were
swayed by the moral appeal, leading them to discount the military

realities. From the very beginning the end was obvious.

During March 1941 the New Zealand Division was shipped across the Mediterranean, moved up through the Greek mainland, and took up defensive positions near Katerini, 300 miles north of Athens.

Charles Upham's platoon found itself in a little Greek hamlet called Riakia. There they stayed for seventen days, digging in, erecting wire, settling their defensive lay-out in anticipation of the German attack that would assuredly come down the road straight into their village.

The ability to lay out and construct a good defensive position depends so much on the type of ground one is offered; but there were many opinions expressed that Upham's positions were outstandingly well done. Here at last he was able to mesh his own downright opinions with those of the text-book writers; and he drove his men on to accomplish a lot of work in a short time. Den Fountaine, then second-in-command of the company, and later to become a full colonel, has since described Upham's work at Riakia as "a marvellous job".

Upham, too, respected the importance of camouflage. He studied it eagerly, made his men work at it hour after hour. It was one of those things he became very intense about. One day he gave a lecture on camouflage to a large audience, expounding his theories with fervour and sincerity. When it was over he stood alongside Frank Hill, a quartermaster-sergeant whom he had known since 1939. "How did I do?" he asked Hill, his voice shaking.

Hill was surprised to notice that Upham was still trembling with nervousness. To a man who is normally intense and highly strung, illness can be a greater burden than to others. The battalion had not been long in Greece before Upham developed dysentery. At first it was not disabling but it saw him becoming irritable and quick-tempered. He became loudly impatient too often and too quickly, and was unduly bitter against the alleged inadequacies of higher commanders. But it was only the approach of real war beginning to expose the depths of his belligerence and hatred for the enemy. Illness merely put an unpleasant sharpness on that side of his character.

On 6th April 1941 Germany attacked Greece and Yugoslavia. They had already been in Bulgaria, on the north-eastern border of Greece. Now they attacked across the border, soon ravaging Salonika and advancing south towards the New Zealand positions near Katerini.

In addition, they swept into Yugoslavia and made short work
of opposition there. That gave them a clear run into Greece by
the central route. If they pressed on down there through the
Monastir Gap they would isolate the Katerini defences on the
east coast.

Barely forty-eight hours passed after Germany's declaration of
war before the New Zealanders were moving back from the
Katerini positions, in realization that the collapse of the Yugo-
slavs opened up Monastir and made Katerini untenable.

Two brigades dropped back to the Mount Olympus area, leaving
the Divisional Cavalry to nibble at the enemy and slow down the
advance. The 4th Brigade (including the 20th Battalion) was sent
over to the central front, on the road running south from the
Monastir Gap, to an area near the town of Servia. There,
Upham's platoon was posted at an important local crossroads to
check the streams of refugees beginning to pour down from the
north. There were civilians with their pathetic burdens, Yugo-
slav troops, Greek soldiers with nothing left to fight with but
courage, and an expected proportion of fifth columnists.

It seemed quite a friendly war at first. Overhead came German
reconnaissance planes, confident in the skies in the absence of
British aircraft, flying casually low over the hill-tops.

Upham waited for the real war. He disregarded the observation
planes. It was futile trying concealment in these positions.

Kippenberger had other thoughts.

"Why aren't your men under cover?" he demanded sharply.

Upham said it was waste of time.

"Then when the real thing comes," Kip continued, "you'll find
your men will be too slow. They'll think it's another snooper.
You'll have casualties."

Upham learnt quickly. During 11th April bombing and
machine-gunning from the air could be seen ahead. Refugees
thickened. More enemy planes appeared above. One German
pilot flew brazenly low over the defenders, waving from his
cockpit. The Kiwis admired his cheek and waved back. The plane
flew on, banked, and swung back along the same route. Another
wave?

War came to the 20th Battalion as the pilot, his little game over,
abruptly dived and strafed them savagely.

Then they turned as they heard the sound of more engines,
coming up from a new direction. Our planes this time? Upham
suddenly yelled: "Duck quick . . . they're Heinkels!" And as his
platoon went to earth, bombs came raining down.

Upham's cross-roads became a favourite target. More and more planes came over, dropping their bombs along the roads, into the villages, seeking out the artillery positions. They had it all their own way. British planes had done their best but there had been pitifully few of them from the start. Upham stood on a large rock as German fighters swept overhead. John McIlwraith, a sergeant of C Company and an old friend, squatted beside him and wondered why Charles wasn't wearing a tin hat. Upham's men often wondered at that later. In Greece, on Crete, into the inferno of Minqar Qaim, through the disaster on Ruweisat Ridge—Upham often wore no helmet, but came on to the battlefield wearing an officer's soft cap, making him look like a casual observer who had wandered into the wrong territory.

It was not till after the war that he offered the only known explanation. Pressed by a friend for his reasons, finally, rather gruffly, he said: "Because I could hardly ever find a tin hat to fit me."

He certainly had a large head—a "leonine head", one writer described it. If he found a suitable hat he would wear it. But if he couldn't get the right size in the first three or four he tried it is likely he gave up the search.

McIlwraith checked the Bren gun in his hands. The next plane that came in low enough he would have a good go at. At least it would make them fly a bit higher—might even get a lucky hit. Over they came, confident, almost contemptuous. McIlwraith cocked the gun, swung the barrel up, and emptied a whole magazine at the nearest plane as it zoomed past at tree-top level. He clamped another mag into the Bren, watched silently as the plane banked round at the end of the valley. It was going to make another run at them. Then there was a voice beside him. "Let's have a go, Mac!" and Upham was eyeing the Bren gun eagerly.

But now the plane was shrieking down at them again, and suddenly Upham was snatching the Bren from him. McIlwraith felt himself thrust behind a great boulder, and saw Upham standing upright in the open, lining up the attacking plane as it roared in to strafe them; and then a long sustained burst from the Bren, and then the plane was above, gone, and Upham was cursing furiously because he had missed it.

Then he was moving away, running quickly from one section to another. "You chaps all right?" he was calling.

By 13th April 1941 New Zealanders sat astride three of the

main lines of advance into southern Greece. Greek armies were on the western side of the peninsula. New Zealand 4th Brigade was around Servia, in the centre; the 5th Brigade on the slopes of Mount Olympus, with the 6th a little to the rear; while a solitary battalion squatted on the extreme east coast watching the Platamon rail tunnel. All these routes converged and joined together as they continued south—so that a successful German attack down any of the four routes would cut off the defenders holding the other three.

That turned out to be the story of Greece. The Germans attacked down every line, suffering heavy casualties at every place where they ran on to the New Zealand defences. But down the western side the Greeks had no weapons to match the German panzers, and it was only a matter of time before the invaders would sweep through to the south, regardless of how long the defences in the centre and the east held out.

Next day, the 14th, the air blitz continued. But already it was obvious that even the new defences could not be held. Enemy pressure increased on the 15th. On the Servia front German infantry moved towards the New Zealanders, but were heavily manhandled. But successes like these had no sweet taste. There was no advance and counter-attack to emphasize the enemy's discomfiture. Minor victories had to be won merely to gain time for retreat. Good soldiers hate that kind of fighting.

Even at Thermopylae the line could not be maintained. Hardly had the New Zealanders arrived there before word came that the Greeks on the western side had broken up and capitulated. The Germans would be in behind Thermopylae before many hours passed. No more could be done for Greece. Evacuation was ordered.

The 6th Brigade held Thermopylae while the other two brigades fell back towards the beaches. Time for evacuation had to be gained. Artillery attached to the 6th fired 30,000 rounds in fifteen hours, then destroyed their guns after they had fired their last shell. Then the 6th turned and made for the coast.

Now the 4th Brigade, the men who had stood at Servia, had to act as the delaying force. While the 5th and 6th went to the beaches, the 4th took its stand near Kriekouki, not far from Athens. They thought they could hold on there for two days, but orders came that they would have to stay an additional twenty-four hours. Kriekouki was christened "Twenty-four Hour Pass."

C Company of the 20th was alongside the road at Kriekouki

Pass. During the three days the battalion was there, many a question was asked why messengers from C Company—from 15 Platoon in particular—kept foraging around for tins of condensed milk.

"They're for Charlie Upham—the boss," came the reply. "He can't eat anything else. Got dysentery. Can hardly walk. Be lucky if he gets away." And for three days his faithful platoon fed Upham with condensed milk while his weight went down and down.

If he couldn't walk around his section posts then he would ride. So Kriekouki became used to the spectacle of Charles astride a donkey, painfully moving along the hillsides, up to Company Headquarters and around his section posts. He rode in to Battalion H.Q. on the final day to thank them for his tins of milk. He looked very sick.

It was difficult to move around. While he did what he could on his donkey, Upham found he had to use Eric Le Gros for more message work than usual. Leggy and Charles bandied abuse at each other. There was probably never a more disrespectful batman. Indeed, the platoon sometimes wondered who was batman to whom.

Leggy returned from a long walk to Battalion H.Q. Charles was sitting on the ground, face drawn, but his voice cheerful as he said: "Thanks, Leggy-boy. Get there all right?"

"Yeah. I found the bludgers. I bet they'll clear out and leave us here . . . you see."

"You reckon, Leggy-boy? I don't. But, here . . . I've made a mug of tea. Have some. You make such a lousy cup of tea I reckon I might do it myself in future."

Leggy took the mug, tasted it carefully, then pulled a face. "Christ, that's awful," he said. "Can't you make better tea than that?"

Upham laughed. "Grateful, aren't you? You know, you're a damned awful batman, Leggy. I should have taken Spout Fountaine's advice and given you the chop months ago. . . . Now, where are my boots?"

Leggy looked uncomfortable. "You mean—the spare pair? Well . . . actually they're gone. I gave 'em to an old Greek geezer when we were passing through Larissa."

"Gave 'em away? What the hell for?"

It took Leggy-boy quite a time to admit that he was one of a number of bright lads who found a bombed-out bank in Larissa. There were banknotes everywhere. Leggy helped himself to a good collection and was still having great trouble finding enough room for them in his pack.

"Well, what's that got to do with my boots?"

"Don't you see, boss, someone had to keep a look-out for the M.P.s. Couldn't expect the old boy to do it for nothing—so I gave him your boots. Do you want a share of the notes? Reckon they're worth a good lot."

Upham looked at him more in sorrow than in anger. "If you weren't on active service, Leggy-boy, you'd deserve to get court-martialled for that. But I suppose the Jerries would have got them if you hadn't. So shut up about the whole thing. Now get me that donkey. I want to go down to the 18th . . . eh, what's that?"

Leggy hastily retrieved the donkey from a quartermaster-sergeant in the 19th, to whom Leggy was hiring the donkey at so much per hour.

Finally, in the nights, the ships came and lay off the beaches, while 40,000 troops were taken off to safety and to fight again elsewhere.

"That's a heavy load, soldier," the Navy type would say, as the exhausted soldier clambered aboard. "Here, I'll look after it." So the soldier gratefully surrendered the pack of extra food, his bedroll, looted money, and precious comforts that he had been jealously harbouring all the way from Monastir. And the Navy man's method of looking after it was to pitch it into the sea. "No room for it, chum—got to get eight hundred men on here tonight. Go on, get down below. You'll find plenty of cocoa and bread-and-butter."

Below decks it was all warmth, kindliness, and generosity.

While down at the southern tip of Greece, at a little port called Kalamata, the New Zealanders took part in the last organized resistance. One by one the beaches had been closed by the advancing Germans until, at the end, the last few thousand defenders gathered uncomfortably in Kalamata. But no miracle of rescue could be done for them, though many could have been saved but for inescapable confusion in a time of great difficulty.

But here in Kalamata, with rescue gone, the New Zealanders still fought. For a few hours lightly armed Aussies and Kiwis disputed the town against the might of a German panzer unit. Jack Hinton, a forthright sergeant of the 20th, won his V.C. as he moved around the streets, destroying enemy nests that were gradually pressing the last Allied troops closer in to the sea. Others fought with him, courageous but hopeless little battles, with the inevitable end only a matter of time.

Looking back on the futile Greek campaign, it gives a little comfort to believe that it served some good moral cause, and that it delayed the eastward advance of Hitler's armies. The truth of history is not so comforting. It is now apparent that the political decision to enter Greece was taken without the fullest military appreciation that was necessary; all the facts were not disclosed to the New Zealand and Australian Governments who were to supply the bulk of the fighting troops; and, from the moral viewpoint, it is an open question whether the helter-skelter withdrawal, so soon after the fighting began, did Britain's prestige more harm than the good created by the noble effort to help a threatened little country.

With adequate air support the original plan might possibly have checked the Germans. But when the Greeks reduced the measure of their own contribution, and Middle East Command had to retain in the desert some of the forces previously earmarked for Greece, the project became more than merely hazardous. It became quite hopeless.

Hopeless causes sometimes have to be fought. It is at least doubtful if there were sufficient reasons for such a hopeless cause as this, weighed against the sadness in 2500 New Zealand homes (or 6600 British homes for that matter) whose sons died, suffered, or went into captivity. It was only the courage and resourcefulness of lesser men that atoned in some measure for the ill-judged decisions of the greater ones.

CHAPTER SIX

INVASION OF CRETE

FORTY thousand men could not have been rescued from Greece if the Navy had delivered each ship-load to Egypt before returning for more. So the majority of the Allied troops were dropped off at Crete, the Greek island lying sixty miles south of the mainland.

By chance, some well-equipped troops were taken straight to Egypt. By equal, but unhappy chance, a great many more arrived in Crete with few arms and fewer supplies. There were drivers without trucks, artillerymen without guns, signallers without wire. These men, of reduced military value when parted from their specialist equipment, had to be fed and clothed like the rest. The 400,000 Cretan civilians also now expected the British forces to maintain them.

Crete possessed some strategic value, and the Germans intended to invade it very soon. It would be an attack from the air with paratroops and troop-carrying aircraft, designed to drop the invaders into several obvious target areas. A seaborne landing would also be attempted, but that could safely be left to the Navy to deal with. But the air invasion could not be stopped half-way. The New Zealanders had nearly a month before the blow fell. They were given an area to defend that stretched from Canea, a town on the northern coast, westward along the shoreline to the Maleme airfield—a strip about ten miles long. It was laced with ridges and streams running from the central mountains to the sea, clothed with olive trees and vines, with only one substantial road that ran parallel with the northern coastline.

It was certain that the air assault would be directed at the airfield and on other flat ground within the New Zealanders' defences.

The Kiwis camped and dug under the olive trees, swam on the beaches and in the streams, and waited—and waited—for the equipment to come that would give them a reasonable chance of fighting the battle on equal terms. But when the battle came, and was fought, and lost, it was not the courage of men that failed. It was the failure to give them the tools of war that rendered their defeat inevitable.

There were few picks and shovels, so men dug trenches with bayonets. Any unit that had a truck was envied. Mortars without baseplates, Vickers guns without tripods, artillery without sights —from the beginning, right through to the end, it was a pauper's campaign.

Major-General Freyberg, the New Zealand G.O.C., was put in command of all Allied Forces. He accepted appointment as a duty, but regarded the chance of successfully defending the island as precarious. He signalled his Government in New Zealand:

"The decision has been taken in London that Crete must be held . . . it can be held only with the full support of the Navy and Air Force. The air force on the island consists of six Hurricanes and seventeen obsolete aircraft. Troops can and will fight but, as the result of the campaign in Greece, are devoid of any artillery and have insufficient tools for digging, little transport, and inadequate war reserves of equipment and ammunition. I recommend that you bring pressure on the highest plane in London either to supply us with sufficient means to defend the island or to review the decision that Crete must be held."

That was on 1st May 1941. The New Zealand Government supported him. Fraser cabled Churchill stating that the situation was regarded as one of the utmost gravity.

But Wellington received no reply to the request that the decision to hold Crete be reviewed. The days and the weeks conveniently passed, until finally it was too late to do anything but fight the invaders with such means as Freyberg had available to him. Middle East Command, under Wavell, did its best to feed in supplies, but it was a profitless enterprise, with ships able to unload for only three hours in the middle of each night. Freyberg realized his peril and sensed that others did not. He signalled Wavell to "introduce a little reality into the calculations for the defence of Crete".

The Germans bombed the island incessantly. Suda Bay, the main harbour near Canea, became a graveyard of ships, with a huge pall of smoke overhanging it night and day. The bombers and fighters paraded overhead, looking for targets, softening up the vital areas where the defenders knew the attacks would come.

The nights were bitterly cold. It was merely in conformity with the general shortage of supplies that there were no groundsheets and bedding, and one blanket had to be shared. Charles Upham and Eric le Gros shared their blanket, and night after night woke in mutual accusation, hotly blaming the other for taking more than his fair share. One night their disagreement reached its climax. Upham suddenly stopped their verbal war. "All right, Leggy," he said calmly. "There's only one way to settle this. You take that end, I'll take this. . . . Now fold 'er over . . . right? Now get your bayonet. . . ."

And with elaborate care they used Leggy's bayonet to split the blanket down the middle, solemnly dividing it into two equal, satisfying, but utterly useless halves.

Invasion came on the morning of 20th May 1941. The battle lasted nine days, but the Germans had won Crete by the evening of the first day. It began like most other days. At six in the morning the planes were overhead, bombing and strafing, but this morning there seemed a greater intensity about it. Yet when this bombardment fell away, and allowed the troops to begin their breakfast, there was little to suggest that this day would be different from the others.

But about a quarter to eight a new attack developed. Overhead the bombers swept in again, fighter planes swooping amongst them, and against vital targets an air blitz of great ferocity was mounted.

Maleme airfield came in for special attention and around the perimeter the intensity of the bombing was so severe that men who had gone through the artillery barrages at the Somme stated later that this was more terrible. Further afield, from out over the sea, the roar of an approaching air armada beat upon the ears.

Then through the bedlam and the fiery skies planes of strange shape were seen manoeuvring, coming in over the island little more than 400-500 feet up. All at once the fury seemed to abate, as if to leave the skies clear for something new. And to the men clinging deep in their slit trenches a spectacle as bizarre and unreal as anything in the history of warfare was unfolded. Black dots suddenly fell from the bellies of the low-flying planes. In an instant the dots were blossoming into parachutes, hundreds upon hundreds of them, swaying swiftly earthwards, filling the sky with their different colours.

There seemed then a moveless pause, as if the defenders were transfixed by this amazing sight. But only for a few seconds. There was no long delay as the parachutes wafted down. On the contrary, they seemed to descend with quick and dangerous suddenness. There was hardly time to aim and fire, but then the crackle of rifle-fire began, swelled into a chorus, Bren guns added their chatter, and the bodies of paratroopers began to twist and squirm as they came near the earth. Many fell out of range of our guns, organized themselves quickly, picked up their supplies and heavy weapons that had floated down with other 'chutes, and moved swiftly into attacking formations.

But those who fell close by the New Zealanders learnt a lesson that Hitler never repeated during World War II. Of 136 who landed near 18th Battalion only two survived. The rest were destroyed in the air or within minutes of their landing. A hundred more dropping near the village of Galatas fared no better.

A wave of paratroopers swung to earth by the lines of an engineers' unit. Their descent was watched by an infantry head-quarters not far away. "Ring up those engineers," the infantry C.O. ordered sharply. "Can't expect sappers to deal with para-troops. Tell them we'll send over help."

Back came the reply. "Thanks, but don't bother. They'll all be dead before you can get a man over here."

The engineers were almost true to their word. 126 men jumped that day into the teeth of the belligerent sappers. A mere fourteen escaped the fate of the 112 others.

These were minor examples of the torrid reception that the defenders of Crete gave Hitler's prize troops on the first day of the battle. The enemy landed 10,000 men that day. By nightfall only 6000 remained active. But the parachutists were not all. Long-winged, stubby aircraft came sidling in over the defences, completely silent, planing steadily downwards, or circling cumbrously like great useless birds. Gliders. Towed six at a time by heavy Junkers planes and released when they crossed the coast, the gliders swept in low over the defences, inexpressibly menacing and sinister.

The glider troops were hotly engaged the moment they came within range. But many gliders chose the safe undefended ground west of the Maleme airfield, bumping and crashing their way to earth, disgorging their crews into sheltered valleys where they could re-form and prepare for battle.

Back in its reserve area near Canea, the 20th Battalion watched the landings and listened to the growing noise of fighting.

Charles Upham said to his batman: "They told us it would be this morning, Leggy. Good Intelligence work somewhere."

"I suppose they knew what time it would be, too," said Le Gros.

"That's right," said Charles. "We were told to expect it between eight and nine o'clock."

"Jeezes," Leggy said wonderingly, looking over the ridges towards the smoke and fire in the direction of Maleme. "Didn't think these Jerries could be *that* accurate. . . . Heh—had your milk this morning?"

Upham nodded rather heavily. His dysentery had become worse. He could take only condensed milk. He was feeling pretty weak.

Then Den Fountaine came running over. He was in command of C Company now that Major Wilson had gone over to organize a crowd of Greek recruits somewhere up in the battle-line.

Fountaine said: "Charlie, some paratroops have come down over there between us and the 19th. Get a few men there smartly and clean 'em out, will you?"

Upham called on a handful of men from his platoon and moved quickly away, down through the trees, along a gully, then up to a ridge. Over the ridge they saw the 'chutes lying on the ground, tangled in the trees. "Cover me!" he said shortly. They knew what to do. They had practised it often enough. The men went to ground, picking their cover, and began firing steadily into the area where the 'chutes lay. Upham went round the flank, moving quickly forward and out of sight. Five minutes later they heard a flurry of shots. Then silence. He was soon back, appearing suddenly out of the olive trees, swinging a German helmet in one hand. "She's right now," he said, his voice sharp with excitement. He didn't tell them any more.

The main German landings were made in three areas. One large group dropped into the Prison Valley, a few miles inland, and quickly scattered some Greek forces; but by the end of the day had made little progress against the New Zealand defence line in that area. Another group landed west of the Maleme airfield and continued to be reinforced throughout the day. There were no troops available to keep them engaged.

The most serious lodgment was made around the Maleme 'drome, held by the 22nd Battalion of 5th Brigade. The fight there went on all day. However, all communications broke down, pockets of paratroops caused casualties if the defenders attempted movement, and the Germans diverted more and more men to the attack on the airfield, the capture of which would open all western Crete to the invaders.

By late afternoon the Kiwis around the 'drome were out of touch with their own headquarters and with one another. Battalion and Brigade Headquarters farther back gained only a confused and pessimistic view of the situation.

With the Germans gradually gaining a foothold on the vital airfield, counter-attack was imperative. If 5th Brigade could not lay on the counter-attack with their own men, then someone else would have to do it—4th Brigade, no doubt. In command of 4th Brigade was Brigadier L. M. Inglis, later to command the division and to become an Occupation Force judge in Germany. With his brigade not heavily handled, Inglis knew that his should be the counter-attacking role, his task to move inland south of the busy 5th Brigade, then turn northwards up the Tavronitis River straight on to Maleme 'drome. He thought he could do it successfully with two battalions. So he asked for orders to counter-attack, conscious that delay would be fatal. All day long he could see the signs of a big enemy build-up proceeding unmolested in the safe areas west of the airfield. That build-up had to be interfered with. Time was of the essence.

But back in the places where greater decisions had to be made there was the knowledge that the enemy were also landing at Retimo and Heraklion, two other airstrips on the island, and reserves might be urgently wanted there; that more waves of airborne troops might any moment descend on the same hills and valleys that would be left only lightly defended if much of 4th Brigade moved away westwards to the counter-attack. A sea-borne landing, too, was known to be in the German plans. Troops had to be kept back to meet that threat.

When finally the word came through to Inglis—"Counter-attack not permitted"—his Brigade Major leapt up and shouted: "Then we've lost Crete! We've lost Crete!"

Inglis snorted: "You don't need to tell me that."

It is idle to speculate what would have happened to the battle for Crete if that withdrawal had not taken place. But un-doubtedly, if the men of the 22nd had been allowed to stay, and a counter-attack had been quickly and strongly laid on, the battle would have run differently.

After the war Inglis spent an afternoon with General Student, the German commander of the invasion.

"What would have happened," Inglis asked, "if I had been permitted to counter-attack you that afternoon?"

Student said: "If you had done so, I could not have held Crete. You had knocked me about so much that day, particularly my paratroops, that I could not have resisted a counter-attack. After the way you smashed up my units on landing, all day long we waited for your counter-attack. We feared it, we thought it must come, and were amazed that it didn't."

CHAPTER SEVEN

CRISIS AT MALEME

The next day, 21st May 1941, saw the Germans massing reinforce-ments into Maleme. Some of our guns still played on the airfield and on the nearby beaches, where troop-carriers attempted land-ings; but by afternoon planes were landing on the 'drome at the rate of one every three minutes. With Maleme secured, the German plan would be to advance east to Canea, rolling up the New Zealanders on the way.

There was sharp fighting with our advanced battalions, but the enemy made little progress against the defences. Smarting under his heavy casualties of the opening day, he was content to concentrate on building up men and supplies, probing forward where he could.

During the day it was belatedly realized at Force H.Q. that all would be lost unless Maleme were recaptured. A counter-attack had to be made. But by day the air strafing was insuperable and prohibited practically all movement. So the counter-attack on the airfield would have to be a night show. It would have to go in that same night—another day's delay would make success impossible. Even now it might prove to be already too late.

It was decided that the attack would be given to the 20th and the 28th Battalions. They would first be moved up to a start line during the early hours of the night; then, when all was ready, they would advance westward, side by side, a distance of about four miles, until they reached the 'drome. They would have to swarm on to the field and capture it before dawn, or daylight would make them open targets for the German guns. The four-mile strip of ground the attackers had to cross before reaching the 'drome was known to be occupied by the enemy. How thick the enemy were, and how many guns they had defending that ground, could be found out only in the face-to-face experience of the night attack. For such an enterprise against unknown dangers, few better troops could have been allotted than the keenly trained men of Kippenberger's 20th and the fiery Maoris of the 28th.

No forward move could be made, however, until an Australian unit arrived by truck from further east, took over the 20th's defence positions, and handed over its vehicles to the 20th to take the men forward to the start line. With the Australians scheduled to arrive about 8 p.m. all would be well; the 20th would embus and move west. By 1 a.m. the four-mile advance against the aerodrome would begin.

Dusk came; drifted into night. Restless and impatient, the 20th waited in their slit trenches amidst the olive groves, listening for the sound of the Australian convoy. They were keyed up for the occasion, ready and eager to fight, all ranks knowing that the counter-attack on Maleme that night was crucial. The hours passed. Eight o'clock . . . then nine . . . ten . . . and Lieutenant-Colonel J. T. Burrows, now commanding the 20th while Kippenberger had a brigade, felt his anxiety growing, as there was still no sign of the Australians. Every hour of the night was precious. It would be madness if his men were still in the open when the next dawn rose up over the vales of Crete. But he was helpless and immobile. The arrival of the trucks was out of his hands.

It was not till 1 a.m.—the very hour when the attack should have been going in—that the first party of the unfortunate Aussies arrived. They had been bombed and strafed when they started, delayed for hours by casualties and wreckage suffered at the very beginning of their move. Even now they brought only enough trucks to lift two companies of the 20th—less than half the battalion.

"Get started with what you can," Burrows was told. "Start the advance with only two companies. The rest will follow."

The attack on Maleme began. They moved off in the darkness, sections spread out, just a few muttered words setting the whole line in motion.

Down into a shallow gully, up the other side, all trying to keep quiet, through a hedge at the top, and across the first field of vines. Then there were trees, looming dimly through the night like broken buildings.

Each man strained his eyes ahead, peering into the darkness, watching the shadowy outlines of the country gradually unfolding. Four miles of this before they reached the 'drome. They were advancing against the line of the country—all the gullies ran across their path, all the vines and hedges had to be climbed through, one after another. They made the first mile in that fashion.

Out on the right somewhere was D Company, its flank advancing along the beach. Then came C Company, and across the road, somewhere in the darkness, the Maoris were picking their way forward. But over them all the dark bowl of the night was already beginning to fade—a new day was not far away, and not a shot had yet been fired.

Then sharply through the night came the first rifle-shot, not a hundred yards away, then another, and another, and suddenly the air was filled with the sound of it. Machine-guns broke into their chatter, and through the darkness lines of tracer came weaving in fiery patterns.

The New Zealanders surged ahead. But they found now, and as the attack continued on and on, that the Germans had spread themselves right through this country, with posts established behind trees, in houses, in ditches, wherever there was cover. Pockets of enemy riflemen and machine-gunners were scattered in depth along the whole route of the advance. As our men pressed forward the fire came at them in the front, from the sides, even from behind.

Upham's platoon had moved steadily forward across the fields, waiting for the first sound, wondering how far they would go before it came. They climbed up a rise, through a small hedge; shook themselves out again into line, then moved cautiously across the open field. There was a large tree square in front of them. They plodded on, each man's feelings and fears like a huge private world inside him. With a dinning gabble, a machine-gun burst into action from behind the tree, only sixty yards ahead.

"Down! Down!" Upham was shouting, and they hurled themselves to the ground. But it was already too late for some. Four of the platoon were hit.

Now came the test of training. Each section-leader had to make his own instant decision. Could his men survive where they were or must they find better cover? Some stayed where they dropped to earth, relatively safe in the undulations of the ground. Others wormed their way on their stomachs to better cover, lay there panting while the tracer bit through the air inches above their heads. Now it was up to the platoon commander. One machine-gun can't stop an advance. His was the next responsibility.

Upham crawled from one section to the next, giving them their orders, showing them the route they had to follow. They all had to get nearer—closer in on the gun. So one by one they moved again, squirming from cover to cover, with Upham in front of them, till finally he had them barely forty yards from the tree. Then they waited for him to make the next move. He told them what he planned to do.

They began firing at the tree, at the gun-flashes, at the patches of deep darkness that lay in its shadow.

Hill-Rennie, the man on the extreme left of the platoon, watched Upham moving like a hunter round to the side, drifting silently from one shadow to the next. The Germans were firing wildly now, conscious that some out-flanking movement was under way, but pinned down by the steady covering fire from the grounded men of the platoon.

Upham was drawing grenades out of his pouches, loosening the pins. He drew one pin right out, held the grenade in his hand, fingers pressed down on the lever.

It was curious the way he was feeling. There was excitement and tremendous tension; but above all he was aware of an icy fury possessing him—not a feeling of hot reckless rage, but a deliberate deep savagery—and it had started the moment he saw four of his boys roll agonizingly to the ground. The first moment they had really seen action—and now they were dead or wounded. The hatred of it took hold of him, the hatred of war, the hatred of the enemy—the enemy crouching behind that tree, just a few yards away in the semi-darkness.

And now Upham was almost behind the tree, his figure a mere shadowy outline as Hill-Rennie peered at the spot. He saw Upham gathering himself up on to his knees, crouching forward, poised as if to spring. This was the moment when one man had to risk everything in a burst of tremendous action.

Upham suddenly moved. In one rushing moment he was up on his feet . . . his arm swung over . . . the grenade arced towards the machine-gunners . . . there was the splitting crash of its explosion. . . .

And he was rushing in . . . hurling another grenade . . . and another straight after it. The succession of bomb-bursts hit against their eardrums like a repeating hammer.

Straight at the German nest Upham was running, and he was firing his pistol ahead of him . . . there seemed to be a burst from a sub-machine-gun, firing straight at him. . . .

The others watched the sudden fury of noise and action. Then he was calling to them in a high-pitched, penetrating voice, and waving to them to come forward. They leapt to their feet and ran to the tree. He was standing there beside the gun, breathing heavily.

There had been eight paratroopers there—seven with sub-machine-guns; another behind the bigger gun that had first torn into the platoon. They were all dead.

"There'll be plenty more like that," he said sharply. "Come on, let's get cracking again. Don't bunch . . . spread out. We don't want to get copped standing here."

They began pushing on slowly again. By this time it was much lighter, and they could see the shape of a house standing on the edge of the road just ahead. Behind it was a shed.

And again it suddenly came—the fiery stream of tracer leaping towards them, and the staccato of the enemy machine-guns, one from a window of the house, another from the shed.

They literally flung themselves to the ground this time, rolling like seasoned veterans into the nearest cover. They got the Brens into action, firing short sharp bursts at the windows, watching for any sign of movement.

Then in the half-light they saw Upham running again, dashing ahead with head bent low, racing past the house and up to the walls of the shed. For a few moments he was protected there, while he edged his way along the wall towards the door. They kept up a rain of bullets to cover him while he crouched there in the open.

It was light enough now to see him reaching for his grenades. They were beginning to realize that he was carrying grenades all over him. One dead German lay with arm outstretched through the outhouse door. They watched Upham pull the pin of a grenade, jump forward and place the bomb fairly in the dead man's hand, then crouch back.

With the explosion, Upham was shouting to them, his voice ringing through the night.

"Come on!" he roared back to them. "Come in quick!" And the platoon sprang forward as one man and dashed towards the buildings.

It was enough. Half a dozen Germans came tumbling out of the house, hands held high. Inside the shed eight more were found wounded.

On again . . . on . . . on. The men of 15 Platoon found Charles amongst them one moment, the next he was out in front, scouting the way ahead. He was talking excitedly, shouting encouragement, drawing them on by his personal example. And all the time the light was growing stronger. More vines . . . more hedges and trees . . . the houses were becoming thicker. There was fire everywhere now, out towards D Company on the right, over the road where the Maoris were, straight ahead where their path lay, and the tracer seemed to draw curved lines across their path, as if to say "this far and no farther".

They couldn't burst through this line of tracer. It was coming in from the right, in long fiery bursts, flashing across their front from a gun way out on the flank. There was no dodging this one. They hesitated, crouching low in the grass. But now Upham was beside them. He was saying: "It's high, chest high. That won't hurt anyone. Come on . . . we're going to crawl through underneath."

And on hands and knees he led them towards the path of the tracer, closer and closer, and they watched him go right underneath it, rise to his feet on the other side. They followed, resisting the temptation to go flat on their stomachs as they crawled past the deadliest spot.

There were few men not afraid. As in all fighting, there were moments of cold terror. But Upham's men found themselves watching the boss, wondering at his apparent indifference to fear, prepared to rush in and follow so long as he led.

Another machine-gun barked suddenly at them. There it was —in that window in the corner. One of our men was hit—in the stomach—and he let out a cry and rolled on the ground in agony.

His mate dashed to him, tried to hold him still. Upham's face contorted. He looked towards the gun and the words came out of him like a vow. "Leave that bastard to me! I'll fix him!" He made this his personal war.

So while the others covered him with fire, he moved quickly round to the flank, Le Gros close behind him. Then when there was no more cover he broke out, rushed straight for the window, grenade in hand. Away went the pin, he threw it like a baseball player, and the crash came as it exploded inside the window.

Le Gros had a Tommy-gun. He kept firing at the window while Upham raced round to find the back door.

Something stuck into Le Gros' back—something like the barrel of a gun. He shouted, stood dead still. In a moment Upham was back, sprinting round the corner of the building, saw the hefty German towering over Le Gros. Upham flung himself at the man, hitting him with his fist, beating him to the ground.

But another German, confused or unheeding, came stumbling in from the fields, making for the house. He carried no weapons. Upham seized him round the neck, started hitting him over the the head with the butt of his revolver.

Gradually he broke the German's resistance, sent him sprawling on the ground. "Get him out! Take him away!" he ordered loudly as his platoon swarmed around.

At this moment Peter Maxwell, one of D Company's officers, appeared in the morning light. He had not had a hard time of it so far—his real fight was yet to come—and he had come over to see if Upham needed any help.

Maxwell said: "Why didn't you just shoot him, Charlie?"

But that was futile advice. Upham had a vendetta now. He would show the Huns they couldn't kill his boys without answering for it.

Forward again. Now into a little village called Pirgos the platoon moved determinedly. It was almost full daylight now. It seemed that every house held a German, firing, sniping . . . They moved from house to house, clearing one after another.

Fire started coming at them from yet another house in front.

Eric Le Gros kept close beside Upham, followed apprehensively as he began walking straight up the garden path towards the house. To make a smaller target Le Gros pressed himself against the wall. Then he watched as Upham began circling around to the back.

Charles turned, appearing to notice Le Gros for the first time. He scowled. "You stay there, Leggy-boy," he ordered.

"No, I'm coming too. What's good enough for you, boss . . ."

Upham turned full round to face him. "I said stay back there!" he shouted. "You get out of this. You'll get killed. . . ."

The platoon moved up cautiously, then demonstrated the art of house clearing. While the rest of the building was kept under fire, one of the N.C.O.s kicked the door in suddenly, threw in a grenade, and they rushed in before the dust cleared.

But now there were casualties coming faster and faster, and the thump of a captured Bofors gun was reverberating through the village. Hill-Rennie and two others crept up the ditch towards the Bofors. They began firing at the gunner, forcing him to keep down.

Upham waited till his men were all firing. Then, dropping to his stomach, he squirmed his way forward, yard by yard, thirty, twenty, fifteen, ten yards, unslinging his beloved grenades as he inched closer.

Then sharply, surely, over swept his arm, a grenade curled through the air, and with a roar Bofors and German gunner were destroyed as the boys raced in to support their leader.

House after house they edged onwards. Daylight now; what hope was there now of capturing the 'drome? How had D Company on the right got on? A lot of fighting over there by the sound of it, and they seemed to be farther forward. They must be close to the airfield.

Now there was a culvert, with Germans holed up beneath it, firing along the road. Colonel Burrows with his Battalion Headquarters was right up now with the assaulting troops, watching 15 Platoon go to work on the culvert. Corporal McKegney had started off with eleven grenades hung around him. They were nearly all gone, but the boss seemed to have an inexhaustible supply.

Next they came to a line of bamboos. Upham broke through them first, McKegney close behind, with Puck Wesley alongside.

The two Germans were standing not five yards ahead, waiting for the New Zealanders to come into the open. They looked startled, but the one with a sub-machine-gun was quick to react. He lifted it sharply to his hip. Upham moved like lightning. His pistol flashed up and he pulled the trigger before the German could steady his gun. The man pitched to one side and the gun dropped to earth. One gone.

But from out on the flank Fountaine saw the incident and caught his breath in sudden alarm. For the second German was raising his rifle quickly, while Upham seemed to be still watching the man who had just fallen. Fountaine could see it all happening, but he was too far away to intervene. But Upham was awake to it. Up came his pistol again. He pressed the trigger.

The pin clicked on an empty chamber. With the vision of the German already about to fire, he seized his other pistol, the Luger, fumbled desperately with it, not sure that he knew exactly how it worked.

He would have been dead an instant later. But Wesley threw up his rifle, fired quickly, and killed the German. The muzzle of his rifle was within inches of Upham's ear as the shot blasted out.

Charles turned quickly to him. "Thank you, Puck," he said gratefully. "I was a goner."

But as the fighting progressed through Pirgos, this morning of 22nd May, the opposition became more inflexible. It was 7 a.m. by now, and casualties were mounting gravely. With Germans established in buildings and behind walls, any movement in the open became more and more hazardous. Obviously the attack was grinding to a halt. Burrows knew that he could get no farther. The Maoris, too, had struck immovable opposition on their inland route.

What of D Company, though, hard by the beach? Striking light opposition in the early stages, they had pushed ahead fast, outstripping C Company on its left. Forward they pressed, till finally, in full daylight, their forward sections reached the edge of the 'drome. There they came under tremendous fire, making it utterly impossible to attempt a crossing of the 'drome, and forcing them to fall back a few chains to a position of cover. B Company, one of those who had made a very late start, followed in behind, and it, too, reached a point not far short of the 'drome. Then it was pinned down by the violence of the enemy fire.

Lieutenant Jack Bain, a platoon officer from Headquarters Company who had followed behind C Company, came up to Upham in Pirgos. Men were lying wounded in the open, casualties were piling up, and progress now was irretrievably halted.

Upham said to Bain: "What do we do, Jack?"

"We'll have to get out," Bain said. "Everything's bogged down."

Upham swore. "If we'd had another hour," he said, "we'd have been through to the 'drome."

"Someone's got close," Bain said. "Listen to that shooting over near the 'drome. Sounds as if D Company's getting stuck in."

Upham said: "We'd better get Fitz here out. He's wounded. Wait till I get a door."

So Charles broke a door off its hinges from a nearby house.

Bain, Upham, and two others lifted Fitzgerald on to the door. Then they started back, straight down the street in full view of the enemy. The others watched, waiting for the machine-gun to mow them down. But the few decencies of warfare were still being observed by the Germans. Fitzgerald was carried safely out of danger.

Around the airfield further progress had stopped. Maxwell of D Company was believed to be holding his ground, rather precariously, a short distance from the edge of the field. It was thought that B Company were near to him. The air was full of planes and it would not be long before troops in the open would be strafed and bombed.

They had done their best, but Burrows had feared it was hopeless from the start. Now he knew that nothing more could be done. Any movement from cover was drawing murderous fire. If he attempted to press the attack any further he would gain nothing and probably sacrifice the rest of his battalion. He accepted the inevitable—that he could not now capture Maleme. He had to withdraw his companies from their exposed positions to higher ground inland.

Runners had to go out to the companies, telling them where to assemble, the points to make for in the hills. But it was a question how many messages would get through. There was no contact with either D or B Companies out near the sea. They could not be left there. Somehow word had to be got through to them, even though the man who took the message would run a very gauntlet of fire. All the radios were out.

Number 15 Platoon of C Company was close by Battalion Headquarters. Burrows moved over to them, found Upham behind a wall. He told him the position, said that word had to get across to the companies on the beach. He wanted Upham's platoon to do it.

"Right," Upham replied shortly. "We'll fix it." He peered cautiously over the wall, looking at the expanse of open ground stretching between his positions and where D and B Companies were thought to be over towards the 'drome. It would be about half a mile across to them, and under fire the whole way. Whom would he send?

Upham crawled over to Sergeant Dave Kirk. ("The finest soldier I ever knew," Upham described him.) He told Kirk what was required.

They discussed the best route. Any route was as dangerous as another.

THE FACE OF A SOLDIER

Upham photographed after the campaigns in Greece and Crete

Too ill to walk, Upham
rides a donkey at
Kriekouki, Greece

"The Victoria Cross
has been awarded . . ."
Surrounded by his platoon,
Upham is congratulated
by Sgt. Bob May. Eric
Le Gros is second
from right

Then Kirk said: "Who's going, boss?"

Upham was busy checking his pistol, seeing how many grenades he had left. His reply was almost absent-minded. "I'm going myself, of course, Dave," he said. "It's a bit dicey for anyone else, though. Don't know who to send."

"Let's get started," Kirk suggested.

Upham looked at him and grinned. "I thought you'd say that."

The two men set off from Pirgos, striking north-west towards the 'drome. They saw two of the enemy crouched in a ditch a little distance ahead. They had to go along that ditch. They had brought a Bren with them. With one long burst they cleared the way.

On and on across this no man's land, until at last they broke out of the bushes and found the airstrip beneath their feet. There, right on the edge, two New Zealanders lay dead, mute proof that some of the Kiwis had penetrated to the limit.

They skirted the edge of the field, right out to the beach. They found some B Company men there and passed on the orders. But D Company, under Maxwell, had already realized the hopelessness of the position and had wisely retired back along the coastline already.

Mortar and machine-gun fire was all around them, planes were zooming down on to the 'drome, and there was great enemy activity.

They started the journey back.

CHAPTER EIGHT

VALOUR IN DEFEAT

By midday on 22nd May the stricken 20th had fallen back into a perimeter in the hills where the disappointed Maoris had also taken up defensive positions. There they sat within sight of the aerodrome, but unable to reach it with fire, watching the troop-carriers running a shuttle service between Maleme and Greece. Thousands more men were landed on Crete that day.

Twice during the morning Upham, Kirk, and others of the platoon crept back to the village to rescue their own wounded boys, carrying several out on doors or improvised stretchers. But by noon all movement was stilled by the German gunners, while aircraft weaved overhead and roared down on any sign of activity.

During the afternoon the enemy pressed hard against the New

Zealanders, searching for a gap in the line. C Company was in an advanced position and several times Upham's platoon was hotly engaged. From one ill-advised enemy attack his men captured a German machine-gun which they promptly put to good use.

Night came with the whole of 5th Brigade, and 20th Battalion, astride the hills two or three miles from Maleme airfield, with the ground in between now a mass of Germans.

With darkness, Upham's platoon heard the Germans moving around them on three sides, machine-gun belts rattling. It had been a grim day—the early-morning drama of the attack on the 'drome, the bitter thought that only daylight had defeated them, the fall back into the hills; then the mounting German pressure of arms against them, with clashes and more casualties. Upham's platoon sergeant, Bert Wallace, was killed that day, and Kirk stepped into the position.

Kirk and McKegney listened to the German preparations in the darkness out front. This would be a hopeless spot to be in when morning came, they argued. And then it wouldn't be possible to get out of it. So they edged over to Upham.

"I reckon we're too far out on a limb here, boss," McKegney suggested. "We'd stand a better show if we dropped back in line with the others, don't you think?"

"What do you think, Dave?" Upham asked.

"Look around," Kirk answered. "There are only seven of the old platoon left. I don't know if these odd one or two chaps who've joined up with us will be any good."

"Why not? They're 20th chaps, aren't they? Not their fault they've lost their companies."

"Well . . . no." Kirk hesitated. Then he grinned. "But some of them saw you in the village this morning. . . . I think you put the wind up them. And I don't wonder."

Upham frowned for a moment, as if trying to understand Kirk's meaning. Then he looked out over the ridge again and, changing the subject, said: "We'll stay here. I don't think it'll get worse."

Meanwhile, Colonel Burrows was waiting anxiously for the night to pass. He couldn't see that he could last another day in this position. Casualties were too high, enemy fire too strong. There were not enough dressings for the wounded. He wasn't surprised when about five in the morning he received orders to pull the battalion out and withdraw eastwards towards its original reserve area near Canea. Move at once. They would retire in groups to Platanias, then re-form to complete the withdrawal to the final rendezvous.

With dawn soon upon them, Upham and the rest of the 20th clambered along the ridges towards safer territory.

But before the 20th completed its retirement to the Canea area enemy pressure became so intense that most of the battalion had to be stopped half-way in the region of the Platanias Bridge and turned round to face battle again. By 10 a.m. this temporary line was manned. There followed a torrid day. There was brisk action around the Platanias Bridge, the Germans being held off by mortars and some artillery fire, and by sallies from our infantry.

From the bridge out to the sea was 300 to 400 yards. Into position there Upham and his platoon were rushed. Enemy attempts to get through along the beach were beaten back, but the defenders came under heavy fire from German mortars. About 4 p.m. Upham heard the last whirr of the mortar bomb above him. He dropped full-length into the ditch alongside, seeing as he dived the body of the man next to him being lifted and shattered by the blast. Something bit into the back of his left shoulder, as if he had been punched. He climbed shakily out of the ditch. The man he had been speaking to a moment before was dead.

He had a feeling of surprise as the blood began to soak from his shoulder and pain began. He crawled over to McKegney. "How are things, Keg?"

McKegney shrugged. "Hickey's wounded. Getting hot, isn't it?"

A voice broke in. "I'm wounded too." It was Leggy.

Upham was all concern. "Sure it's all right, Leggy-boy? Here, let's have a look...."

"Or-r, 'tisn't much," Leggy said. "But these ruddy mortars ..."

The rest of what Leggy said was drowned as another mortar bomb seemed to burst all around them, and he was heard to declare ever after that it was like a ball of fire dropping into his lap.

There was something still stuck in Upham's shoulder. He could feel it there. A mortar fragment. He moved over to Dave Kirk.

"I've got a bit of shell in my shoulder, Dave. Here ... dig it out, will you?" And he handed Kirk an open pocket-knife.

"Eh?" said Kirk. "Dig it out with a pocket knife? Hell, I'm not a surgeon. Get on back to the R.A.P."

"Take it out!" he repeated sharply.

Kirk shrugged and took the knife. "There are two pieces in there," he said, looking at Upham's bare shoulder.

"Go on, get on with it" Charles retorted.

So Kirk tentatively prodded at the wound with the knife,

apologizing profusely for the pain he knew he must be causing. Out came one piece of metal.

"I can't do the other bit," he declared. "You'd better get back and have it done properly."

Upham thanked him for the homespun surgery, ignored the other suggestion. So Kirk went off and found Den Fountaine. Fountaine came up, promptly ordered Upham to the R.A.P.

The M.O. dressed it quickly. "That'll fix it," he said. "But there's no transport back for you. You'll be walking wounded. You'll have to foot-slog it back to the A.D.S."

"Walking wounded?" snapped Upham. "Like hell—I've got a platoon down the road there." He stumped off angrily, went back to the remnants of his platoon overlooking the Platanias.

The long day drew to its end. Maleme airfield was now securely in the enemy's grasp. At other points in the island he was not bothering to engage in battle. Maleme would do. Crete could be won from there. A twelve-mile advance eastwards from Maleme would see him in Canea and the harbour of Suda. That was all that was necessary.

At nine o'clock that night orders came to C Company to leave the Platanias and complete the retirement to the old reserve area east of Galatas, not far out of Canea. Under cover of darkness the line thinned out, and exhausted men silently and thankfully withdrew.

The next day—the fifth day of the invasion—was moderately quiet. There was a continuation of heavy mortar attacks, aggressive enemy patrolling, and the usual air bombing and strafing that stopped all movement by day. Canea itself was by now almost in ruins.

Freyberg, reporting to Middle East H.Q., said that the scale of air attack had been far worse than anything he had visualized. This, combined with the exhaustion of his ill-equipped men, told him that the end was near. If there had been deep, well-sited defence-works in a dozen strategic positions, with enough men to hold them in depth, the defenders might have withstood the savagery of the air assaults. But fighting in the open, with poor equipment and food, few digging tools, broken communications, and the enemy possessing unchallenged use of the air, left men with only their doggedness and courage.

Fortunately for New Zealand, Prime Minister Fraser was at this moment in Cairo. He watched the development of the battle with growing anxiety. To any but the blind, the total extinction of our forces, or their evacuation, was only a matter of time. He had some reason to believe that few people outside Crete appreciated the gravity of the situation. He cabled Churchill:

"In the name of the New Zealand Government I would strongly urge that all possible additional support by air and sea be immediately provided, and especially the full air assistance that can be released from all other quarters, including the United Kingdom."

Churchill replied:

"Although I sympathize and share your feelings of anxiety I cannot accept the implications of the final sentence of your telegram. The suggestion that we are holding back air assistance for the sake of the United Kingdom is really quite unfounded. . . ."

It is easy to understand Churchill's touchiness. He of all people would have known by then that both the Greece and Crete episodes had been, in the almost total absence of air support, futile and hopeless from the very beginning, and that inspiring words and moral pride were little consolation to troops cowering behind rocks and in ditches while an unopposed enemy air force smashed at them without respite.

The sixth day, 25th May, was a day that is remembered; remembered for its dramatic contrasts of quietness and fury, of collapse and defiance, of great heroism amidst exhausted defeat.

Early in the day all troops were warned that a massive enemy attack must be expected. The front line was held by the 18th Battalion, its right flank resting on the beach, joined on its left by some spare units who formed a bridge across to the 19th, lying a little to the rear. As a second line behind the 18th, a Composite Battalion lay in anxious wait, its motley gunners and truck drivers ill at ease with the weapons of the infantry.

The morning passed quietly—almost peacefully—if one excludes the steady bombardment from German mortars, machineguns, and aircraft. To provide a force ready for counter-attack, two companies from the 20th Battalion were sent forward from their reserve area. These comprised the remnants of the former B, C, and D Companies. Upham and his platoon were among them. They were held in the olive trees just north of Galatas, their commanders Fountaine and O'Callaghan waiting alongside the Brigade Commander Kippenberger for the orders that would assuredly come. Planes found them there, and for an hour they were heavily bombed and strafed.

By four o'clock in the afternoon the Germans were ready to make their assault. The mortar fire increased, hundreds of bombs crashing down on the thin New Zealand lines. And into the dust and torn air thirty Stukas came screaming, adding their dive-bombing to the onslaught. Forward then came the German infantry: under sheer pressure of lead and fire the right flank of the 18th was overwhelmed.

Now Kippenberger had to move fast. With his line broken, he had to call on the two reserve companies from the 20th to prevent a complete break-through. Fountaine and O'Callaghan were ready for their orders. Out they raced from the olive trees with their men, directing them into position as they ran. They found the right of the line all but gone. Dashing into whatever cover was available, the men opened fire. Grimly they held their places during the remainder of that vital afternoon, while the German forces beat against them.

By now Upham's arm was in a sling. His shoulder wound was painful, his dysentery no better. But he refused to yield. He had to hold a ridge. Leaving his men below the brow, he crawled forward alone to the top, and studied the confident advance of the enemy. He waved back, waited while Kirk brought up the rest of the platoon. Then into position.

Now he received his second wound. From a machine-gun burst an almost spent bullet plunked into his right leg, low down, passing through the anklets he was wearing. He bent down, tore the anklet away, saw that the bullet had not gone in far. It wasn't till a fortnight later, back in Egypt, that the festering wound forced itself on his attention. Then he bent down, squeezed at the flesh each side of the wound and prised the bullet out.

The attack was not long in coming.

These Germans were from the 5th Mountain Division. Good troops. Well trained and efficient, they moved steadily towards the New Zealanders. Half an hour later they reeled back, every attack beaten down by the shaggy remnants of the 20th. In front of Upham's withered platoon they left forty dead.

But the others made their way round the flanks and the Kiwis began to suffer, not only from fire in front, but even from behind. The Germans besieged Galatas village, deep behind the front line.

Upham now was in a state of exhilarated defiance. The enemy machine-guns, firing from close range, were the main trouble. He had to detect them, point them out to his riflemen, have them destroyed. So in an audacious game he paraded up and down, exposing himself long enough to draw enemy fire, enabling him to pin-point each gun that began firing at him. One by one his men shot them out of the battle.

"There Charlie was," McKegney said later, "telling us to keep down, keep down, and all the time standing there in the open himself, his arm in a sling. You'd have thought he was planning to stay a couple of months. Charlie knew, I suppose, that if we didn't stick it out for a few hours the whole div might have gone west."

Meanwhile Brigadier Inglis, commanding 4th Brigade farther back, realized that the New Zealanders were being engulfed. Scraping the bottom of the barrel, Inglis sent forward signallers, the Kiwi Concert Party, and even the 4th Brigade Band, all to act as riflemen. Here, indeed, was resolution in desperation.

Just on dusk another strong attack was made by the Germans in an effort to capture the village of Galatas. This brought them so far forward that the two companies of the 20th under Fountaine and O'Callaghan were in danger of being cut off. They had to be pulled back to maintain a line with the others.

The orders came through to Upham. He could withdraw his men all right though it would mean fighting part of the way. But there were other troops in the line beside him whom he would have to warn. So he ordered Kirk to take the platoon out and himself went across to the others to warn them that they might be cut off unless they, too, pulled back.

Kirk, however, found the way out was all but closed. So, taking the fight to the enemy, he vigorously counter-attacked, inflicting sharp casualties and making good his ground to the rear. Even then, he found himself out of touch with the rest of the company, and joined in spiritedly in the famous counter-attack on Galatas that took place soon after. Kirk and his men rejoined their company early next morning after holding an advanced salient right through the night.

Kirk won the D.C.M. Upham said of him: "He was the really superb fighting man. A crack shot, he always carried a Bren gun and used it with deadly effect, and was one of the few men who could fire it accurately at close range like a Tommy-gun. . . ."

Meantime Upham had returned from warning the other front-line troops to find that Kirk had safely disengaged the platoon and was piloting them back across the ridges. Upham was alone, and now had to find his own way back to the new defence line. He began picking his way. The Germans were already infiltrating forward and it was obvious there were some of the enemy between him and safety.

He came out from a grove of trees to find that he would have to cross a hundred yards of open ground. That was dangerous. He paused, looked back. At that second the shots came.

In an instant he saw the two Germans. They were moving towards him through the trees, just two men on their own. Two more shots cracked at him.

Back on the far side of the clearing one of Upham's platoon was watching. He heard the shots, saw Upham twist round to look, then: "Charlie . . . the boss . . . he's copped it!"

He saw Upham reel, collapse to the ground, one arm flung above his head as he fell.

The two Germans must have seen it also. Satisfied, they continued moving carefully forward, looking for the New Zealander's body.

But Upham had only tripped over a tree-root. He squirmed his way through the grass to the nearest tree, noticed with satisfaction that there was a low fork in the trunk.

He had a rifle again. But with his arm in a sling it was a heavy, almost useless weapon for a one-armed man. In the fork of the tree, though . . .

Cautiously he raised his head, peered through the fork. He could see the Germans moving steadily towards him. With his good arm he lifted the rifle, rested the barrel gently in the fork, made sure it was cocked, the safety-catch off. Two of them to get.

Only one hand to hold the rifle, to pull the trigger, then work the bolt after the first shot and bring the second round into the chamber.

They looked good men—they were moving carefully, not exposing themselves unnecessarily. They had sub-machine-guns. They came closer. Twenty yards . . . fifteen . . . ten. And they were cautious now, because they could see the clearing ahead. They were peering into the grass looking for his body.

Closer . . . closer. Eight yards . . . seven . . . six.

He lay dead still, hardly breathing. Close enough.

He squeezed the trigger. The crack of the gun seemed to shout back from the trees. He saw his man pitch forward.

Like lightning he shifted his hand to the bolt; a moment's fumbling would be fatal. Seized it, drew it back, pushed it home again, with the other man looming over him. When he shot the second German the man's body fell against the muzzle of his rifle.

. . . Close enough.

The same attack that nearly cut off Upham's men saw the Germans sweep into Galatas. Their pressure in this area indicated that they wanted possession of the town by nightfall, and they rapidly swarmed into its little houses and set up their guns around the town square.

Kippenberger decided that he must strike, and strike boldly. Two British tanks were handy, one commanded by the notable Roy Farran, and two companies of the 23rd Battalion came up, tired but in good heart. Farran clattered into Galatas, spitting fire, and returned to report that the town was "stiff with Jerries".

Kippenberger told the two companies that there was no time for reconnaissance; the tanks would move in, the infantry would follow in behind the tanks, single file on each side of the road, and take everything with them.

Then Farran said: "I've got two wounded men inside. Could any of your New Zealanders take their places in my tank?"

Volunteers were called for. Farran says: "About three hundred volunteered," which is a pleasant but inaccurate exaggeration. However, two men were quickly found who could fire Vickers guns. They were sent up the road for a rapid lesson in tank fighting, while the infantry waited silently by the roadside.

Now there were odd stragglers also joining in, glad to be given the chance of hitting back, linking themselves up to the two queues waiting on the roadside. There were groups from the 20th, some men of supply units, a few British officers, and all sorts of scattered remnants who refused to be left behind.

Ten minutes sufficed for the men to learn their jobs in the tank. They returned. Then with barely another word the infantry moved off, tanks in front, Galatas in the dusk ahead.

Beginning at a walk, soon the men broke into a run to keep up with the tanks. And then, as the buildings of Galatas loomed up 200 yards ahead, there suddenly arose a clamour from the throats of men that still rings in the minds of those who heard it.

"The whole line seemed to break spontaneously into the most blood-curdling shouts and battle-cries . . . our chaps charging and yelling. . . . One felt one's blood rising swiftly above fear and uncertainty until only an inexplicable exhilaration quite beyond description surpassed all else, and we moved as one man into the outskirts."

So wrote the men who took part in this remarkable episode. Into the town they charged, along the lanes, over the walls, through the gardens, in and out of the buildings, shouting, fighting, and always driving forward. They were fired on from all sides, from roofs, doorways, and windows. They died quickly and freely, but the rest forged on. The noise was overwhelming.

The Germans broke and ran.

There are many who say that this hour was the fiercest fought by New Zealanders in the whole war. There could surely be no other hour to match it in the superb rallying of men to a desperate call; no other engagement could share its spirit of sudden bold retaliation, crowned as it was by complete success.

But by early morning the implacable logic of wider strategy had ruled that Galatas would have to be yielded anyhow. Broken as the line was, a withdrawal to a shorter defensive position was essential, one that the available fit troops would have a chance of holding.

To Freyberg the end was in sight. Only eight artillery pieces left, communications gone, his battalions still resisting doggedly, but cut to shreds, exhausted and disorganized, a prey to any enemy plane that cared to look for a target and spray it with fire. He signalled Wavell:

> "The troops under my command here have reached the limit of endurance. No matter what decision is taken by the Commanders-in-Chief, from a military point of view our position here is hopeless. A small, ill-equipped, and immobile force such as ours cannot stand up against the concentrated bombing that we have been faced with during the last seven days . . . the troops we have are past any offensive action."

That night saw our men falling back again, forming a new line at what became known as 42nd Street.

The chain of command from Force Headquarters through to the lower echelons had by now almost completely broken down. Men on the spot had to make decisions.

It was such a decision that led to the affair at 42nd Street. Two brigades—the 5th New Zealand and an Australian brigade—found themselves alongside each other, holding a line that followed the road called 42nd Street. They thought they were in a reserve area and that other troops were out in front between them and the enemy. But as the day advanced—and it was now 27th May, the eighth day of the battle—the two brigade commanders came to realize that there was nothing out front. All forward opposition had been trampled down.

Soon enemy forces made their appearance, driving swiftly eastwards. On the spot, the unit commanders decided that there was no future in quietly letting the enemy build up in front, and that it was futile thinking they could stem an enemy assault. No —the decision was made that when the enemy came to close quarters the defenders would open fire and charge forward.

The Maoris of 28th Battalion began it, most witnesses agree. Bayonets fixed, they waited behind the walls and in the ditches. Then from a man who could contain himself no longer there came a shout. In an instant it was echoed by a score of others and a line of men suddenly leapt into the open.

Forward went the Maoris "with an élan almost incredible in men who had already endured so much" (so wrote one historian). Within seconds they were followed by the 21st Battalion, the 19th, the 22nd, the 23rd—such of them as still remained. It was a scene of mass reaction—they all went forward, walking grimly at first, then running, firing at the grey uniforms in the grass, behind the trees and hedges, using the bayonet ruthlessly on those who resisted. It was no panic charge of a distraught rabble. Officers kept the men to their senses, keeping interval to save casualties; but on and on they went. The uproar swelled over the peaceful fields of Crete.

For the enemy, the sight of troops advancing into the fire with such sharp pugnacity was too much. They fought for a moment, wavered, then fled. And they were destroyed as they ran.

In a spirit of exhilaration for which there can be no words, our men swept the Germans back from 42nd Street nearly half a mile.

Our own casualties were surprisingly light. For the enemy it was a sad day. The 1st Battalion of 141st Regiment, fighting its first engagement, was all but eliminated, and other units were sharply cut about.

Out of defeat and adversity, history tells us again and again that the greatest deeds are born: little wonder that Churchill later referred to the New Zealand Division as "that ball of fire".

In all the annals of warfare have men behaved more nobly?

Charles Upham would have been in his element at 42nd Street, allowing even for his one useless arm, his wounds, and his dysentery. But, with the rest of the 20th, he was already farther south, marching into the interior of the island to protect the escape route that all Allied forces now had to follow.

Evacuation had been ordered. A little fishing village on the south coast, called Sfakia, was the only place left from which the Navy could take men away. It was a march of some forty miles to the south coast. The road seemed to lead upward all the way, with interminable zigzags, hairpin bends, and over mountain ridges reaching 3000 feet. To men who were fresh and fit this would have been a physical effort of some magnitude. But to the Kiwis, Australians, and British troops who were exhausted from lack of sleep, short of food and water, defeated by the weight and shock of never-ending air attack, whose courage had been futile in the absence of adequate fighting equipment, here was the culminating ordeal.

To fall behind was to be taken prisoner. To continue ahead was to drive the body to unattainable lengths of endurance.

Over the whole nightmare road was a mass of disorganized stragglers, men who had lost or left their units, painfully fighting their way southwards, trying to attach themselves to organized parties. For it was soon known that parties who were still armed and organized would receive priority in evacuation.

The road was littered with abandoned equipment of all kinds. The dead lay there too. The wounded, the weak, the ones who fell out, lay with them. Some even struggled onwards on hands and knees.

No more moving description of those terrible few days could be given than that of D. M. Davin, in his official New Zealand history of the campaign in Crete. He sums up the agony, the courage, and the despair of it all in these words:

"Trucks would pass ruthlessly along the column, ignoring the appeals of wounded men who would not fall out while their legs assured them that they might still be free. Or sometimes a truck would stop and one of its occupants would gruffly get out to make room for a man on foot whose condition was so bad that the passenger could not bear to ride while he walked. And of those who marched some went stonily on, ignoring the appeals of companions who could go no farther; while others showed an awareness of something greater than their own exhaustion and did their best to struggle forwards, a wounded companion slung on a blanket or a wooden stretcher between them. And time and again the sight of a man stumbling along with an arm around the neck of each of two comrades who took turns carrying his rifle stressed its echo of Calvary."

At the end of the journey, on the hills looking far down to Sfakia on the coast, the road petered out entirely, and goat-tracks had to be followed down the hillsides for the last few miles.

So in the course of several days thousands of the beaten Allies converged on Sfakia. While the Navy worked like demons to take them off, necessarily by night, they lay up in the caves and the stony gullies that ran sharply down to the rocky coast. As they waited their turn, the enemy came closer and closer, pressing on the outer ring of defenders, forcing the line to be contracted shorter and shorter, and the men in the hills packed tighter around the tiny village.

On 30th May two companies of the 20th were carrying rations from the beach up to the rearguard forces. They were close to the lower end of a long ravine known as "Rhododendron Valley", hard by Force Headquarters. Inglis and Kippenberger were standing there talking, discussing the orders for the embarkation of troops that coming night.

With startling suddenness, the sound of firing came to them from the direction of the ravine, only a few hundred yards away.

Inglis ran to a knoll, raised his binoculars, and saw Germans advancing down the ravine. Here indeed was trouble. The Allied rearguard was out holding the main approach road to Sfakia, some miles away. But now the enemy were within the perimeter, almost on top of Force Headquarters itself.

Inglis and Kippenberger moved into action. The former rushed orders to 18th Battalion to mount men on the eastern slopes of the ravine. Kippenberger told A Company of the 20th to block the mouth of the ravine, and ordered Fountaine of C Company to get men up the cliffs on the western side.

Fountaine ran over to Upham. "Get your men up there, Charlie!" he called, pointing to the precipitous hills. "Get on top of them. And you'd better move fast. They're in a hell of a flap at Force H.Q."

Upham looked at him. He was shrunken with illness, weary beyond description, still unable to eat, his wounds a dull heavy drag on his determination. But there was a shadow of a grin on his face as he said: "Oh, tell 'em to go to hell and not get excited." He turned to Dave Kirk beside him. "Get the boys moving, Dave. And tell 'em it's a five-minute job."

Upham led his men to the foot of the cliffs and they started climbing. They had been on their feet day after day; they had marched over the mountain passes, and now, at the last, the sheer walls of the ravine were so much torture.

Slowly they inched their way up the 600-foot walls of the ravine. It became apparent to the watchers below that Upham intended to get right on top of the Germans, to be able to fire down directly from overhead.

They toiled wearily on. Some of the party were disposed in positions on the hillside; then Upham pushed farther ahead with three other men. For another half-mile his small group crawled on, clambering painfully ever higher. It seemed to the men that he would never stop.

General Freyberg was watching. It seemed to him they were climbing very slowly. An hour had gone by; an hour and a half; it was nearly two hours now since the first outbreak of firing.

After the war Freyberg returned to his battlegrounds on Crete and looked closer at the cliffs Upham's men had scaled. "I can understand now," he said, "why they seemed to take so long."

But finally the group of gasping battle-worn men came to a spot where Upham said: "This'll do. Now use tracer. Got to see where you're striking." They got the Bren ready.

Far down below they could see the Germans moving from cover to cover in the ravine. They were right on top of them. The hillside was so steep that Brown, who had the Bren, had to be held by the legs so that he could lean over far enough to fire.

"Right, let her go!" Upham said.

Hopelessly caught by the plunging fire, the Germans ran desperately about, but they were doomed. One after another they fell to the fire sweeping down on them from overhead.

"Here, give me a turn!" Upham shouted excitedly. He took the Bren, saw that there were still a few left to account for. He aimed carefully, fired, and picked off all of the enemy who still survived.

Of the fifty Germans who came down the ravine that day, twenty-two were killed by Upham's men. The rest were mopped up by other troops surrounding the valley.

The slow, aching climb down the hillside began, and when they reached the bottom again there was Burrows.

He was waiting to tell the officers about embarkation that night. His news brought a sigh—one officer and forty men of the 20th would have to stay behind. There was not room in the boats for all.

Fountaine assembled his company, told them the story, and asked for any volunteers to form part of the forty to stay behind.

The men who had climbed the cliffs, still hot, weary beyond words, their legs weak and shaking, paused. Then Grooby, the C.S.M., stepped forward. At once Fraser, the C.Q.M.S., followed, along with Kirk and Vincent. And then Fountaine's company, barely forty in number all told, shuffled forward in line with their N.C.O.s. They would all volunteer to stay.

It had to be done by drawing lots. Fountaine went back to Battalion H.Q. with the names of the men.

Burrows met him. "I suppose Charlie Upham wants to stay too?"

Fountaine nodded. "Doesn't think it's right to go off himself while some of his men are left behind. He'll stay with them if he gets half a chance."

Burrows looked serious. "Watch him, Den. Make sure yourself that he embarks. I didn't tell you before, but Kip's given me special orders about Charlie. He said Charlie must go off tonight; *he's not to be allowed to remain under any circumstances.* So keep your eye on him."

Fountaine understood. He knew that, already, wherever men gathered in small groups and talked quietly about the last ten days, Upham's name was being mentioned. So quickly had the word spread that a legend was already in the making.

Afternoon drew into evening. Men who were embarking handed their water-bottles and their rations to those staying behind. There were unhappy, strained farewells. Fountaine was never far from his company, and he kept his eye on Charlie Upham.

There was a time when he thought he had been outwitted. Upham disappeared. But not for long. He was back soon, feet dragging, his wounded shoulder hurting abominably. But he felt pleased with what he had done. Because he had always loved animals, and couldn't bear to see them suffer. In the midst of all this human ordeal Charles had noticed that the Cretans, who had wisely deserted their village, had left behind a few mules, still closely tethered. They had no food. They would soon die. He stumbled over the broken ridges to the mules, untethered them, set them free to forage in the grass. Then he made his way painfully back to his men.

Night came. An armed cordon ringed off the beach, allowing through only those who were to be evacuated that night.

The hours passed. Then out of the dark came the ships' boats and the landing craft and men began to clamber aboard.

Kippenberger stood and counted his men of the 20th as they passed through the cordon. He saw Upham come through, a "walking skeleton", he described him later. Upham was weeping, in a medley of utter exhaustion and illness, and from bitter frustration at not being allowed to stay for another crack at the enemy. To have to leave some of his own men behind, and go off to safety himself when he felt he could still fight, was galling to him. That he was already physically far past the point of effective soldiering he did not accept.

Den Fountaine said: "I actually had to hold Charlie and literally drag him off."

CHAPTER NINE

THE VICTORIA CROSS

THERE were new huts at Helwan for the New Zealanders, there was accrued pay, and there was a week's leave—survivors' leave, they called it. Off they went to Luxor, to Palestine, to Alex. While they were away reinforcements came marching in.

Upham did not forget the promise he had made on the hillside overlooking Maleme, just after the failure of the counter-attack on the 'drome. A slap-up meal at Shepheard's, he had said. So he kept his word. He turned on a worthy feast for his boys—but, alas, there were only five of them: Kirk, Le Gros, "Shorty" Christian, and two others. The remainder of his band were left on Crete or were in hospital.

Meantime Kippenberger collected eye-witness accounts of Upham's conduct on Crete. One report from a captain of the 20th said: "He showed a total disregard for his own safety, very seldom using cover, and always moving around his platoon cheering his men on. . . . Coolness, leadership, and unremitting attention to his men. . . ."

And a corporal wrote: "After being wounded on the third day he carried his arm in a sling and was in constant pain. . . ."

Another said later: "I was with him at Maleme and history will tell how magnificent he was. Some people are under the impression that he was foolhardy and reckless, but in my opinion he wasn't. There was method and cool reasoning in all his actions, he summed up the situation quickly, and his courage and determination ensured success."

Yet another opinion was: "He seemed to have a battle sense and to work by instinct. He never took useless risks and seemed to know just how much he could accomplish. . . . He was able to move faster and march with less fatigue than any of the men ten years younger."

Worn out after the campaigns in Greece and Crete, Upham was in hospital for some time, with sinus trouble adding to his burdens. He was finally discharged, to find that the battalion was toiling through a series of ambitious manœuvres, along with many other units, in the Nile Valley, watched by great numbers of men of high rank.

It would be inconvenient for him to rejoin his platoon immediately, it was said, so they seized on him to act as one of the umpires of the exercises. Part of his task was to approach a New Zealand brigade with the news that an enemy tank force was advancing on them in great strength. What would be the New Zealand Brigadier's orders?

Upham thought his duties as an impartial umpire should not override his loyalties to the New Zealand Division. So before delivering his news he prudently ferreted out the "school" solution. *Withdraw*—that's what the New Zealand Brigadier would be expected to order.

Thus, when the imaginary tanks hove into sight, and Upham stood alongside the New Zealand commander to ask for the Brigadier's orders, he got some satisfaction out of telling him in advance what the mighty ones said should be done.

"Withdraw?" the Brigadier expostulated. "Not on your life!" And he didn't.

That night, as the great ones gathered in solemn conference to debate the lessons of the exercise, Upham arrived to take his seat as the most humble of the umpires. Somehow he arrived at the wrong door, for, as he entered, he found himself alongside the microphone that was to be used by the speakers. Glancing over the parade, Charles paused a moment at the sight of so much rank—he had never seen so many generals and brigadiers in one place. He couldn't repress the involuntary remark: "My oath, what a galaxy of bloody talent!"

In an instant all the noble heads turned on him, and he realized that the microphone had been switched on. His cheery remark had gone booming down the hall, a diverting introduction to the evening's business.

Some weeks later the division was sent to do amphibious training at Kabrit, in the Canal Zone. Enemy air-raids on the Canal were increasing, culminating on 8th September with an attack that had the authorities expecting a parachute landing. It was battle stations for everyone.

Some of C Company of the 20th were hardly prepared for it. There had been something of a party, heads were unsteady, and the air-raid alert caught men confused between the necessity of getting out of certain clothes and into others. These things are very difficult to work out in some circumstances. One of those who found it difficult that night was Fanny Hill of 15 Platoon. He staggered from his bed of confusion to the assembly point, oblivious to the fact that he was clad only in his boots and identity disc.

Upham saw him, swallowed hard, then moved up to him and put his mouth close by Fanny's ear. "What the hell are you going to do to the paratroops?" he shouted distinctly. *"Kick them to death?"*

From Kabrit the division moved out into the Western Desert again, there to improve the defences of the Baggush Box, 160 miles west of Alexandria. There was battle training in the sand, swimming in the Mediterranean, digging in the stones, each company living a self-contained life in a manner where men really came to know their fellows. More exercises were held there early in October, watched, it was said, by every brass hat in the Middle East.

During a pause in the manœuvres Upham slipped off his web gear and laid it on the running-board of an A.S.C. truck. He moved away a few yards to attend to something else, turned back, found that the truck was gone. With it went his Army pistol and binoculars.

This is serious, the Army always says to such an occurrence. That's what they told him now when he privately mentioned his loss, though he delayed putting in an official report.

Upham frothed and fumed, pointing out how absurd it was to worry over it so much when he had seen literally millions of pounds worth of equipment readily cast aside on Greece and Crete. Anyway, he argued hotly with anyone who cared to discuss the subject with him, if he *had* to produce a pistol and binoculars he'd get them soon enough the next time he was in action. Couldn't they wait till then? His pride was hurt. Rather sheepishly he asked the men of his platoon if they would help him look.

Not merely the platoon but the whole company volunteered, and a good part of the following day was spent in an emu parade up and down a large area of the nearby desert. It was amazing what things actually were discovered, including some ancient Roman coins, so it is said, a broken Grecian urn, and a sheet of paper containing some Cairo addresses. But no sign of the pistol and binoculars.

"The driver pinched them," was the general verdict. And so upset was Charles over the whole trivial incident that a meeting was held and the suggestion put forward that, to save Charlie's face, a volunteer would have to pinch a pistol and binoculars from some *other* officer in some *other* unit. Because otherwise a court of inquiry would have to be set up.

Eventually, all hope gone, Charles had to make an official report admitting his loss. He wrote it out that evening, handed it in, and roamed around like a bear with a sore head. He was too annoyed with himself to bother listening to the mess radio when the news from London came over.

But at 9 p.m. those listening heard a news item that had them leaping from their seats. In the warmly modulated tones of the B.B.C. came the announcement:

"The Victoria Cross has been awarded to an officer of the New Zealand Military Forces, Second Lieutenant Charles Hazlitt Upham, for gallantry in Crete."

There were several officers present when Charles was first told he had won the V.C. The news seemed not to register immediately on his mind—like the way a man acts and looks when he thinks people are talking of someone else. There was no expression of surprise. He seemed neither excited nor overcome. Just a slightly puzzled, almost defensive, attitude. And after a silence that seemed to indicate distrust and disbelief he at last spoke.

"It's meant for the men," he said harshly. "My men—by God they could fight! You know, those chaps can do anything. . . ." and he continued talking rapidly, almost wildly, about the merits of his platoon, as if trying to postpone the fact that he himself had been singled out. Yet deep in his mind he knew it all on the instant. He knew immediately that his life now would be different, that he would be constantly trying to escape from a position of fame; and he knew that he was going to be hurt by the belief that the Victoria Cross was being awarded for something that was no more than a man's ordinary duty. "He had done nothing . . . nothing. An officer must lead . . . an officer must urge them on . . . but it is the men who do it . . . he hadn't won anything . . . his men had won it . . . yet he would have to suffer the humiliation of receiving an award that belonged to his men, not to him. . . ."

So ran his thoughts in those first few hours, and Charles Upham has never really overcome that first feeling of embarrassed defensiveness. It has remained with him throughout the years.

Then only three days later came another announcement. The

Victoria Cross was awarded to Sergeant Jack Hinton for bravery at Kalamata, in Greece, where he had been captured in the final resistance. It was not enough coincidence that both Upham and Hinton were from the 20th Battalion, but both belonged to C Company. And then to C Company came a D.C.M. for Dave Kirk, and an M.C. (Greek) for Major Wilson, the officer commanding C Company who lost his life on Crete while temporarily leading a Greek battalion.

Up went a notice in the lines: "Join the 20th and win a V.C.", and Colonel Burrows, now doing a tour of duty at Base, wrote an amusing letter to Kippenberger concluding: "It would be a convenience if in future the names of members of the 20th Battalion who win Victoria Crosses be published in one list and not on different days as appears to be the present practice."

Meantime, the 20th were having military competitions—tactics, drill, weapons, grenade throwing, etc., and this engendered a brisk enthusiasm. Platoon drill would be one of the hard ones for Upham's 15 Platoon, for they couldn't trust him to give the orders at the right time. On the morning of the drill competition he stood talking with Bob May, rather glumly thinking that he didn't stand much chance. He would let Bob take as much of the drill as possible. He said: "Well, Bob, we'd better get going . . . and—Bob . . ."

May looked at him enquiringly. "Yes?" he asked.

"I think, Bob, you'd better salute me this morning."

And May solemnly agreed.

But in the culminating competition for a platoon attack Upham's clumsiness with drill was of no account. With great vim he led his platoon against the imaginary enemy and the obstacles that the umpires threw in his way. He won easily, with a clear margin over the rest of the battalion. To those who may have wondered if Charles Upham was merely a brave individual there now came the realization that he was also a shrewd, quick, and determined tactician. He seemed to know the right thing instinctively.

But something worse than military tactics faced him on 25th October. Into the desert came the New Zealand Mobile Broadcasting Unit, intent on recording an interview with the new V.C. to send back to New Zealand. Norman Johnston, a prominent post-war advertising man, was in charge.

Perhaps forewarned, Upham was in his dug-out and had placed Eric Le Gros on guard outside. "No, he'll see no one," Le Gros firmly said to Johnston, in the best manner of the millionaire's butler. "He doesn't want to talk about the V.C. Of course, if there's anything you want to know . . . ?"

Johnston assured him that it was only Upham they wanted. But it needed Colonel Kippenberger's active assistance before Charles was persuaded to even talk with Johnston.

There was a long argument. Upham was like a rock, feeling that to broadcast a message would be a form of self-aggrandizement.

Kippenberger played a major part in the argument, deftly translating Johnston's suggestions into language that might appeal to Upham's feelings.

"You see, Charlie, this might be the only chance you'll get of paying a tribute to the men you fought with. Johnston's not asking you to say anything about yourself—talk about your men if you'd like to."

It was that sort of argument that finally, very reluctantly, won him round. He agreed to broadcast a message. If they left him alone he would write it out. Johnston and Kippenberger left him to it.

Johnston came back a couple of hours later. By that time Charles was in a fever of nervousness and distress. The sheets of Y.M.C.A. paper looked as if they had been through a washing machine.

The microphone was set up. Upham began the first take.

It wasn't long before he let slip one of his more powerful expletives. Johnston grinned, said: "Let's try it again." They did. On the third try they made a success of it.

And the words that thousands of New Zealanders heard over the air a few weeks later were these:

"I wish to thank all those who have sent me cables from New Zealand and England. I have been very fortunate indeed, having the very best of commanders above me and the very best of N.C.O.s and men in my own platoon, as well as right throughout the New Zealand Division. It was very easy to do any job under those circumstances. It was the men in my own battalion, not myself, who earned the distinction. Their morale was the highest in the whole army. Nothing could stop them.

"We left many friends killed over there. Men we will never forget. I will mention the names of some of our own company— Major Wilson, Sergeant Wallace, Sergeant Mussen, Corporal Herbert, Corporal Malloch, Lance-Corporal Skilton, Privates Allen, Atkins, Boyd, Burns, Brown-Pride, Gilligan, Hislop, Watson, and Woods; not to mention Sergeant Hinton and hundreds of others left wounded in Greece and Crete. I hope the people in New Zealand remember them, lying in hospitals and prisons all over Europe. Do all you can to send them food and clothing. These men were not captured whole and unharmed like the Italians we ourselves took, but were wounded and sick men who struggled and fought right on to the last.

"After the war we must do all in our power to help the Greeks with food and clothing and stud stock to help build up their country again. The Greeks were very staunch friends of the New Zealand soldiers and hundreds of us owe our lives to the big-heartedness of these people.

"The division over here is going from strength to strength and the morale of our own troops is unsurpassed. You will hear more from us again. We have a great little army up here in the sand-hills.

"I would like the New Zealand Government to know that it is impossible to send over too much New Zealand tobacco to the troops. It is very much appreciated here. Kia Ora."

The men of my battalion . . . the men who had died . . . send food to the prisoners . . . help the Greeks . . . tobacco for the troops.

It was no artifice of construction. Upham simply was not capable of mentioning himself. In or out of action, his thoughts were constantly of other people. His modesty was almost an obsession.

Johnston packed up his equipment, well satisfied in a rather awed way, for this had not turned out to be the kind of talk he had expected. He went back to Battalion H.Q. and asked Kippenberger to say a few words as a postscript to the broadcast.

Kippenberger agreed, made some notes, and recorded the following:

"I am speaking as Upham's Commanding Officer. Upham is the first New Zealand *officer* to get the award of the Victoria Cross probably since the Maori Wars. He is very distressed, genuinely distressed, that he has been singled out for this award, as he has the idea that a great many men who served well and gallantly deserved to get it instead of himself.

"Nevertheless every man in the company and every man in the battalion is satisfied that the award was made to the right man. He was unquestionably the paladin of the battalion, unquestionably the finest fighting soldier that it had throughout the operations. The exploits for which he has been awarded the Cross—a whole series of dazzling exploits—any one of them deserve an award. . . . During the whole affair he was suffering from dysentery very badly indeed. He had contracted it some five weeks before in Greece. He was unable to eat bully beef and biscuits, which were the only ration in Crete. He lived simply on milk which the men of his platoon found for him. He was a walking skeleton when the affair ended."[1]

Nine days later the whole of 4th Brigade was astir early. This was to be a spit-and-polish day. The Commander-in-Chief Middle East, General Sir Claude Auchinleck, would review the brigade in a ceremonial march past, and the feature of the day would be the presentation of high awards won on Greece and Crete. Charles Upham was tense and tight-lipped as he began dressing for the parade. Le Gros was helping him.

"We've got to do this right, Leggy-boy," he said nervously. "All the top-hatters are going to be there. Make sure again all that gear's ready."

"Everything's jake, boss," Le Gros said cheerily. "You don't look too bad. And I've cleaned those boots about six times . . . they're *your own* boots, you know."

"My own boots, eh?" Upham said, looking down at them. "Well, I suppose that's something to be thankful for. Come on, Leggy, I've got to get moving."

"What about a brandy before you go?" Le Gros suggested.

"No, Leggy-boy, not today. But you have it. Do you good."

"Well . . . I dunno, boss," he said innocently. And he watched as Upham began walking over to Company Headquarters.

"And tell that Auchinleck," he called out after him, "that we don't want any more shambles like that last show. Give 'im the works."

Upham waved back absent-mindedly.

Then into the dug-out that formed the Company Orderly Room, where a number of officers and N.C.O.s were waiting. Terry Madsen, the C Company clerk, watched Upham sympathetically. Fancy a man like that being in such a state of jitters, he thought. Upham was pacing up and down, highly strung, thoroughly miserable. Madsen tried to soothe him. "Take it easy, sir. Give it an hour and it'll be all over."

Upham grunted, went on fretting. Then the message came in: *"Ceremonial parade postponed twenty-four hours."*

It was all Madsen and the others could do to save Upham from becoming a casualty then and there. But next day saw it through.

[1] Both broadcast talks reproduced by permission of the New Zealand Broadcasting Corporation.

Looking spruce and somewhat better composed, Charles paraded with the rest of the brigade. It was a day of brilliant sunshine. First there was an inspection by Auchinleck, accompanied by General Freyberg. Then, with the troops lined up in formation, three names were announced: Kippenberger, to receive the D.S.O.; Lynch, to receive the M.C.; Upham the Victoria Cross.

The three officers marched out, lined up in front of the Commander-in-Chief. Auchinleck handed the official citations to General Freyberg. "You read them," he said.

There was a brisk wind blowing. The citations were long. So Freyberg turned to Brigadier Inglis. "You read them," Freyberg said.

Inglis condensed the citations quickly, read out a neatly turned précis. Then, as each man stood to attention before him, Auchinleck bestowed the awards. He talked quietly with each man.

"Congratulations, Upham," he said. "New Zealand will be very proud that you've won this decoration."

Upham fought his battle to the last. "I didn't win it, sir."

Auchinleck's eyes smiled. "Then if you didn't, Upham, I don't know who did." And that was that.

Retiring from position in front of the C.-in-C. Upham retreated twenty paces before recollecting that he was required to salute. He promptly, if belatedly, did so, to the great relief of his senior officers, who at the same time noticed that under his puttees he was displaying a pair of yellow socks. Yellow socks! Shades of Sandhurst. What a mixture of a man, they thought. On one hand an intense desire to do the correct thing militarily and to fight the war to his utmost; at the same time an innocent indifference to many of the traditions and formalities of military life.

The answer was—some things really matter; some don't. Upham always sharply classified things into one division or the other.

That night in his dug-out Kippenberger thought over the events of the day and decided to write a letter to the Headmaster of Charles's old school, Christ's College. He said:

"Dear Mr. Richards,

I would like to congratulate your college on Upham's V.C. We are extremely proud and pleased that he belongs to this battalion, as does Hinton, and nothing in my service has given me such pleasure as the preparation of the recommendation and citation. The latter was really a masterpiece of under-statement.

Quite apart from having won this decoration, Upham is an outstanding officer of whom you may justly be proud. His head is not in any way turned, nor likely to be. It really has been rather pathetic watching him meet the attacks of photographers and reporters. He did it very well, though with desperate reluctance. I only induced him to speak for the wireless by pointing out that it gave the opportunity to mention some of his men who had died. . . .

I am sure you will not think it a presumption on my part to congratulate College on this decoration, which General Frey-berg told me was about the best earned he had ever known.

With kindest regards,

Yours sincerely,

H. K. Kippenberger."

Elsewhere throughout the world, as tales of heroism in defeat began to be announced, tributes appeared in the Press.

The *Daily Herald* of London wrote of the exploits of Upham and of Hulme, another New Zealand V.C. winner. The headline was: "NO HEADLINE CAN TELL THE HEROISM OF THESE MEN."

But *The Times,* in its third leader of 15th October 1941, pro-duced a piece of treasure.

"FOR VALOUR

In the Baghdad of the Arabian Nights it used to be ordered that the story of any notable achievement should be written down in letters of gold. Is gold good enough, we can but ask, for the achievements of the two New Zealanders who have been awarded the Victoria Cross for valour? The story of Second Lieutenant Upham covers nine days. During the whole time he was suffering from dysentery and could eat very little. The ordinary mortal, who knows to his shame how a little indigestion can upset both his eye and his nerve on the golf course, will feel that on the least eventful of those nine days Mr. Upham's courage was superhuman. Courage moreover, in this case, meant something far more complex and intellectual than was demanded, say, of even the officers in the charge of the Light Brigade. All the time, and not only on the fifth of those nine days when, painfuly wounded, bruised and starved, he bagged his brace by shamming dead, or . . . when by exposing himself he tricked the enemy into doing the like, he was think-ing, planning, pitting his wits against the German strength. We all like to think that in the excitement of battle we should be able to do deeds of which the mere thought turns us cold in repose; but the story of those nine days includes not only the hour after hour of silent endurance through which discipline helps to fortify the least heroic, but also the deliberate courting of danger in cold blood for the sake of the platoon, of the Army, of New Zealand, of the British Empire, and the free world. And Sergeant Hulme, that deadly stalker of snipers, he too has won his V.C. as much by his brains as by his contempt for danger.

These deeds were done in Crete. Deeds as brave and as ingenious are still being done in Crete by Britons, by Cretans and others, though few or none can be told to exalt us with the honours that they deserve. Deeds that can only be done through the highest forms of intellectual and physical courage are being done on all sides in this war-stricken world; and, perhaps for the first time in history, civilians have been free to reveal the same combination of initiative, endurance, and self-forgetfulness even unto death which is the constant glory of our sailors, our soldiers, and our airmen. The men of Talavera and of Waterloo were heroically brave; but there may be some excuse for asking whether the nature of modern warfare has not raised the standard of courage to heights unknown before. If it should be so, and if brainpower, initiative, and resourcefulness are necessary to courage of the highest order, it may be surmised that the free peoples are more likely to produce that order of courage than any others. The forces of the whole Empire, from every continent, of every race, know that they are fighting for freedom, with their own home-people passionately in support of them. Out of all this devotion to an ideal, this rivalry in the service of a sacred cause, there must grow a great glory of courage, before which all men and women of good will must feel as proud as they are humble."

The citation upon which the King approved the award of the Cross read as follows:

"8077 Second Lieutenant Charles Hazlitt Upham.

During the operations in Crete this officer performed a series of remarkable exploits, showing outstanding leadership, tactical skill, and utter indifference to danger.

He commanded a forward platoon in the attack on Maleme on 22nd May and fought his way forward for over 3000 yards unsupported by any other arms and against a defence strongly organized in depth. During this operation his platoon destroyed numerous enemy posts but on three occasions sections were temporarily held up.

In the first case, under a heavy fire from an M.G. nest, he advanced to close quarters with pistol and grenades, so demoralizing the occupants that his section was able to 'mop up' with ease.

Another of his sections was then held up by two M.G.s in a house. He went in and placed a grenade through a window, destroying the crew of one M.G. and several others, the other M.G. being silenced by the fire of his sections.

In the third case he crawled to within fifteen yards of an M.G. post and killed the gunners with a grenade.

When his company withdrew from Maleme he helped to carry a wounded man out under fire, and together with another officer rallied more men together to carry other wounded men out.

He was then sent to bring in a company which had become isolated. With a corporal he went through enemy territory over 600 yards, killing two Germans on the way, found the company, and brought it back to the battalion's new position. But for this action it would have been completely cut off.

During the following two days his platoon occupied an exposed position on forward slopes and was continuously under fire. Second Lieutenant Upham was blown over by one mortar shell and painfully wounded by a piece of shrapnel behind the left shoulder by another. He disregarded this wound and remained on duty. He also received a bullet in the foot which he later removed in Egypt.

At Galatas on 25th May his platoon was heavily engaged when troops in front gave way and came under severe mortar and M.G. fire. While his platoon stopped under cover of a ridge Second Lieutenant Upham went forward, observed the enemy, and brought the platoon forward when the Germans advanced. They killed over forty with fire and grenades and forced the remainder to fall back.

When his platoon was ordered to retire he sent it back under the platoon sergeant and he went back to warn other troops that they were being cut off. When he came out himself he was fired on by two Germans. He fell and shammed dead, then crawled into a position and having the use of only one arm he rested his rifle in the fork of a tree and as the Germans came forward he killed them both. The second to fall actually hit the muzzle of the rifle as he fell.

On 30th May at Sfakia his platoon was ordered to deal with a party of the enemy which had advanced down a ravine to near Force Headquarters. Though in an exhausted condition, he climbed the steep hill to the west of the ravine, placed his men in positions on the slope overlooking the ravine and himself went to the top with a Bren gun and two riflemen. By clever tactics he induced the enemy party to expose itself and then at a range of 500 yards shot twenty-two and caused the remainder to disperse in panic.

During the whole of the operations he was suffering from diarrhoea and was able to eat very little, in addition to being wounded and bruised. He showed superb coolness, great skill and dash, and complete disregard of danger. His conduct and leadership inspired his whole platoon to fight magnificently throughout, and in fact was an inspiration to the battalion."

Back in the desert Charles was fighting a losing battle against the legend growing up about him. Men who had helped dig the defences at Riakia in Greece, or had clung to the ground under the bombs that plastered Hellfire Corner in the Servia Pass, talked about him in the evenings, when there was little to do but commune with one's fellows. They told the stories of the counter-attack on Maleme 'drome, the defiant resistance on the hills, the grudging withdrawals, the price the Germans paid for every advance, and the final drama around Sfakia. And throughout the whole division conversation never went far before Upham's name was mentioned, and the stories about him exchanged, to be told again the next night, and the next.

Upham shrank from it all. Notable people came to see him, and he avoided them whenever he could. New Zealand's High Commissioner in London, William Jordan, visited the New Zealand forces in the Middle East. He went out to the Western Desert to the 20th Battalion, and then with the C.O. on to C Company.

Upham glimpsed them in the distance and promptly disappeared.

The official party arrived. "They want to see Lieutenant Upham," came the word. Actually Jordan wanted more than that. He hoped to arrange to take Upham back with him to England.

Platoon Sergeant Bob May paraded 15 Platoon, but with no appearance of the platoon commander himself. May kept an impassive face. He knew Upham had gone to earth in his dug-out, hoping that May could handle the situation and see the visitors politely off the premises. May handled it nicely, telling some persuasive white lies in the process.

Later, when Kip discovered that Charles had been close at hand the whole time, he sent a warning to his over-sensitive V.C.: "Next time I'll charge you with cowardice."

It was inevitable that Charles would receive congratulations whenever he met new people. At first embarrassed, he soon developed a technique of his own which did not give offence to the well-wisher, but nevertheless indicated that the subject of the V.C. was not welcome. In reply to the congratulations, Upham would give as short a "Thank you" as he could and immediately embark on a rapid discussion of the weather, or the state of farming in New Zealand, or any other topic that would serve to divert attention from the subject of himself.

When his own V.C. ribbon arrived he made no effort to attach it to his uniform. It lay around his dug-out unused. This didn't suit Eric Le Gros, who gained a good deal of reflected glory from his boss's distinction.

"What'll I stick this on?" he asked one day. "No good leaving it lying around." Charles shook his head.

"Go on, you've got to wear it, boss," he insisted. "Chaps'll think it funny if you don't."

"No, Leggy."

"You won't? All right, if you won't, *I'll wear it myself.*" And there is reasonable ground for believing that he might have done so had not Kip taken a hand at this time and ordered him to wear his ribbon.

But it was only half a victory. The V.C. ribbon must be worn on the inner side of all other ribbons, that is, nearest to the centre of the chest. Charles found in this a sufficient excuse for mounting his ribbon so far to the inside that it was mostly covered by the lapel of his jacket.

For Molly McTamney the V.C. was, of course, something that any fiancée might well dream of. Perhaps it gave cause for fear, for men of that kind were liable to be where the bullets flew thickest and death was close at hand; the winner of the Victoria Cross is for ever singled out from his fellows.

But Charles gave her few crumbs from his own plate of memories. Not once in all his war-time letters to her did he refer to the deeds that won him the Cross, and on only one occasion did he ever refer to the V.C. or to the fact that he had won it. On that single occasion he wrote to her saying: "Please don't put V.C. on your envelopes."

Freyberg once chided him for not wearing the ribbon on one of his uniforms. "Put it up immediately!" he ordered. "It is an insult to the King not to wear it."

A week later he was guest at a dinner, where he met the General again.

"Pleased to see you've got your ribbon up," Freyberg remarked.

Charles looked at him with a rather malicious twinkle. "Yes, sir; and you've got yours up too, sir; but mine at least is in the right place."

Freyberg looked down, then laughed as he saw that his batman had mounted his own V.C. ribbon the wrong way.

War heroes can be a great inspiration to people on the home front, and it was inevitable that plans were mooted for sending Upham back to New Zealand for a tour of duty.

One day the Acting Military Secretary, Captain Guy Rhodes, received a visit from Upham. They knew each other well. Rhodes was one of the original officers of the 20th, had gone through Greece and Crete with it, had become its Adjutant, and was now relieving in a Base appointment while convalescing from a spell in hospital.

He was astonished to see the state Charles was in. The man looked worried to death and thoroughly nervy and upset.

"They tell me the Military Secretary is arranging to send me back to New Zealand," Charles said miserably.

Rhodes nodded. He understood that was in the wind.

Tears actually came to Upham's eyes. Almost like a frightened boy, he pleaded with Rhodes that they shouldn't do it to him, that he be left in peace with his platoon in the desert. He was appalled at the thought of missing the next campaign. Rhodes explained that it was out of his hands. But Upham pleaded his case in other ears also, and it wasn't long before Rhodes received official word that Second Lieutenant Upham would remain with the division after all.

His platoon were glad to keep him, not only for his example and his toughness, but also for his kindness. He scrounged hard for his men, intent on getting them the best of everything. He gave them presents that he received from home, rushed hotly to the defence of any of his men in trouble.

By November 1941 the newly named 8th Army was ready for another offensive in the desert. While Wavell's forces had been engaged in the fruitless campaigns in Greece and Crete, Rommel had become well established in North Africa. But now it was the Allies' turn to take the offensive.

Every unit organized its men for the campaign. As always happens, a group of men had to be left out of battle so that if disaster occurred there would be a kernel of experienced men around which the unit could be re-formed. Kippenberger of the 20th chose his officers to be L.O.B.—six of them. Amongst them were Maxwell, prominent for his performance in Crete, and—to the surprise of many—Charles Upham himself. Upham's reception of this news was unbelieving, then bitterly hostile.

When he finally knew it was true, his face flamed, he grabbed his equipment and threw it on to the ground, exclaiming: "What the hell am I doing here anyway?" He could not understand that Kippenberger was doing it not only for his own good, but for the good of the men he would lead into action.

But Howard Kippenberger, one of the most thoughtful and able military leaders New Zealand ever had, judged his man right. He knew Upham's courage, his ruthless singleness of purpose. He wanted him to have time to add a life-saving share of sober cunning to his other attributes. But at the time it made Upham thoroughly sore and bad-tempered. He was moody and un-approachable.

However, when the first disappointment wore off, his disposition improved. He set to work preparing for the return of the battalion, improving the dug-outs, making sure that when his boys came out of the battle they would find as much comfort as reasonable ingenuity could provide for them.

On 11th November the division moved forward to battle. "We felt like runners, tense for the pistol," graphically wrote Kippenberger.

Sidi Azeiz, Fort Capuzzo, Sollum—it was all success at first. But then, against well-prepared opposition, Point 175, Sidi Rezegh, Belhamed—names that still ring in chill memory—were taken by the New Zealanders only after heavy fighting. These battles opened up one of the main objectives of the campaign—the relief of Tobruk—and on 27th November 1941 the 19th Battalion found its way through, joining up with men from the Essex Regiment patrolling out from the town.

The relief of Tobruk is now merely an incident of history. And hardly had it been accomplished before Rommel's tanks, returning from a useless foray towards the Nile, threw themselves at the Allied infantry standing on those desert ridges.

One by one the New Zealand battalions were engulfed, the

corridor to Tobruk was broken again, and all the successes of the previous few weeks seemed lost. Out of the battle zone the New Zealanders withdrew, proud, it seemed, of their successes, bewildered by the turn of events that had reduced several battalions to mere shells, bitter at the thought that so much sacrifice had been suffered for so little gain. There were hard criticisms of Allied command, whose policy had committed the infantry to battle in isolated groups, without adequate tank support.

But in the end it seemed that Rommel lost most. While cutting deep into our infantry, he nevertheless saw score upon score of his own precious tanks succumb to point-blank artillery fire, saw them fight with less than equal success against the British armour until, at the end, he had a bare forty tanks left. He couldn't hold Cyrenaica with that; so back from Belhamed, from Sidi Rezegh, from Tobruk, he retreated, and left the field to the battered opposition, who hardly realized they had won a victory.

Upham's long, restless wait with the other L.O.B.s came to an end. He saw the pitifully few remnants of the 20th come back, looked almost in vain for any men of his precious 15 Platoon and of C Company.

Those that returned Charles met warmly, showed them to their quarters like the manager of a hotel. He had worked hard to have the dug-outs in good order, to have all possible comforts laid on ready for them. He moved several of the men in the ranks into the comparative grandeur of the former sergeants' mess—and that was luxury.

They told him the story of the campaign as they sat in the cool evening air. He sympathized, and he scowled, and he shared their pride and their anger. And, with an almost dog-like affection and respect for his leadership, some went away saying: "It wouldn't have happened if Charlie had been there."

Thousands of reinforcements came up from the Nile Delta to fill the ranks of the division. Seven out of the ten battalions required new commanding officers. Upham became Company Commander of C Company.

The Baggush Box was surrounded by mine-fields, measured by the square mile and by tens of thousands. One mine-field lay close to C Company, necessitating a long detour to Battalion H.Q. and to the main supply road.

Upham asked the new Battalion Commander, Colonel Burrows, for permission to open up a route through the mine-field to gain better access. Kippenberger had now become a brigadier.

BATTLE OF MINQAR QAIM

Surrounded by the enemy, New Zealanders build their sangars on the open slopes of the ridge

The battle opens with an artillery duel

New Zealanders crossing the River Po. At the top of the embankment on the far side Charles Upham leapt from his prison truck and ran for the trees in the background

Upham's daylight escape attempt from Weinsberg prison camp. Still entangled in the barbed wire where he fell, Upham is smoking the cigarette that saved him from being shot only a few moments before

Burrows said: "It's a dangerous job. Get the engineers."

"No," Charles replied. "We can do it. There are a few experienced miners in my company."

"All right. But be careful. You haven't any mine detectors. What'll you use?"

"We'll prod for them with bayonets," Upham said.

Burrows went over later to see how Upham's miners were getting on with the job. He found the rest of the company keeping a safe distance away. Working on the mines was Charles himself, assisted by two men.

Upham and Dave Kirk were finishing the lane a few days later. A call came through for Charles to go to Battalion to pick up three new junior officers. So he left Kirk to finish off, jumped in the company pick-up, and drove himself over to meet the new men.

Coming back with them, instead of travelling round by the road, he drove straight across the desert to where Kirk was finishing lifting the mines. "Finished the track, Dave?" he called out.

"Yes, but we'd better have another check."

"I'll soon check it," Upham said.

He promptly installed one of the new officers in the driver's seat, pointed out the supposedly cleared lane, and told him to drive the pick-up through it to Company H.Q. beyond.

The truck moved off gingerly, the three new officers facing the realities of war rather earlier than they had expected.

"You're a bit tough on them, aren't you?" Kirk suggested. "They're so new they might blow themselves up."

"If you say the track's cleared, Dave, that's good enough for me," Upham replied. Then he added tartly: "They've had it safe long enough. This won't be the only mine-field they'll have to drive through."

Kirk shrugged. He knew his officer well, but there was a hard streak that he could never penetrate.

With his obstinacy, Charles would never let up once he started on anything. One evening near Christmas 1941 he set out with a friend to walk to another unit about half a mile away. It was very dark. They walked for twenty minutes, then for an hour. Two hours passed—and still the destination eluded them. With a persistent dogged fury at his own failure, Charles insisted on walking and walking; and it was not till 3 a.m. that his friend persuaded him to rest till daylight.

Then he got pneumonia and jaundice. Feltham, the Battalion M.O., called on his patient a few days later. He found Upham sitting up in bed devouring a New Zealand mutton-bird—and it is doubtful if there is a fattier, greasier dish in the whole world of gastronomy. Upham would never acknowledge weakness, or accept the symbols of it.

In January 1942 the New Zealanders were having more amphibious training at Kabrit, in the Suez Canal area. There Upham rejoined his company after his sojourn in hospital.

One thing he had to straighten out immediately. Some transport drivers, past masters at this sort of thing, were living in a cave. Headquarters Company, to whom they really belonged, thought they were under control of C Company. C Company thought they were back where they belonged. But Upham soon put that right. "We knew all good things come to an' end when we heard you were back," they said ruefully.

Next, an Army film unit wanted to make a propaganda film showing the slickness and efficiency of our Middle East infantry in rapid debussing. The way a well-trained section could leap from its truck and dash into battle positions would make a good film.

It was not unexpected when Upham's C Company at Kabrit was called upon to provide men for the film.

He had moved cautiously into the job of Company Commander. At Kabrit the Company Orderly Room consisted of a small tent in which the company clerk Terry Madsen slept. There was just room, in addition, for a primus, a tin or two of coffee, and the telephone. One day Charles happened to be in B Company lines.

He returned to his own headquarters looking rather worried.

"Terry," he said, "I've just been to B Company. You know, for Company Headquarters they've got a ruddy big E.P.I.P. tent, with tables and chairs. They've got trays marked 'In' and 'Out'; and they've got papers clipped together hanging on nails with names on them like 'Returns' and 'Action Pending'. We don't seem to have any of that. Do you keep any files, Terry? If you do where in the hell are they?"

Madsen grinned cheerily. "Right here, Mr. Upham," he said, and dived under the pillow on his bed. Everything was neatly filed inside a rubber band.

"What about 'Ins' and 'Outs', and 'Action Pending', and that sort of thing? Don't you need a bit of a system?"

"It's all here," Madsen said blandly, tapping the rubber band.

"Well, look, Terry. Don't say what you're going for, but make some excuse to wander over to B Company. Have a look round their orderly room—make sure there's nothing you're overlooking."

Madsen shook his head patiently, but went over and had a look nevertheless. When he returned he reported that B Company didn't do anything he didn't do.

"Ask yourself who'll be ready first to move in a hurry," he pointed out to Upham. "You see, it all gets bunged into this old ammo box and shoved on the truck; and then I wait around for you others to get packed up."

Upham's face suddenly cleared. "Well, that's just how it should be, Terry. You just carry on the way you like it. To hell with 'Actions Pending'!" That suited Terry.

CHAPTER TEN

IN SYRIA

THIS is the Djedeide Box. In Syria. It is astride the Bekaa Valley and will stop the Germans from penetrating south down the valley. The enemy may come swiftly through Turkey and sweep into Syria. He will find a number of sympathizers here. Once through Syria he can put an intolerable squeeze on the Suez Canal.

Inside the Djedeide Box three brigades will sit, complete with supporting arms and all their supplies. If the enemy by-passes them they can debouch and attack him on the flanks or in the rear. To stop him driving through the Box it will be a mass of concrete emplacements and dug-outs, heavily wired and mined, bristling with armament. It will need a lot of work to make it ready.

On the eastern slopes of the valley the 20th Battalion began its digging. There was hard rock, necessitating much help from the engineers with their explosives; but there was plenty of cement, with paint and camouflage material to follow, and no enemy in sight. As a result the defensive positions were well done.

Upham, commanding C Company—and now a captain—was almost fanatical over the siting and digging of his defences. Kippenberger, Brigadier of 5th Brigade, saw them. "Perfectly constructed," he said. And after the war he told an interviewer that they were the best and most skilfully prepared company positions he had ever seen.

Over his diggings Upham presided like a mother hen with

chickens. There must be no tell-tale tracks, not even footprints, leading to his dug-outs, except down the hard lanes where they wouldn't show. No aerial photos would give him away.

Free from the acute pressure of war, the New Zealanders expectedly got themselves into a little trouble. Bob May, now C Company's sergeant-major, found Upham a doubtful quantity in the conduct of orderly-room trials.

"What am I supposed to give this joker, Bob?" he would ask. "What's the usual thing?"

May would read out the passage from the book. "A fortnight's pay is the maximum."

"Now look here," Upham would say to the miscreant in front of him, "you're a good soldier. What's gone wrong with you since you came up here? Walking away from your post; getting shikker. Look—if I let you off with a warning, what about giving me your word of honour that you'll play the game for the next three weeks?"

The word-of-honour method worked all right out in the field. But when the troops were close to Baalbek, doing guard duties, temptations were too great. However, Upham found that few men let him down once they realized that the contempt of the boss was more effective a punishment than his fines. To have a V.C. despise you often hurts.

But then, while Charles was still concerned over the number of his men going A.W.L., who should completely disappear without trace but Eric Le Gros himself. "Araq" Le Gros, some called him, because Leggy was a connoisseur in Middle East beverages.

"I beat it for six days," Leggy explained. "I holed up in a tent in the 26th Battalion lines and they never found me. There was a bit of a party on there—and it never stopped. I couldn't have got home if I'd tried. Then I heard that the M.P.s were searching every tent. Well, by this time I'd got hold of a dog. So I started off back to the 20th with the dog. I didn't want those M.P.s to catch me."

Upham was standing by his tent when Le Gros' bedraggled figure came slowly into view. He watched him approach.

Leggy pointed vaguely in the direction of the 26th.

Upham looked him up and down. "My God, you look terrible," he said. "You'd better——"

But at that moment Le Gros' newly acquired dog rushed forward, jumped up, and deposited its muddy paws on Upham's stomach.

Leggy thought this wasn't a very tactful homecoming.

"Don't hand me on to Burrows," he pleaded when he came up on charge. "Burrows will slaughter me."

"I'll put you down for fourteen days C.B., Le Gros," Upham said sternly. "But I don't know what'll happen to my boots. Who's going to clean them? And after this . . . you'll have to go out on parades like all the rest. That'll keep you off the plonk."

Some solid drinking went on in Syria. Saturday night was always the night of the big do. Sunday mornings were greeted with many mournful eyes. But on Sundays there was Church Parade, and some sort of turn-out was expected. Charles himself took charge of the "Other Denominations" parade.

One particularly heavy Sunday morning saw Sergeant Beechey line up the parade of "Other Denominations". Upham arrived to take over, looked with astonishment on the pitifully thin muster —barely enough to comply with the Prayer Book's promise— "where two or three are gathered together . . ."

Charles eyed his tiny squad confidently, returned Beechey's smart salute, and announced loudly: "Must be a hell of a lot of R.C.s this morning, Sergeant."

Upham was not a religious man in the sense of being an ardent churchman. His religion was a way of living—a respect and awe for things of nature, a personal morality based on honesty and trust, and a hatred of badness. But he conformed to, and respected, the rituals of religious worship.

He had a profound respect for all ministers of religion, regardless of their denomination. A difference in dogma meant little to him. Perhaps his belief in the efficacy of the cloth stemmed from the time at Christ's College when girls from the Christchurch Girls' High School were invited to the college dance. They were allowed to come, but had to be chaperoned.

"I'll be chaperone," Charles announced confidently to his schoolmates. Sure enough, when the taxi called for the girls, there sitting in the front seat was the very guarantee of respectability—a figure in clerical vest and dog-collar. Charles found that by reversing his college waistcoat, and turning his stiff white collar round, he could quite well pass for a clergyman in the dim light of the taxi. It worked all right. The girls made it to the dance.

Colonel Burrows knew Charles probably better than anyone else: Upham, with his outspoken attitude towards most things military, a mixture of shyness and truculence; Burrows, All Black footballer and first-class cricketer, a model of tolerance and determined wisdom. Upham would do anything in the world for two people—one was Kippenberger, the other Burrows. His belief in their judgment was almost as strong as his hatred of the enemy.

Burrows says: "I remember only one occasion when Charlie was drunk. That was in Syria."

So it was. Peter Maxwell, John Phillips, and Charles had decided to visit the 18th Battalion mess. Things went swimmingly there. Brigadier Inglis was present and in top form. There was a ditch they fell into when they started for home, and by the time they reached the 20th lines it seemed a crying shame that the rest of the battalion should be sleeping and not joining in the general fun.

"Let's wake up old Ralph," someone suggested, and with a little difficulty they identified the Nissen hut in which Ralph Patterson, the battalion second-in-command at the time, was sleeping. "Here, get some stones." They began throwing stones on the tin roof of the hut. This made a very satisfactory clatter.

The fact that no one seemed to be wakened by the din served only to increase their efforts, and a veritable rain of stones thundered joyously over the head of the second-in-command. Then they extended their activities to the huts of other officers.

"What's wrong with them?" Upham shouted thickly in disbelief. "Come on, we'll go *inside* and wake 'em."

But by this time the clamour had begun to worry the camp guards—was it a raid by a few daring Syrian bandits—a fifth-columnist trying some sabotage perhaps? And in the end a sentry decided he needed help from his sleeping comrades in the guard-tent. Raising his rifle, he fired a shot into the air.

"Garn!" Upham roared. "Couldn't hit us if you tried!" So they trooped inside the huts and made themselves thoroughly unpopular.

Then the Colonel arrived on the scene. All three would report in the morning, and a fair matting it promised to be. Upham's only excuse at the time was a somewhat unsteady claim that "You couldn't do that in *my* lines, sir"—as a kind of complaint that anyone could sleep through such a shower of metal on the roof.

The morning came. Phillips and Maxwell made their way sorrowfully to Battalion Headquarters by the usual track. But Charles now realized how silly he had been. Throughout the wigging that followed he stood looking at the floor—utterly mortified, pathetically ashamed.

Burrows, a school-teacher by profession, told them that the

incident was on the level of the pranks he expected from his twelve-year-old boys. If they were going to behave like that when they took too much liquor then they'd better watch their liquor.

In a spirit of shamed self-denial, all three voluntarily promised to go on the water-wagon for several weeks ahead. Burrows accepted that promise curtly, dismissed them, then rose from his chair and shepherded them across to the officers' mess. There was a mess rule that no one could shout a drink. Burrows thought the occasion allowed him to break the rule, and he restored their self-confidence by a quick round. So much for their self-denial— but this was an order.

Resolution and hardness on the one hand; shyness and intelligence on the other. With such a mixture of human qualities Upham was always something of a character. His response was always unpredictable. And amongst his worst qualities was his often unreasonable pig-headedness.

As he always had been, Upham continued to be a thorough pest to the Q.M. staff. By constant arguing he obtained for his men the best of what was offering, always pressing for more and for something better. So keen was he to see his men equipped with more grenades that he offered to pay out of his own pocket a reward for every extra grenade his men could acquire from other sources.

He was keen like that on vital equipment, yet casual and rough in matters of personal appearance. As for shaving, for example, he could have won the title of the fastest and worst shaver in the British Commonwealth.

For variety, company commanders inspected one another's companies. Peter Maxwell of D Company came over to inspect Upham's.

Maxwell stopped disapprovingly in front of one C Company stalwart. "Did you shave, soldier?" he demanded, looking at the stubbly chin. The soldier shifted uncomfortably. Then his guilty eyes turned slowly and became riveted on Upham's jowl, with its stalks paralleling the mown tracks like a tornado's swath through a forest. Maxwell followed his eyes, swallowed slightly, then turned back to inspect the man's rifle.

"Humph. Must have spent your time cleaning your rifle." And he passed on.

There was a message waiting at the orderly room when this inspection was over. Upham was to report at Battalion Headquarters.

There Colonel Burrows said to him: "Charlie, the Brigade is

sending two officers to inspect some defences in the Lebanon. They are being dug by an artillery regiment, but they want some New Zealand infantry officers to report on them, and make any suggestions. Brigadier Inglis has chosen Johansen of the 27th as one. You're the other. You'll be in pretty classy company, I dare say, so watch your step. You're going the day after tomorrow."

Late one afternoon Johansen and Upham reported to the headquarters of their artillery hosts. They were rather surprised that first evening when, on entering the mess, they noticed a bottle of Scotch on a sideboard bearing the label "The Colonel".

The Colonel himself arrived soon after. It had apparently become the unit tradition that the Colonel's entrance should be solemn. It was indeed. With all standing at attention, the C.O. walked slowly down the length of the ante-room in dramatic silence.

After mess Upham and Johansen were beckoned to join him, and the labelled whisky bottle was uncorked. Under the balm of good spirit the chill of exaggerated formality began to thaw. But it was inevitable that the talk should turn to Singapore, which had fallen to the Japanese only a few weeks before.

Drinking freely, Charles became more and more talkative over the subject of Singapore. He had strong opinions about it. But the Colonel, after analysing the reasons for the capitulation, just as strongly declared that no other course had been possible.

Then Upham blurted: "There can be only one man to blame for the fall of Singapore, one man only, and that's the one at the top."

"Oh?" said the Colonel icily. "And how do you make that out?"

"Because all the evidence points to it," Upham retorted. "And I reckon the men in charge there can't have known a bee from a bull's foot."

The C.O.'s face flushed. "I'll have you know, Upham, that the commander at Singapore is a personal friend of mine."

"I don't care," Upham shot back, "if he's your favourite uncle."

"Then I'll have an apology from you, Upham, forthwith!"

"That'll be the day!" Upham flashed, and he banged his glass down on the table.

The Colonel stood up abruptly. "Leave the mess at once!" he ordered.

"And you!" Upham snapped, his temper aflame. He rose sharply, turned, and marched out.

Johansen, distressed by the sudden clash, stood up and said steadily: "I'm afraid I must withdraw also."

But the Colonel took him by the arm, guided him back into a chair saying: "Perhaps we've had too much to drink. Let's forget about it."

It was some time before Johansen could get away. Then, to his surprise, he found Charles outside their tent, leaning on the tailboard of the truck they had brought with them, and inside the truck all their gear, ready packed for home. Batman and driver were there too, fully dressed, roused out of bed by Upham and given orders to prepare to leave.

"About bloody time," Upham growled at Johansen. "We're off home. What have you been doing—sucking up to that bastard?"

Johansen took no notice. He was senior to Upham. Quietly he told the batman and the driver to return to their quarters and go back to bed. They wouldn't be leaving that night, after all.

Finally he produced another bottle. "Now come on, Charlie. We'll have this in our tent. What the hell do you think the Brig would say if we beetled off home without making our report?"

It took some time, and a fair part of the bottle, to mollify Charles, but in the end his anger died and he agreed that they would stay to complete their task.

Next day they began work. The Colonel ignored them. Just as well, perhaps, for it wasn't long before Upham's forbearance was strained too far. The whole defensive area was a complete and utter failure. Whatever mistakes were possible to make were made. The concrete could be seen miles away; most of the positions were hopelessly sited. "And as for camouflage," Upham said, "you might as well have painted red, white, and blue flags all over them."

Then they made their first report to the officer appointed to receive it. There were two stages in their task—first to report on the existing positions; second, to peg out better ones. They decided to report first, do the pegging-out later. They said what they thought.

And then, to their amazement, the officer said: "Look . . . don't bother to do any more. Just put in a report that everything's satisfactory and forget about it."

Now it wasn't only Upham who rushed to the lines and ordered the batman and driver to pack up for home. Johansen piled into the truck in a spirit of cold fury. He, too, wasn't going to have any more of this. Off they set for the New Zealand Division again.

"You're the senior," Charlie said, as they arrived in their old brigade area. "You'll have to tell the Brig. But I'll have the drinks ready for you when you come out."

Johansen did the best he could with Brigadier Inglis, but Inglis told him that, whatever the circumstances, his job was to get the proper positions pegged out. He and Upham would return and complete their assignment. So back they went and, keeping their tongues well in check, worked day and night on the defences, marking and pegging, until at last the artillery regiment, and its Colonel, could expect to survive for a time if the invasion came.

The few days' special leave in Beirut that followed were like nectar.

The New Zealanders learned about mules in Syria. To carry supplies to troops stationed on trackless mountain ridges mule units were attached to the division.

The mules arrived with strict trade-union rules about them. They were not to be used for more than so many miles per day, nor were they to carry more than a certain weight. Charlie Upham thought a man could carry that weight himself.

To the officer delivering the mules Charles said: "What's the use of a mule if it won't carry more than a man?"

The officer began patiently to explain that it wasn't so much what they carried but what they saved a man from having to carry. To Upham, with his remarkable stamina, that was no argument.

He launched into a long description of what he thought the mules ought to carry. The argument developed hotly, the visiting officer stoutly defending his animals. It ended up with Charles claiming, with no justification whatever, that the man didn't know anything about the ruddy mules and "Anyway, they're too damned fat!"

This put the mule officer into a towering rage and he threatened court-martial and other awful things.

For several days a number of the officers were away from their units doing tactical exercises without troops, the officers themselves forming platoons and taking turns in assuming command. These were live-ammunition exercises, not mere paper battles.

It came Upham's turn to command a fighting approach through the foothills and up a valley. Then, at night, the mules would be used as they moved into steeper country.

The advance began in the afternoon, Upham leading the way, with Johnny Sullivan, the 20th's Intelligence Officer, alongside him. Sullivan had to point out the route.

The platoon had been going two hours, and had made its way well up the valley, before Sullivan came back to Upham with a worried expression. He said: "Charlie, I'm afraid I've made a mistake. I've guided you up the wrong valley. We can't get up here any further; we'll have to go back nearly to the start line, then head off to the left a bit to bring us on to the proper route."

Upham said: "That's a pity, Johnny. But don't worry. We're not going to turn back. There's no time for that. We'll go straight ahead, up over the ridge and down into the proper valley the other side."

Sullivan told him he didn't think it could be done. He thought it was impossible. The hills were like precipices.

"But that's what we'll do," Upham said quietly. "We won't go back. We'll get there somehow."

He led them on and on; and later Sullivan acknowledged that what he had thought impossible Upham was able to accomplish.

As night came the mules were brought up and assembled for the next move forward. But this had to be a silent move. So Upham issued orders to the other officers to muffle the hooves of the mules with sandbag material. It was a more difficult job than it sounded, and Upham watched indulgently as his officer-troops struggled to make any progress. Finally he smiled knowingly and said: "Hold it. You townies just haven't got *any idea*. I'll do the job myself."

So, watched by the officers, he called up all his skill in animal handling and began wrapping up the hooves one by one. It was hard work, and it seemed to get harder. He was breathing heavily by the time it was finished. He tried not to show that the job had all but beaten him too.

"It's a matter of understanding animals," he explained in a kindly way. "You've got to keep the beggars still. Now, if we're all ready, we'll get started."

It was true that the mules had kept still. Whether that was a tribute to Upham's powers no one knows. But the stoical animals had stood fast, had reluctantly allowed the mufflers to be put on, and continued standing immobile until the job was finished.

But now, as Upham's triumph was about to be demonstrated, and the mules to advance silently over the rocky paths, a tele-pathic signal must have passed from one beast to another. Almost as one, they started squirming and twisting, pawing at their own hooves, scraping and rubbing.

In horror Upham watched the awful spectacle. For within a minute every muffler lay loose on the ground, tattered and stripped, and the uncovered mules stepped delicately away from them in quiet satisfaction. Upham's fury was nearly catastrophic.

As May 1942 came round, all battalions went out eastwards to the Syrian desert to conduct manœuvres. Those units who were near the frontier at Aleppo performed with more enthusiasm than discretion, and an international incident, with interesting possibilities, was narrowly averted when the Kiwis advanced cheerfully across the frontier into Turkey.

Charles's men of C Company had the task of advancing along an oil pipe-line to hold it against imaginary enemy forces who would be seeking to cut the line. It was a hard march out, the men moving all night on foot, with the imaginary enemy certain to be defeated in the imaginary battle next morning. But whether or not the enemy were defeated, certainly one would expect some interesting re-deployment, flanking movements, platoons in attack, forming a rapid box, etc., when the end of the march was reached.

Morning came with the troops tired but expectant.

There appeared a liaison officer in a car, complete with map showing the last-known battle positions. Upham studied it.

"Well, what will your orders be?" the liaison officer asked.

"You tell me first what the school solution is," countered Upham.

"The school solution is to withdraw," the liaison officer said brightly.

"Withdraw!" exclaimed Charles, his jaw dropping. "After marching out all night—now we march back?"

"That's right," came the cheerful reply. "That's the school solution."

"Well I'll be ... !"

Upham had a remarkable flow of language, very apt for an occasion like this.

It was while battalions were on manoeuvres that word came to return rapidly to camp. Back they went, and packing up began. New Zealand? The Pacific? India? Or the Western Desert again?

Wishful thinking clouded judgment, but there was certainly the example of the Australians, who had already packed one division back home to meet the threat of the Japanese.

Terry Madsen, C Company clerk, said to Upham: "What do I do? If we're going home I'll want these files, these 347Bs, and all this junk. But if we get sent up into action they'll be a damned nuisance."

Upham looked at him solemnly with his serious deep-fire eyes. "You pack for action, Terry," he advised.

CHAPTER ELEVEN

BREAK-OUT FROM MINQAR QAIM

ROMMEL was to blame. Having been driven out of Cyrenaica in January 1942, he had edged back to a position near Gazala and Bir Hacheim, but then both sides had lain dormant for several months.

On 27th May he struck fiercely. Within eight weeks 8th Army was decisively defeated, despite outnumbering Rommel's forces almost two to one, despite numerical superiority in tanks and artillery. The German commander did it by concentrating superior forces against the isolated Allied groups that were thrown in piecemeal against him.

Over the mountains and down the valleys of Syria the New Zealand convoys roared out, through the orchards of Palestine, the sand-wastes of Sinai, past Cairo, the Delta, and on to Mersa Matruh, far west of Alexandria. And as they moved into the desert they encountered 8th Army in retreat, thousands of vehicles crowding the road as they all poured eastwards. Around Matruh the division spread out into defensive positions, and there waited for the enemy.

But anxious that his division should not become a beleaguered garrison force in Matruh, Freyberg urged that he should be given a more fluid role. This was done, and the division was ordered to hand over the defence of Matruh to other troops and to move south into the desert to the area of Minqar Qaim. There it was to operate as a mobile force to hold the low ridges in that region, and wherever possible to use its mobility to attack and delay the enemy.

While this move was in progress the 20th was given the task of guarding a party of New Zealand engineers who were laying 9000 mines in the path of Rommel's advance. They would follow the division to Minqar Qaim later.

The mines were to be laid on the site of an old mine-field for which no plans existed. There would be risks, there might be casualties from the old mines. But this gap in the line had to be closed.

The engineers, assisted by Indian troops, laid their mines. Protecting them sat the 20th, with Charles Upham tensioned like a spring in anticipation of the action that all knew was impending.

After helping with the mines the 20th rejoined the division at Minqar Qaim, but was almost immediately ordered to embus again and move northwards. As the men were climbing into the trucks, a drone came from the skies. Eyes turned upwards. Then a flare floated down. Charles was away from his company at that moment, but in the light of the flare he came racing back, shouting to his men to run for a wadi some yards away. They fled there as the bombs came tumbling down. More than twenty Stukas pounded the column.

Upham and Sergeant Monteath of Battalion Intelligence found themselves diving for the same slit trench. Monteath won.

"You young devil!" Charles shouted good-humouredly, his face alight with the sharp drama of the dive-bombing attack.

But Monteath wondered why Upham was bothering about a slit trench, for next second he was standing up, searching the wadi for his men, and shouting at the top of his voice for them to engage the planes with small-arms fire.

Spending the night northwards of the division, the 20th returned to Minqar Qaim early on the morning of 27th June. Everybody then dug in as well as they could amidst the hard rock and stones. Here now was almost the whole division, lying along the Minqar Qaim ridge, with its artillery and trucks hard by. The 4th Brigade, with the 20th, was out on the flat ground east of the main ridge.

It was at this stage that the division learnt that the commander of 8th Army had been relieved of his post and Auchinleck, Commander-in-Chief Middle East, had assumed personal control. There were orders to make a stand in the Mersa Matruh area; orders to retire to Alamein; orders to retire but only after offering stubborn resistance. It is still a matter of doubt which orders were finally given to all formations.

All that the New Zealand Division appreciated as dawn came on 27th June was that they were on an "island" in the desert, with few battle-worthy troops near, and Rommel's flood was about to pour upon them. At 7.30 that morning the 21st Panzer Division began its advance from its overnight positions. The German 90th Light Division moved ahead also. Within the hour the enemy had run against the spikes of the New Zealand Division sitting astride Minqar Qaim. Artillery on both sides opened the battle, the Kiwi twenty-five-pounders effectively keeping at a distance a screen of tanks that ushered the panzers on to the battlefield.

With the gunners running the battle so far, more ominous

signs appeared at 10.30 a.m. when a patrol from the Maori
Battalion sighted an enemy column moving into position some
three miles away. It was advancing on a front a mile wide, led by
its tanks, behind them up to a thousand trucks laden with
infantry. Almost leisurely its artillery came into action, then its
mortars, while the New Zealanders answered in kind with a
steady, watchful enthusiasm.

The exchange of high-explosive shells continued the rest of the
morning, while the infantry in their slit trenches or stone sangars
watched and waited. Towards midday it was apparent that a
great mass of the enemy was passing across the north front of the
division and there were signs that some of it was then turning
southwards so as to cut off the New Zealanders from the east.

By early afternoon Rommel had four armoured divisions in
the Minqar Qaim area. The New Zealanders were obviously in
for a warm time, but they wondered, as the day advanced, why
the Germans were so reluctant to move in to the attack. It was
a reluctance born of knowledge that by nightfall they would have
the New Zealanders completely surrounded.

There had been a lull in the shelling, but about two o'clock
the enemy guns broke into fresh life, followed by the mortars.
Whereas earlier in the day the New Zealand guns had been the
target, now the Germans began shelling the infantry positions
as well.

Charles Upham had one of the company's three-ton trucks and
had driven it from the escarpment down towards his company
lines. He was sitting on the bonnet looking out over the desert.

"Bob," he called to C.S.M. May, who was near him. "There's a
primus in the back. What about boiling up? I reckon we won't
have time later on."

May climbed into the back of the truck to get the primus.

There was a sudden crash, the sound of breaking glass, and
the truck gave a convulsive lurch. Bob May found himself leaping
for safety out of the back of the truck. "What was it?" he asked.

Upham, still sitting on the bonnet, said casually: "An eighty-
eight went right through the back, out through the windscreen.
But where the hell is that primus? Come on, get a move on, Bob."

The next shot smashed the tail-board.

"This is getting a bit hot, isn't it?" May suggested. "We're the
target, I think."

Upham shrugged. "Near misses don't hurt. . . . Come on, Bob,
get that primus cracking or we won't get a cup of tea before the
damned show starts."

But now tanks suddenly appeared through the dust, and all along the front German troop-carrying trucks came heading in. Here now came the attack—infantry jumping down, like ugly flowers suddenly sprouting all over the desert, mortars and machine-guns being mounted and beginning to fire. "Hold it!" Upham was shouting, with his men itching to fire.

They waited till the enemy trucks closed to a range of 400 yards; only then did the New Zealand infantry and anti-tank gunners open up.

Out swarmed the Germans, racing for cover in the low desert scrub. They were good men, too, men of the Panzer Grenadiers. Like well-trained campaigners, they dropped swiftly to earth, began returning the New Zealand fire spiritedly.

The Kiwis clung tight to their slit trenches. If one merely put a hand up above ground level it felt as if the Germans were all firing at that. The whole battlefield seemed to be alight, the air thick with fire.

And then, to the stupefaction of his company, there was Upham above ground, running from post to post in the open. "Don't waste your ammo!" he was shouting. "Ease up on it. Keep it till they come in!" And across the flat to the next group of slitties . . . a few shouted words . . . then running on to the next. . . .

"Keep watching! You'll never kill a German like that, son," he called to a new hand lying deep in his trench with his face buried in the sand. And as he raced around, from one section to another, the mortars seemed to follow him, and the small-arms fire tore at the stones around his feet.

"That's Upham," the gunner said to his mates as they rammed round after round of twenty-five-pounder ammunition into the gun. They were firing over open sights now, at lowest trajectory, their shells screaming out straight over the heads of the C Company infantry. They could see that infantry officer running around the field right in front of their gun, crouching as he dashed through the haze of smoke, dust, and fire.

"Blast him—he'll cop one from us in a minute," they complained.

Out on the exposed front a platoon thought the pressure was becoming too severe. They started singling out, falling back towards the main company position. Upham rushed over towards them.

"What the hell are you doing? How many casualties have you had?"

They told him.

"Hold on here!" he ordered. "Let me know when you have thirty per cent casualties. Then I'll see about it. But we've got to stay put in this show. We mustn't budge an inch."

Runners were needed to take messages out to the front, across to companies on the flanks. Upham went himself, rather than ask his men to face the fire in the open.

From early in the engagement Upham had made a discovery. The enemy fire was well disciplined, but it was inaccurate. A man might be hit by mischance, but unless he stood still the risk of being hit was worth taking, when morale and control needed someone prepared to move around.

His company mortars ran low in ammunition. Rather than have his men seen coming back from the firing line, he ran back himself, ferried fresh supplies out to the mortar-men.

"He was always a hard man to get on the phone," Colonel Burrows said. "He never seemed to be at Company H.Q. Someone would go for him. Then he would come on the line breathless, as if he had been running."

Lieutenant Moodie with his anti-tank guns had earlier sent his batman to Upham's Company H.Q. to act as liaison with the rifle platoons. As the battle grew more torrid he looked over towards C Company, expecting to see his man come crawling back with any necessary information. He didn't envy the man his job. The air was too deathly.

Then across the flats Moodie saw Upham coming in person. The German fire was heavy. Upham was wearing a soft hat and, as he ran, he leant to one side, holding his hat down on an angle as if to keep out the bullets, like a man battling against the wind.

In the midst of Moodie winning his own M.C. that afternoon, he did not cease to wonder at the spectacle of Charles Upham moving continuously around the field, spending more time above ground level than below it, shouting, running, encouraging, swearing.

Bob May was now out on the right flank with one of the platoons. There was a machine-gun out beyond the mine-field giving them a bad time. Try as they might they could not locate it. He sent a message in to Company H.Q. to ask if anything could be done about it.

Upham peered into the sun. The desert was trembling with heat, and the ground itself was lost in a mirage-like haze. Trust the Huns to pick the right angle to attack from. You couldn't tell what was what out there. That glassy shimmering spot way out—

was it a truck, a tank, a group of men, a big gun, just a patch of scrub? But out of the haze the Germans were steadily coming. He had to try to identify something. And where was that blasted machine-gun that was worrying Bob May's boys?

A truck driver named Falconer was standing near him. "Come on, Scotty," Upham called suddenly. "Get your truck going. Take her down there by Company H.Q."

So Falconer gingerly manœuvred his big three-tonner into a spot near the slit trenches that formed the headquarters. What a spot for a truck! Out there in the open, in plain sight of the enemy, Falconer thought that he wouldn't have a truck to drive much longer.

And then, as men of Company H.Q. watched from the shelter of their slitties, up on to the truck Upham began climbing. Up on to the step, on to the edge of the tray, then with a squirm to the very top of the cab, and Upham drew himself upright, standing on top of the cab with his legs apart. Deliberately he raised his binoculars and gazed steadily towards the advancing Germans.

Terry Madsen looked up at him in dismay. No time for politeness. "Get down, you idiot!" he shouted.

"Get down, boss! Get down!" they yelled to him. "They'll hit you."

Upham, his eyes glued to his binoculars, called back to them: "They've been trying all day. Haven't hit me yet."

There was a pause, while they shrunk into their trenches as a burst of machine-gun fire seemed to whistle only inches over their heads. And then Upham's voice came clearly down to them again. "Half right, near that black rock—it's a tank, about twelve hundred yards. Four fingers left—two more tanks and one truck. Jerries getting a gun into action. About a span to the left again— looks like a mortar, moving in closer, about six hundred yards. . . ."

And when he had calmly seen all he wanted he climbed down steadily.

They looked at him in anger rather than awe. The boss had no right to do a thing like that. Brave if you like, but that sort of bravery went too far.

The afternoon drew on to evening. Nowhere did the enemy break through the steady, controlled fire of the New Zealand infantry. Nor did they risk throwing their tanks into the muzzles of our guns. It was a duel of bullets and shell, not a personal conflict. German infantry who tried to come to grips were beaten back.

But the events of the day were no comfort to the New Zealanders. They were now attacked on three sides; artillery ammunition was down to thirty-five rounds a gun; they had no tanks; and the evidence grew ominously that during the day the Germans had thrown a ring right around Minqar Qaim. The line of retreat to the east was cut. The Germans did not need to make a frontal attack. Next day, with all their divisions in position, they would chew up the New Zealanders piece by piece.

Freyberg realized that to save his division he would have to break out of the circle. It would be a gamble, but there was little choice. But he had barely given the preliminary orders before he himself was wounded, and Brigadier Inglis took command of the division. Burrows moved up to become Brigade Commander.

Inglis directed that the break-out should be done half an hour after midnight. It would have to be a surprise affair, with no warning, no artillery preparation. The whole division would have to withdraw furtively from its battle positions, assemble in the darkness, then wait for zero hour. Then the chosen infantry would make a silent approach against the Germans lying directly to the east. As soon as they were detected, they would charge ahead with bullet and bayonet. They would punch a hole right through the enemy line.

Behind them the transport would have been formed up waiting, with the rest of the division sitting silently in the trucks. And when the assaulting infantry signalled that a breach had been made, the trucks, the guns, the ambulances, everything would pour through the gap.

Night came, and a clear moon rose like a ghost over the desert. 4th Brigade assembled in the dark, pulling back from their slit trenches out in the open, forming up in silence on the start line, their transport drawn in tight behind them.

Two battalions were late reaching the start line and the clock had advanced to 1.45 a.m. before everyone was ready. For the commanders this delay was a period of anxiety. Once before, at Maleme, Burrows had had to make an attack when his troops had not arrived in time. The delay spelt failure on that occasion. Now at Minqar Qaim, with Burrows commanding 4th Brigade, he had to wait and wait till all were ready.

But to the men in the ranks, who nevertheless knew what was ahead of them, the delay was just another excuse for sleeping. They dozed where they lay, and when they felt the nudge in the ribs from their section-leader they woke calmly and quietly, knowing that the time had come.

But it was not all grim. There was the spectacle of big "Snowy" Smith of the 20th, a soft-spoken, likeable giant of over six feet, who was gravely concerned because the rim of his tin hat was very shiny and conspicuous. With some glee he unearthed a desert topee, anchored it firmly *on top* of his tin hat, and thereby made himself about seven feet tall. It certainly hid the shiny rim of his helmet. In such fashion he prepared to advance against the enemy—a most impressive sight, an excellent landmark to steer by, and no doubt a formidable and startling apparition to the unsuspecting Afrika Korps.

And when at last they were all ready Burrows said quietly: "All right. Let's get started."

There was bright moonlight over the field, but the night seemed dark. It was all silence, just the rhythmic chuffing of men's boots against the sand and the stones, rifles held high, men walking forward with fear and hope in their hearts, wondering when the earth in front of them would awake and blaze. They were walking towards the enemy, to punch the hole right through the line, to make the gap through which the New Zealand Division must escape.

They walked 200 yards . . . 500 . . . 1000 yards. And still no sign of the enemy. Then a single shot came . . . another . . . and in a moment the whole front erupted into flame.

Ahead of the advancing troops a thick curtain of fire was flung up, the interlocking tracer forming an impenetrable screen. Into the teeth of the fire the New Zealanders flung themselves. For the 19th, in the van, it was not so difficult at first, for they found only light opposition straight ahead of them. But on the left the 20th, charging down into a gully, ran into the thick of the German defences. Into there the 19th turned also to help their friends.

Here in this wadi war was fought savagely. Germans in slit trenches were bayoneted or shot. Men following behind did the same to their bodies, for fear that a German might be shamming and would fire on them from the rear. German trucks burst into flame. Others were used in desperate efforts to escape the ruthless New Zealanders.

Through the wadi they poured, shooting, grenading, bayoneting, shouting, and yelling. With the 20th rushed Charles Upham. Those who saw him at the start noticed the huge load of grenades he carried, some said in a sand-bag, but certainly in a stuffed haversack slung around his shoulders. Charging into the wadi in the very front of his men, he left the bayoneting to the others, concentrated on the trucks and other vehicles with his arsenal of grenades.

The weirdness and drama of that night is still fresh in the minds of those who took part. The sheer audacity of the plan . . . the chatter of machine-guns in the darkness . . . the lines of tracer that men seemed just to ignore . . . the leaping fires of burning trucks . . . the shouts and screams.

They watched him with his bag of grenades, tossing them at every target he saw, regardless of the risk of wounding himself from the explosion of his own bombs. It was throw . . . throw . . . rush in . . . another truck—throw . . . rush.

There were many who saw him that night. But none can say for sure how often he dashed in against the enemy vehicles, heedless of the fire pouring at him, and flung his grenades at them. ("Perhaps six or seven," Upham grudging acknowledged after the war—but there were more than that.)

He was fired at by German Tommy-gunners from the back of one truck as it strove to escape. He yelled at them, rushed in with a grenade, and destroyed them all. Time and again Upham leapt upon their trucks as they were getting under way, bombing them into wrecks or setting them afire.

There were German staff cars too, for it seemed that the 20th had crashed right into a German headquarters. Upham was seen with his pistol, firing into the cars as they lurched away, few of them escaping; and as he raced up alongside one laden car he wrenched the door open, flung in a grenade, and slammed the door shut on its hapless passengers.

Through to the other side of the German lines the battalions fought, leaving behind chaos and destruction. They emerged into clear ground, and suddenly all was still. Up went the flare signal that the gap had been made, and towards the gap poured the transport that had been waiting at Minqar Qaim.

The 20th emerged from the battle all fiercely excited and stimulated. They saw Upham, his voice still high with tension. Fraser, the C.Q.M.S., looked at him in amazement. "What's happened to you?" he asked.

For Upham was covered in blood. Not then, not till the following night, did he report for medical treatment for his wound. From the grenades he had been distributing on the enemy he had at the same time peppered himself with grenade fragments.

All he said was: "This show tonight will make bloody history." It did for him, but he didn't mean it that way.

But to mention Upham is but to name one man whose exploits

in the break-out were dramatic. There were dozens of men whose courage and dash were unseen in the darkness, whose heroism burst and flamed in moments of mad confusion, where men singly and in concert performed one of the epics of World War II.

It was not the effect on the Germans, or on the New Zealanders, that was the feature of Minqar Qaim. It was simply that, by a display of daring and fearlessness that has few equals, the division escaped annihilation. That was as good as a victory.

Minqar Qaim was a glorious feat of arms.

CHAPTER TWELVE

DISASTER AT RUWEISAT

THOUGH delayed by rearguard actions like Minqar Qaim, Rommel's forces were now in full cry. Auchinleck's 8th Army was falling right back to its final defence line at Alamein, where the available route to the Nile Valley narrowed to a front of thirty-eight miles—the Mediterranean bounding it on the north, the Qattara Depression on the south. Along this front the Allied forces were strung thinly, gathered for the most part into a series of strong-points, but with few units other than the New Zealand Division in good fighting shape.

Given a mobile role in the defence line, the Kiwis now faced a long period of almost continuous movement and manœuvre. Ridges were occupied one day, abandoned the next, an attack mounted in the evening, the captured ground relinquished next morning.

It was a case of the defenders struggling to upset the balance of the enemy, who themselves were at the point of exhaustion and at the extreme end of their supply lines. Most attacks had little chance of success; but there was such weakness on both sides that almost by accident the battle for the Middle East might have been won and lost in a few fateful hours.

To those who saw or heard the official orders from on high, cynicism came easily. It might be a convenient Army expression, but civilian soldiers did not enjoy the hypocrisy of being ordered to "take ground to the eastwards"—when that was the direction of their own bases and rear units, and the enemy were still all in the west.

But on the other hand there was no fear of using the words "withdrawal" and "evacuation" in other contexts. "The Chief has decided to save 8th Army" was the condescending message that emanated from the staff at Middle East H.Q., prefacing secret plans for the retreat to the Nile and for complete withdrawal from Egypt.

Weary beyond words, C Company of the 20th came one night to their latest defensive area. Upham pointed out to his platoon commanders the sector each was to occupy. The men began the chore of digging, just as they had done the previous night, and again early that morning. There were, as usual, not enough picks and shovels to go round.

Colonel Burrows was back again as Battalion Commander. He had a new car, too; and somehow Charles had managed to acquire the old one—a Ford V8 which his driver Hopgood greatly admired but which presented an attractive target to the enemy. Burrows arrived in the company area, walked briskly over to Upham.

"You're in the wrong place, Charlie. This is part of D Company's ground."

Thin and unkempt, Upham looked at him wearily. "I'm in the right place," he said doggedly.

"Charlie, I'm sorry, but you're in the *wrong* place. Your position is over there." Charles looked where the C.O. was pointing.

There was a pause, silent except for the sound of Upham's heavy breathing, and the ring of picks and shovels.

When would they really fight? When would the brass hats learn that his men were getting more tired and sick every day? When would someone come out with a confident plan for a real showdown—a battle where his men could show their mettle? Never apparently—just dig and dig. And the frustration and exhaustion of the past few weeks suddenly boiled up inside of him. Not looking at Burrows, just staring into the desert, Upham began to swear, first softly, then with increasing venom. He swore at the Army, the war, the Germans, the "higher-ups"; he swore at Burrows, he swore at the desert—in an outpouring of emotion that violent language seemed to relieve.

It was not for nothing that the other man was known as Gentleman Jim. Because Burrows just stood and listened gravely while the worn-out figure of Upham abused him, along with the rest of the world.

When the pot of emotion ran dry, and Upham just stood there glaring, Burrows looked at him in the desert twilight and said softly: "I understand, Charlie. But I repeat—you're in the *wrong* place. You should be over there."

Like an exhausted and sad schoolboy Upham muttered: "Yes, sir," and walked heavily away. He had been spoiling for a fight with anyone, even Burrows, but the soft words and the refusal to argue had turned his wrath to water.

Burrows continued on his way to see Kippenberger at 5th Brigade H.Q. He thought he might see Inglis there too. He hoped so, because there was something he wanted to say to both of them. Strange it should be about Charlie Upham, whom he had just left. But it had taken days to check up on all the facts, and to make sure that what he had to say to Inglis and Kip was the result of sober judgment. He had waited till the drama and excitement of Minqar Qaim had died down to make sure that his thoughts were not exaggerated by the stimulating events of those hours. He had had to speak to a few reliable witnesses, too.

He found Kippenberger there. "It's about Charlie," he explained.

"Yes, how is he?" Kip asked with quick interest.

"Tired, like the rest of us; and savage. He wants a showdown. But I want to talk to you about Charlie at Minqar Qaim. Kip, Charlie's got to have *another* V.C.—for Minqar Qaim. . . ."

The 20th were moving east, exhausted after three simmering days of constant movement. Hoppy Hopwood drove Upham's V8 car. Upham, Le Gros, and Terry Madsen stretched out on the cushions asleep. Charles's last words had been: "That's our convoy, Hoppy. Just follow it."

Hoppy followed. But sleep bore him down too. He allowed the car to weave to a halt, slumped forward over the wheel. . . . When he awoke an hour later his own convoy was out of sight. But there was another going the same way. Starting up the engine again, he joined in the queue, then started to sweat.

He decided the best thing to do was to tell the boss as soon as possible. So he leaned over, shook Upham by the shoulder, till he stirred him into wakefulness.

"Captain Upham! Captain Upham! I've lost the convoy. I'm sorry, but I couldn't keep awake."

"Wish way we goin', Hoppy?" Upham muttered.

"Towards Alamein. But I dunno where this convoy will take us to."

"That'll do, Hoppy. Just keep going. I don't care a beggar where we are."

When dawn came they found themselves very close to home, were soon in their own company lines.

Charles was wanted immediately at Battalion H.Q. He went with Hopgood in the car, left instructions for a group of slit trenches to be dug for his headquarters while he was away.

On his return the trenches were ready, the one for his own use being deep, well covered, comfortable. He looked at it appreciatively, complimented the men on a good, thoughtful job. Then, pointing to the trench, he turned to Hoppy and said: "This one is for you, Hoppy."

It was typical of him to insist on the best being given to the man who had had the least sleep.

The company truck was well laden with sticky bombs, hand grenades, and bed-rolls.

Charles was some distance away when the truck caught fire. As he raced towards it he could hear the bombs beginning to sizzle, the flames starting to lick all around the boxes of ammunition and grenades. The driver, Ben Gurdon, was up on the back of it throwing off the bed-rolls.

"Get off, you fool!" Upham shouted as he raced up. "Those bombs will go up. Get off, you bloody idiot, you . . . !"

But by the time his oaths had finished he was up on the truck himself, throwing off the rolls, dashing sand over the flames, time after time ordering Gurdon to jump off. Ben Gurdon disregarded him. Together they cleared the truck, subdued the fire.

At last they climbed down together, grimy, covered with sweat and sand, the taste of burnt cordite still in their mouths.

"Well done, Ben," Upham said quietly.

11th July 1942. Midday
The New Zealand Division received orders to take part in an attack on Ruweisat Ridge, an important feature overlooking the battlefield of Alamein. It was held by the enemy, who were also believed to have advanced posts out on the flat, south of the Ridge, and across this flat the attack would have to be made.

The division would move forward to secure a start line within range of Ruweisat, and there await orders for the actual assault. When the time came it would be a night attack.

Tanks would be needed to protect the western flank of the division as it moved forward, Inglis claimed. The enemy held all that ground to the west. They wouldn't let the New Zealanders move across their front towards Ruweisat unmolested. And when the infantry had captured the Ridge, and daylight came over the desert, they would need tanks to guard them while they sat on the exposed slopes and dug in.

"Strafer" Gott, commander of 13th Corps of which the New Zealand Division formed part, thought Inglis was seeing difficulties that did not exist. But he agreed that assistance was needed. So it was ordered that the tanks of the 1st Armoured Division would provide "full fire support and flank protection".

The division mounted its trucks and moved across the desert to the start line. The enemy picked up the mass movement, thumped shells at the trucks as they advanced, flailed them with artillery and mortars as the trucks stopped and disgorged their men.

The shells continued to fall, but in textbook fashion the infantry shook out into extended formation, began to plod steadily forward. They reached the wadi where they were to assemble for the main attack and disappeared into its safety. They dug in there. But there was no attack that night. Nor the next night; nor the next.

They all waited in the wadi. The shells continued to fall on them. And Inglis was disquieted to hear that the tanks would not now move forward with his men, would not protect his western flank during the advance. He demanded that the tanks be placed under his command. Gott refused.

At the very least, Inglis demanded, would the tanks advance at first light, following the infantry assault? By then his men should have captured and be sitting on Ruweisat Ridge. They'd be easy targets unless tanks moved in to protect them. They told him this would be done.

And the thousand and more New Zealanders who were to lose their lives or liberty at Ruweisat Ridge would have wished that Inglis could have received that promise in some signed watertight legal document.

Then the word came: "Attack to start at 11 p.m. this night, 14th July. Contact with the enemy expected at 1 a.m. Capture the Ridge by 4.30 a.m." It would be *six miles* altogether.

The tanks are promised at first light, Inglis reminded himself again and again, as if to allay his feeling of uneasiness.

4th Brigade was on the left, 5th on the right. Each brigade had two battalions forward. It was dark. There was hardly a sound other than the creak and clink of equipment as men rose to their feet, spread out into formation, silently accepted the orders to be moving.

For some reason C Company seemed disturbed just before zero

hour. Intelligence Officer Johnny Sullivan was with them, showing them the start line, pointing out the axis of advance. They
would have to wait, anyhow, until the 18th and 19th had moved
off. The 20th were only in the second wave.

The leading battalions went two and a half miles before
striking the first enemy posts. As the first volleys split the night
air, they rushed out into line, then advanced on the enemy at the
double. Grenades, bayonets, bullets, hand-to-hand fighting; and
everywhere it was success. Some posts gave in quickly; others
fought bitterly to the last. And as soon as one post was subdued,
another straight ahead sprang to life, and they had to rush that;
or maybe it was to the flank; and even some behind. The Kiwis
tackled them all, charging in one direction and another, but
always making ground forward to the main objective on the
Ridge.

Within the first hour the company and platoon commanders
were thinking: If these are only the outposts it's going to be
pretty hot when we hit the main defence line on the Ridge. This
is much thicker than we expected. But it's going famously. Very
few casualties. The enemy being smashed up. We've lost touch
with the platoon on our left—perhaps they went in the direction
of that blazing truck; perhaps they veered off to that machine-
gun far out on the left flank; and we haven't the faintest where
Company H.Q. is now; but the Ridge ought to be straight ahead
—another couple of miles perhaps.

And as they went on, capturing and destroying, wading through
a very hot-bed of enemy resistance, the New Zealanders were
thinking in terms of victory. Did it matter that communications
were breaking down early? Companies were losing touch with
their platoons and with their battalions. Battalions could not
raise Brigade. Perhaps it did not matter, they thought, for the
battle on the Ridge was still to come; these were just the furious
preliminaries.

Moving off half an hour after the assault battalions, the 20th
had the task of mopping up the "left-over" opposition. They
pressed forward quickly, urged on by the sound of the fire-fight
crackling and exploding a mile ahead of them. Burrows, in command of 4th Brigade again, was travelling close by the 20th, and
had to prevent them moving at the double in their anxiety to
catch up with the war.

It was quiet going at first, but soon they came upon the relics
of the fighting left behind by the assault units. They were sur-

prised to find that the enemy's outposts had been so thick and formidable.

Now and then a stray enemy post, overlooked by the battalions in front, came to life, and the 20th had to engage and subdue it. The approach of New Zealand bayonets was usually sufficient, but once or twice Upham's men of C Company had to pause impatiently while the enemy were routed out with bayonets and grenades. D Company were also briskly engaged for a time, and then the whole battalion was pinned down for over half an hour by some accurate mortaring.

But Upham and his fellow-officers of the 20th became seriously worried. Things were not as they should be. The 18th and 19th had blazed ahead, smashed through the enemy apparently, and ought now to be in contact with the main defences somewhere about the Ridge. Yet out on the flat, short of the Ridge, there were more and more tightly held enemy posts, coming to life like a mass of erupting volcanoes in the very middle of the New Zealand supporting arms. It shouldn't be. They were getting in the road of the main battle up front.

Then through the darkness Upham heard the distinctive clank of tanks. He called Bob May over to listen.

"Ours, I suppose," Charles ventured. "If they're Jerries there'll be trouble in the morning unless they're cleaned out. They'll be in behind us."

Brigadier Burrows was worried too. Concerned with the silence from his battalions up near the Ridge, and with the fact that the battle apparently still needed to be fought on the flat, he decided that he must get news from his forward units. The radios were out; telephone lines had failed; there was no communication except by personal contact. So he went over to Manson, C.O. of the 20th, and said: "Ian, get someone to go forward and find out what's happened. Take this jeep."

Manson decided C Company should send someone up. He went over to Upham and gave him the orders. "Detail a good man, Charlie. The Brig wants the whole story from up front."

Upham said shortly: "I'll go."

Manson and Burrows were not surprised. Charlie would always do a job like that himself. They saw him hand over his company to C.S.M. May, clamber aboard the jeep alongside the driver, then roar away into the desert battlefield ahead.

It was not long before the jeep came under fire. Annoyed at this interruption, Upham had the driver cruise round till shortly he came upon an enemy post that had been knocked out. There he obtained a German machine-gun complete with tripod and ammunition. He mounted it on the jeep, then continued forward.

There were still enemy posts in all directions, still actively hostile. He was amazed that so many had survived the onslaught of the attacking battalions. Shots came at them from all sides, but Upham swung the captured gun at them, firing pugnaciously at anything that seemed troublesome. He was tempted to run in to the attack, but he knew his first job was to get information, so he contented himself with short bursts of fire in retaliation, then veered away out of range.

Farther and farther ahead they went, weaving round enemy dug-outs and weapon pits. He came upon enemy tanks, looming up through the fading darkness. Sharply he detoured away.

The dim shadow of the Ridge was right in front of him when he saw his first New Zealander. It was Doug Green, commander of an artillery troop, who had gone forward with the 19th Battalion to observe for his guns.

"Where's the 19th?" Upham shouted.

Green told him they were only a short distance away.

"What about the 18th? How have they got on?"

Green had no idea, but he offered to help. He would like to know, too. So he climbed on board the jeep beside Upham and away they went together, touring the battlefield in search of the battalions.

But now things were much thicker. There were Germans and Italians everywhere around them, some in confusion, pulling guns out by hand and with ropes. Enemy tanks were moving around, trying to protect the infantry in their withdrawals. Flares were going up, tanks firing, red tracer bullets from machine-guns curling through the darkness.

Roaming backwards and forwards, Upham's jeep then ranged over all the battlefield worth mentioning. They did not come upon the 19th again, which by now was near its objective on the Ridge; they ran through elements of the 18th and 21st, both of which had become disorganized; and, although they were not aware of it at the time, they passed beyond the line of our forward troops and into the thick of the German and Italian masses that had now fallen back over the Ridge to safety beyond.

Several times their jeep stuck in the sand, and it needed their combined shoulders to heave it out again. The second time it stuck, Green realized that there were scores of enemy infantry within a few yards. Green silently indicated them to Upham, furtively cocking his Tommy-gun as he did so.

"Never mind," was the reply. "They're mostly Wops. Come on —let's get the jeep out." And totally disregarding the Italians milling around, Upham put his shoulder to the back of the jeep and heaved.

They toured on. They would see a light in the distance. "Let's try over there," Charles would say, and they would scud off in that direction. It would turn out to be a German truck trying to tow out a gun; so they would swerve away and look for something else. It was a fantastic adventure. They came upon few New Zealanders, but all over the field they were running into German and Italian troops, bursting in and out of them, often in a flurry of shots, then racing away.

They stuck again. More Italians this time, completely surrounding them. Out they clambered, began hurriedly pushing at the jeep.

Without a tin hat as usual, Upham was not a clearly identifiable figure in the gloom. Whether it was by some telepathic projection of his personality, or by a laughable mistake, it is hard to say; but within a few moments Green found that Charles was directing a few Italians to help free the jeep. They crowded around, seemingly anxious to assist, pushing and shoving willingly, until with a roar the wheels took up again, the New Zealanders jumped on board, and off they went with barely a wave to the lugubrious but obliging Italians.

There was a tearing, scraping noise, and the jeep slowed down. They looked out. Trailing behind were yards of barbed wire, inextricably caught up in the axles underneath. They had to trail it the rest of the way around Ruweisat.

Next there was a sudden tilt, a slow slide, and in a moment the jeep was on its side over the edge of a dug-out. And more Italians everywhere. These looked more belligerent.

Charles sized them up, then advanced suddenly towards them with angry gestures that left only one interpretation. In a jiffy a party of Italians pounced on the jeep, righted it, saw it rev off into the night, with Charles still waving his fist at them in mingled contempt and appreciation. And, as they raced this way and that, the truth of the attack on Ruweisat began to dawn on Upham. From his extraordinary reconnaissance the facts began to emerge. They were unpalatable, but not yet dangerous.

The facts were these—that a grave miscalculation had been made as to where the New Zealanders would meet their main opposition. The main enemy line would be on the Ridge, or just short of it—so it was thought. That's where the battle would be.

There would be mere outposts out on the flat. They would have to be rolled up during the march in, but the leading battalions would have to reserve their main effort for the big assault just near the Ridge.

But the truth was that the outposts, whose resistance so puzzled the Kiwis, were in fact *the main enemy defence line*. The New Zealanders had burst their way through them, fought on to the Ridge, and driven the enemy off it. That was victory. But out on the flat the so-called outposts, which had been treated rather off-handedly, had come to life again. They formed a fiery barrier between the battalions who had broken through the supporting troops behind. Inside that barrier the enemy were as active as ever, and they had tanks coming in from the western flank to help them.

On the Ridge, the battalions found themselves broken up, irretrievably in some cases. The nature of the fight on the flat, with sections dashing off in all directions, caused cohesion to be lost. The Ridge, a mere forty-foot elevation in the desert, was no landmark, and few troops found themselves on their true objective. But they were at the Ridge—that was what mattered most. The morning would see the sorting out.

Upham and his crew turned the jeep round and headed back towards the south, weaving its way through enemy ground as if in a snake-dance.

It was coming light when it plodded back to Burrows, its enemy machine-gun still mounted, enemy wire draped around it like a fancy dress. Upham told what he knew, then hurried back to rejoin his company.

Almost full daylight. Closer to the Ridge. Only a shallow depression to cross before the short climb up the Ridge to the summit. The 20th were heading for a trig marked "Point 63", but I.O. Johnny Sullivan had realized they were off the line, that Point 63 was a little distance away to the right. They would have to climb the Ridge first, then move along the top to the trig.

To the lip of the depression they came. Burrows was up with the 20th, still praying that his other battalions were safely dug in ahead. Once across the depression, then up to the Ridge, and all would be well.

And in a sudden moment it became all noise and fire, the red jets of tracer were leaping towards them, and the flashes and spits of flame were coming from half a dozen guns, down there on the left, in the depression, about 400 yards away. They flung themselves to earth. But not before they saw, only too clearly, that the enemy had armoured cars down there and, farther back, almost in the shadow of those mounds, the unmistakable outline of the things they most dreaded—*tanks*.

Burrows summed up the situation instantly. It was serious—perhaps vitally serious. He shouted to Manson of the 20th to go in with the bayonet.

Manson looked at it quickly. He saw there was no time for fancy tactics. It had to be done on the run, straight into them.

He dashed over to Maxwell of D Company. "Get straight on to the Ridge, Peter!" he called. The trig had to be taken as soon as possible. It was a commanding position. He shouted to Washbourn's A Company to keep on the ground, await developments.

Then he was over at Upham's company, on the left flank, the fire pouring at them in a never-ending stream. He ordered Upham to detach from the rest of the battalion, wheel left, and make an assault on the German guns. Just for a second, as his eye swept down the bare fire-whipped slope, Upham's face set. He could see what had to be done. He could see what was likely to happen.

And then that old exultation and burning feeling seemed to sweep up inside him. He was up on his feet, and his voice was ringing out: "Come on, C Company! Come on! Come on!" and from the ground his men sprang up, swung left into line, and followed behind him, charging down the slope into the dip.

It was a long dash down the hillside. It had to be an assault into the very muzzle of the guns, straight down the lines of tracer, straight towards the German armour. And as Upham ran, and he saw them all running with him, unhesitating and unflinching, a savage pride possessed him. What men they were! What bloody heroes!

Now they were down into the hollow. Here were enemy trucks, guns, infantry. The fire came at them in vicious streams, the tracer like streaking red tennis balls.

"Come on now! Come on . . . into 'em!" Upham was shouting at the top of his voice as he ran forward. Hundreds of yards away, up on Point 63, all around the battlefield, they could hear his voice, rising above the din of battle as he roared his encouragement and his hate.

But a frontal attack is a brutal business. Ian Smith and Edwyn Shand—two of his platoon commanders—were killed in the first minute. Men were dropping all along the line. And with a wrench that threw him to the ground, Upham was hit in the left arm, a tearing wicked wound from machine-gun bullets that ripped

Upham receives his first V.C. from King George VI at Buckingham Palace.
Jack Hinton, another New Zealand V.C., waits his turn

Evening Post, Wellington

In typically casual
clothes, Upham says
goodbye to Molly as
he leaves for Greece

Amanda, Caroline,
and Virginia

Green & Hahn, Christchurch

through his biceps and smashed his arm at the elbow. He got up and staggered on.

Now they were into a mass of slit trenches and in amongst the trucks and the guns. It was cold steel and grenade work. One of the machine-guns was silenced.

There were the tanks ahead. They were moving from one mound to another, sheltering hull down, firing from behind each one. German infantry were running back, seeking protection behind the tanks. And his men now were at the armoured cars, swarming over them.

Upham's mind was hazy with the shock and pain of his smashed arm. He told Bob May to take over command of the company, for he didn't know how much longer he could keep going. But he was still in front, shouting and exhorting, cursing at his arm, while from their position on the Ridge, men of D Company looked down and saw him with his grenades, and they marvelled as they watched him lead the rush against the remaining machine-gun post and destroy it with bombs and bayonets.

It was all smoke, noise, confusion. For five minutes his men seemed to be everywhere, running and firing and shouting, and the terrible sounds of close fighting were like bedlam. Then all of a sudden it was still. It was suddenly all over, as if some weird signal had stopped it. The shots were still coming, but the fight had finished.

And as through a red curtain Upham looked around dazedly. He saw where they were. They were through the enemy, clear of the depression, up on its farther slopes. And in the depression? Where the enemy had lain in wait for them? It was cleaned out—swept absolutely clear; everything in it was either destroyed or captive in our hands.

Even the tanks had gone—now withdrawn out of range.

Upham felt something like awe. He had thought it wasn't possible. Face taut with pain, he looked around wonderingly. They had two German officers on their hands and forty other German prisoners, and well over a hundred Italians; they had enemy guns, a German Intelligence truck full of battle-maps.

Up on the Ridge he could see the other New Zealanders moving around, apparently secure on their target. He said slowly: "This is the greatest victory yet." Surely all enemy strength had now been broken.

He closed his eyes while Le Gros put a field dressing round the wound. It was a bad one this time, he knew, a really bad one.

Now Johnny Sullivan came hurrying over. He looked critically at the wound, realized instantly that Upham was in poor shape.

"You'll have to get to R.A.P. as soon as you can, Charlie. I'll try and jack up a truck."

Upham looked up at him without speaking.

Sullivan went on: "Like me to look after things for a while? We've got to push on up the Ridge, you know. What do you say, Charlie?"

Upham nodded heavily. "You take over, Johnny, till I get my arm patched up. Then I'll be back."

Sullivan looked at him silently. He thought it would be a long time before Charles would be "back". Be lucky if he didn't lose his arm.

Johnny Sullivan took over C Company, moved it into a stronger position on the Ridge. Then a small truck came on the scene and in it Charles Upham was taken away to the R.A.P., now established on the slopes of the Ridge further along. Le Gros would not leave his side.

Now it was daylight. From the Ridge there was the spectacle of masses of German trucks and men milling about to the north and west. Their guns were already bombarding the Ridge, where our men were finding that digging in was all but impossible. There was solid rock a few inches beneath the surface, so the best that could be done was to build sangars. They were little protection against air-bursts from the German artillery, a technique now being widely adopted.

Many commanders were desperately trying to find routes up to the Ridge from the original start line. Not only was the intervening area bristling with enemy who had survived the initial sweep by the New Zealanders, but now into that area more German tanks had moved. They edged up towards the rear of our positions on the Ridge.

Where was our own armour? Where were our tanks that were to be up at first light, protecting the New Zealanders on Ruweisat? The question was asked at the first flush of dawn, again and again as the hours advanced. And men, with feats of gallantry too many to be chronicled, braved the no man's land that now separated the Ridge from the Kiwis' supporting arms, to appeal for the tanks to move up, as promised. Nothing happened.

It was not long after dawn before those on the Ridge saw a long column of men marching westward, shepherded by tanks. At first they could not identify the marching column; then they didn't believe it; and when they finally knew it was true they couldn't understand how it could have happened. For the column of men was the bulk of the 22nd Battalion, who had made good their ground to the foot of Ruweisat during the night (a mile or two to the east of the 20th) but now at dawn were surrounded by German tanks and left no choice but to surrender.

Brave men can attack tanks and achieve short-lived success. But once the anti-tank guns are blown out of the battle, and the enemy tanks hunt together, unprotected infantrymen can do nothing but rise from their sangars with arms raised. So it happened to the 22nd, to all but a few men on the flanks who managed to run and survive.

Thus came New Zealand's first disaster of this day, almost apologetically, and indeed it remained unknown to the brigade and divisional commanders until late in the afternoon, so complete was the disruption of communications.

The hot sun mounted over Ruweisat, and the men clung to the ground, divorced from the guns that could have helped them, proud of their success during the night, wondering when the promised tanks would come forward to their aid. And hour by hour the shells and bullets poured in from the Germans reorganizing out on the plains.

They shelled the R.A.P. also. Already it was overcrowded. No casualties could be evacuated. Feltham, the 20th M.O., looked at Upham's arm. It was a horrible wound. He wanted to give him morphia. Upham refused, fearful that his usefulness might be affected. Feltham dressed it, then discussed with him how the R.A.P. could escape the shelling. A white towel. One that already had a red stripe down the middle. "Don't make it look like a white flag," Charles said. Make it into a red cross. There was only one source of red colouring. Plenty of it. They collected some in a mug. Carefully they painted another large red stripe across the towel, forming a cross, then draped it in view of the enemy.

The gruesome but effective flag was honoured by Rommel's men during the rest of the day.

Fretting and impatient, his arm like red-hot steel, Upham could not rest quietly at the R.A.P. It was pitiful and frustrating there —more wounded than could be cared for lying around in the open, waiting with growing disillusionment for the arrival of ambulances and medical supplies. But, as the hours advanced, the exhilaration of the night attack was giving way to bitter realization that the infantry were isolated on Ruweisat Ridge, cut off from artillery, reinforcements, and supplies, communications lost, with the long-promised armour still somewhere over the horizon. He got to his feet for the hundredth time and filled another pipe. It wasn't easy with one arm in a splint—and the pain of it made him giddy. Then in a moment of sudden decision he was walking away, head down, shoulders hunched, walking away from the R.A.P. over the Ridge. He headed towards the area where he had left the remnants of his company. What good was it hanging around amongst the dead and wounded? He could still walk and think. He could fight them one-handed if he had to. He did it on Crete. Three hours at the R.A.P. were long enough.

Bob May saw Charles coming back unsteadily. By now C Company were so reduced by casualties that they had joined with A Company into a composite group. But the numbers were thinning all the time. Wounded men were leaving for the R.A.P. almost every minute. They were so vulnerable on the bare slopes of the Ridge, completely exposed to the enemy shells and mortars.

Upham walked in amongst the sangars, caught sight of a captured eighty-eight gun and walked over to it. With one hand he struggled with the breech mechanism, trying to disable a vital part so that it would be useless to the enemy again. May walked over to him.

"What are you trying to do, boss?"

Upham scowled at him. "Get back to the men!" he snapped. "Keep under cover!"

"O.K., O.K.," May said apologetically. (Why did Charlie always get so savage during action?) "Just thought you might want some help."

"Well . . . perhaps I do," Charles replied in a milder tone. "Here, Bob, give us a hand with this damned gun."

The German gun-crew were still lying nearby, all wounded.

"Those Nazi bastards don't look so clever now," Upham said. He looked at the way their wounds had been neatly dressed. "Our boys fix them up?"

May nodded. Then he caught his breath, for Upham had advanced towards the wounded men, was standing over them, looking down with contempt. May thought—he hates Germans so much he's capable of anything, but surely he's not going to abuse them now.

Then May wondered if he had really ever understood Upham at all. For Charles was bending over the wounded men, giving them each a long draught from his own water-bottle. The Germans drank gratefully. Le Gros looked on open-mouthed. He had never expected to see his boss giving water to a German.

Bob May came up close to him, whispered: "For Christ's sake, Leggy, take Charlie out. Get him back to the R.A.P. He's out on his feet."

Meantime those in high command had become fully aware of the peril that beset the division. The night thrust had been almost too successful, the dash of the New Zealanders had carried them through the enemy lines on to Ruweisat, and all had seemed well.

But by day the ground between the Ridge and the start line had bristled with enemy guns again, forbidding any reinforcements, while enemy tanks had moved in and already swallowed up 22nd Battalion. Desperate measures were needed to save the rest of the infantry from the inevitable armoured counter-attack.

But it was after two o'clock in the afternoon before our tanks made any contact with New Zealand troops—even then only partial contact. Their advance into the battlefield was so timorous that by four o'clock requests to rush urgently to the rescue of 4th Brigade were met only by a proposal to send forward a "reconnaissance" tank.

Let that heat-laden day drag round to 4 p.m. Exposed all day midst the gravel and the sand, with no supporting arms, no tanks, no supplies, few communications, the New Zealanders became more and more conscious that a victory was being slowly turned into defeat.

Consolidation must follow attack. But the enemy line, broken and dissolved into scattered elements, was being allowed to revive, those who had retreated were re-forming and hitting back, counter-attack was imminent. Why wasn't something being done? Where were the tanks?

The War Diary of the German 15th Panzer Division echoed their thoughts. It said: "It was most astonishing that the enemy could not exploit his penetration into a break-through by pushing his tanks forward."

At 4 p.m. the counter-attack came. The enemy had had all day to prepare it carefully. Through the dust and smoke the tanks came heading in, heedless of the small-arms fire, singling out the handful of anti-tank guns and silencing them one by one.

Liaison officers raced back, urging our tanks forward. If they were coming forward at all it had to be now or it would be too late. Enemy guns were plastering the Ridge with their fire, the German tanks were looming up closer and closer, wondering why it was being made so easy for them.

Through the murk came armoured cars, manœuvring with skill

and speed, racing on to the infantry posts with machine-guns spitting. In from the west rumbled the tanks, German infantry sheltering behind them. Ruweisat Ridge was drenched with fire. Gone now were our own anti-tank guns, gone any means of defence against the enemy. And as the guns of the tanks swivelled down on to them there was no more to be done, nothing more to be said. The tank commanders stood up in the turrets, waving the men up from the ground.

As the wave of enemy machines advanced on 20th Battalion, Charles Upham looked around the R.A.P. again. Half his company seemed to be lying there. He had never seen so many officer and N.C.O. casualties.

He began stumbling over the fire-torn Ridge towards the 20th again.

Peter Maxwell saw him heading towards the exposed slope where the remnants of C Company were awaiting the assault.

"Where're you going, Charlie?"

"If we're going to be cleaned up I'm going to be with my boys," Upham replied, moving doggedly on.

"You bloody fool, Charlie. You'll stop it for good before you reach them. And if you do you won't get a doctor for hours. Stay with the R.A.P."

"Like hell!"

He reached the broken rocks where his men lay, just as another mortar bomb seemed to burst all around him.

His leg crumpled under him as the shrapnel bit in. He went sprawling in the dirt. Now, if he wanted to fight any longer, he couldn't even walk. He lay there helplessly. But what did it matter now? All was lost.

Here now were the tanks and the cars, sweeping in amongst the 20th, rounding up the New Zealanders as they rose from their sangars, hands up sheepishly. Upham lay on the ground, watching it coming closer, savouring the bitterness of it. One arm, one leg, one man for whom the war was ending in pain and humiliation.

Leggy was beside him.

"You've still got time, Leggy-boy. You can make it if you run for that little wadi. . . . Go on—you're not wounded—scram!"

"I'm staying with you, boss."

"O.K., Leggy. But what about that truck? I told you and Jack Coyle to make a break for it in that truck. Why didn't you give that a go?"

"Jack did. Last thing I saw he was going great guns. But I didn't want to."

Buck Carnachan edged over to the pair of them. It had been an unhappy day for signallers like him.

"What's the meaning of it all, boss? Looks like the biggest schemozzle of them all—and I've seen a few. What's gone wrong?"

"I'm sorry, Buck, really sorry." Upham sounded apologetic, as if the disaster was all his doing.

"Well, have you got a spare fag you can give me? Might be the last I'll smoke for a while."

Upham handed him a cigarette. They still had a minute or two before the tanks would reach them. While Carnachan lit up Upham told him of the rules in P.O.W. camps. "Promote yourself, Buck. Here, take two of my pips. Make yourself an officer. Then you'll come into camp with me—in an officers' camp. You won't have to work. Don't see why we should work for the bloody Hun. Take 'em."

But Carnachan shook his head. "Too late, thanks, boss. Truth is, I've just promoted myself to sergeant—I altered my pay-book just before I crawled over here to you chaps. Don't think I'd better try another forgery."

Charles grinned weakly. "Good on you, Buck. Now tell Leggy to try and scrounge me a cigarette, will you. That one was my last."

Buck looked at the butt of the one Charles had given him. "Oh Christ!" he said. "Did I take your last ruddy fag? What a hell of a day!"

The leading tank loomed out of the dust, only fifty yards away, its guns swivelling towards them. The end was close at hand.

CHAPTER THIRTEEN

VALLEY OF THE SHADOW

AN overnight stop at Daba . . . hardly more than a few tents in the desert, surrounded by slit trenches and barbed wire. One night at Daba . . . just one more night of pain and exhaustion, of the spectacle of men whose spirits struggled more and more weakly against the growing tortures of the body.

The searing days in the jolting trucks when men's wounds and broken bones threatened to drive them crazy in the never-ending torment. Or were the nights worse? Nights when it was still, and the agony seemed to come flooding in with the darkness and the thirst.

It was better that first day after Ruweisat, when the wounded prisoners lay together in the open, the enemy trucks and tanks laagered around them, while the British guns shelled them all indiscriminately.

And now at Daba, on the slow journey westwards with the prison-of-war convoys. . . .

The tent was for wounded officers "with no future". Beau Cottrell, one of A Company's officers from the 20th, lay there crippled, his Achilles tendon shot away. No more for him the roar of the crowd as he ran on to the Rugby field in his All Black jersey. There were other New Zealanders in the tent beside him. They had little to do but endure their sufferings, talk of the disaster at Ruweisat, and wonder how many of their friends had survived. Already they knew that no less than five New Zealand battalions had been cut to pieces.

A small man who seemed to be unwounded made his way into the tent and gently roused one of the officers. The wounded man turned over carefully, looked up and asked: "Found them yet?"

"Yes, boss. All the boys are together."

"Well, you hop back there, Leggy-boy. See how they're placed for water, will you?"

Leggy nodded, glad to get out of the tent again. The smell of death and badness in there was too strong. He went across to the other tents and dug-outs he had found, saw Bob May there with all the others, and enquired about the water situation.

He returned and reported to Upham. Sitting up on his stretcher, Charles called loudly for attention. He demanded the chief medical officer. That, of course, was impossible, he was told.

So he shouted louder . . . and louder.

One of the wounded, tongue in cheek, called over to him: "That's it, Charlie, throw your weight about. Flash your ribbon at them. They might take some notice then."

Charles scowled. Because he hadn't got his ribbon. When the truck had picked him up off the battlefield, lying there helpless with one leg completely numbed, he had ripped the ribbon off and thrown it away in the sand. If he had kept it he would have received preferential treatment, he thought.

So he renewed his protests and finally made himself heard. There was enough water for the wounded officers—why not the men? They listened to him, and in the end the extra water ration went over to the wounded prisoners of the 20th.

But the arguing was a painful process. Every move now was an agony. His whole body seemed alight. His mind was often hot and wandering, and he knew that several times he had faded out into unconsciousness. In between times he awoke and for a few minutes then his mind was sharp and vivid, turning over like an express train as if there was little time to lose.

It was inevitable for prisoners on both sides to be relieved of anything of value. But as Upham lay on his back, he protested volubly as the Italians looted the wounded prisoners. He knew that many of his own men would do the same, but he wouldn't countenance it himself. Apart from its illegality, he regarded it as degrading as much to the looters as to the victim.

Perhaps it was the force of his personality, or the cold flash of his peculiar eyes, or merely the vehemence of his protests, but the Italians shrank from robbing him. Not so lucky were the others.

Beau Cottrell found himself politely relieved of a beautiful watch that he treasured—a presentation to him back home. A young German took it from him. Cottrell lay suffering with his smashed heel, but grieving more at the loss of so prized a possession. Charles lay beside him. Upham said suddenly: "Here, Beau, you take *my* watch."

Cottrell gave a short laugh. "No, thanks, Charlie. Mine's gone, that's all that matters."

"Go on," Charles said irritably. "I don't want this one of mine. And, anyhow, the bloody Ites will pinch it off me sooner or later. Go on, take it!"

"No, thank you, Charlie old man. I don't want your watch."

"Well, if you don't want it they aren't going to get it." And Upham lifted his hand, flung the watch from him. It skidded into the sand a few inches from Cottrell's stretcher. He turned his back on Cottrell, satisfied now that neither was going to suffer more than the other. Beau would have no watch. Neither would he. And he would save himself the ignominy of having it filched from him later. Let it rot in the sand. But before they shifted him Beau Cottrell rescued Charlie's watch. He kept it with him during the years of captivity that followed, brought it back to New Zealand, and to this day still produces it on demand, with its initials *C.H.U.* on the back. Charles has always point-blank refused its return.

Now it was Mersa Matruh. Or he thought it was. Things were not so clear. The men were different. They were all separated. Leggy had been taken off. Beau had gone. In fact, as Upham woke up this morning and looked dazedly around, he couldn't see anyone he knew. They all seemed to be Italians. No New Zealanders at all.

They were on the concrete floor of a cellar; in an old stone barracks building in Matruh. His head seemed like a detached balloon; his arm was living fire. It had had nothing done to it apart from the simplest field dressing. The stench of it was appalling. And the smashed bone was sticking out through the bandage in a way that seemed to tell him he had no hope. It was full of maggots, too.

The smell of blood and putrefaction in this place was overwhelming. Something was going on, some activity, but all he was conscious of was the pain, the presence of other twisted bodies, the terrible sounds of human agony. His mind went out and he lapsed into unconsciousness again. . . .

It was evening. He came sharply awake at the sound of screaming and looked around. In the dusk he saw the figures of them all, sprawled out across the floor. One look at the man next to him and he knew he was dead. He must have been dead for days, too. The sight and smell of it were unbelievable.

In a glance he could see that these were all badly wounded men—no "walking wounded" here. They looked like the very worst cases.

Then as the night came more was added to their sufferings. For British planes came over, deluging the town with their bombs —severe, merciless bombing, more than these broken patients could stand. Many gave way to their terror, and screamed and thrashed about in agonized helplessness. Even when it was over, and they managed to sleep, the fear poured from them again in uncontrollable nightmares, the shock and agony of their wounds making a pitiful blend with the mental torture of the falling bombs.

Next day came, and perhaps his mind was a little clearer. He could see around the cellar now—yes, they were all Italians. He was the only Allied prisoner there. They were all in a very bad way.

The scene in the cellar was indescribable. Even in his illness Upham found it staggering to his senses. For men lay dead in the rapid decomposition of the tropics. Clearly some had lain like that for days. Some orderlies came in and dragged their corpses across the floor, hauling them unconcernedly over the bodies of those still living.

Those alive had plumbed the depths of degradation, as many lay feebly in a mess of their own excreta, crying continuously for water and aid, while others burst suddenly and terrifyingly into the wildest screaming. A few, and a very few, lay like stoics as life ebbed from them.

Night came yet again after a day of alternating sleep and consciousness. Again the bombing, again the spectacle of men in the ultimate torments of mind and body. And on top of the bombs came shells from the Royal Navy, bombarding Mersa Matruh to destroy the few buildings that remained standing.

Hysteria, terror, and mortal agony reigned in this fearful cellar. And Charles Upham began to doubt his own sanity as he clung to the life which others were yielding without pride. The pain of his arm was shocking. It would have to be amputated, he knew. And he came to realize that the reason for this ghastly underground pit was to assemble cases requiring amputation or the most drastic forms of surgery. He was resigned to it. Take the arm, he felt. In its present state it would soon lead to his death unless medical treatment was forthcoming.

And he found that down here was where the actual operations were done, too. There was no privacy. It was all just one filthy, communal operating theatre, where those waiting for the surgeon lay cheek by jowl beside those writhing fresh from the scalpel, and those for whom mercy had at last gratefully intervened. There were no drugs, no apparatus, little water. For the victims it was life or death, and it was mostly death.

The Continental doctor approached his amputation patients with a surgeon's knife, a little machine like a hinged paper-cutter, and a saw. As the orderlies closed around the victim, the dreadful details of the operation were spared those others who were looking on; but Upham saw, with cold horror, the blood-encrusted saw being wiped again and again across the doctor's trousers.

The clumping feet of the orderlies woke him. They were coming over towards him . . . the doctor behind them . . . and with them the saw, the thing like a paper-cutter, and the kit of instruments. He wondered hazily if this was his turn.

But no—not yet. It was for the man next to him, a twisted figure with both legs mangled, for whom there was no hope but double amputation.

The orderlies seized the poor fellow, prepared his body quickly, and held him firmly down. Only inches in front of his eyes, Upham stared aghast. The man struggled weakly, making pitiful sounds beneath the hand that was clapped over his mouth. His eyes bulged.

One . . . two . . . and as the cleaver went into the second leg an awful jet of blood spurted from him, straight on to Upham's chest. He recoiled in nausea. The man gurgled, his throat rattled and choked, and in less than a minute he was dead.

And if that were not enough the grisly team was now advancing on another stricken fellow. Upham could not tear his eyes away. The spectacle was so macabre, so shocking.

This was another leg amputation. Again the dreadful process of holding the man down, hand over his mouth, and the butcher-cum-surgeon sliced around the leg in a jiffy.

It was off, and again the blood came, pulsing out of the hideous stump in great bursts, splashing on to the man next door while one of the orderlies was jumping around trying to avoid being soiled.

And then, as if to cap all other horrors, Upham saw the orderly with something in his hand, and he was trying to jab it on to the bleeding flesh, trying to hold it there and at the same time dodge the spurting blood. And the object he was holding was—*a hot iron*: he was trying to cauterize and seal off the wound with this ghastly relic of surgery a century out of date. The victim died while they were still working over him.

Upham felt absolutely shattered by these sights. The experience of them was like tearing open some black door and exposing a terrible world beyond, of which he had never known before. How could it be possible? Was he really still alive or was this just the tortured living-on of the mind after death? Was this appalling place really true?

He was aware of the night coming again, and the terror that it brought once more. It was misty in his mind and even the terrible things were like fantasy.

Next morning he awoke. Instantly he felt that something was different. Yes, while he had slept someone had been in and removed part of his bandage. It was lower down, and now high up on his biceps there was a ring drawn with some coloured material like chalk, right round the upper arm. He was feeling bad . . . he didn't bother at first to guess what it meant.

But now in came the orderlies . . . over towards him . . . and now the doctor . . . the kit . . . the saw . . . the thing like a paper-cutter . . . the hot iron. This was his day . . . his turn.

Quickly they moved him on to a stretcher. They told him—yes, he knew—that the arm had to come off . . . they could not save him otherwise . . . they couldn't devote the time to dressing it. Amputation was all they could offer. Otherwise the gangrene would spread, there would be more infection, and in the end certain death.

He knew now, of course. The chalk mark was the guide line for the surgeon. Hoping against hope, he asked how they would do it . . . what anaesthetic?

The doctor said casually: "There isn't any anaesthetic. We haven't got any."

And suddenly he knew—if they did it, it would kill him. In his state of health he could never survive the awful shock of such an operation. He had always hated and dreaded pain . . . why should he be butchered now? Perhaps the others had agreed for fear of being left to die a worse death, of being utterly neglected. Well, he could look after himself better than they.

They prepared him. He protested once; then twice; and again. Until all of a sudden they stopped and looked at him, and realized that he was having the effrontery to refuse their treatment.

Just for a moment the doctor paused in surprise. Then impatiently he pushed Upham off the stretcher, gave him not one further glance, and called sharply for the next case, the next sacrifice. They had given him his chance. He had rejected it— they wiped their hands of him.

But, as he lay on the floor shocked and shaking, Upham knew, with complete certainty, that he had saved his own life. He had been within an inch of giving it away, under the guise of medical treatment. Now he felt he could live, he could get better, he could fight for himself. All he had to do was find someone who would dress his arm decently.

The days seemed to pass on and on, and Charles faded in and out of consciousness, too ill to sense the passage of time. Once he became aware that a British doctor was bending over him, a fellow-P.O.W., and that his arm was being dressed expertly.

And then things seemed to become straighter and his mind clearer. He was still in the cellar, but the hot dizzy feeling in his head was subsiding, and the arm no longer felt as if his whole body was tied on to it, with leaden weights attached. He could soon walk again, shakily at first, enough to move around the cellar and restore some decency to his person, to feel the strength starting to ebb back little by little, and for his mind to begin thinking: get well, the quicker the better; for until health was regained there could be no escape.

He was still in the war, even if he had to fight it behind prison wire. But war, and escape, would have to wait on recovery. It would be senseless breaking off into the African desert without food, with few clothes, a recent leg wound, and a hideously shattered arm that they had just put in plaster of Paris. He must wait.

That he should even think of the future was proof that he was alive again. But he had passed well down the long Valley; he had wandered deep into the Shadow, and he had felt close the enveloping folds of its mantle. His life could never be quite the same after that.

The hospital ship leaving Mersa Matruh for Italy did not want prisoners on board with lice in their hair or filth on their clothes. So Charles Upham found himself walking slowly up the gangway with his head shaved clean, feeling faint and sick from a touch of sunstroke on his uncovered pate. Walking up a gangway completely naked was certainly a new experience. He supposed they would give him fresh clothes on board.

The Italian girl standing on the deck looked for one moment at the stark New Zealander, adorned only by his identity discs and plaster cast, before turning casually away. Charles's embarrassment was replaced by a sharp feeling of hatred at finding himself subjected to such humiliation.

They took him below. There he would be the only New Zealander.

Half-way across the Mediterranean the ship was attacked by British Hurricanes. Upham did not know if the ship was correctly marked with the insignia to protect it from enemy attack, but he knew the ship was being used for more than hospital purposes. There were a number of Italian soldiers and German officers on board, all combatants, merely being transported to Italy on tours of duty.

As the planes swung away, it was against Upham that the Italians turned their wrath. For a few hectic moments he feared they would pounce on him and cut his throat, so hysterical and violent was their reaction. The Germans on board smoothed out a ticklish situation.

But they, too, looked on Upham as special bait. They taunted him with German victories, revelled in the way he flared up in reply.

The ship brought them into the port of Reggio, on the southern tip of Italy, right opposite Sicily. He would disembark here, they told him. He would be walking past crowds. Just as a precaution, they would have to handcuff him. It would be rather awkward, of course, with one arm in plaster.

Upham said nothing. He did not mind. As a prisoner he intended to treat his captors roughly. He fully expected to be treated roughly in return. They gathered around him when the manacles were put on, sitting jovially around a table in the officers' quarters. Despite his truculence and barely concealed contempt for them all, they liked to hear him talk. They knew him now as a V.C. winner, a genuine war hero. It added a little glamour to their own lives to spend time talking with such a notability.

The word came to go. They were all ready. Upham was sitting on one side of the table. A large water jug stood on the table near the opposite side. With a casual expression Upham rose from the table, his knee out in front. Up went the table suddenly, over went the jug, and the water splashed into the laps of two German officers.

He apologized quickly. After all, a man in handcuffs is inclined to be clumsy. But they had good reason to doubt the sincerity of his apology.

It was time to disembark. Barefooted, with no more than a shirt and a pair of shorts, still in handcuffs, Upham was directed down the gangway and on to Italian soil.

Here it was a parade. People lined the streets of the town, waiting for their men to leave the ship and march up from the wharves.

First some Italian soldiers emerged. They marched smartly into the town and the crowd cheered them to the echo. Then came Italian wounded. Abruptly the cheers ceased and, as one, the crowd burst into bitter weeping. Then cheers again for the Germans. Then the prisoners.

As if the parade were all for him, Upham was led along the street on his own, walking uncertainly between the lines of citizens.

The hissing and booing grew. Some spat at him as he shambled past, arms crossed in front, looking left and right in contemptuous acceptance of the spectacle they were making of him. It seemed that the whole town was on the street that day, and all subjected him to abuse as he walked past.

All? All except one. For as the procession neared its destination Upham saw a little Italian girl run out from the crowd, a child of six or seven perhaps, quite uncomprehending the reason for this demonstration. All she saw was a ragged-looking man stumbling along, ill, barefooted, one wrist fastened to the other, and with one arm in plaster. She ran towards him. Into the cradle made by his two arms the little girl gently laid a bag of sweet fresh pears. Then shyly she turned and ran back into the crowd. Perhaps Charles Upham's head rose a little higher as the procession moved on.

From Reggio the prisoners travelled north by train. They sat him in a compartment with some German officers, who continued the mild baiting that had been their amusement on board ship. They had food and wine. The food they shared with him, but when he asked for a portion of the wine they brusquely refused. He seethed at the awareness that their good-humour was simulated, merely a cloak for their more natural arrogance.

He chose his moment. Then, in an unmistakable gesture, he suddenly rose from his chair, put his knee under the table, and heaved.

The effect was just as he planned. Into their laps the wine cascaded, over their conceited uniforms it spread its stain, and Upham laughed aloud in rich satisfaction. It was almost too good to be true that he had pulled the same trick twice! The rest of the journey was not so polite. Never mind—that round was his.

Into Naples they swung, then on trucks to Caserta Hospital, a short distance out of the city. On the third floor of a large stone building seven wounded officers found themselves together in one room—Upham with his broken arm, Beau Cottrell with his Achilles tendon, Major Lynch of the 18th, grievously wounded, and four others.

There began then at Caserta the months of waiting and futility that only prisoners of war can truly understand.

The transition in Upham's life from his intent war-making to the dreariness and clogging tempo of prison camp affected him deeply. For a man of his far-ranging independence, confinement was almost more than he could stand.

But for the first long months it was a matter of keeping alive. The only problem was recovery, and that was hard enough. They attended to his arm and managed to save it, but only at the cost of his general health falling perilously low. The Italian doctors did their best with the equipment available, and the attention given the wounded was reasonable and considerate. But, as the months of 1942 passed, more and more Allied prisoners came flocking in. Food became shorter, medical attention more hurried and less frequent.

They were grey months of suffering and sickness. Probably only Upham's wiry constitution and implacable determination enabled him to survive. He lived through it. So did Cottrell. But all the other five officers in that room died there.

Charles spent many hours sitting beside Major Lynch, trying to introduce a little cheer into his last days. It was something to be able to move about, not to have to lie abed suffering month after month.

"You know, Beau," Upham said to Cottrell, "what a little thing it takes to floor a man. Look at you now—just a little nick through the heel, and you're not worth a tin of fish. You with your one leg, me with one arm—we'll go into partnership after the war, eh, Beau?"

Cottrell said: "You'd be no good, Charlie, if you thought of coming into partnership with me in law. My God, you'd look awful in a wig and gown."

"And you'd be no ruddy good, Beau, if you're thinking of coming into partnership with me on a farm. We need two-legged men on the farms."

Hour after hour Charles sat alongside Lynch and Cottrell, talking and joking, recalling rather desperately some of his funniest experiences back in the New Zealand mountains, to help keep his friends' minds off their own suffering.

He was too ill himself to give anything more than passing thought to the question of escape. Survival and recovery were all that mattered just yet. His own shaky health was dragged down further by an attack of jaundice, and then he endured weeks of debilitating toothache. While prepared to let them treat his arm, he obstinately refused to accept dental treatment. It was too personal, too close and intimate. He couldn't stand that from people he loathed.

And so the dreary, painful months began to crawl by, death and suffering the chief companions, little left but an indomitable will to overcome the despair of his environment.

Upham's health sank very low at Caserta. He might easily have gone the way of his five companions in the room but for a transfer some months later to another hospital in the north of Italy, at Castel San Pietro, where he remained about four months before being moved on again in March 1943. They were months of slow recovery. Food was good, medical attention adequate, and all prisoners admired the kindness of the nuns who nursed in the wards.

But, like Caserta, it was overcrowded. Wounded men lay in all the passages. There was no room for any recreation except singing.

Slowly the glimmerings of health began to return. From the lethargy of deep illness Upham's spirits began to stir again. No longer dangerously ill, but still weak and emaciated, Upham now began to display the first glint of rebellion that later dominated his prison life. There was an Italian security officer at Castel San Pietro whom, for lack of a better name, they called Rat-face. Rat-face always carried an evil-looking knife, a most sinister weapon. It seemed to typify his mean personality and, to Upham, it was a symbol he was not prepared to accept. Charles might have been content if Rat-face had carried a revolver. But to have a man parading in front of him armed with a *knife* seemed to Charles to be a psychological wrong that needed righting. He did it by fright.

One morning, as Rat-face moved slyly down the room, the prisoners eyeing him with casual disinterest, Upham made his gesture.

Abruptly he stepped out from his bunk, walked a few paces firmly towards Rat-face, and stood belligerently in front of him, feet astride.

"Give that to me!" he demanded sharply. And with that he reached out and laid hands on the knife.

Rat-face leapt in surprise, clapped his hand over the scabbard, and stepped hurriedly backwards, jerking the knife-handle out of Upham's fingers. He looked up into those frozen blue eyes that were beamed on him like enemy searchlights fastened on a defenceless aircraft.

For several taut seconds the two men stood facing each other. Then Rat-face seemed to shrink, he stepped back another pace, then turned and retreated ignominiously in the face of Upham's silent challenge.

Charles stood and watched him hurry out. Then he looked around and grinned. He felt good. He felt marvellous. He had, for a moment, acquired the moral ascendancy over his captors. That was all he wanted. His spirit was coming back.

CHAPTER FOURTEEN

ESCAPE AT THE RIVER

LEAVING Beau Cottrell still incapacitated at Castel San Pietro, Charles was transferred to a normal P.O.W. camp in March 1943. Here at Modena (not far from Bologna) he found himself again amongst friends—Neil McPhail, Dick and Wally Ormond, Tiny Armour, Tom Bromley, Wynne Mason, Bill Allan, Doc Beattie, and others.

The other P.O.W.s there had little enough for their own comfort, but when they saw Upham come in, obviously still weak, they immediately made everything stretch a little further so as to provide for his well-being. He came in wearing only a pair of thin Italian trousers and a shirt. It was only a matter of seconds before Dick Ormond forced him to accept a heavy, warm, polo-neck sweater—a garment which Charles kept to the end of his war-days, and which probably saved him from dying of cold more than once. Someone else had a spare pair of boots, and each man contributed a little from his own meagre supply of tobacco.

Modena was a new camp, well constructed, and with good food. Some of the camp appointments reached quite a level of splendour, with marble generously lavished on washrooms and lavatories. It housed about 240 New Zealand officers and 800 or so South Africans—and it was here that Charles developed some of the friendships with the South Africans that he still treasures. There was Neville Holmes, a South African lawyer who later became a Supreme Court judge, and Sir de Villiers Graaff, one of that country's personalities and leader of a political party.

Charles arrived at Modena still suffering from his wounds and illnesses, but fit enough now to take part in regular P.O.W. camp life. He was quiet to the point of moodiness at times, preferring a serious argument with a close friend to cards or singing.

Few knew him better than Neil McPhail, and there were few whom Charles liked better.

They were sitting together peeling potatoes.

Upham wound up the long argument by saying: ". . . the Huns caused the war, they began it, and they'll start another war unless we wipe all their industry off the face of the earth. No armistice terms, just destroy the whole ruddy lot. There's never been a good German yet."

"Oh, I don't know, Charlie," McPhail said. "Blame Hitler and the Nazis if you like. And blame the German people for not stopping him when they had the chance. But there must be good Germans, just like there are bad New Zealanders."

Charles's eyes suddenly flashed. "Good Germans? There are *no* good Germans. There never has been a good Hun."

"Oh, come off, Charlie. I don't hold any brief for the ruddy Huns, but there have been good ones . . . in the arts, for example. Take music . . ."

"Music! Music!" and with an oath Upham threw down the potato knife he had in his hand, jumped to his feet, and stalked away.

He refused to speak to Neil McPhail again for a whole week.

But that was part of Upham's make-up—an implacable hatred of the enemy. It was part of that same attitude that made him refuse to learn Italian or German. He knew it would help him if he were to escape, but he could not demean himself to do so. Likewise, he persistently refused to look at any enemy news-papers, or to give more than a contemptuous glance at enemy notices or orders that appeared in English.

Charles was so continually arrogant to the Italians and Ger-mans that trouble seemed to be just round the corner, day after day. It was like that on the night of Tom Bromley's birthday. It had become a custom that a certain amount of vino would be saved up for birthday celebrations. As the night drew on, the others faded from the party one by one, leaving Bromley and Charles alone at the finish. But these two were tipsily determined not to go to bed.

"I won't go to bed till Tom goes," Charles declared thickly.

"And I won't go to bed till Charlie does—good old Charlie." So said Bromley.

And nothing would make them decide who should go first.

So amid the clamour of their arguing, and the weary shouting of their friends, it was not surprising that the captain of the guard should decide to look in and see what the row was all about. It might be a diversion to cover an escape. He would count the bodies.

Inside the hut the first man his eye met was Upham. Here was a prisoner still fully dressed. The Captain naturally turned his attention to him. Unhappy decision!

The restraint and self-control of all the long months of con-finement were dissolved in the warmth of the vino. Straight in front of Upham was the symbol of the enemy.

Like a man unleashing a savage dog, Upham launched into an abusive tirade at the unhappy Captain. He swore at him, shouted at him, let his feelings run raw and wild in a truculent display of simple hate and temper.

As men turned over in their bunks and peered at the two figures in the gloom of the darkened hut, they gained different impressions of what happened next. There certainly was con-fusion, with other P.O.W.s jumping out of bed and hurrying to

Charles's side. They simply had to save him from getting in too deep. There are some who say that Charles finally leapt on the startled Captain, seized him by the throat, and began to shake him savagely. Questioned after the war, Charles cagily said: "I might have."

Whatever did happen it is, at any rate, common ground that his hut-mates leapt into action, dragged Charles reluctantly away from his victim, and then poured soothing words over the head of the affrightened Captain. The episode had gone too far already, and they feared its consequences. Only two things saved Upham. One was the immediate intervention of his friends. The other was the solemn assurance given the Camp Commandant that Upham was so drunk that he mistook the captain of the guard for his mate Tom Bromley, with whom he was having an argument.

For the first of many times Upham went to the "boob".

With health returning, Upham began to look for freedom. He thought that escape from the punishment cells at Modena would be easier than escape from the compound or the barracks. So by some carefully phrased insolence he obtained another short gaol sentence and cheerfully went off to the boob.

It was a simple plan. If he could get out on to the roof of the cell-block he would have fewer obstacles to surmount before getting free. And they'd never expect an escape from the security cells—that sort of thing isn't done. But the cells had one weakness—they had plasterboard ceilings. He had no tools. All he had was his bed.

Upending the bed was hard enough, for his arm was still withered and weak. But he got it there at last, standing it up vertically at a spot which would be screened from view if someone opened the door.

He waited till he judged the guards were out of hearing. Then, with a physical effort that almost broke him, he lifted the bed bodily upwards and crashed its end against the ceiling.

His strength wouldn't have allowed him to do it more than three or four times, for the strain seemed prodigious; but on the second lift the plaster cracked, and a large slab fell away. . . . One more heave . . . and a hole big enough to squeeze through gaped in the ceiling.

He propped up the bed like a ladder. He doubted even now if he would have the ability to climb up. But, with the fervour of escape, extra strength seemed to come. Before he was fully conscious of it, he seemed to have his hands, then his knees, at the rim of the hole, and he was dragging himself through.

Inside the ceiling now. One glance inside the cell, of course, and he was doomed. From now on he would have to work like a demon. It was only a matter of wrenching off a few tiles, then he'd be out on the roof, with the whole world at his feet.

He grabbed at a tile, shook it, felt around it, wondered why it wouldn't shift. He tried another. Not a budge there either. Quickly he shifted position, attacked the tiles at another spot, until with a dawning exasperation he realized that every tile was tightly wired down in place.

If only he had a hammer, a screw-driver, a nail-file even—anything at all. But his fingers alone were not up to a task like this—not in the time available. It was only after he had twisted and picked away with his fingers, with little success, that he heard the sounds from below. He heard his cell door opened, heard the uproar when they saw his bed upended, and the hole in the ceiling.

They caught him there, crouching under the roof. But it took them quite a time to find him in the shadows.

As 1943 advanced there was not so much enthusiasm for escape schemes. The war had at last turned in favour of the Allies. From a low point in August 1942, when the Axis forces were deep into Egypt, were pressing on Stalingrad, and had much of the Russian oil-fields in their hands, the tide had changed.

In the Pacific the Americans had come ashore on the Solomons and were taking the first land offensive against the enemy there. By December, Montgomery's 8th Army was sweeping across North Africa, and the first great amphibious campaign of the war saw landings in Algeria and Morocco with the Americans now, at last, involved in the land fighting.

By May 1943 the war in Africa was over and the whole continent of Europe was now the target for the next Allied assault. The great German war machine, which three years before had seemed so invincible, was on the defensive, suffering its appalling losses at the hands of the Russians, enduring destruction at home from the bombs that the British and Americans rained from the skies.

Then in July came the invasion of Sicily. Mussolini resigned that month, his Fascists were broken up, and in a few weeks the armistice with Italy was signed.

To meet the likelihood of an armistice the British War Office had sent an instruction to almost every P.O.W. camp in Italy. All personnel, it said, were "to stay put when war ends"; they were to organize themselves into military units and await orders; arms and assistance would be flown in; officers were to be prepared to take command of nearby other-ranks' camps.

That was the order that every Senior British Officer in P.O.W. camps received. No order cancelling or amending it ever arrived —nor was ever given. The failure to amend that order was one of the war's most obtuse blunders, with grim results that were all too quickly glossed over. Those who disobeyed and broke away into the Italian countryside mostly reached safety.

In Modena, where almost all New Zealand officer-P.O.W.s were held, preparations had been well made. There were plans for taking over a nearby airfield with all its aircraft.

Then to Colonel Shuttleworth, the Senior British Officer, the Italian Commandant added confirmation of what Shuttleworth had already been ordered. It was best, the Commandant said, for the prisoners to remain where they were. The Germans were "pulling out of Italy", and a British force had already landed near Genoa and was heading eastwards.

Shuttleworth passed on this information to his fellow-officers at a parade. He told them the orders he had received.

But by 2 p.m. on 9th September Shuttleworth feared that he had been betrayed. He called the camp together, told them that the situation was so uncertain that any who wished to go could go—but they would have to move quickly.

At 2.30 p.m. German troops swept into the camp and took over.

Upham was in the camp hospital as these fateful days were unfolding. He was still wasted and gaunt, and was running a high temperature, as the news of the armistice swept over the camp. Sinus trouble had been plaguing him, bringing such severe headaches that he had blacked out twice in the last few days. On the second occasion he was taken off to hospital. But he was not going to witness these events from a hospital bed, so, as rumour after rumour flooded in on the inmates of Modena, he found his way out of hospital and back to his friends.

Charles Upham, Johnny Sullivan, one or two others—they gathered together to debate the latest news.

They argued it out and in the end agreed it was their duty to obey the orders that had been given. They would stay in the camp; the proper course was to stay.

Upham was weak and shaky. He was glad to return to the

hospital. He was still there when the arrival of the Germans showed how Shuttleworth had been deceived.

With the Italians drifting away, and the Germans moving swiftly to regain control over the prisoners of Modena, Charles spent the hours in hospital fretting at his weakness and roaming the buildings on the look-out for escape openings.

It mightn't be so hard to escape from the hospital. But something was radically wrong with that idea, and it took a little time before Upham recognized what it was. It was a matter of conscience.

The hospitals—the Red Cross—they had been good to him, he pointed out to a friend. Wouldn't it be an abuse of the Red Cross if he used its freedom to aid him in an escape? If a man did that, would hospital and Red Cross privileges for other prisoners be tightened up, perhaps withdrawn? To Upham the answer seemed clear.

So he left the hospital again, this time in pyjamas, carrying his clothes, and walked back into the compound. He knew the first convoys for Germany would soon be leaving. Once back in the compound, away from the hospital, he could carry out his break, and there would be no reprisals on the people who had shown consideration towards him.

One of his friends of 20th days, Evan Wilson, saw him come back inside. He knew Upham was still a sick man.

"What are you coming in here for, Charlie? You'd be better to stay with the sick."

Upham replied: "I'm going to make a break for it, Evan; but I won't escape from the Red Cross. That's why I'm here."

Charles had his plans ready. He knew of an enlarged drain where he could hide. Others had similar ideas. Hiding-places were being rapidly constructed in ceilings, under floors, in short tunnels, in angles of buildings, all by men who reasoned that they could hide up quietly for a few days while the Germans took over and removed the prisoners; then they would steal out and break off into the fields.

Upham found the M.O. beside him.

"Don't do it, Charlie. You're not well enough. You'd never survive two or three nights in the open. Chaps in good condition can face up to it, but you just couldn't make it."

Upham looked at him soberly. "I'm ready to take a chance. What show have I really got, Doc? Go on—tell me straight."

"You have no show at all, Charlie," the M.O. told him. "None whatever. The condition you're in—you're a dead man if you go. That's certain."

Upham accepted his verdict.

On 12th September 1943 the Germans started shipping out the Allied prisoners of Modena. Many were taken to the local railway station, where they entrained for Germany. Others travelled the first stage of the journey, from Modena to Mantua, by motor-truck.

Charles Upham was amongst those sent by road.

German S.S. troops guarded the convoy. The prisoners travelled in open Army trucks, one S.S. man driving, another armed guard sitting beside him. There were no guards in the back of the trucks with the prisoners. But immediately behind every truck-load of P.O.W.s came a truck manned by armed guards, who could cover both the prisoners in front and those on the truck immediately behind. So the convoy was spaced—one P.O.W. truck, one S.S. guard-truck, and so on.

On each guard-truck, a machine-gun was mounted, able to fire instantly in case of trouble, either to the front or behind. The S.S. guards were all heavily armed.

Out of Modena the convoy swung, turning north towards the Reich, first stop Mantua. Between the two cities lay the River Po.

Charles recognized that once they reached Germany prospects of a successful escape were very poor. The farther north they travelled, the more slender became his chances.

But in a convoy like this it would be madness to try it, except under the most favourable circumstances. The trucks were following one another so closely that any man leaping to the ground would come under fire in a matter of seconds.

But he decided to keep his eye on the road and the surrounding countryside. Something might turn. Any decision would have to be a quick one.

Nor was it any use making a break while the daylight lasted. It would need to be getting dark—not so dark that he couldn't see the road and the cover that lay in the fields alongside, but dark enough to avoid being a sitting shot for the S.S.

His restless eyes peered from side to side as the afternoon hours advanced, but the trucks churned remorselessly on almost bumper to bumper. Once or twice his pulses stirred as the convoy approached a wood, but the S.S. seemed to sense the danger, the trucks closed right up, and the man behind the machine-gun looked far too attentive. By sundown he realized how hopeless it was.

It was coming dusk when they reached the River Po, and the convoy began the slow crossing of the river on a pontoon bridge from the southern to the northern shore. Upham looked ahead with dull interest. On the northern shore the road, after leaving the pontoons, crept up an embankment about thirty feet high, then ran along the top.

They were half-way across the bridge. When they reached the other side and the truck started climbing up the slope what would happen at the top? Coming off the pontoon bridge perhaps the S.S. truck might fall behind. So—if a man jumped from the truck when it reached the top of the embankment, and leapt down into the fields beyond, he would be shielded from the guard-truck behind for a few seconds.

Quickly he nudged his way to the rear of the truck, saying nothing, getting into position in case the chance came. His truck was off the bridge now, grinding up the slope of the embankment.

Yes! It was the time, the chance! For Upham saw, in a moment of savage satisfaction, that in crossing the pontoons the convoy had become strung out. The nearest S.S. truck was lagging behind. It was only just coming off the bridge.

On to the top, speed dead slow. The guard-truck was churning up the slope behind them. He could see beyond the embankment now. First there was a low bank, about three feet high, rising up from the road. But beyond that there was a long thirty-foot slope down to the fields.

Long lines of vines down there. Poor cover. Some trees about 150 yards away. He would have to make it to there. It was too far. They'd be firing at him before he'd gone half the distance. He wished it were darker. But there might not be a better opportunity. Better to take the risk now, when he still had a chance, than later on when there'd be no chance at all.

In a flash he made the decision. He chose the very spot, the very instant. He grasped the tail-board, braced himself for the effort, then flung himself over. He hit the ground hard, went crashing on to his face, and felt the sudden sharp distress of being "winded". He groped to his feet, staggered to the three-foot bank at the side, climbed up it, then seemed to pause an instant on the very summit of the embankment.

It had all happened before anyone realized. And now he literally threw himself forward, lost his footing, went sprawling, rolling over and over down the slope. His withered arm gave him an awful twinge.

Near the foot of the bank he scrambled to his feet, set off running towards the trees as fast as he could. The going was flat, but he had to run down the lane between the vines.

He seemed to have gone only a few yards before the bullets came. The S.S. men, well-trained marksmen, were into action in seconds. Leaping from their guard-truck, they lined the top of the bank, had a clear view of Upham as he raced across the fields below them. With sub-machine-guns and rifles the fusillade started, fire pouring towards the hapless man as he sprinted for cover. He felt the bullets around him, whipping past his ears, plucking into the earth at his feet. As he ran from the bullets, he felt more scared than ever in his life.

Gasping and lurching, Charles covered the first hundred yards, knees like jelly, incredulous that he had got so far without being shot down. It had been too close—the spot was all right, the light not bad, but that guard-truck had closed up rather too quickly.

There was a grove of olive trees and undergrowth ahead. If he could reach it, hide there till dark, they might miss him. The guards couldn't let the convoy remain stationary for long in the fading light. Others might make a break. Anyway, he was finished —he couldn't run much further. He dodged again and again. They hadn't hit him yet. They never could, these Huns.

And in a sudden moment he found himself crashing to the ground. Something had hit him, tripped him up, sent him sprawling headlong. But there was no shock, no pain.

In an instant he realized it. He had been hit all right—but on the heel of his boot. In a flash it had tumbled him into the dust.

He crawled into the grove, dragged himself out of sight, lay there helpless and panting.

There were shouted orders in German. While some remained on the embankment covering the fields, about ten S.S. men climbed down the slope, spread out carefully into extended order and began moving steadily to the spot where Upham had last been seen.

It was rapidly getting darker. They moved down through the vines, arms at the ready, while the convoy waited. Charles heard the searchers coming closer. He lay dead still.

Then he couldn't believe it—they were passing him. They must think he had gone further on.

He raised himself cautiously on hands and knees, looking at the backs of the S.S. men as they began probing at the undergrowth, working further and further away from him.

But one S.S. man had lagged behind the others, unseen by Upham. He caught sight of the dim shape crouching in the leaves, sprang at the prisoner with a shout of triumph, and delivered a mighty kick. It struck home, sent Upham pitching on to his face. Then he covered him with his rifle while the rest of the guards came racing back.

They led Upham back to the trucks, surrounded and tightly held.

As the group came into earshot of the waiting prisoners, they heard his voice, cursing loudly, working out his disappointment in a verbal barrage. But Upham's onslaught was not all. The Feldwebel in charge of the guard ordered the S.S. man who had recaptured Upham to stand before him. Then, in full view and hearing of the P.O.W.s—several of whom understood German— he gave the successful soldier a vicious dressing-down. The escaper should have been shot immediately, he stormed. He should never have been merely recaptured and returned to the convoy. By refraining from shooting the escaper he had encouraged all the other prisoners to attempt it. He was entitled to shoot fugitives in the act of escape. There was no excuse for not having done it that night.

They loaded Charles on to a truck again, but this time into the Guard Commander's truck, where he would travel with S.S. men all around him. They still found it prudent, however, to bind a length of wire clumsily round his wrists.

The journey towards Germany continued.

First night the convoy lay up in the Mussolini Stadium at Mantua. From here they were put aboard trains next morning and headed towards the Brenner Pass. Then on through Austria.

The discomfort and privations of travelling in crowded cattle-trucks, forty men in each, were beyond words. Five days in the cattle-trucks saw them finally right across Austria into Silesia. There, near Breslau, they were left at Lamsdorf, one of the largest P.O.W. camps in Germany, known as Stalag VIIIB. This was a sprawling, ill-disciplined camp, holding over 30,000, many of them rationed out to working-camps in the district. It was an unlovely place, and one of the worst controlled.

They spent a week at Lamsdorf before travelling again, this time far to the west. Again the journey was made in cattle-trucks, a period of four days' acute misery, until finally they were disgorged at camps in the vicinity of Strasbourg, close to the French border. Many of them, including Upham, were held at Stalag VC at Offenburg.

A fortnight later they were on the move again, this time finally to Weinsberg, Oflag VA, about seventy miles to the north-east.

CHAPTER FIFTEEN

WIRE-BREAK AT WEINSBERG

WEINSBERG held about 140 New Zealand officers, as well as many hundreds of South African, Australian, and British prisoners. It was to be Upham's home for nearly a year. There were old friends again in the hut Charles occupied. Johnny Quilter, Tiny Armour the lawyer, Humphrey Hall with his architecture, Dick Ormond, Gordon Washbourn, Wally Ormond, Neville Holmes, Johnny Sullivan—all of them had something to contribute to making camp life bearable.

With Neville Holmes, the South African lawyer, Upham became on close terms. They shared the restlessness that never let them desist from thinking of escape. Neville's legal logic was a complement to Charles's intuitive kind of judgment, and the pair found a deep satisfaction in the sharing of ideas to which each contributed so differently.

Years later Neville Holmes wrote from his position as a Supreme Court Judge in Pietermaritzburg:

"Captain Upham had many friends among the South Africans. It was a privilege to enjoy his friendship. He was not a parade-ground soldier, but his exploits in action were legion. In appearance he was slight, with a magnificent head, and he was astonishingly wiry and strong. He was "Charlie" to everyone, and he hated sham, and was no respecter of rank without merit. I never knew a more generous nature. For example, it was always a great day for a P.O.W. when a clothing parcel arrived from home. But when this happened to Charlie he would empty the contents on the table, pick out one or two items he needed urgently, then call out: 'Anyone need a shirt? Who wants socks? Anyone short of blades?' Small wonder that he had the respect and affection of every man in the camp. He was very well read (he had even read the Bible right through) and his general knowledge was amazing. Above all he loved to talk about farming, and one of his favourite cronies in this respect was Lieutenant Sir de Villiers Graaff. Charles was cast in an heroic mould, but withal he retained the warm human touch. . . ."

He had many an agreeable argument about farming with John Riddiford, whose family have farmed many New Zealand acres for several generations. Upham was a South Islander, Riddiford a Northerner. Charles advocated South Island Corriedale sheep, Riddiford argued for his Romneys, with which his thousands of acres were handsomely stocked. One day when the mail arrived Charles seemed to be unusually eager to hand it around. After flicking through the envelopes he loudly announced: "Another one for you, John. Been torn about a bit. No postmark."

Riddiford gratefully opened his extra letter. It appeared to be from home, signed by his farm manager. Riddiford thought the writing wasn't as familiar as it ought to be—but there was the signature.

He read the letter, and his jaw dropped.

> . . . and, Mr. Riddiford, I decided to sell all your Romneys. I only got fifteen bob a head for them. I have replaced them with Corriedales at 35s. each . . . and I'm afraid I've had to shoot all the old dogs, including your favourite Spot. . . .

Into the blank horror that was rushing through Riddiford's mind came a sudden doubt. He looked up, then glanced quickly again at the strange writing on the terrible letter.

"Charlie, you——!——!——! . . ." and he sprang in loud pursuit of the practical joker. Shrieking in mock terror, Charles fled.

In community activities Upham took his part. Though by nature a lone ranger, and one who preferred the company of one or two men to that of a crowd, he did his share.

In sport there was basketball and some baseball, in both of which he was an aggressive, militant sort of player, some would say "over-enthusiastic" at times. He gave all he had at the time.

In between spasms of enthusiasm and heartiness he occasionally dropped into periods of acute moroseness. Like a caged lion he paraded the camp, frustrated and depressed, his hatred of the enemy completely stultified by the physical confinement.

There were days when he refused to get up from his bed, lay there hour after hour with the blankets pulled right over his head, like a wounded beast. It was useless interrupting him—he would snap back a curt reply or just burrow deeper into his melancholy. Prison for him was a mental torture to be endured over and above the physical fact of confinement. When he was feeling well he maintained his self-respect by hating and baiting the guards and working on escape schemes. But if he was off-colour the misery inside him closed around and he went to earth, locked away from everyone else.

"It's under the gym," they whispered. "Johnny Royce has got it worked out. While we dig we'll have to get a bit of an orchestra going—you know, practising and all that; have a few stooges around."

"You and I keep together, Charlie," Neville said. "The break-out will be in pairs."

The tunnel started. The orchestra scraped away, hiding the sounds of excavation beneath.

And, like all tunnel jobs, hiding the spoil was the most difficult task.

Upham and Holmes worked on it together, taking their turn with the others who were included in the "break".

Plans began to be made for the big night. They would hold a concert in the gym, right on top of the tunnel, and have the band playing flat out, community singing, lusty choruses, all hiding the inevitable noises accompanying the final burst. Invite the Camp Commandant and the guards—they might thin out round the wire. Then . . .

"I'm sorry, we've had it, boys," Johnny Royce told them dolefully. "The game's up. They've found the hole."

A careless tunnel-digger had left a mud-covered singlet lying in the gym. Hauptman Knapp, the Security Officer, had spotted it, and guessed its significance immediately.

But next morning their spirits soared again. There had been rumours, but now, this morning, they saw it themselves for the very first time.

It was a slow drone on the horizon at first, gradually louder and louder, way up in the sky; closer and closer it came; and the sirens wailed, and then the air seemed to throb as the noise pervaded everything. Like schoolboys welcoming home the conquering team, they rushed out into the open, shouting and cheering, heads craned into the skies trying to pick up the planes.

There was one plane, then another, then another, then a dozen, twenty, fifty, and men grew hoarse with excitement and wonder as hundreds upon hundreds of bombers sailed majestically over them into the heart of Germany. It was the most exciting and uplifting experience these P.O.W.s had ever known.

During the day that followed orders were issued that all men would return to their huts during an Allied air-raid. There was silence now from the German propaganda machine, which had so stridently proclaimed that no enemy aircraft would ever cross the Rhine in daylight.

Then, early next morning, as if to drive home the lesson of the day before, over they came again—snarling steadily into the Reich, so many that men could not keep count. Five or six hundred of them, and right over Weinsberg. It was cheering and laughing again.

"Go on, you beauties. Go on! Go on!"

But now the men were being rushed back into their barracks. Reluctantly they obeyed, feeling consciously superior to the guards who herded them in. All were pushed inside, except one.

It would, of course, be Charles Upham who stayed outside.

He remained standing in the open, cheering the planes, until a section of guards, with fixed bayonets, came over towards him at the double. Condescending to go inside, he turned at the door and shouted to the German officer: "No planes across the Rhine, eh? What do you think those are—ruddy ducks?" And he waved his pipe at the bombers cruising through the upper air.

Next there were orders about pamphlets dropped by Allied planes. Prisoners were required to retire to their barracks during the passing of enemy planes; but in addition any man picking up a pamphlet dropped from the sky would be instantly shot.

Orders like that were made to be defied by men who constantly believed in challenging the authority of the enemy.

Down the pamphlets fluttered over Weinsberg a few days later. Into the huts the P.O.W.s were rushed, while the guards paraded the open ground to pick up any pamphlets that fell inside the camp.

Upham spotted one floating down near his hut. Poised in the doorway, he waited for the right moment. Then he rushed out right past two of the goons, plucked a pamphlet out of the air before it even reached the ground and doubled back towards the hut at top speed.

With shouts and clicking of rifle-bolts, the two guards gave chase.

Charles bolted in through the door, thrust the pamphlet into the hands of the first man he saw inside, then dived for his bunk.

Green & Hahn, Christchurch

"I'd always be jealous of my friends on farms"

Green & Hahn, Christch

Charles Upham at home on his New Zealand farm

The guards burst in. Upham was lying in bed, snoring gently.

"Captain Oopham—I want to ask you some questions," Hauptmann Knapp said.

"UPham, not OOpham," Charles explained.

"Yes, Captain Oopham. Now, I have a report that you and another New Zealand prisoner have been detected making measurements near the fence. And a map has been found beside your bed. Your explanation, please—that is, if you have one."

Upham looked serious.

"Yes, I suppose I had better explain, Hauptmann Knapp. I confess we were making measurements. And seeing that you've found our map I suppose the game's up. There's no use trying to hide it from you. You'll find all the measurements on the map. I'm very sorry about it."

Knapp rubbed his hands. "Ah ha, Captain Oopham. You are being sensible at last. But you will realize this is very serious, very serious. Now, let me look at the map."

The sergeant beside him smoothed out the map, drawn carefully in ink, with many signs, directions, and measurements.

A minute went by while Upham tried to conceal his feelings. Then Knapp suddenly jumped to his feet. "Out! Out!" he shouted. "Take him out!" And Upham, chuckling, was unceremoniously removed and taken back to the barracks.

Along with Ian Reid and several others, Charles got a lot of fun out of standing by the wire, taking useless measurements in a furtive manner. It always worked. The guards would rush off in a great state to report. And the maps. Many happy hours could be filled in concocting the most ridiculous false maps. They always got a bite, too. Maps showing the lay-out of Christ's College, or an imaginary desert island, with hidden treasure, always set the Germans running.

"Tom Bromley says it's only twenty feet from his hut to the wire. It'll have to be deep, because I reckon they've got underground mikes."

"What about the spoil? Where'll we put it?"

"Try distributing it around first. Then, if we're in a hurry, put it up in the roof. It won't be a long tunnel, so there won't be too much spoil."

"All right. Count me in. When do we start digging?"

"Tonight...."

They tried scattering the clay about the camp, carrying it

around in bags slung inside their trousers. But this was a dangerous method. Weinsberg had a lot of black coal dust, and clay showed up on the black surface like a painted sign.

It was a slow method too. So they soon decided to stow it all in the ceiling—Humphrey Hall, Bill Allan, Neville Holmes, Charlie Upham, John Riddiford, to name but a few of those who worked on it.

Out went the tunnel, snaking underground towards the fence. In came the spoil and, with ever-increasing difficulty, was spread over the ceiling in the hut.

As more and more came in, so the ceiling sagged down and down. It became a question of which would happen first—the tunnel breaking out, the ceiling breaking down, or the goons breaking up the whole thing. It seems that the microphones behind the walls detected this one. A friendly goon said: "Walls have ears...."

With the failure of these two tunnel schemes it was obvious that something better planned and better constructed would be necessary. Experience gained from the other tunnels would be valuable, but this time two important points had to be covered: first, it was simply not good enough having a tunnel break ground just outside the wire. The ground was too open, and the heartbreak would be too severe if the hole were detected at the very end, when all the work had been finished. Second, a better place for hiding the spoil had to be found.

A group got together on it. There were some New Zealanders, some South Africans led by "Div" Graaff and Neville Holmes, and a number of British Army officers. They soon solved the first problem. Rather than bring the tunnel up through open ground, they decided to surface it inside a storehouse that stood outside the wire. It would need a careful survey to determine exactly when the tunnel should become vertical, so as to come up right beneath the floorboards of the storehouse, but, with a surveyor and a Senior Wrangler in the group, no trouble was expected on this account.

The second problem did not permit of any clever solution. There were just no satisfactory ways of hiding soil. It was no use trying the ceilings again. That was old-hat. Instead, they decided that wardrobes in the hut be emptied, then soil packed tight into them.

So the digging began, and this became a splendid tunnel. Stooges were well organized to warn of approaching guards; the

Senior Wrangler used logarithms and other devices to determine exactly how far the tunnel had to go before driving up to the surface; and into the large wooden wardrobes in the huts the soil was compressed.

The day came when the tunnel was due to surface. Little trouble with this was expected, as the surveyor and the Senior Wrangler had made their calculations with deliberate care. But, just to be sure, the tunnellers were to stop about a foot beneath the surface and carefully probe up with a long thin stick.

"She'll be all right," the Senior Wrangler said smugly. "We won't see the stick. It'll be rapping under the floorboards of the shed by now."

Then, with something approaching panic, the escapers, watching casually from inside the wire, saw the end of the probe break up through the ground and wave about in mid-air—six feet short of the storehouse!

There were frantic signs and messages. With great relief the probe was retracted before being seen by the guards, and the tunnellers were set to work burrowing a further six feet outwards.

They did it, surfaced safely inside the shed. Now all was ready. The break would be next night. Then one of those chances intervened.

On the morning of the great day a German workman arrived in the escape hut to mend the fireplace—a job that had been standing idle for months. One of the wardrobes was in his way. Putting his shoulder to it, he expected to ease it quietly along a foot or two. But it wouldn't budge. No wonder—it held about a ton of soil. He tried again.

"Give you a hand?" the conspirators offered genially, with a remarkable show of friendliness and co-operation.

With many willing words they eased the puzzled workman out of the way and laid gentle hands on the wardrobe. With happy smiles they pressed against it; then a little more strongly; then with every ounce they possessed. But it was as immovable as the Rock of Gibraltar. They nearly died trying to shift that wardrobe.

Very puzzled indeed, the workman wandered off.

Hauptmann Knapp arrived within the hour and opened the wardrobe. It had been a beautiful tunnel.

Undismayed, ten of the conspirators, Holmes and Upham prominent among them, set to work on another. This time it would be a different approach. Not for them this time the meticulous care, the long weeks of toil and cunning. No—this would be a crash project. Dump the soil wherever they could—

and the best available place was in the lavatory cubicles. That wouldn't escape detection for long—but maybe long enough to enable the hole to be rushed through.

They began work like beavers. It needed only a suspicious guard to open the closed door of the lavatory in the course of a casual inspection—and that is exactly what happened.

Appell! Roll-call!

The prisoners stood in line, five deep, and the goons went down the front line, counting the numbers—five, ten, fifteen, twenty, etc.

Upham was at his rebellious best on *Appell*. He loathed the compulsion of it and he showed, by every means he could other than downright disobedience, that he accepted nothing. If to bait and infuriate them was the only way he could continue the war, then he would do it.

No smoking on *Appell*! The orders were clear and strictly enforced.

Upham stood in the front rank, looking calmly ahead, and puffed at his long curved pipe.

The guard sergeant stopped in front of him, pointed at the pipe, and rapped out an order. Upham knew what he meant.

Leaning slightly forward, he inhaled, then removed the pipe slowly from his mouth so as to comply with the order. Then he breathed out, long and slow, and the smoke wreathed and circled about the face of the sergeant. The guard captain strode up. He snapped an order at Upham to produce his identity disc.

Charles knew what was being said. He stood still, made no move.

The order came again. Upham slowly shook his head, pretending not to understand. Then the order was given to the ranking British officer standing nearby.

"He orders you to show your meat-ticket, Charlie."

"I know he does," Upham replied sharply. "And tell him if he wants to see it to come and get the bloody thing himself."

It was Christmas Eve 1943. Weinsberg was enveloped in snow, and it was still snowing. Some of the Germans were celebrating the day well, drinking the wood alcohol issued to them for their cigarette-lighters.

Clear as crystal the idea swam into his mind. How simple— why hadn't anyone else thought of it? Christmas Eve. . . . The way the Jerries were tearing into the plonk there wouldn't be many of them sober by midnight. Sentimental about things like Christmas, they'd have a good sing-song and booze-up tonight. And the guards—the ones in the towers, those who patrolled outside the wire, the pairs who prowled around inside the compound—all they'd be thinking of would be the end of their watch, stamping their feet to keep warm, shaking the snow off their shoulders, keeping under cover if they could. They'd be thinking: no prisoner would be crazy enough to try to escape tonight, in a blinding snowstorm, with almost a gale beating the snow in under the doorways and against the windows. And the dogs would be frozen stiff, too. It was tailor-made, Upham thought. The Krauts who went off duty about midnight would be relieved by those who'd been drinking flat out all evening.

And if he made it—there'd be a fair number away on leave . . . not so many to chase after him in the morning.

Aitken of the 19th Battalion had made a saw out of a watch-spring and one day he had sawed through the bars on one of the hut windows. Now was the time to make that pay off.

It was after midnight, still snowing hard, when Charles pulled the bars aside, wriggled his way through, and dropped softly into the thick snow outside. He told no one he was going. He went like a shadow, and in a second the snow outside had swallowed him up.

But he couldn't take any risks. The searchlights on the towers were constantly playing backwards and forwards over the compound, searching along the walls of the huts, running their beams around the wire. They were not so effective in the snow, but he still had to contend with them . . . and the picquets . . . and perhaps the dogs.

He went across on his knees, worming his way through the slush. He watched out for the searchlights, froze like a statue when they swung near him. But he was safe so far. For he had reversed his clothing. He had his white underwear on top of everything else and he knew that only a very sharp-eyed sentry would pick him out. He had merged into the snow.

Here was the trip-wire. Now the double-apron fence. Through it, and he was at the foot of the main wire. Now just climb over.

He crouched low on his haunches, listening for the patrols and the sentries. Just as he had guessed: not a sound of them—they'd be under cover somewhere, sheltering from the cold and the snow.

Alongside a post he rose to his feet, began to climb the wire. It was easy. Up and up he went. He was almost contemptuous at the simplicity of it—just climb over the wire in the middle of the night. Odds all in his favour—the combination of Christmas Eve boozeroo, the white ground, the snowstorm—and he was almost at the top now, a triumphant feeling starting to well up in him. Then ...

Crack ! ! The rifle-shot came from right beneath his feet. Starting convulsively, he lost his footing, clutched wildly with his hands, missed, and in a flash was falling backwards off the fence. Down he crashed into the snow, inside the compound, waiting every second for the *coup de grâce*. He lay there rigid, unable to see a thing.

The seconds passed. Nothing happened. Looking round, Upham could see only a few feet through the white gloom. He could see no one, but the shot had seemed to be right under him.

Perhaps the sentry had been half asleep or half drunk, fired at the blur on top of the fence, then convinced himself that it must have been a ghost. Upham's instant disappearance from the top of the wire, with hardly a sound as he fell into the soft snow beneath, may have convinced the German that it was imagination, after all.

He was soaked through. He was wearing every stitch of clothing he possessed, and he couldn't live outside in the European winter in wet clothes. He daren't attack the fence again. Next time the German would know he hadn't been mistaken.

So he crawled cautiously through the snow, back to the hut, along to the window, shivering violently. He made good his ground to safety inside without any alarm being sounded.

It had been a good scheme, he reckoned afterwards. Might easily have pulled it off. But that wretched sentry must have been standing silently in the snow, only a few feet from where he tried to climb the wire. Five yards further away and he might have made it.

"Nev," Charles said to "Judge" Holmes many weeks later as they strolled around the compound. "This tunnelling business is a dud. The Jerries are up to all the tricks now. I reckon we have to think up a different line."

"All right, Charlie, but let's look at it. There are only three ways of getting out: first—through the main gate; second—a tunnel; third—over the wire. Well, "Div" tried it through the gate but didn't get far. No one can work his trick again. And there'll have to be something pretty new in the way of tunnels to have any show."

"That's what I mean, Nev. The only thing is—over the wire."

"But how, Charlie? I know you almost made it on Christmas

Eve—but there were special circumstances that night. There's no snow now, summer's coming on. You can't try that one again."

"I know, Nev. But I still reckon the wire's the thing."

"All right; then which way? Cut the wire or climb over the top? Whatever way you try you've got this against you—get out of the hut first—and I suppose we can do that if Aitken's still got his saw—but outside there are the damned dogs. You've got to beat them to the wire. Then the lights, the goons, and the guns."

Charles said: "I can poison the ruddy dogs. And I reckon I know where I can get a pair of wire-cutters."

"Right-oh, Charlie, I'm with you. Let's talk about it."

It wasn't long before they had the wire-cutters.

They agreed there was a chance. If they waited for the night of an air-raid, when the floodlights were switched off, they might get through the wire, then strike out for France or Switzerland.

First, more bars on the hut windows had to be filed through. They managed this one day on the pretence of washing the hut windows.

Charles tried many schemes for poisoning the Alsatian dogs that roamed the camp at night, but none of his poisoning plans seemed to make any noticeable increase in the death-rate of the dogs.

Then, in company with Neville, he made a number of night-time reconnaissances round the wire, having several narrow escapes from the beasts, and causing a good deal of jitteriness amongst the guards.

When their turn came they decided they would have to risk the dogs. . . . They made their preparations.

Then one night the air-raid sirens wailed again. Holmes waited beside the gear, checking that both of them had all they required. Charles waited at the window, watching the perimeter lights.

The lights blacked out. He walked quickly along the hut.

"They're off, Judge," he said laconically.

"Then so are we, Charlie," Holmes replied, bending down and picking up his gear. Without another word they moved to the window, lifted out the severed bars, quickly squirmed through, and dropped to the ground outside.

They moved out of the deep shadow of the hut, bending over almost double, treading on tip-toe, making across the open to the point in the wire where they had decided to make their break.

They reached the trip-wire, stepped over it carefully.

Then there was the double-apron fence. They dropped on their stomachs and wriggled through beneath it.

Now just the main wire ahead—first the inner fence, then tangled wire beyond, then the outer fence. Then freedom.

No sign yet of any dogs. They came to the inner fence. They lay on their backs while Holmes took firm hold of the bottom wire with his two hands. Upham got out his cutters. It was pitch dark. They had to feel for everything. But so far so good. Luck was with them. Thank God the dogs hadn't found them yet. Upham squeezed the cutters.

The wire parted with a "ping" that seemed to resound all over the camp. "Oh, hell, that'll wake 'em up," Charles breathed. He thought of the man on the tower, barely thirty yards away. Surely he must have heard it.

They lay dead still for a full minute, frozen into position, waiting to hear the sound of an alarm. But still their luck held.

Then Holmes whispered: "O.K., Charlie?" and he reached up cautiously for the next strand, took hold of it, while Upham lifted the cutters. As he groped in the darkness, Charles had a momentary feeling that something was going wrong with their scheme. With an air-raid alert on, normally there would be the sounds of ack-ack guns in the distance and often the great drone of the bombers cruising overhead. There would be noise. It wasn't usual for everything to be so quiet.

He closed his fingers around the handle, whispered a word to Neville to hold the wire steady, and prepared to squeeze the cutters again. . . .

Then in a blinding instant all the camp lights flashed on, the floodlight on the tower drenched them in its beam, and the "All clear" siren wailed through the night. Everything was visible —the huts, the wire, the two escapers—all silhouetted in brilliant clarity.

With a gasp, both men dropped on to their faces, pressing themselves into the ground. There was just a chance the men in the towers would not be looking their way at that vital moment.

They lay there motionless, keeping their faces and hands covered, knowing that one false move might be their last.

Holmes whispered: "We're for it now, Charlie. We can't get through with all the lights on. They'll see us here any moment."

"I know. I know. We've had it. We'll have to try to get back. What do you reckon—go separately or keep close together?"

"Separately, Charlie. . . . I'll follow about five yards behind you . . . but for God's sake keep flat on your stomach . . . we might make it if we go slowly."

"O.K., Nev. I'll make for that nearest shadow—by the corner

of the hut." They shrank away from the fence, clawing their way over the ground on their faces, making every movement slow and deliberate, freezing into stone whenever the big lights swept near them.

The temptation to jump up and run blindly for the hut became almost irresistible. But they crept on like snails, knowing that was their best way of survival.

They reached the shadow of the hut at last, edged their way along to the window with the bars sawn through, and climbed swiftly in the moment the next searchlight went past. . . .

There would be just a chance they could repeat the scheme during the next air-raid, but Hauptmann Knapp put a stop to that. For next morning, to their chagrin, they watched Knapp snoop suspiciously round the wire, saw him find the cut strand, and watched him go swiftly into action.

Knapp knew how to deal with prisoners who had wire-cutters. There would be things he could do with the dogs, with the lights, with alarm wires, with patrols outside, with special searches of the huts. The wire-cutting men wouldn't put it across him. Knapp gave them only one chance. He probably wondered if that devil "Oopham" was one of them.

Meanwhile Upham sat back and brooded. He was sure it could be done over the wire. The two of them had come pretty close to it. But at night there were the dogs, the lights, the noise. That's when they expected a man to try to break. Funny if a man tried to go through the wire in daylight, wouldn't it? They'd never expect that.

And, as the thought wandered into his mind, something gripped him. A wire-break in *daylight*! What could be more totally unexpected? Of course it was hopeless, ridiculous. The guards would see a man at the wire, cut him down before he was through the first couple of strands.

But what about climbing over the top?

First there was the trip-wire. The prisoners were not allowed over that. Next you came to the double apron, which would take a little time to clamber over, or underneath. And then you came to the main fence.

There were two main fences, really, with a gap in between them. Each was of barbed wire, about ten feet high. In between them was this gap, filled with concertina and dannert wire. It all presented a fair maze to get over—but it wasn't impossible. The stuff lying in the gap was the trouble. Perhaps he might swing from the top of one fence to the other. But the time! Surely it would be impossible to go across in less than a minute. And there weren't ten seconds when every stretch of the wire was not under close and direct surveillance.

Still—what a thought! Dare say nobody had ever thought of climbing the wire in broad daylight. Just not done. He chuckled. Might try it some day.

"John," he called out suddenly. "You're on the Escape Committee. Anybody ever got over the wire in daylight?"

John Riddiford looked surprised. "In daylight, old boy? Come off it. Nobody's that crazy. No one can do it even at night . . . or perhaps you didn't hear about those two chaps last night? . . ."

Upham threw a sock at him.

It was a fortnight later, a fortnight in which Charles Upham had become more sour and depressed than ever. He couldn't stand it much longer—just the hopeless waiting and waiting. He couldn't wait any more.

They'd landed in Normandy all right. But it was going slowly. There was no sign of the Jerries packing up. They were as tough as ever. And he was not so sure about this bombing. Chaps came in who said how Berlin was being smashed up—they'd passed through in trains—and Mannheim, and Hamburg, and Essen, and Frankfurt. But it seemed to make the Jerries fight harder.

He couldn't stand it. He had to do something. He just couldn't stand being an animal in a cage any longer.

There were no escape schemes on foot now. Not worth while, they said, now that the Allies had landed in Europe. War would be over soon, they claimed. Who said so?

It was Sunday. Summer in the Black Forest. He'd been nearly a year in Weinsberg. If he had to stick it out any longer he'd crack up. He knew it. He felt the crisis coming on.

Upham wandered around the compound on his own, smoking his pipe, restless and miserable. He looked again and again at the guards slowly walking their beats, at the man up in the tower with his machine-gun, and hated them more each time.

Just where he was looking the wire took a right-angled turn. There were always three guards patrolling outside the wire along this sector. It meant that every inch of the fence was always under the eye of at least one guard. In addition there was always the man up in the tower. He could see everything. In fact he could see rather more than he ought to today. He was having fun watching the couples out in the fields. But one glance and he could see the whole of the wire.

One man always in the tower . . . three men always patrolling the wire . . . Upham had studied them countless times, wondering if there could be any possible chance. . . .

He watched them with lack-lustre eyes as he walked aimlessly around the compound, his spirits almost at zero. Let those guards give him just one decent chance—he wouldn't even care if they shot him. . . .

And in one sudden instant he froze, and his breath caught. Something inside him was ringing and ringing, like a sharp, shrill bell.

He watched the guards. He watched them walk up and down, once, twice, three times. And he began counting the seconds.

Steady. Steady. Count the time again. Watch how they did it. Was it the same every time? Yes, yes, it was! And the man in the tower was watching the boys and girls.

And instead of the first amazement there was a savage exultant feeling coming over him. A chance! A chance! This could be the moment, the impossible, hopeless chance that came only once in a blue moon.

For his hungry eyes had seen what no one else appeared to have noticed. There were not *three* guards patrolling the wire today. *There were only two.*

Only two guards instead of three. When they marched outwards they left a blind spot behind them—they paced slowly away from each other, then turned. He counted again deliberately. Forty-five seconds.

There was a space of forty-five seconds in which the angle of fence was not being watched! Except by the man in the tower.

Forty-five seconds to get through the wire! Once they turned again they would see him. And the man in the tower with the machine-gun could see him the whole time.

Out through the wire were German washing-huts. Hide there till dark. No use rushing it, clambering over the wire in a hurry. They'd hear him. No—a steady, careful climb, hand over hand, then a jump from the top of one fence across to the top of the other, leap down to the ground, and fly for the huts. He could do it in forty-five seconds if luck was with him all the way.

The daylight break! The escape they had all scoffed at as impossible. Well, it was not! It *could* be done. Split-second timing. But over the wire in broad daylight! They'd think he'd gone round the bend.

He moved back calmly to the hut, unhurried, but his heart

beating fiercely inside. He got out his escape gear, all in a little haversack.

When he was ready he went out and looked for "Judge" Holmes.

Holmes was lounging in the sun, doing nothing. He saw Upham approaching, carrying his haversack.

Upham spoke to him and his voice was a little thick. "Judge, I'm going out over the wire. Get the boys to make a bit of a show, will you—down there under the tower. Keep the goons looking down. A fight, or anything you like—you know. Start when you see me at the trip."

Holmes saw the look on Upham's face. He didn't argue. Lately he knew that Charles had been feeling desperate. It was no use trying to stop him when he was in a mood like that. He said quietly: "How on earth are you going to do it?" Upham explained shortly.

Holmes nodded rather sadly. He said: "I'll fix the diversion. You can leave that to me. And . . . good luck, old boy." Then he got up abruptly and moved away, so Charles couldn't see the look on his face.

Holmes spoke quietly to half a dozen friends. One by one they sauntered casually to the place Charles had indicated.

Upham waited in the doorway of the hut until they were all ready. Then he moved out across the compound, slowly and inconspicuously, and stood languidly beside the trip-wire. He looked out to the main fence, deciding exactly where he would climb.

Then he gave Holmes the signal.

The men under the tower started to argue. One man shouted. Another shouted back at him. Suddenly one lashed out at the other, and they rushed together, fell wrestling to the ground. The onlookers gathered around, some calling encouragement. The man in the tower heard the commotion, looked down and watched the fight with interest.

Upham had his eye on the guards, waited till they passed each other and marched outwards. Then he quietly stepped over the trip-wire, advanced across the forbidden ground to the low apron fence.

He was up and over it in a few seconds.

And now he was at the main wire. He seized the strands, began climbing steadily. It was easy. In no time he was at the top.

All around there were dozens now watching. Others were catching sight of him for the first time and were staring in amazement. A wire-break in broad daylight! What maniac was trying that!

Some who recognized his small wiry figure called out softly to those near: "It's Charlie Upham." There was a sudden aching sympathy for a man who would dare such fearful odds.

But there were some who said: "He must be mad." They waited for the volley of fire any moment, waited to see his body crumple up and fall from the wire to the ground, like a sack of old clothes. But those who said that hadn't counted the guards today.

The fight became more furious and several others had joined in, while Upham paused for a second at the very top of the fence.

Now, with studied care, he lifted one leg across, and he was astride it. He was in full view of the goon on the tower if he were only to look. But a real mêlée had developed below, and that was more interesting.

Upham swung his other leg over, measured the distance across to the outer fence. It was a fair leap, but it was his only chance. Down between the two fences was a maze of tangled barbed wire. He couldn't climb down there and up the other side. No, he had to jump. If he could make it to the other fence it would be just a swing over the top, then a leap to the ground, and a wild sprint for the huts. With any luck they wouldn't see him at all. He climbed down one stand, paused, then crouched for the spring. About thirty seconds gone!

Then, as he gathered himself together . . . snap! A staple flew out the nearest post and the wire Upham was standing on went suddenly slack. Desperately he hurled himself out, lunging for the other side. But the broken staple had spoilt his leap. He fell short, came crashing down into the rolls of barbed wire lying between the two fences. The moment that staple pulled, he knew he was lost.

He heaved and wrenched at the wire, swearing and cursing, tearing his hands and his clothes. If he could free himself, dive at the other fence, climb over it even under fire, there would be a chance—just run for it over the fields, with the odds against him.

But the more he strained, the tighter the grip of the barbs.

He was aware now that the sentries were patrolling back towards him. There was still the faintest hope that they might not notice him lying amongst the wire—they might possibly just walk past.

But now, suddenly, he was aware of a face—a German face, eyes bulging—staring at him from outside the wire. A man with a working party, just going past, and he had caught sight of Upham, and his jaw had dropped in startled amazement. And then the workman's voice was raised. He was shouting. The guards looked round. They all saw Upham. They were running. The alarm was on. Whistles were shrilling. Rifles unslung, bolts clicking, the pelting of racing feet.

Meanwhile some of the diversion party were dashing to the spot. They'd seen that Charlie's jump had failed. Any moment now and the shots would blast the summer air. Charles Upham, hero and gentleman to them all, would get the treatment that was allowed. A prisoner may be shot in the act of escape. They surged to the wire, calling and waving, hoping to stop the guards from shooting.

Others stood transfixed, staring at the spot, waiting for the inevitable. That any man could attempt such a thing . . . the sheer bravery of it . . . the desperation . . . the terrible sadness of it.

There was pandemonium as the guards dashed to the scene.

The first guard arrived with his rifle at the ready, finger on trigger. Simultaneously, Charles whipped out the compass he had so laboriously made, tried to throw it back inside the compound. His hand caught, the compass dropped to his feet. So he kicked at it, and it scudded along the ground inside the wire. Peter Maxwell was there, one of the first to reach the scene, bent down quickly and picked it up.

The guard's rifle swung towards Maxwell and he shouted. There was an instant when it appeared certain he would shoot Maxwell, who had turned to run, but the rifle pointing at him held him fast.

Then Upham suddenly called: "Hey!"

Diverted, the guard swung back on Charles. More prisoners were on the spot, shouting at the guard, warning and threatening him not to fire.

The man hesitated. Upham was lying absolutely still. And in that hesitation the moment of killing was lost.

But now a corporal of the guard was on the scene. He was angry. He feared the consequences of a prisoner having almost outwitted his patrols. He had drawn his pistol and looked dangerous.

He shouted in German. He declared he was going to "finish off" the prisoner. He would shoot him there and then. The P.O.W.s tried to dissuade him. Keep him talking till his temper cooled.

He was standing by the wire, pistol raised, jaw set. It might be any moment. Then Upham, in almost exaggerated slow motion, made a cautious move. So far he had been lying motionless, knowing that any move would assuredly result in a bullet.

But now, as the corporal aimed his pistol, Upham moved one hand carefully to his pocket and he drew out—the others strained to see—he drew out a *cigarette*. Then he took out his matches, struck one and, doing everything with studied slowness, lit the cigarette.

An English major watching the drama didn't dare look away, but breathed to his companion "My God, what nerve!"

The corporal looked on, pistol still ready, but hesitant now, undecided what to do. The sight of the cigarette being lit had thwarted him. He knew he couldn't shoot now. There was something about the demeanour of the man caught in the wire that deterred him.

The Senior British Officer was there, pushing his way to the front.

"Are you all right, Charlie?" he called.

Upham growled "Yes."

"What are you going to do?"

"Nothing. They can damned well come and get me. And I refuse to be shot by a bloody corporal. Tell 'em to bring an officer."

"Judge" Holmes whispered to one of the New Zealanders: "Did you hear that? Charlie's dictating who he's going to let shoot him."

There was a stalemate. The P.O.W.s still crowded close to the wire, the guards trying to clear them back. The Germans were still talking loudly and gesticulating.

At last the man arrived—Hauptmann Knapp himself, his podgy little figure rolling from side to side as he bustled along.

He took in the scene swiftly, gave sharp orders to the other prisoners to move back. They obeyed.

For a few seconds he watched Upham lying in the wire, puffing unconcernedly at his cigarette. Then: "Captain Oopham, what are you doing there?" No reply.

Louder: "Captain Oopham, what are you *trying* to do there?" Again silence.

"Captain Oopham are you all right?"

Upham puffed a cloud of smoke into the air.

Hauptmann Knapp appeared to sigh. He unleashed something from his shoulder, stepped closer to the wire, aimed it at Charles. It was a camera. He took three photographs. At last, he thought, here was concrete evidence about this dangerous prisoner. Then he called: "You can come out now, Captain Oopham."

Again Charles ignored him, went on smoking. There was quite

a long pause. Then Knapp said, quite softly: "You are a very, very brave man, Captain Oopham. Now please come out."

The Senior British Officer intervened, and it was only when he finally ordered Charles to pick his way back out of the wire that Upham agreed to do so. He was promptly led away to the cells.

Something new was added this Sunday afternoon to the legend of Charles Hazlitt Upham.

Colonel de Beer, a South African, was the Senior British Officer at Weinsberg at this time. Knowing the record Charles Upham already had with the Germans, and having seen the performance at the wire, he felt very anxious about Upham's safety. He feared that the Germans might seize this opportunity of disposing of a very recalcitrant prisoner—and if they explained that Upham made another bid to escape from the cells there would be no one to deny it. Twice now German guards had refrained from shooting Upham in the act of escape. Any guard who now took the law into his own hands and finished off Upham while in custody would probably receive an official rebuke but unofficial congratulations.

So almost immediately after Upham had been taken away, de Beer applied for an interview with the Camp Commandant.

He was promptly escorted in.

He announced that his visit concerned the New Zealand prisoner Captain Upham, now in the cells. The Commandant looked smug.

Colonel de Beer came straight to the point. "All I want to say is this—this man Upham is *the ace soldier of the British Empire.* If anything happens to him I will see that you are held personally responsible after the war. That's all." The warning was well timed. News later reaching the New Zealanders confirmed that the question of shooting Upham was indeed mentioned the morning after his arrest.

The guard corporal was brought before the Commandant. He faced a tirade for not having shot the New Zealand officer the moment he saw him in the wire. Why was he not shot? Why was it not done immediately and then there could have been no complaint?

But the corporal, indeed all the guard, knew about Upham. With Hauptmann Knapp himself, they shared an admiration for the New Zealander, a reluctant respect that stemmed from Upham's complete refusal to submit, and his never-flagging antagonism.

Many Germans are single-minded people. Those in Weinsberg recognized in Upham a similar quality and they admired him for it.

The Commandant railed and stormed at the corporal. Until the officer in charge of the guard, stung by the criticism, finally burst out: "Well, Herr Oberst, the prisoner is in his cell, and you have your pistol."

Such an insolence might well have driven the Commandant to precipitate action, had it not been for de Beer's timely threat. As it was, Upham received the customary sentence of thirty days' solitary.

It was his morning exercise time—half an hour marching in a circle around the parade ground. The sentry stood in one spot, rifle under his armpit, and Charles was required to walk around him in a circle.

On a parapet above was a man with a machine-gun. His job was to cover Upham with the gun every pace he took. As the prisoner marched around the circuit beneath, the barrel of the machine-gun followed him like a shadow.

The Germans were taking no chances this time. The goon standing in the centre was routine. But the special machine-gunner overlooking the parade ground, whose job was to keep Upham in his sights every second, represented the measure of Knapp's respect.

From the prison compound the other P.O.W.s could see it, and they marvelled at the spectacle—one machine-gun allocated to cover one solitary man, traversing steadily backwards and forwards as the prisoner went about his exercise.

Charles paced his circuit patiently. They had taken his boots away and given him wooden clogs, which were awkward to clump about in. Pity the wire-break hadn't come off! He would have been in France by now. There wasn't much chance of escaping from this place, even though it was outside the main wire. The goon with the rifle was too close, the goon with the machine-gun too dangerous—though he reckoned a man continually traversing a machine-gun would not be able to fire accurately very quickly.

The goon with the rifle looked a fairly old codger—an old "blood pressure", unfit for the front line. If he could shoot an elephant at ten paces he would probably have been on the Russian front.

Then Charles suddenly noticed, with a feeling of amused contempt, that the old boy's rifle was not cocked. He looked belligerent enough, watching Charles intently with his hand along the trigger-guard and the rifle under his armpit. But to fire he would have to open the breech, then close it, before being able to shoot. Silly old codger.

Upham hardly thought of escape, but he was as determined as ever to harass the Germans. The circuit went on and on, Upham's head down, round and round in his own footsteps, the goon patiently turning and watching him.

Then, without warning, Charles suddenly jumped round, faced the way he had come, and set off walking rapidly in the reverse direction. That was all—he just turned round quickly.

But the goon! Charles nearly burst out laughing as he saw the guard leap in startled surprise, fumble stupidly with the bolt, open and close it, then look at Upham again, his eyes wide in sudden apprehension. It was as good as a play.

But the steady circuit resumed, and slowly the guard's anxiety faded.

Next exercise time Upham did the same thing again—and once more the ludicrous display of startled fear on the part of the goon.

Upham thought this was good fun and well worth the money. If the goon carried his rifle cocked then he wouldn't dare try it —the fool might fire it off by accident. But there must have been some orders about carrying round cocked rifles.

Then another idea drifted into his mind.

On one side of the small parade ground stood a barrack-room occupied by the guard. It had a door opening out on to the parade ground. There was another door on its far side. Out beyond that there was a wire fence dividing the guard-house from the main road down to the village. He thought about it.

Why not, anyhow? He hadn't much to lose. The risks—the goon with the uncocked rifle; the goon with the machine-gun. The first couldn't fire instantly. The other would probably fire inaccurately. The main trouble would be his wretched clogs.

The next exercise time came around. A good time too. Over in the camp there was an *Appell*. Everyone was paraded. There would be lots of guards on duty there.

Yes—he would try the sudden jump round again. By now the old boy wouldn't get excited about it—he was almost getting used to it.

He began the circuit. Round and round—everything exactly the same as before—round and round, head down, everything the same.

But imperceptibly Upham began widening the circle, just

faintly, doing it so gradually that the goon became used to the distance separating him from Upham.

Round and round, a little bit wider, a couple of circles like that, then a fraction wider again—and he checked to make sure that the rifle was not cocked again. Wider . . . a little wider.

And the circuit was now taking him close to the door of the barrack-room. He kept going steadily, everything the same as usual.

He passed the door of the barracks, plodded on, gathering breath, digging his toes into the clogs to give him a better grip.

He came round to a point opposite the door again . . . moved past it.

Then like a flash he leapt round, sprang into action, and dived straight for the door beside him.

The goon had hesitated when he saw the turn—just the same silly jump the New Zealander had done before. But by the time he woke up to the realization that here indeed was something real, the quarry was out of sight, in through the barracks door, racing across the room inside. Upham dashed straight for the far door, was through it and outside again, running towards the fence and the main road beyond.

He knew the machine-gunner could see him, would have the gun trained on him in a matter of seconds. He was entirely in the open. But it was one of the fastest things he had ever done. Surprise was on his side.

Only the fence to climb. It was of netting, about six feet high, but the mesh was too small for him to climb up the wires. But there was a sloping stay-post . . . he ran to it . . . up the face of the post, over the top, dropping to the ground beyond. Now on to the road.

Best plan—run straight down the road until he could break off into cover. But first—put some distance between himself and the camp.

He sprinted down the road, the clogs thudding awkwardly on the bitumen. Back in the camp the whistles shrilled again, the shouting, rushing, the panic—and on *Appell* the prisoners of Weinsberg knew that something serious was on once more and it would be that man Upham again.

But it was not to be. Charles had hardly covered fifty yards down the road before he ran straight into a group of German guards returning to camp. He darted to one side, but they were at him in a moment, surrounding him, pawing at him while he cursed and struggled.

They led him back to the cells, unrepentant and still aggressive. The whole affair had taken less than a minute.

Why hadn't the machine-gunner fired? How had Upham managed to get as far as he did?

The way it was between guards and prisoners it wasn't long before the man on the parapet told his story to one of the New Zealanders.

"I saw it all happen," he claimed. "I could have shot him down any time after he ran out of the barracks. But I could see the guards down the road and Captain Upham was running straight into them. I knew they would catch him."

Then he went on to admit that another reason he withheld his fire was out of sheer admiration for such a bold but hopeless attempt.

Hauptmann Knapp mounted a *second* machine-gun on the parapet overlooking the parade ground.

Upham was allowed back amongst his friends before he was taken from Weinsberg. He had his last breakfast with them.

"Judge" Holmes says: "I think the whole camp was sorry he was leaving. I remember the morning he left. His immediate friends gave him items of food for his journey—and at this time food was as precious as uranium. I cooked him a tin of hot porridge. Charlie was touched, but all he permitted himself to say was: 'You old beggar'."

Then they took him away.

"This time, Captain Oopham, it is the end of the road for you. You are being transferred to another camp—to Oflag IV C."

"IV C? That's a Straf-lager isn't it? A punishment camp?"

"Oh no, I would not call it that. IV C—it is just a camp you cannot escape from. There are some very interesting prisoners there, what we call the bad prisoners. No escape. Oflag IV C is in Saxony—at a little place called . . . now let me see . . . ah yes, a little place called . . . Colditz."

CHAPTER SIXTEEN

TWELVE HOURS

THE German Commandant now had a deep anxiety that Upham might still escape; and the transfer to Colditz would provide the prisoner with opportunities he dared not let him seize. So it was the measure of the Germans' respect that, as the train settled down for the journey eastwards, Charles found himself alongside not merely one guard, not even two, but no less than three stalwart custodians.

One was a sergeant. He was content with a pistol. The other two were one-stripers, one of them armed with a pistol and sub-machine-gun, the other with a pistol and rifle. Quite enough fire-power to keep him subdued, Upham thought.

But they were quite agreeable company. Past the age for active service, they were still useful for the immense guarding and occupation duties Germany had to perform. They were not of the arrogant Nazi type, not like the Gestapo men who came through the train. On the contrary, Charles found them considerate and helpful, provided he co-operated. But he soon knew they were afraid. They were afraid of him physically, and not for a moment did they relax their concentration on his every movement. But, more than that, he could see they were literally terrified at the possibility of his escaping. They acted as if their lives would depend on it—and perhaps they would.

The journey took over three days. One of them would get out at the stations and bring in the food for all of them to share. One would sleep while the other two watched the prisoner. Never did they allow him the slightest rope.

It was a tedious, yet interesting, journey. The train would halt for hours on end, held up by the effects of Allied bombing on station yards or bridges ahead; or it would alternately race and crawl, go on to sidings, reverse into loop lines; and all along the route Upham saw the devastation to industry and transport that the war was now bringing to Germany.

The train was chock-full. Among the passengers were German civilians moving east to escape from the battles drawing near their homes; there were wounded German soldiers; and threading through them hour after hour were the Military Police and the Gestapo.

The M.P.s were looking for deserters, and every man in uniform was closely examined. They were tough, heavily armed, and they looked well fed. In contrast, the German soldiers and civilians appeared thin and miserable.

Upham had heard from other prisoners about the Gestapo. He now saw them in action. Every passenger was scrutinized care-fully, all papers examined slowly and suspiciously. Upham found he was the only one not having to fumble with his wallet every few miles. The Gestapo, too, looked affluent and over-healthy, like fat stock, and their uniforms were smart and new.

It was on the second night, as they clattered farther and farther eastwards, that Upham realized his time was running out. These three goons were intelligent enough to prevent his escaping unless he took some unprecedented risk. They were so afraid of anything happening that they would obviously take great risks themselves to stop him, for fear of the punishment they could expect if their captive made a successful break.

He knew he had to try somehow, somewhere. But the hours dragged past to the tune of the clacking wheels and nothing happened to give him hope. Hour upon hour he sat and brooded, and it grew in his mind that each minute saw him farther and farther away from freedom.

It was in the deadest hours of the night, about three o'clock in the morning, when Upham decided the time had come. This was not an occasion when opportunity would be presented to him. It was too late for that. His only chance lay in taking the kind of risk he had always shunned—stepping into danger without being able to assess the chances of success. He said he wanted to visit the lavatory. One of them—"Blue-Nose", Upham had dubbed him—came along with him, saw him into the little cubicle, and stood guard outside. They had allowed him that amount of privacy, even though a desperate man could perhaps effect an escape through the tiny window. But there was no risk, they must have thought, of a man hurling himself from an express train travelling at top speed. For that reason they allowed him to visit the toilet only when the train was travelling fast.

But that was the very risk Charles decided he now had to take.

He tried the window. No, of course they wouldn't leave it so that anyone could just push it open. It was well nailed up. Well, that meant he would have to smash the glass. He broke the glass quietly, peered uncertainly through the gap into the black night outside. The window was so small he didn't think he could possibly get through it. No chance whatever with his heavy coat on, and with the small pack of belongings that he rarely took off his shoulders.

He looked out again. It was pitch dark. The train was roaring through the night. He could see absolutely nothing. For all he knew they might be travelling alongside a river, along a mountainside, on top of an embankment. Many men, he knew, who had jumped from trains had simply thrown themselves to instant death as they were dashed against rocks, posts, or in one or two cases straight over the edge of precipices. And at this speed . . . it was the sort of risk he would never dream of taking—the dangers were so great, and he could not judge the chances of success.

But now time was short. For once he had to risk everything.

Swiftly he peeled off his pack and his coat, wrapped one around the other, then stretched out, and threw the bundle out of the window. Now to follow himself.

He began to edge himself through. The window was still too small for a comfortable exit, and he feared he would stick halfway. He hesitated as he lay twisted in the window space, peering into the night, hoping to pick up the nature of the ground alongside the train, but it was all just one rushing blur.

It was madness, he thought. And for a moment an inner voice seemed to be calling: "Go back, go back!" And he would have tried to squeeze back inside again were it not for the thought of his coat and pack lying on the railway track down the line. He felt really scared.

Then sharply came a rattling of the door-handle and Blue-Nose was calling: *"Aus! Aus!"* That was enough.

In a moment of sudden resolve he pushed harder, balanced for a moment, and then was gone. . . .

The incredible feeling of hurling himself out into space . . . the dread of it . . . the sharp clutch of fear as he knew he was on the way . . . the roar of the wheels as his last thought. . . .

Something seemed to whip at his feet and then, in an instant, a tremendous crashing impact of his whole body . . . his head blazed . . . and he knew no more.

Slowly his brain came awake . . . ever so slowly, it seemed, and with every moment the splitting pain in his head grew worse. He was lying huddled up on the ground, and for a while he had no idea where he was or how he had come there. It was a half-world from which he was reluctant to fight clear. Every moment seemed such an agony. Then suddenly he was sharply awake. He knew everything—the train . . . the window . . . the jump . . . the black night . . . the shattering impact.

He was lying across railway sleepers. But they couldn't be the ones his train had run on. No—he could see now—there was a double railway track. When he leapt he had hurled himself out on to a parallel line. He must have hit his head against the rails, or the wooden sleepers perhaps. Which meant the train must have gone *that* way. He got to his knees, peered through the darkness in the direction where his train had disappeared. There was not a sound up there, not a sight of anything. So far, so good. The train had gone on. They mightn't have missed him yet. How long had he been unconscious, he wondered.

But there was no time to lose. Old Blue-Nose would be breaking in the door before long, staring in horror at the open window, rushing back to his fellow-guards, stopping the train, alerting all the search forces. They would have patrols out in no time. He had to be under cover before daylight.

Every bone aching, he dragged himself to his feet, blessing his luck to find that he had no injuries apart from his appalling head. Urgency lending him wings, he began immediately trudging down the railway track, heading westwards away from the train that had been taking him to Colditz.

He had one thought: get farther west, then find cover for the day.

He tramped steadily on. What real chance did he have, he wondered. Couldn't speak German, no false papers, no German money, no maps. Still—might meet up with some foreign workers. And if not—well, he'd give the Huns a good run.

He had been walking more than a mile down the line before he came upon his coat and pack. They were intact, but he shuddered again as he tried to work out how fast that train must have been travelling.

It was bitterly cold, and he was grateful to snuggle into the coat again, and to feel the reassuring pressure of the little pack over his shoulders. He hardly noticed the darkness beginning to fade. On and on he stumped, mile after mile, following the line until daylight would enable him to see the lie of the land. He had to be careful of another train coming along, but he would have plenty of time to get down out of sight.

The dawn was coming quickly—he could see a clear quarter-mile now. Nothing suitable on either side of the line; just cultivated fields. Hopeless breaking off into that kind of country. Better stick to the railway as long as he could.

Lighter now, and he glanced behind. . . . He stopped.

He turned deliberately full round and narrowed his eyes. Was that someone way back along the line? Could it be someone walking along the tracks, following his own footsteps, perhaps half a mile back there?

Yes, it was someone, all right. Might be a farmer or a workman taking a short cut to work. Nothing to worry about that—he could out-distance him if necessary. He turned sharply round and began walking again, clapping on the pace. A strange man seen walking the railway tracks would excite suspicion in this kind of country. And every young German was trained as a junior Nazi scout, on the look-out for escaped P.O.W.s. He needed cover pretty soon.

Then he breathed again. Not far ahead, off to the south of the line, lay a wood. He would move off there, get deep into a thicket for the day, reconnoitre just before dark, then travel again during the night. He hurried along now, keen to reach the haven of the trees. It was still very early, very unlikely for anyone to be about. Make the last few hundred yards at top speed, duck off to the side, and he would be safe for the day. He decided where he would leave the tracks. He was right alongside the wood now, but it didn't please him so much. For it was a plantation, not a natural wood, and the trees grew in straight rows. You could see right down the lanes between them. But that couldn't be helped. He had no choice.

He paused as he prepared to strike off away from the line . . . looked back again. . . . There, curse it, was that same figure, but perhaps even a little closer. That fellow must have been really tramping to have made up ground like that. But he was still a long way off.

Upham stared hard . . . and he had a haunting feeling that the man up there was Blue-Nose. Absurd, he sharply rebuked himself. Turning away, he quickly ran off the lines, into the shade of the trees, and moved rapidly down one of the lanes. He would get right into the centre.

The sight of that figure far up the line made him uneasy. Surely they wouldn't waste time sending a man along the railway on *foot*. And surely the train must have gone several miles before they discovered his escape. No—he was getting too suspicious; the simplest explanation was that it was a workman hurrying to a nearby farm. The places where they would be watching for him would be railway yards, picture theatres, isolated barns or hay-ricks, and in the ditches alongside the main roads. They wouldn't expect him to walk along the railway, as plain as a wooden duck moving across a shooting gallery.

Still, the thought of it made him restless. He would see what this plantation was like. He would reconnoitre around it, decide where to make for after nightfall. He would have to lie up all day.

He tramped through to the far end of the wood, peered cautiously out over the countryside beyond. He would have to make south, or south-east perhaps. Maybe his best hope lay in going east towards the Russians. Next night he would go across country, pick up some food, make the journey in bounds. He found himself a deep thicket. It was broad daylight now and no time to be lost in making himself inconspicuous. Pressing in under the branches, he burrowed a hole midst the leaves, curled up gratefully, and closed his eyes.

He awoke stiff and sore. From the way the shadows lay he judged it was late afternoon. He must have slept about eight hours. That was just what he wanted. He would be out on the edge of the wood by nightfall, ready to move into the open as soon as it was dark. But there was something wrong—he felt it.

Carefully he rose to his knees, then crawled to the edge of the thicket. Parting the branches with elaborate stealth he peered out. The figure of a man was standing there, right at the end of the lane, looking straight down towards Upham. And, even as Upham stared at him, the figure began to move, with slow, cautious steps, like a man who is waiting for something to happen in front of him. And he was coming, slowly but steadily, straight down this very lane. Upham watched him in cold tension. The deliberate, methodical approach of the man worried him. . . .

And then, like a flash, he knew, for coming out of the trees on each side of the man were three others, and they all had rifles.

He squirmed his way past the nearest tree, into the next lane, then began jogging silently away from the spot, at right angles to the lane down which the searchers were advancing.

He paused when he saw the light increasing ahead and he knew he was approaching the edge of the wood on that side. He drew himself in close beside a tree, looking back to see if he could pick up the other men as they passed down the lane.

Then again, with a feeling of urgency, the warning bell seemed to be ringing inside him. Almost by instinct Upham turned round, looking out towards the edge of the plantation.

Right on the edge there, rifle in hand, stood a figure, peering uncertainly in Upham's direction. The outline of the man was familiar, the way he held the rifle, that cant of his head. *It was Blue-Nose!*

Blue-Nose himself, whom he had left in the train, now patrolling through this very wood, looking for his precious prisoner.

That meant five men. Blue-Nose and four others. And Blue-Nose was now starting off slowly, pacing down the lane towards Upham, towards the centre of the wood.

The searchers were going through the wood at right angles to one another. That was grim enough but, given luck, he might dodge them, keeping in the sector away from them.

Upham planned it out rapidly, moving like a shadow as his brain ticked over. He had never felt so alert, so much now dependent on his wits. Deliberately he began running at an oblique angle, to take him away from the two paths that the searchers were following. He ran through the trees as fast as he dared, trying hard to make no sound . . . on and on, until at last he reckoned that he had crossed almost from one side to the other. Somewhere on the way he must have crossed behind the first party of men, but he had not sighted them.

Now he was panting with the running, trying to think what plan they would follow. They would divide the wood off into squares. He would have to keep moving either ahead of them or, better still, behind them. Move into a square they had just left. It wouldn't be impossible with only five men to beat.

His mind was still dwelling on "five men" before the signal lights abruptly changed. For now there, far down the lane in which he was standing, there was *another man*—another searcher, carrying a rifle at the ready, moving confidently, looking right and left as he strode down the lane. Upham darted out of sight, peered back towards the railway end of the wood. And there . . . oh my godfather! . . . there was another . . . and another! Eight of them now!

He ran quickly now, deep towards the centre again . . . paused . . . pressed himself up against a tree while he got his wind back. Up this lane? Yes—but up at the end of it there was the next man—only a hundred yards away.

Upham slid round into the next lane—looked up it, caught his breath in desperation. There was a man coming down this one too. Chancing being seen, he dashed across the space, into the shadow of the tree, looked up the next lane. There was a soldier moving down there, too. No time for planning now—just jump where the whip cracked, and he had to chance it again to leap across this lane in the hope that there would be clear territory ahead.

The shout from somewhere out to the side of him was like a battle-cry. He wasn't surprised to hear it. It had to happen pretty soon.

Like a hare he darted away from it, doubling back across the lanes, and as he ran the shout seemed to be taken up around the wood, like voices echoing back from a dozen mountainsides. He found himself wondering—how many of them altogether?

And he ran this way—and there was one man running towards him . . . he veered off sharply . . . but there was another down there . . . again and again he swerved away . . . but it seemed everywhere they were coming at him . . . he tried in all directions, but they were always there, some running, some moving steadily . . . all with rifles.

At last as he stood at bay he could watch them coming. From where he was he could see down several lanes, and there was a rifleman advancing down every one . . . coming in on him fast.

Run here . . . but again they were in front of him. It dawned on him ominously—there was a cordon around the whole wood. They had surrounded him while he slept. Now they had spotted him, they were moving in steadily, in a circle, narrowing him down.

He could see most of them now—there must be a whole platoon of infantry on the job. He had only one chance—if it were a single ring closing in on him he might dash straight through it—like the night at Minqar Qaim. There was nothing else left.

He began running again, straight towards the ring of searchers. Perhaps it would surprise them.

Sixty yards . . . fifty . . . thirty . . . and he saw the look on the face of the man he was racing towards. Then . . .

Crack!! The rifle-shot echoed through the wood like cannonfire. *Crack! Crack!* And all around him now the shots were coming, and he felt the dry "phew . . . w . . . w" as the bullets plucked the air close by his ear. The man in front of him was firing too—point-blank range. They seemed to be all running in on him.

And he knew the game was over.

He knew when the lure of escape no longer blinded him to the prospect of certain death. His time had run out . . . he knew it . . . and it was no use any more. The next few bullets would strike him down, but he threw in his hand before the inevitable end.

Hands raised in surrender? No—not for him. That was too humiliating a gesture. When he knew it was all over he stopped running abruptly, then deliberately sat down on the ground, watched them as they paused uncertainly.

They must suspect him, for they came crowding in to a range of about a chain; but there they stopped, covering him with their weapons, while the shouting and calling continued.

Fully two minutes passed, while Upham remained sitting on the ground in simulated indifference, before they finally moved in cautiously. In they came. Yes—there must have been an entire platoon.

They searched him meticulously. They told him later that if

they had found any German food on him he would have been executed for "pillage". But now—here was old Blue-Nose. The old codger would probably slap him over the head with his pistol-butt.

But that was strange. Old Blue-Nose was coming up with his face wreathed in smiles, and he put his hand on Upham's shoulder as if he were greeting a long-lost friend. He almost drooled at his delight in recapturing the fugitive.

In contrast to the rough reception Upham expected, he had never found himself so popular. Blue-Nose was full of concern for his welfare, and fussed around him like an over-indulgent nanny. Charles found himself grinning at the experience, but the truth was obvious enough: this was one of the greatest days in the old boy's life—the day his prize prisoner was recaptured.

Charles was led out of the wood in a spirit of camaraderie and effusive goodwill. Blue-Nose explained that it was he himself who walked back down the line—it was he whom Upham must have seen a long way back—for Blue-Nose correctly judged how the fugitive would behave. He trailed him along the line, not anxious to catch up too soon, and saw him disappear into the wood. Then he phoned for help and the local military commander provided a force to surround the plantation.

Upham was at liberty for just twelve hours. It was well worth it.

In another train the journey to Colditz continued. But now there had to be more care still. The guards couldn't risk a second escape. So for the remainder of the journey Upham sat hand-cuffed to one of them.

The guards tried now to take Upham with them when they got out at stations to obtain food. But the restaurant people brusquely refused to have the prisoner inside or to serve him with any food at all.

What, then, to do with him?

So they hit on the convenient idea of handcuffing Upham to a post on the platform, in a position where they could keep an eye on him while they bought their miserable black bread and soup at the restaurant counter.

A group of young Luftwaffe toughs strolled by. They stopped and stared. Then one of them, a petty little brute with a pasty face, after making sure that Upham was securely tied, came up bravely and lashed out with his foot. The kick caught Upham on the side of the knee. It hurt.

That seemed good fun for these young worthies. One after

another they stepped in and contemptuously added their kicks to the assaults of the first comrade. Upham could do nothing but endure their violence with a black heart, while they vented their cruelty and hatred on him until they tired of their sport.

The kicking and roughing-up he suffered on that station platform remained one of Upham's most vivid war-time memories. Even over the mellowing years he has found it hard to forgive. So often a person forms his opinion of a whole nation from the actions of a degraded few; and in modern times so often the leaders of a nation set the pattern for those few.

Bruised and humiliated, Upham was led back to his seat in the train.

CHAPTER SEVENTEEN

COLDITZ CASTLE

THEY marched in past the sentry at the gate, then over a bridge across the moat; beyond that an archway with another gate and sentry; then through yet another gate, up a sloping cobbled walk, and finally into a courtyard entirely surrounded by high buildings.

He had arrived in Colditz.

The Germans called it *"Sonderlager"*—Special Camp. To it they sent the most desperate and troublesome of all war prisoners, not for punishment, but because Colditz was reputed to be escape-proof.

The story has been told elsewhere how the ingenuity of a number of Allied prisoners destroyed the reputation of Colditz's invincibility. They beat it, they beat the walls, the precipices, the mass of sentries, the Gestapo inspectors, the German officers who came to know everything that could be known about escape technique and stratagems. And, despite all these, the escapes, fabulous and well-nigh incredible, continued.

Built and rebuilt, altered and added to over four centuries, Colditz was enough to make the bravest quail. Its great walls—seven feet thick in places—its gloom, the five-storeyed buildings rearing up around the tiny courtyard, its rigid discipline—all bore heavily on the aggressive spirits of those confined there.

When Upham arrived in the late summer of 1944 the years were taking their toll of the occupants. Sickness had increased, the mental balance of many of them was insecure.

Just before Upham's arrival the prisoners had realized there was a traitor amongst them. Information obtained by the Germans could have come only from the mouth of a man who knew the prisoners' secrets. So the senior Allied officers decided that every new arrival should receive a private screening from his fellow-prisoners.

Martin Gilliat—then acting as Adjutant of the British prisoners and later to be an official in the household of the Queen Mother —heard of the new arrival. He went to Fred Moody, a New Zealand medical officer in the fortress.

"Fred, I'm told another New Zealander was brought in last night. Name of Upham. See if you can check on him, will you?"

Moody was interested in this new arrival, particularly as no combatant officer from the New Zealand Division had yet been sent to Colditz.

The new man was having a shower. Moody stood in the court-yard, edged along till he was within earshot of the grilled window of the shower-room. "What d'yer know, Kiwi?" he called out softly in unmistakable New Zealand accents.

A pause. Then: "Who are you?" came the cautious reply.

Moody told him, gave him some identification.

Upham whispered: "What the hell is this place? Looks bloody awful to me." Moody gave him more information, meantime keeping an eye on the sentry in the courtyard. "Do you want any food?" he asked.

"No."

Then they talked guardedly, Upham still cautious about Moody's identity, Moody asking questions to satisfy himself about Upham.

When they had satisfied each other the voice came out through the grill, wary but eager: "Any chance of getting out of here, Doc?"

"Not much," Moody whispered back. "But I'll tell you about things when they bring you out." Then the sentry moved him on.

Moody went before the prisoners' Security Committee a few minutes later. He told them what he knew. "I know it's Upham," he said. "He comes from Christchurch. Father's a barrister. Went to Christ's College. I heard of him at O.C.T.U., and I was on Crete when he got his V.C. I remember the boys in the 23rd at Maleme talking about Upham of the 20th tearing the Huns to bits."

In a few hours Moody helped Upham to settle in, took him to the Canadian mess—the group that shared one eating table—and introduced him around. Once again Upham asked: "Now tell me, Fred, what's the story about escaping?"

The doctor answered: "No hope at all. The Huns have sewn up just about everything now, and there's not much escape activity—not like there used to be. If we stick out the winter, looks as if it might be all over. Most fellows think escaping isn't worth the candle now. Whatever you try here it's a death or glory business. You can get killed falling off the roof, or down the cliff, and the goons will shoot you without hesitation if you're caught. But if you've got any ideas you have to register them with the Escape Committee. Dick Howe's in charge—and he's got to give you the O.K."

It did not take Upham long to realize that Colditz had reached the stage where it was almost completely escape-proof. Mike Sinclair, an unquenchable escaper, had just made his final bid from Colditz and had been shot dead just over the wire. The impersonations, the tunnels, the long ropes, the drains—all had been tried before, some successfully; but now the loopholes were sealed.

Upham, moreover, was not well enough to attempt any escape that involved climbing. His arm was stiff, ruling out any prospect of climbing the steep ridges of Colditz's jagged roofs.

Charles was rather a solitary figure. The misery of Colditz seemed to dampen the active side of his character; only now and then did his fiery spirit emerge.

Mickey Hargreaves (a New Zealander in one of those mysterious British parachuting units) and Fred Moody became Upham's closest friends, and the only ones in whom he confided. They tried to draw him out sometimes, to set him talking about the old days on the battlefields of Crete or North Africa. And once when Moody talked about fear, and questioned him about it, Upham spoke as if he didn't understand, finally blurting out: "I got so bloody angry with them nothing else seemed to matter."

Dick Howe undertook the task of teaching Charles how to cook. Now this was rather different from cooking in a shepherd's hut on the slopes of the New Zealand Alps, or with a section in the Western Desert. Cooking at Colditz was a fine art. As Howe puts it—one had to start with practically no ingredients.

Dick Howe gave Charles a lesson in making soup. First the two of them ransacked the swill-tubs—the scrapings from the kitchen. What they wanted were peelings, because here and there some of the vegetable would still adhere to the skins. These minute prizes were carefully gathered together and fried with a little fat. Then unlimited quantities of water were added, depending on the number who were to partake of the meal. Any odd scraps available would be added by way of seasoning. Result—tasty soup.

"Having mastered this art," writes Howe, "Charlie went from strength to strength until he became a very accomplished chef, which under those conditions was most important."

But among the hungry grey faces of prisoners enduring the last winter in Colditz, Upham made no special mark. They recognized his restrained hatred, the intolerable burden of close confinement which he suffered just like them, the deep longing for freedom, the determination that nothing in the end would defeat him. But if any picture of Upham remains clearly in their eyes it is only of a tough solitary man plodding round and round that dreary courtyard, head sunk, brow furrowed—still the caged lion, but now with the heart being crushed.

Nevertheless, while towards his fellow-prisoners he was a mixture of warmth and dourness, towards the Germans he never varied. His attitude remained one of constant antagonism and contempt.

Counting the prisoners was a procedure that infuriated Upham. The British contingent would stand casually in their ranks, reading or chatting, while Hauptmann Pupcke made the count. Pupcke was not disliked by the prisoners, but he was an awfully poor counter.

"This damned counting business makes me bloody angry," Charles said on a dozen occasions. "And here's old muck-up Jack coming," as Pupcke entered the courtyard to begin the business of counting.

Pupcke liked everything lined up nicely. He gave orders that no one should smoke on *Appell*.

Upham stood in the front rank, waiting to be counted, smoking his pipe. Pupcke stopped in front of him, pointed at the pipe, and barked. He seemed to take a long time to say what might have been said in a few words. All he was doing was ordering Upham to remove the pipe.

Upham looked at him steadily, took the pipe out, and said: "Oh, go shoot yourself." Then he replaced the pipe.

Hauptmann Pupcke looked quickly at the interpreter. "What did he say?" he asked in German.

Fred Moody, standing alongside, nudged Charlie. "Don't cause any trouble, Charlie. No point in it today."

Pupcke faced Upham again, rapped out in English: "Stand to attention!" Upham took no notice and went on smoking.

Then Pupcke stormed at him, all to no effect. He tried persuading, then ordering, then shouting. And then, tolerant German that he was, he suddenly stopped, smiled, and said magnanimously: "Perhaps there's something wrong with him." He took no further notice of Upham and resumed his counting.

It was a near thing on another occasion. Again Charles was in the front rank, reading, this time with a cigarette in his mouth.

The Security Officer, Hauptmann Eggers, was doing the count. He walked slowly down the line, counting methodically; then came to Upham. In a high-pitched voice he shouted at Upham to take the cigarette out.

No one expected Charles to obey. Nor did he. He stood still, looking up from his book in a bored way, still smoking.

Slowly Eggers raised his open hand, drew it back, then slashed Upham violently across the face, sending the cigarette flying.

Nothing would then have saved Eggers' life had it not been for the violent intervention of Upham's friends.

His face "like a bayonet charge" (says Dick Howe), Upham threw himself at Eggers. Almost as quickly, his friends on each side grabbed him. Livid with rage, Upham struggled furiously with them, obsessed with nothing else but getting at Eggers to avenge the insult he had suffered. Eggers backed away hurriedly. With difficulty they restrained him, and Hauptmann Eggers was quick to dismiss the parade.

It was an incident that could have had a more serious ending.

There occurred also at Colditz a flare-up with a German officer that Upham now describes as his "nearest thing". The Germans had had a fright and, fearing an escape, had sounded the *Appell* siren just on midnight. This was not uncommon.

Stumbling and cursing, the prisoners gathered their coats about them and filed out for the count. A number of men were called on to show their identity discs. They did so—all except Upham. When asked for his he threw it on the ground in front of the inspecting officer.

He was ordered to pick it up. He took no notice. Again and again the orders were given. Upham said once: "Pick it up yourself," then kept a defiant silence. Having taken his stand, he was not going to shift. The German officer finally gave up speaking, drew his revolver, and cocked it, then advanced on Upham and pressed the muzzle against his stomach. "Pick it up!" he ordered for the last time.

Upham was always an expert at judging a risk, knowing how far he could risk himself or his men without incurring too great a danger. This time he knew where he stood. He could tell it in the manner of the officer standing before him.

For a long twenty seconds he stood there, eyes blazing. Then, defeated in the face of death, he relaxed, bent down, and picked up the disc, handed it over.

He made it appear, however, as if he were conferring a favour.

Those alongside agreed that Upham could never have been closer to it than in those tense moments.

Sometimes there was fun, even with the Germans. And when these prisoners of Colditz had fun it was hilarity unlimited. It had to be.

Appell! And this day the prisoners knew that Pupcke was the Orderly Officer of the day, and that he would accordingly be making the inspection and doing the count. There would be nothing drastic.

They filed down into the courtyard in bored disinterest, shuffled into their ranks, and waited for Pupcke to appear. Punctual and punctilious, it wasn't like him to be late. But no sign of him. Ah! At last, there he came, entering the courtyard almost at the double, looking red-faced and bustled. It seemed clear that the good Pupcke had been away from the Castle, had just made it back to the fortress in time for the parade.

With no time to collect himself, Pupcke advanced to the front rank and began his task. It was his habit to lean close to the front-rank men. He passed down two or three of the files . . . then paused, because the first man had begun giggling. Seeing nothing to giggle about, Pupcke continued the inspection. But as he went steadily on, so steadily did the giggling turn into chortles . . . and the further he went, the less they could restrain themselves. They began to laugh, louder and louder, and by the time the startled Hauptmann had reached the end of the line the noise was swelling into uproar.

"Three cheers for old Pupcke!" someone shrieked, beside himself with mirth, and the prisoners cheered hilariously, letting their feelings burst out in a positive furore of helpless laughter.

It seemed so uproariously incongruous for the precise, rigid Germans—these inhuman guardians of Colditz—these automatons who possessed few, if any, human weaknesses. But there, dear old Pupcke, he went blissfully down the line, more and more puzzled, with his breath stinking of liquor, and around his mouth a generous plastering of rich red lipstick, implanted on him in broad tell-tale imprints.

Winter dragged on, and 1945 came round. There were concerts and plays in the camp theatre; there was the stimulation of hearing the B.B.C. broadcasts from the secret radio in the attics. The war on land was advancing into fortress Germany.

There was the interest of seeing Colditz being used for hostages. Inside its walls were assembled a number of prisoners closely related to prominent people in the Allied war effort—Giles Romilly, who was Winston Churchill's nephew; Captain the Master of Elphinstone, a nephew of Queen Elizabeth; Lieutenant Lord Lascelles, nephew of King George VI; some prominent French and Polish generals; and Lieutenant John Winant, son of the United States Ambassador to Britain. It was obvious why they were being held. Their lives and safety were to be traded by the Nazis at the time of reckoning.

Three Americans also enterel Colditz, captured from an unsuccessful parachute mission into Hungary. One of them, Colonel Duke, had been advertising manager for the American magazine *Time* and became one of Upham's close friends.

As the final months drew on, agonizingly slowly, escape seemed futile. Unnecessary risks were no longer wise.

Nevertheless, Charles Upham and Peter Winton made some explorations. They revived interest in the old drains, one of the earliest of schemes, thinking that a few innovations might see them pay off again. But time was on their side now. Closer and closer came the war.

On Tuesday, 10th April 1945, the war on land came within earshot of Colditz. Used to the crump of bombs falling on Leipzig, twenty-five miles away, now the prisoners could distinguish the unmistakable sound of shell-bursts in the distance. There were few *Appells*. Colonel Tod began spending a good deal of time in conference with the Commandant. Just as freedom was approaching, he sensed that the safety of his fellow-prisoners was now at its most critical stage. One false move by the German Commandant, or one tactical error on his own part, could mean bloodshed in the Castle. The inmates of Colditz were not people to be trifled with at this late hour.

Next day, Wednesday, the noise of battle drew nearer.

Thursday. Earthworks and defences were being hastily constructed in the village below and orders came for the hostages to be removed from the fortress to the final mountain redoubt in Austria.

Friday; then Saturday. And all that day the shells whined and screamed over the Castle, and a few slammed into it. Tod told the prisoners that the German High Command had ordered that they be evacuated farther east, out of reach of the approaching Allies. He gave the Commandant the answer: "We refuse; we will resist, by force if necessary, any attempt to shift us. Responsibility for bloodshed will be on the head of the German authorities, particularly the Camp Commandant."

By nightfall that day the Commandant had yielded to the inevitable and arranged terms of surrender with Colonel Tod. It was only a matter of hours now.

Sunday the 15th. By 11 a.m. American tanks were seen in the streets of the village, infantry moving in their wake and clearing the houses. It was only half an hour later when four Americans of a reconnaissance section walked through the castle gates. Inside they found the senior British officers ready for them and the Germans lined up in formal surrender.

They went down from Colditz into the village—tramping up and down the streets, looking into the shops. Some walked in and unashamedly took the cameras and the binoculars they wanted. Upham felt he couldn't do that. He saw some eating utensils in a hardware shop that lay unattended. They represented normalcy to him. He walked in, helped himself to a plate, knife, fork, and spoon, then walked out. He saw others with the cameras and the watches. Then he headed for the headquarters of the American unit who had captured the town. He knew exactly what he wanted to do.

"Why not?" the sergeant asked in reply. "Plenty of it. Help yourself." And he helped Upham select the goods he had come for.

Upham changed into the American combat uniform, fitted on the boots and the U.S. helmet. Then the arms—the Tommy-gun, the revolver, two grenades, compass. . . .

He prepared to go into action with the Americans.

For four days Charles stayed with the U.S. forces in the Colditz area, clothed and equipped as one of them, waiting for the call forward. He was intent on fighting the war to the last.

But the inexorable pressure of higher orders finally caught him up. "Under no circumstances are released P.O.W.s to be permitted to join active service units, unofficially or otherwise. P.O.W.s are to be evacuated without exception." He couldn't beat that order, so reluctantly he left his Americans and was soon part of the great movement back towards England.

CHAPTER EIGHTEEN

TELEGRAM IN THE STUDIO

FROM Europe the flood of released prisoners streamed towards England, among them 9000 New Zealanders. Then, armed with a free rail pass, and with twenty-eight days' leave, they roamed every corner of Britain.

Charles Upham waited impatiently for his own "processing" to be completed. Molly was in England, and when reunions are close time never passes more slowly. Fretting, but at last freed, he rushed to find out where she was. The clerk seemed to be awfully slow in looking up the records. "Miss McTamney, sir? Actually she's not here. She's not in England at present."

"What?" almost shrieked Charles. "Then where is she?"

"In Germany, sir." Yes, she was in Germany, working with the Red Cross Auxiliary not far behind the lines.

Leaping for pen and paper, Charles dashed off an urgent appeal. "Come out of there," he demanded. "It's dangerous."

He grabbed another sheet of paper, dashed off an application for permission to return to Germany. Even Charles appreciated the twist of it. Here he was, just freed from Germany after spending nearly three years trying to escape from it, now appealing to go back.

But Molly worked things her way, and the week-end saw her winging back to England to the meeting both had been waiting for so long. There she was at last. He had never seen her before in her war uniform.

And for her—there at last was the man whose letters and postcards had been so homely and placid that she sometimes wondered if he were the same man the newspapers wrote about.

There was just that one week-end when they saw each other. Molly had to fly back, but their plans were made before she left.

While she was away, and Charles waited again for her return, he was meeting all the old faces again—his friends from Crete whom he had left bitterly on the beach at Sfakia, those who had never returned from Belhamed while he sulked as an L.O.B., and the mass of others who had been scooped up in the man-made disaster on Ruweisat Ridge.

And there, at last, was old Leggy; Leggy the incorrigible, as bright and chirpy as ever. And who other than Leggy would have turned P.O.W. life into that of a country gentleman, waited on hand and foot by a family in Poland who protected and fed him? Charles and Leggy-boy walked through London arm in arm.

Then a letter arrived with a coat of arms on the envelope. It read:

"... The King will hold an Investiture at Buckingham Palace on Friday the 11th May 1945 at which your attendance is requested...."

Charles was allowed to take two guests. He took Molly and his sister, Mrs. G. H. Holmes-Siedle, who lived in Hampshire.

King George VI pinned the V.C. on Upham's tunic—as if to perpetuate the temporary investiture in the desert that seemed so long ago.

There were many being decorated and the King had time for only a few words with each.

"Well, Captain Upham," His Majesty said, "I believe this is not your only award. I'm told you've just received a Mention in Despatches for your attempts to escape. Congratulations for that, too. Tell me, though, what have you been doing since you arrived in London?"

"Mostly eating, sir," the lean ex-Colditz veteran replied.

They came away from the Palace and walked through St. James's Park. There was plenty to talk about. Relaxed and cheerful now, Charles was chatting freely when a stern voice stopped him.

A brigadier stood disapprovingly above him, one of the very old school. "Don't you Colonials salute your senior officers any longer?" he demanded pompously.

Charles looked startled. He hadn't even noticed the old boy approaching. Then his rancour rose. The old bag—fancy making a point of it when a man was walking with his sister and fiancée, the war over, and using the incorrect and offensive expression— "you Colonials".

Restraining his temper he said quietly: "I'm sorry, sir, I didn't mean to be disrespectful. I didn't see you approaching. I would have saluted if I'd seen you, of course." Then his impish malice came through. "But actually I've just come from the Palace, sir, yarning with the King, *and he didn't seem to be fussy about saluting*."

The Brigadier swelled and seemed about to burst. Then suddenly he noticed the crimson ribbon on Upham's chest. His eyes popped. Then he clicked to attention, swung his arm in salute, turned about, and marched stiffly away.

"Application declined." Oh well, perhaps it's all for the best, Charles philosophized as he read the reply. He had felt so strongly about it at the time.

On his way out from Germany Upham stopped at a transit camp near Weimar, and had gone with a party to inspect the nearby concentration camp of Buchenwald, where countless atrocities had been perpetrated by the Nazis. This experience quickened his resolve, for he had been toying with the idea of joining some unit after the war for the purpose of tracking down these Nazi criminals. One or two he had met in the camps he wanted to see brought to justice.

So, as he arrived in England, one of his first moves was to enter his name for the Occupation Force—for police duties, he asked. That would be the quickest way to have some of those old scores settled.

But no—there was a rule against ex-P.O.W.s being accepted, and his application was "declined".

On 20th June 1945 Charles and Molly were married quietly at Barton-on-Sea, Hampshire. There were few people present, for Charles wanted nothing but quietness and solitude.

They honeymooned on the Isle of Wight, in the New Forest, and in Scotland. Friends provided them with cars. Then back to a flat in London, where at last Charles began to feel the freedom from the great military maw, and he was able to sink gratefully into the total privacy and seclusion of his own home.

The ships were sailing for New Zealand. Charles was posted to one of them. The shipping clerk told him: "Sorry, sir, but wives aren't allowed. Have to wait for normal civilian transport."

Upham was never one to throw his weight about or seek the intervention of any of his superior officers. He accepted without demur what the clerk told him. For Molly it was cruel to have to part so soon. But now only time separated them. Perhaps a boat for civilian passengers wouldn't be too long.

Molly stayed on in the London flat, a welcome figure at the New Zealand Fernleaf Club (where the division forgathered) and a close friend of Lady Freyberg, who throughout the war had worked actively behind the lines in helping the men of the New

Zealand Division. The two were having tea together at the club one day. "And how's Charles?" Lady Freyberg asked conversationally.

"All right, I should hope," Molly replied. "I suppose he's somewhere off Africa now." Lady Freyberg looked startled and put her tea-cup down. "You don't mean to say they've sent him off without you?"

Molly told her the story. The wheels turned, the cables flew, and in no time orders came through that Molly was to have a seat on an aircraft made available to her immediately.

But Molly, like Charles, did not like to gain any advantage from his renown. If it was good enough for her to be flown out, why not all the other wives? No, she would be glad to have an early sea passage—but wouldn't take advantage of the offered air trip.

So on 2nd September 1945 Charles stepped ashore at Lyttelton, New Zealand, to face alone the wave of public acclaim that was to sweep over him in the weeks that followed.

Only relatives were admitted to the railway platform as the troopship steamed in. There were his father and mother—and no words can ever describe the first moment of reunion with loved ones. Unrecognized by the rest of the crowd, Charles was quickly passed through, and within minutes was on his way home; quietly, without fuss—that is how he wanted it.

Back into the old living-room at 32 Gloucester Street that he had last seen in December 1939—nearly six years before. For the last time he swung his kit-bag off his shoulder, tumbled it on to the floor. One waits so long for homecoming. Then when it comes it seems to arrive so quickly.

Tea, chatter, the feel of the old sofa, the way one can completely slouch only when one's family are present; all of them feeling for a subject of conversation with just a little discomfort. It would take some time for them to know him again. He remembered. Some presents. He jumped up, opened his kit-bag quickly, and rummaged inside it.

"For you," he said to his mother, producing a scarf. She scolded him for bringing so magnificent a scarf, with European embroidery on it that few people in New Zealand would ever see.

Then a meerschaum pipe for his father, presents for the others.

And then his hand touched something else in the kit-bag. He drew it out. "Something else for you, Mother," he said almost diffidently.

Mrs. Upham opened the little box, looked at the Victoria Cross lying inside.

The Press soon cornered him. Would he give an interview on the exploits that won him the Cross? He declined. What about impressions of prison life? He agreed to that, and local dailies gave him two columns. "Wherever New Zealanders were imprisoned in Germany or Italy," he said, "they invariably got the enemy down by a mixture of ridicule and defiance."

His old pre-war friends were so proud of him, but he felt their pride was misplaced. "Congratulate the boys of the division," he said. "Not me."

Allen Shand had known Charles since his mustering days. They spent some happy hours together, for, with Allen, Charles seemed able to relax more freely. It suited him to talk about farms and animals.

A few days after Upham's return he was walking in Cathedral Square with Allen when they stopped to speak to a little old lady whom Shand knew. He introduced Charles to her. But she was obviously rather deaf and had trouble in hearing the name.

"And have you been overseas?" she asked sweetly, smiling pleasantly at Charles. Shand bent his head closer. "Yes, he has," he said clearly. "He got back only three days ago."

The little old lady's eyes lit up. "Oh, how lovely," she said. "Then you must have come home on the same ship as *that wonderful Captain Upham*." Shand guided Charles away tactfully.

But a more difficult occasion now forced itself on him. He was to be tendered a civic reception by the city of Christchurch.

Held on 10th September 1945, Charles awaited this ceremony with distress and embarrassment. And when the speakers paid their tributes to him, telling of his great deeds that were matched only by his great modesty, Charles sat on the platform with his eyes on the floor, feeling miserable. When he finally rose to speak he was greeted by a storm of applause. Unnerved, he fumbled for his opening words, began with the shakiness of the veriest amateur. The crowd felt prouder of him than ever. Everyone loves a nervous hero.

"I should like to point out again," he continued, "that this honour is really due to the division as a whole. I am only one unit in the division. There were thousands of better soldiers than I was." (There was some happy disbelieving laughter at this remark.) "In the Army, as you all know, everything is cut and dried—already planned by someone else—and carried out by the people underneath. The only way to get things done was by taking risks, and those who took the risks were those who did not come back. . . ." Then he proceeded to appeal for help to the less fortunate, to those who had lost the "men who had taken the risks and died".

"If we are going to make all this worth while," he concluded, "we have got to get rid of want and misery in other parts of the world. Before this war the world's riches were pretty badly distributed and although they changed hands considerably during the war" (more laughter) "they seemed to do so in big lumps."

For a speech from a man who hated speaking, it struck just the right note. He walked out, tremendously relieved it was all over, to the sound of sustained cheering and clapping.

There was no man whom Upham respected more than Professor Eric Hudson, Principal of Lincoln College, where Charles had taken his farming and valuation courses. So when Hudson came to him and said that the College wanted to commission Archibald F. Nicoll to paint a portrait of their former student, Charles could do little but agree.

Almost simultaneously the old boys of Christ's College arranged a similar commission with Nicoll—so the two portraits were begun.

It fell to the lot of Charles's mother to make him report for the sittings. Charles fumed and did everything he could to escape—but Mrs. Upham got him to the studio by hook or by crook. Nicoll worked patiently on. Professor Hudson did not dare tell Upham that Nicoll had estimated the sittings would extend over six weeks.

Resigned to it, Charles took his place in the studio on Wednesday, 26th September 1945. Nicoll started the day's work. After a while a telegram boy was admitted. "Telegram for Captain Upham," he said.

Charles thanked him, ran his finger through the envelope, and drew out the telegram. It was from Wellington—from the Hon. F. Jones, the Minister of Defence, he was surprised to see.

"Head still a moment, please, Charles," Nicoll pleaded.

Charles kept his head still, holding the telegram out in front so he could read it. It was not long. He read it slowly twice.

With no change of expression he carefully folded it up again, replaced it in the envelope, put it in his pocket.

Perhaps his shoulders drooped a little, or his eyes dropped to the ground, for Nicoll said again: "Hold it, Charles, just a few minutes longer." Charles resumed his pose, held it stoically.

The studio was silent again as they worked on.

CHAPTER NINETEEN

DESERT ECHO

FAR back in July 1942, after the division had broken through the German ring at Minqar Qaim, Jim Burrows had gone along to Kip one evening to talk about Charles Upham.

"Kip," Burrows had said, "Charlie's got to have *another* V.C. . . . For Minqar Qaim. . . ."

So all the necessary evidence was collected, all the reports made out. They went through to General Inglis. He decided what recommendation he would make, what award was fitting for Upham's conduct in the desert at Minqar Qaim.

But then came the business of Ruweisat Ridge, the triumph of the infantry, the shambles of their capture. And, as Upham went into captivity, the tales were told again and again of how he had acted in those dramatic hours. It had been Upham on Crete, Upham at Minqar Qaim, now Upham at Ruweisat. What could be done about a man like that?

"Another V.C.? Not likely. Not many officers get the V.C. Certainly not a second one."

"But they're recommending him for a V.C. for Minqar Qaim— and he deserves it."

"Then what about Ruweisat? He ought to get one for that."

"He can't have *three* V.C.s, old man, can he?"

What was to be done? Here were the reports on Minqar Qaim; here were the reports on Ruweisat. Upham figured in them both. Each report seemed to support the claim that the Commonwealth's highest awards would be appropriate for *each* of the two occasions.

But as the dust settled over the African battlefields, those in authority decided that the exploits of Charles Upham should be rewritten, no longer in separate reports, but in combined form. General Inglis prepared a new comprehensive report, complete with its sworn statements and proofs. It went through to London.

But Upham was now sunk into the deep heart of the enemy prison system. Was it appropriate that a very remarkable award should be made to a man *in absentia*? On went the war, more urgent files covered the stories of desert gallantry, and the years of conflict slowly passed.

Then war in Europe ended and the prisoners flowed back to England.

General Inglis would never forget the epics of Minqar Qaim and Ruweisat. He saw no reason why mere passage of time should gloss over the courage of former days.

He went to Freyberg. "Upham's back," he said. "He's sick, pretty worn out, but he'll be all right in time. He's got a Mention in Despatches for his escape attempts. But what about that award for him? It's lying in War Office—never been looked at since Alamein."

"I'll see about it," Freyberg promised. It was decided that a draft citation should be submitted to Buckingham Palace, to be studied by the King himself. The papers finally reached King George VI.

This is what he read:

"From Jun 27 to Jul 15 1942 Capt Upham performed five acts of conspicuous gallantry. He was with his company during all the fighting that took place during this period, though he was wounded on three different occasions—on the night Jun 27/28; on the night Jul 14/15 and again on the afternoon Jul 15. On the first two occasions he rejoined his Company as soon as his wounds were dressed and after the third occasion, when he could no longer walk, he was taken prisoner of war. He showed fine leadership at all times and under his command his Company earned a remarkable reputation in attack. Capt Upham's complete indifference to danger and his personal bravery has become a byword in the whole of the N.Z.E.F.

Jun 27th: During the afternoon, when the Germans attacked the N.Z. positions at Minqar Qaim, the enemy made several attempts to clear a path for their tanks through our minefield. One forward section post of Capt Upham's Coy was occupying an important position on the edge of the minefield, and it was very heavily shelled and machine-gunned. Capt Upham walked forward over the ground that had no cover of any sort and which was swept by enemy fire, stayed with this section for a short period and came away only when he had assured himself that it could carry on and hold its ground.

Night Jun 27/28: During the night when the N.Z. Div broke through the Germans at Minqar Qaim, Capt Upham led his men in inspiring fashion and his Coy overcame several enemy posts. The attack took place in very bright moonlight and at one stage a truck full of German soldiers was seen moving slowly through the soft sand. Capt Upham and a Corporal ran forward together, and in spite of heavy Tommy-gun fire from the Germans they reached the side of the truck and with hand grenades wiped out the entire truck load and left the truck in flames. Not one German left the burning vehicle. Capt Upham was slightly wounded in both arms from the explosions of his own grenades. He did not report to get his wounds treated until the following night when the Div was back in new positions, and he then rejoined his Coy.

Night Jul 14/15: During the attack on El Ruweisat Ridge Capt Upham's Coy was part of the reserve battalion which, during the six miles advance, was about two miles behind the leading battalions. Wireless communications had broken down and Capt Upham was instructed to send forward an officer in a 'jeep' to contact the forward battalions and bring back information. He went himself instead and after being fired on by an enemy post procured a Spandau gun and set it up in the car. He had several further encounters with enemy posts but by operating the gun himself while the driver of the 'jeep' drove through anything in their path, he contacted the forward troops and brought back the necessary information.

Just before dawn, when the reserve battalions and the anti-tank guns were almost on to their objective, very heavy fire was encountered from a strongly defended enemy locality. There were four machine-gun posts and about five tanks. Capt Upham's Coy was the leading Coy and he quickly directed the attack on the two nearest M.G.s, which were using tracer bullets. He personally led the attack on one post which was silenced and the enemy bayoneted. During the attack Capt Upham was shot in the elbow by a machine-gun bullet and his arm broken. He stayed with his men until the objective was captured and until positions were consolidated. He then reported to the R.A.P. and then, with his arm in splints, went back to his Coy and stayed with it all day under the most trying conditions of heavy enemy artillery and mortar fire. The enemy made a strong counter-attack late in the afternoon, and Capt Upham was again wounded by mortar fire. He was no longer able to walk.

Capt Upham was taken prisoner of war on 15 Jul 42."

Freyberg had by now returned to the division in Italy. Kippenberger was the highest ranking New Zealand officer in England.

One day he was walking in the Strand when an Army despatch rider braked to the kerb alongside him. Would he telephone his headquarters immediately?

The message from H.Q. was brief: the King wished to see Major-General Kippenberger urgently. It was not long before the General was in His Majesty's study. They had a sherry together.[1]

The King turned the subject to Captain C. H. Upham. He remembered Upham's investiture only a few weeks before. Then, indicating the papers lying on his desk, he said: "I've spent an hour going through these new papers about Upham. I suppose you know—he has been recommended for a Bar to the Victoria Cross."

Kippenberger nodded.

The King continued: "It has very rarely been done, you know, General. Only twice before in nearly ninety years."

His Majesty studied the papers again for a minute. Then, looking up, he said firmly: "It would be very unusual indeed. But tell me, Kippenberger, what do you think? *Does he deserve it?*"

Kippenberger replied slowly: "In my respectful opinion, sir, Upham won the V.C. several times over."

The King looked at him thoughtfully for a few moments.

Then he said: "Well, thanks very much, General. Now . . . how are your arrangements going for getting your men home to New Zealand?"

Archibald Nicoll worked away silently. Charles sat in wooden stillness, prepared to co-operate only because it would see the unpleasant duty out of the way all the sooner. Sun streaked in through the skylight, the traffic noises of Christchurch coming as a subdued murmur from a distance.

Nicoll spoke. "You know, Charles, these two portraits are going to be different. You've got a different expression now from when I sketched the first one."

"What do you mean—different?"

"Well, your expression for the first portrait was more direct, more self-confident. That's how I've shown it. But today, I've really just observed, you're looking different. You're looking more withdrawn, not so confident, a bit cynical, if you don't mind my

[1] The conversation that follows is as reported to the author by the late General Kippenberger.

saying so. That's how I have to paint you, you know—just as I see you"

Upham grunted. So he looked different already, did he?

They worked on again quietly. Just an occasional word, a little lift of the head perhaps, a slight change in position.

Then almost before they knew it the man was in the room.

"I'm from the *Star-Sun*," he said briskly. "Heard I'd find you here. I understand you've had a telegram this morning, Captain Upham. We've had a flash about it. Could you confirm the news?"

Upham stared at him coldly. Nicoll paused. "What on earth is this all about? Was there some bad news in that telegram, Charles?"

Then Upham began arguing defensively with the reporter, a feeling of dismay growing on him second by second. Somehow he knew what he was in for. It was not exciting. It was frightening and depressing, making him feel that he would be a fool in the eyes of his friends. It was all a mistake. He was no different from the others. Why make him the one to be singled out and pointed at?

Then, as the reporter pressed him further, he despairingly handed over the telegram. The newsman read it eagerly, then handed it on to Nicoll. The telegram from the Minister of Defence, sent from Parliament Buildings, Wellington, read:

"I have learned with very great pleasure that you have been awarded a Bar to the Victoria Cross for most conspicuous bravery and devotion to duty in action. . . . The Prime Minister desires me to convey to you on behalf of the New Zealand Government his heartiest congratulations."

Archibald Nicoll looked up at Charles, his mouth open and his eyes wide. "And this is the wire you got this morning, Charles? And you just stuffed it in your pocket and said nothing? Goodness gracious me!"

The reporter from the *Star-Sun* went into action. He talked, and he questioned, and Nicoll resumed painting, and Charles continued sitting, fighting a losing battle. That night the paper said:

"Captain Upham, whose present role of artist's model does not sit altogether comfortably upon him, said that he had no idea of what particular incident might have prompted the recommendation for this new award. He was wounded in the El Ruweisat engagement and, as he put it, 'things were a bit hazy'. Captain Upham does not accept the view that he is now a figure of almost unique fame. 'I never did anything out of the ordinary, I can tell you that,' he protested at the suggestion that the whole Empire would be talking about him today. . . .''

In the hours that followed, the news that a New Zealand officer had won the Victoria Cross a second time swept the newspapers of the Commonwealth. The award of the Cross is reserved for valour of the highest order, and the comparative handful of men who receive it are for ever singled out from their fellows.

But for one man to win it *twice*—here indeed the unattainable, the impossible, had occurred.

Streamer headlines all over the British world hailed the news:

"HIS VOICE WAS HEARD ABOVE THE BATTLE"

"FIRST DOUBLE V.C. OF THE WAR FOR AN INCORRIGIBLE HATER"

"NEW ZEALAND HERO"

As if a torrent had suddenly been unleashed, a flood of admiring publicity suddenly descended on the reluctant Upham. To his family the news came bewilderingly. In the streets of Christchurch that day Charles's father found himself beset. A well-known local figure, he could make no headway along the footpaths on his way to lunch. He tried crossing the street. Cars stopped beside him and hands were outstretched towards him. It was difficult to reach the other side. There were more waiting for him there.

Towards evening, as the flood of telegrams and cables began to cover the Uphams' drawing-room, and the phone beat a never-ending clangour, Charles looked around for a place of retreat. There were reporters in the front hall, people waiting at the door, and so-called friends demanding to speak to him on the telephone. He darted into the bathroom, locked the door, and looked despairingly out of the window.

Mrs. Upham rang Allen Shand.

"Allen—do you think you could come over? There are newspaper reporters at the doors and Charles has gone and locked himself in the bathroom. His language is terrible. I think you might be able to help."

But Charles didn't wait. Finding a way out, he slipped unobtrusively to a friend's flat, let himself in like a fugitive from justice.

"Peter," he beseeched, "what's all this bloody rot about this Bar? What's it mean?"

"Oh, come off, Charlie. It simply means they've awarded you another V.C. That's all."

"But what on earth for? Are you sure that's what it is?"

Upham looked appealingly at his friend, hoping against hope that Peter was wrong, that his own understanding of it was wrong. Perhaps the explanation would come out later—something like merely a confirmation of his first V.C., but surely not *another* V.C.

"Read the paper yet, Charlie? They've printed the citation. It's for Minqar Qaim and Ruweisat."

Upham shook his head as if bewildered. "It's wrong, Peter, it's wrong. They shouldn't give it to me. What about all the others? We all did exactly the same things. Why pick on me? It just makes me a bloody fool."

Upham sneaked home that night hoping not to be seen. But outside the house there was gathered a group of boys from Christ's College, his old school. They stood outside the gate, sang the school song, and did a haka. Charles walked down to the gate, and looked in the eyes of boys who now occupied his old desk and his old bed, eyes that shone now with open hero-worship. To wish them all good luck was about all he could manage.

Meantime at the Christchurch Officers' Club they were talking about the effect it would have on Charles's life.

"What can we do for him? This sort of publicity will just about put him out on his feet. He loathes it so much."

One of them said: "Best thing I can think of is to pull any strings we've got to get Molly back as soon as possible. That would help."

London papers whose dead-lines missed the announcement made up for it in their next editions.

"FIRST COMBATANT TO WIN V.C. TWICE"
News Chronicle

"AT THE BOTTOM OF O.C.T.U. CLASS—BUT HE'S NOW A DOUBLE V.C."
Daily Sketch

"DOUBLE V.C. FOUGHT ON TILL HE COULD NOT MOVE"

"WON FIRST V.C. AS LIVE SKELETON"

and alongside a happy photo of Molly:

"SHE'S THE WIFE OF A DOUBLE V.C."

There had been two others in history who had won the Cross twice. Arthur Martin-Leake, of the Medical Corps, won his Cross in the Boer War for saving wounded at Vlakfontein on

8th February 1902, and gained his Bar on the Western Front in 1914. Noel Chevasse, another medical officer, performed the double during the Great War of 1914-18, again for saving wounded men under fire.

Theirs were great deeds. But never had a combatant soldier won two Crosses. That after nearly ninety years the feat should be performed by an inconspicuous man from the Dominions, one who impressed his instructors so little, made the event more remarkable.

Charles hated the publicity that followed.

When he arrived at supper-time at a smoke concert given to welcome home a draft of 650 men from England the hall rose and cheered. Charles acknowledged the acclamation, and all the other tributes, with polite modesty. Inside, his heart craved to be relieved of it all.

The local Christchurch paper's leader said:

> "Captain Upham's outstanding characteristic, apart from the determined courage and soldierly skill which earned his decorations, is the extraordinary modesty with which he wears them. . . . That he should wish to give the credit for his exploits to the men who served with and under him is typical. . . . Those who were privileged to hear his reply to the citizens' welcome in the Civic Theatre will remember not so much what he said as the manner of his saying it. He is no public speaker in the accepted sense of the term, but the sincerity of his utterances touched his audience to profound admiration for the qualities of heart and mind that they unconsciously revealed. . . ."

From men of his old platoon and company the letters arrived. There were messages from the Indian Army, from Returned Servicemen's Associations, from Governors-General, Prime Ministers, Archbishops, and Mayors. From England came a message from two ex-Colditz pals : "Many congrats. If you ever want two good stooges send for us."

And: "Hope Knapp reads English papers."

Charles set himself the task of answering every letter by hand, spurning the temptation of having a standard "thank-you" letter typed above his signature. It was a formidable task.

Then there came honours from one after another society and organization—life memberships, special functions, eulogies. And when the Lincoln College Old Boys' Association amended its constitution so as to provide for Upham to become its one and only life member the speaker said: "His brilliant leadership was exerted whether he was wounded or whole, well or ill, exhausted or rested, and he set an entirely new standard for those who would win the words 'For Valour'."

From the Prime Minister himself came an offer to fly Upham to England for the investiture of the Bar.

"I'm sure you understand," Charles's parents said to reporters, "that Charles is really tired and over-wrought with all this publicity." Charles and his mother stole off to an inaccessible seaside haven at Diamond Harbour, not far from Christchurch, but where there were no roads, telephone, or mail delivery.

For a fortnight Charles sank gratefully into the seclusion he longed for, free from the turmoil and the adulation, free to think of his own future and the life to which he would soon have to introduce Molly. He knew it must be farming. He could do a job as a farmer. He wanted nothing else than the sense of owning his own acres, far away and isolated, roaming for miles in the open air that no one else challenged. That would be real freedom, he thought. His own farm. . . .

Others, too, began thinking that Charles Upham should have his own farm—and what more fitting than that his fellow-citizens should give him one?

By now Charles was a public figure whose every word was listened to. Unused to public speaking, he found himself in positions where he was disclosing more and more the philosophies that had so long been private to him. Now, when he expressed his views, people listened.

It was just so on 11th October. That day the Government tendered a complimentary State Luncheon to all the New Zealand winners of the V.C. They gathered in the capital city, Wellington, at 1 p.m., Parliament itself specially adjourning to mark the occasion.

Deputizing for Prime Minister Fraser, who was ill, Mr. Walter Nash spoke feelingly of the debt due to our servicemen, and the special regard the country had for its greatest heroes. Then after a toast proposed by him, and seconded by the then Leader of the Opposition, Sidney Holland, Upham was called on to reply on behalf of the other V.C. winners present.

Speaking with his usual sincerity, Charles began by saying that the only circumstance that had brought him to the function was that he was the representative of 100,000 others whose exploits were as fitting of the reward as his. "Those exploits were only made possible through the sacrifice of others," he said. "In my case there were many others who did more than I did, but many were killed or wounded." He continued on to extol the virtues of the ordinary fighting New Zealand soldier. Then he concluded in a manner which, from its simplicity and earnestness, moved every one of his listeners. "One thing I want to ask . . . when these men come back people who are in a position to do so should show their thanks in a practical way. There will be among them men who are maimed, still suffering from wounds, ill, or mentally ill. They'll need homes, furniture, and jobs. Please show them your practical help and your greatest patience."

Charles returned to Christchurch after the luncheon to find that a committee was being formed. Its object—to present a farm to their famous, favourite son.

Ever since the Bar had been announced groups of people in Christchurch had been discussing some suitable form of public recognition for Upham's distinction. Such an honour as he had brought to his home town should not be merely accepted and unmarked. Even the Government had thrown out feelers for a "National Gift".

Those who knew Charles best were aware that his heart was set on becoming a farmer. He could become one all right. It was only a matter of how large a mortgage he could afford to shoulder. Those closest to him knew that he had little, if any, savings, and that his only cash resources would be Army back-pay.

On 17th October 1945 the Mayor of Christchurch called a large public meeting. One speaker said: "My committee believes that if Mr. Upham were financially independent his influence for good in the community would be given wider scope." He referred to Charles's exploits, predicting: "School children of the future will read in history books of his deeds of valour."

The meeting was of one mind. The war had revealed a man of greatness. Let him now be freed from the burden of onerous financial commitments—surely he had earned such a position?

They decided to launch a public appeal for £10,000, to be subscribed by the people of Canterbury. With that money they would buy the farm of Upham's choice and install him on it.

The appeal was immediately opened to the public and as quickly adopted by the proud people of Canterbury. The funds rolled in, reaped by the enthusiasm of the scheme's sponsors, aided gladly by the Press, local bodies, and other public organizations.

Over his head Charles saw it all happening, aware that something had started that he couldn't stop. In front of him loomed the wonderful prospect of a farm that he could call his own, debt-free, a gift from people who had not been called on to suffer and endure as he had done—a home for his bride.

Worried and uncomfortable, Charles thought it out from every angle. Of course it was a wonderful opportunity. The people of Canterbury might well resent it if he just brusquely refused.

But to Bill Allan, a friend of Weinsberg days, he confided his fears. "What would be the good, Bill, of having a farm, and every second person going past saying 'I put a hundred pounds into that place'? I'd never feel it was really mine."

"How could I accept it?" he said to his mother. "I'm alive and well. Think of the wives of those who haven't come back. I don't need the money; they do."

Mrs. Upham thought the same, but she asked Charles what he thought would happen if he accepted the gift.

"I'd lose all my friends," he replied surprisingly.

Charles waited for a time when he knew he would be alone for an hour. Then he got out pencil and paper, began to compose a letter. He laboured slowly over every word, intent on making sure that the letter expressed his feelings exactly.

When he was at last satisfied with his draft he wrote it out carefully in ink, sealed it up, and arranged for it to be delivered. It was addressed to the Mayor of Christchurch, Mr. E. H. Andrews.

"As you can imagine" [it began], "I am having great difficulty in composing this letter which I want you to read and pass on to the other gentlemen of the committee which met in this city and decided on behalf of the Canterbury Province to present me with a gift of money to purchase a farm.

I am deeply conscious of the honour intended to be bestowed upon me and I shall always carry with me the knowledge in my heart that the people of Canterbury wished to pay me such a wonderful tribute.

The military honours bestowed upon me are the property of the men of my unit as well as myself, and were obtained at considerable cost of the blood of this country. . . ."

In Christchurch the newspapers carried Charles's letter, handed on to them immediately by the mayor. The rest of it read:

". . . Under no circumstances could I consent to any material gain for myself for any services that I, in conjunction with 100,000 more, rendered to the Empire in her hour of peril, and

I most humbly request that you will understand my position in having to decline the Province's most generously intended gift.

This, as you all know only too well, was a war for survival; and if we had not had wholehearted support from all members of the Empire we would not have attained victory over our enemies. It would be unworthy of the occasion for any member of the Empire to have benefited in any way through having carried out his or her duty during the last six years.

Some of us have been fated to play a more glamorous role than others. Many serving overseas have not returned; others have returned unable to live a full life, condemned to disability and sickness, while I am little the worse for my experiences.

Could I suggest, sir, that the fund which you all so generously proposed to give me be used to alleviate genuine distress among the children of those men who gave their all for us, and to help brighten the lives of those men who because of some war disability are unable to lead a full life in the community.

Trusting, sir, that you will not think me ungracious and that you will convey my wishes in this matter to your fellow committeemen,

I am,

Yours sincerely,

Charles Upham."

The publication of this letter roused the people of New Zealand to an admiration and respect for Upham's personal character that had previously been reserved for his deeds on the field of battle. Now they saw that his personal qualities matched his heroic record.

Naturally leader-writers in the Press seized on such a display. One wrote:

". . . No one will read without sincere emotion the words that have come straight from the heart of this very great young New Zealander. . . . Independence and sincerity of spirit shine through his gracious refusal of a gift which lesser men would have found it difficult to reject. . . . His thoughts are still with those who lost their lives. . . . It may be hoped that his wishes will become the wishes of the people of Canterbury and that they will respond even more generously than they intended to the raising of the Charles Upham Fund to widen opportunities for the children of the fallen. It is a conception worthy of the man."

Canterbury did indeed respond to the new appeal and to the new object of Upham's choice. Over £10,000 was soon subscribed, while meantime the committee discussed ideas for carrying out the spirit of the gifts and the purposes Charles had in mind.

Finally the announcement was made. The money would go to a Charles Upham Scholarship Fund, to be held and administered by a group of trustees who would award scholarships to the sons of servicemen, tenable at either Lincoln College or Canterbury University.

Noble and generous in its conception, the Charles Upham Scholarship Fund remains to this day a living memorial to the stature of one man whose greatness has been that of character as well as action.

CHAPTER TWENTY

THE NEW LIFE

DEEP in every man's heart is the picture of the home, or the farm, that he would like. So it was with Charles. Before the war he spent some time working for Douglas Macfarlane, a sheep farmer in North Canterbury, who owned an isolated station known as Rafa Downs. When he dreamed of a farm, he dreamed of a place like Rafa.

It was before his return from England that Douglas Macfarlane rang Charles's parents and said: "I'm thinking of cutting up Rafa Downs into three farms and selling off two of them. I know Charles always liked Rafa, so I'd like to keep one of the two for him if he wants it."

Finding two ex-servicemen to settle on Rafa Downs became the task of the Land Settlement Board. One man was immediately available, but the other was not so easy to find. Phil Bennett, himself an ex-serviceman of the 1914-18 war, was the Board member given the task of locating a suitable second buyer.

Charles returned to New Zealand and Bennett very soon told him that a portion of Rafa Downs might be available to him. He found Upham very interested, but chary of any suggestion that he might receive special treatment.

"There'll be no special treatment," Bennett told him clearly. "If you take this farm you'll pay for it just like any other returned man. You'd better come to Wellington and talk it over."

Upham hedged. He muttered about publicity, his dislike of

being recognized and stared at. Bennett understood, and promised that the visit would be arranged secretly.

Indeed it was. An Air Force plane with a spare seat for Charles was laid on, and a few days later he was met at Wellington airport and brought to the Waterloo Hotel. Bennett was there waiting.

Bennett said: "First of all—is there anything you'd like to do—anything you want?"

"There's only one thing I want," Upham said shortly. "I don't want to be treated differently from any other bastard."

Bennett recoiled. He had expected the man to be highly strung and defensive—many ex-P.O.W.s were—but none had expressed themselves quite so violently. He paused, looked Upham over steadily, then said: "And why the bloody hell should you be?"

Upham stared at him for a few moments; then almost together the two men smiled at each other. They got on famously after that.

Charles's purchase of his portion of Rafa was put through the normal channels—the same mortgage obligations, the same interest, the same terms of repayment, as applied to thousands of other returned men going on the land. Meantime, he remained at his parents' home in Christchurch, waiting for Molly's return from England.

He lived, and behaved, as he chose. He bought a new hat, along with other civilian clothing. The hat looked far too new. He didn't like new things. They made one conspicuous. He pulled it around, kneaded it between his hands, then finally held it under a tap and rolled it dry in front of a fire. He wanted it to look old.

"I love horses," he blandly explained to his parents when one day they found a horse grazing on the lawn at the back of the house. "A man on a farm needs a horse and gig," he added.

"A *gig*?" they asked, prepared to be understanding, but a little stupefied at this one.

"Yes, a horse *and gig*. Mother—you'll have the first ride. I'm getting a gig tomorrow."

Sure enough, he arrived home next day with the horse harnessed to a genuine gig, fresh from the pages of the *Tatler* of 1905.

"Come on, Mother. She's an old race-horse, but I can hold her all right. One of you others hold her head, will you? Yes, I know the step's a bit high."

Mrs. Upham drew a very deep breath. It was trial enough to have a famous son. But now to have a horse and gig stabled on the back lawn, and to be asked to make a spectacle of herself like this on the sober streets of Christchurch—surely this was carrying independence too far.

Charles saw her hesitate. As if to reassure her he said: "You hop up first. Actually the moment she feels anyone on the step she tries to take off. So I'll follow up behind you quickly to make sure you get aboard all right."

Mrs. Upham had secret thoughts that it might work out quite differently—possibly that she might turn the corner into Rolleston Avenue at full gallop, clinging to the step with one foot, with Charles running vainly a hundred yards behind.

But, as she said later, she was determined she was not going to show that she was afraid or that she regarded this enterprise as at all odd. If Charles wanted to ride around in a gig, well, she'd humour him. The returned boys had had enough to put up with. Let them have their way when they came back home.

Manfully she approached the gig, placed her foot on the step, and, with an agility that surprised even herself, leapt up to the seat. Charles followed, and in a trice they were swinging away down Gloucester Street.

Charles smiled at her indulgently, as if to confirm that her unspoken fears had been groundless.

Past staring pedestrians they swung into Rolleston Avenue. Here now were the gates of Christ's College. Past them they swept and along the drive of stately homes that face on to Hagley Park. Turn right again, up through the suburban streets, into the city itself.

That this was an odd thing to do never occurred to him. He did it simply because he loved being close to a horse again; and he would never refrain from doing anything he wanted to simply because it was not "conventional". His mind possessed no sham, no shop-front concealing the wares behind. . . .

December was not long in coming. As the happy day came near, Charles took the overnight sea ferry to Wellington, where, at long last, Molly waved to him from the deck of the *Mooltan* as the ship came alongside.

As 1946 dawned, it was all activity as they moved to Rafa. Their new home was still in the architect's hands, the road to it was just being formed, but the farm was theirs to look at and to plan for.

Given the temporary use of a farmhouse nearby, while their own home was abuilding, Charles and Molly set about the making of their new world. For the site of their homestead they chose a high plateau that gave a vista of twenty miles of coastline.

Then came the announcement of the Victory Parade to be held in London, and that a New Zealand contingent would travel there for the occasion. As New Zealand's most illustrious son, Upham's name was freely mentioned as one of the certainties for the trip.

Only a few days passed before the phone at home rang. It was the Minister of Defence himself, the Honourable Fred Jones.

"We would like you to go to London for the Victory Parade, Captain Upham," came the request.

Charles called up all his reserves of tact and found several convincing excuses for refusing. Then there was another phone call from a high military figure. Again he refused.

A day or two passed, with Charles still determined, knowing that the draft of men to travel to London by sea was already assembling. Den Fountaine, one of his oldest friends of the 20th, would be one of the senior officers commanding the contingent— so there would be old times to talk about. But he looked out over his broken farm and counted the months before he could make it even modestly self-supporting.

The phone rang again. "Captain Upham? Hold the line, please. The Prime Minister wishes to speak to you." And the voice of the Premier, Peter Fraser, came through the under-sea phone cable. It was a long talk, the first of several, but Fraser won in the end. He put it on the basis of duty, and a call to duty was Upham's weak spot. So they flew him to London.

Reporting to New Zealand Headquarters in London, he was told a room had been set aside for him at the Fernleaf Club, where he could stay in reasonable comfort.

"Where are the others staying—the rest of the New Zealanders?" he asked.

"Oh, they're under canvas in Kensington Gardens," came the reply.

"That's where I'll be," Upham said shortly.

The march past at the Parade was a spectacular occasion, with the forces of the Commonwealth presenting a very pageant of the earth's people. The V.C.s were in the rear rank and on the flank nearest to the saluting base. Charles himself was on the nearest end of the line. But he had never been a good parade-ground soldier, and it was only because the others liked him so much that they didn't berate him for the New Zealanders' scraggy display as the last rank marched past the King. For Charles unconsciously began stepping short, and at the vital moment the New Zealand line became a dog's leg.

Whether or not the King noticed it, it did not dim his warmth when a few minutes later he sighted Upham amongst the troops lining the walks in Kensington Gardens, down which His Majesty slowly moved. Signalling the Queen to join him, he moved to Charles, and the three talked animatedly for several minutes.

The phone began ringing again in 1950. This time it concerned the opening of a memorial in Greece, erected by that nation to the memory of the British, Australian, and New Zealand forces who had come to Greece's aid in 1941. Would Charles consent to go as part of a very small New Zealand delegation?

Once more the Minister of Defence rang. Once more the call came from the Prime Minister. But Charles seemed adamant this time.

Then Kip rang: Major-General Kippenberger—then editor-in-chief of the official New Zealand War Histories, with his two painful artificial feet.

"Charlie—I'd like you to go to Greece," Kip said.

"I can't—I've got my shearing to do."

"I knew you'd say that, so I've already arranged with one of your neighbours to do it for you. So you'd better come. In fact you're booked on the plane two days from now."

"Will you be going?" Charles asked.

"Yes—just the two of us," Kip said.

It was a rush to get ready for the official luncheon at the Palace. Kip was still doing up his uniform jacket as they boarded the taxi. It would be inconceivable for them to be late—at the very function where they were to be officially received and honoured by King Paul and Queen Fredericka.

"Oh, my God!" Kip said suddenly. "Look at my medals. These Greek ones—they're upside down. Help, what'll we do?"

Charles said: "Well, it's too late to turn back. We'll change them over as we go."

So as the taxi sped across Athens they wrestled with Kippenberger's coat, got it off over his shoulders and then, while he sat in his braces, they feverishly undid the offending medals, turned them round, and pinned them on again. Kip was in a bath of perspiration, and only just struggling into the jacket again, as the taxi door was swung open by the officer of the reception guard.

The presentations were almost immediate. His Majesty . . . Her Majesty . . . Her Royal Highness . . . His Excellency . . . the Prince . . . General . . .

The two New Zealanders passed slowly down the receiving line. Then Kip came to the Crown Prince of ——. They shook hands, exchanged a word, and then Kip's eyes became suddenly riveted on the row of medals adorning the Crown Prince's chest.

For a second he was speechless and his jaw seemed to drop.

Because the Crown Prince wore the same Greek decorations as Kippenberger did himself. But—one of them was *upside down*, just like Kippenberger's had been; not only that, another was on *sideways*.

Kip's eyes fell to the ground, and he suffered yet a further blow —for below his brilliant uniform the Crown Prince was wearing *suède shoes*.

"We needn't have bothered, Charlie," Kip whispered as they passed on down the line.

For Charles the function became a great success. After lunch King Paul drew him into a corner, and for about an hour monarch and man had their heads together, swopping reminiscences, laughing hugely at each other's jokes. Then it seemed quite within recognized limits when Charles cheerfully asked Queen Fredericka what it was really like to be a Queen. Just as cheerfully she replied: "One thing I like about it is that I always get the best seat on the train."

All in all, it seems to have been a very successful party.

CHAPTER TWENTY-ONE

PASSING DAYS

THE years are passing now over Charles's and Molly's home on Rafa Downs. It is seven miles to the nearest pretension of a settlement at Hundalee, which is hardly more than a general store. From Hundalee the road follows the rushing Conway River, crosses over, then opens out into the coastal slopes. From the rocky shore of the South Pacific the land sweeps first gradually, then steeply, up into the hills. Here on the seaward slopes, in secluded freedom, locked by mountain and sea, Charles has his peace. Around his home the sheep multiply each year, his cattle grow fat, more of his 1200 acres become fit for grazing, and the brutal labour of the first hard years is a little lighter.

They have three children—all girls. Twins first—Amanda and Virginia (whereupon an old 20th friend infuriatingly said:

"Charles, you can't help doing everything *double,* can you?").
Then came Caroline, the youngest.

They have had their years of difficulty, like many others. But
Charles had his farm in good shape by the time a world rise in
wool prices suddenly made the burden easier. It was hard labour
at first! Hardship struck them early. In December 1946, before
the house was even finished, and they were living with friends on
another part of Rafa, Charles suffered an accident. While pouring
petrol into his car by the light of a hurricane lantern, he spilt
some on the grass. There was a flash and a flare, and in a moment
his trouser leg was alight.

"Your husband's swearing terrifically," a friend told Molly.
"He says it's nothing, but I think he's been burnt. He's beating
himself with a sack."

Next morning Charles again said that there was nothing wrong,
and that he was fit to drive the hundred miles to Christchurch for
a conference with the builder. He drove the car silently, deliberately proceeded with the conference, then made one or two calls
he had planned.

Only then did he consent to go to hospital for examination.
Within an hour he was in the operating theatre. Charles was in
hospital and convalescent home for over four months.

There have been attempts to persuade him into politics, but as
yet he has not succumbed. Locally, however, he has taken his
share on Boards and in small public administration. More
recently he has been appointed to the Board of Governors of his
old school, Christ's College.

He has gradually, but reluctantly, become accustomed to his
role as an heroic public figure. In the early post-war years his
rejection of this role was uncompromising, and he defiantly shut
himself away on his isolated farm. That was at a time when he
was less tolerant, and more dogmatic, about many things on
which he has since mellowed.

But while resisting the status that his decorations imposed on
him he has never shirked that status if he thought it a point of
duty. At Returned Services' Association functions he has readily
accepted the role of speaker, he has opened bridges, given away
school prizes. When New Zealand undertook to send troops to
the fighting in Korea, Upham lent his name and his voice in a
national radio appeal for volunteers. And, in a smooth reversal
of his former role as the recipient of awards, Charles has himself
reviewed troops and has pinned pilots' wings on Air Force cadets
at their passing-out parade.

Especially amongst his old battalion comrades there has never been anything held back. Charles never passes an old 20th man in the street. There is a barman here, a tobacconist there, a man driving a taxi, working in a shop, office or factory, a farmer from the Canterbury Plains. Each is met with a warmth and affection that shows no reserve. Eric Le Gros, too, sees Charles from time to time, and they chuckle together over some of their unmilitary adventures.

The 20th had its birth in Christchurch, and every few years its reunion draws hundreds of former members. Upham never misses, and there are the shouted greetings, the back-slapping, the drinking of good beer, the silence for the fallen, and the pride which all of them feel, not just for Charles and their other decorated men, but for one another.

It was not till 1952 that "Hoppy" Hopgood managed to attend his first 20th reunion. It was a far cry back to the days in the desert when he had been Charles's driver.

What a queue of V.I.P.s, Hoppy thought—Freyberg himself, Kippenberger, Jim Burrows, General Inglis, Charlie—all standing in a row shaking hands.

"Here—sign this, boss, will you?" Hoppy asked, pushing a menu card towards Charles.

Upham looked up. His face broke into a smile. "Hoppy! It's you!" Then he whispered surreptitiously: "I say, Hoppy . . . like to take the truck tonight, no questions asked?"

The Queen and the Duke of Edinburgh, the Queen Mother, Anthony Eden, Montgomery . . . as royalty and other notables travel through New Zealand it is always Charles Upham requested by the Government to be amongst the special guests. It is Upham who often appears alongside them in the Press photographs.

"What were you and the Queen nattering about all that time, Charlie?"

"Come on, Charlie, give a little. The Queen was talking to you so long it made the party look like a duet. What does she know?"

Charles shrugged his shoulders, looked rather wonderingly over to where the Queen was now busy talking with another group. Then he turned back and said: "What does she know? I'll tell you *one* thing. She knows a bloody lot more about horses than anyone else I've ever met. And that's what we were talking about."

In 1956 came another journey overseas when the Victoria Cross Centenary Celebrations were held in London. With other New

Zealand holders of the Cross, or their next of kin, Charles and
Molly flew to England in an Air Force transport and shared in
the ceremony.

He is still a complex personality. Now and then he will show
a spark of that old irrational obstinacy, and some of his opinions
may appear too rigid in these modern days when "flexibility" is a
convenient word for vacillation. But the tales told about him, his
own humility, and his utter indifference to personal appearance
(despite Molly's efforts) have long conspired to present a false
picture of his personality; that is, to those who do not really
know him.

The true picture today, however, is of a man deeply thoughtful
and intelligent, one whose opinions are sought and respected. He
has become the confidant of many of New Zealand's leading
figures. They like to hear him talk, for they find his views always
fresh and refreshing.

The keen brain, capable of dedication to a single, unwavering
object, cloaked in modesty, and, sometimes, roughness—that is
the picture.

He doesn't swear as much as in the old days. To his family and
friends his voice is quiet, his manner calm. But once in a while,
if a sharp word is called for, there is a lift, a ring, to his voice that
has almost an electrical effect. The voice rising above the din of
the battlefield seems suddenly real and understandable.

And what of his attitude now to his awards—still the only combatant ever to have won two V.C.s?

The same as ever; just like the reception in London in 1956
when Admiral the Earl Mountbatten approached Charles and
noticed he was not wearing his medals—as prescribed by the order
of dress for the occasion. When he asked him why, Charles rather
sheepishly produced them from amongst the loose change in his
trouser pocket, saying: "My wife made me bring them."

On his way to London in 1956 an interviewer pressed him to
describe the circumstances of the occasions for which he received
his two V.C.s. Charles is older, wiser, than in his more brusque
earlier days of fame. So this was his answer: "The circumstances?
Well . . . it is a long time ago now. I have *forgotten*." Forgotten?
you ask.

Locked deep away in memory, perhaps, so deep that few people
have ever known the real thoughts, the real attitude of mind, that
accompanied the deeds of those long-gone, more dramatic days.

But forgotten? No. And as the years relentlessly push further
into history the events of 1939-45, may the rest of us never forget,

or allow to be forgotten, how the young men of those times struggled to preserve their world for the younger ones who enjoy it today.

Surely they were the men with the Mark of the Lion upon them.

Soon after the war they published a book about the prisoners of Colditz.[1] There are portraits of many of the captives, with pen-pictures of their doings and their personalities. It is a book which is a monument as well as a history. Opposite a full-page portrait of Charles Upham are a few words, set in small type in the centre of an otherwise empty page, and looking insignificant, though in a way impressive, against the blank whiteness of the rest of the sheet. The words are:

CAPTAIN C. H. UPHAM, V.C. AND BAR

New Zealand Military Forces

An officer and a gentleman—determination and singleness of purpose personified—loyal, constructive, quiet, unassuming, and friendly.

[1] *Detour.* Edited by Lieutenant J. E. R. Wood, M.C. (Falcon Press).

THE GAUNT WOMAN

John Blackburn

*"The Gaunt Woman" is published by
Jonathan Cape Ltd.*

The Author

John Blackburn is by trade a bookseller. He would rather have been a lion tamer or a racing motorist, and so to fill up what he thought was a lack of excitement in his life he became a thriller-writer. His novel, *A Scent of New-Mown Hay*, was a great success when published here and has now reached the half-million mark in America. It is being filmed in "Smellorama".

CHAPTER ONE

At nine o'clock sharp, Sir Martin Rolfe, Financial Adviser to Her Majesty's Treasury, was at his desk. By eleven he had read and answered the thirty-two letters which required his personal attention, and spoken on the telephone to the minister, an air chief marshal, and a trade union leader. By twelve he had given his comments on a road development scheme, two defence estimates, and a pay claim in nationalized industries: total sum involved—one hundred and thirty million pounds. At exactly one minute past twelve he initialed the last folder and closed it.

"Well, that seems to be the lot." Rolfe's voice had every trick of modulation that Winchester, Cambridge, and generations of security could give, but it sounded like a machine; a beautifully-tuned instrument which could repeat sounds but had no life of its own.

"Yes, that should be quite satisfactory, I think." He pushed the file away from him and leaned back in his chair, feeling the tiny, familiar stab of pain that the least effort seemed to cause him nowadays: too many conferences, too many decisions to be made, too many memories—too much of one memory in particular. He put the last thought quickly out of his mind, and reached towards the box his secretary held out to him.

"Thank you, Mr Arabin." He took a cigarette and lit it with his own lighter. This was the end of the ritual which told him his morning's work was finished. He waited impatiently for the man to gather up the papers, and leave him with his own thoughts for half an hour: the only waking period he allowed to them.

"Excuse me, sir. I hate to bother you about something which is probably trivial, but . . ." Michael Arabin spoke slowly and carefully as always. He had been over two years in England, but he still had to be careful. Figures of course were easy for him—figures and balance-sheets added up the same way in any language, and he could read them like a novel. But the turn of a phrase, the exact meaning and pronunciation of a word so often evaded him, and he spoke slowly and carefully, as though his job depended on it; it probably did. His employer was not a man to suffer fools gladly.

"Well, what is it, Mr Arabin?" Rolfe pulled hard at his cigarette, watching the grey smoke drifting upwards to the ceiling like the trail of the lost years which had made him what he was. Yes, always upwards; honorary professor of a Cambridge college, chairman of twenty committees, author of a dozen standard works on economics, chief financial adviser to the British Treasury. "I thought that was the last of them."

"Yes, sir, the last of the official correspondence, that is." Arabin reached in his pocket and placed something on the desk. "This came in the morning post, sir. As I said, it is probably of no importance, but I didn't like to open it."

"No, I can see that for myself." Rolfe leaned forward, looking at the envelope in front of him. It was crumpled and stained and looked quite out of place against the gleaming mahogany of the desk, the snow-white blotter, and the shining row of pens. The address was written in a sprawling hand that might have belonged to a child or a very old and feeble person.

Sir Martin Rolfe
c/o The Home Office

Above the address there was another line printed in thick black ink:

Let him open this himself if you value your jobs

"How very curious, Mr Arabin." The man had been with him for some time now, but Rolfe would never think of dropping the formal title. "This seems a little stronger than normal, but it will be one of the usual things, I suppose; the work of a lunatic or a beggar. How many did we get last month? Yes, seventeen I seem to remember. What poor, foolish people there are in the world!" He picked it up and reached for his paper-knife.

"Yes, sir, you're most probably right. All the same"—Arabin broke off slightly and there was an odd look of embarrassment on his face—"all the same, I wouldn't open it if I were you. I'd just put it in the fire. You see, when I was a young man I studied calligraphy, and there's something about this writing I don't like; something very unpleasant about it." He watched Rolfe's hand sliding the knife into the flap of the envelope, and he thought of the coldness of the man, and his ruthlessness, and the long years he had spent climbing up to his present position. He must have made a lot of enemies on his way; a whole army with reasons for hating Sir Martin Rolfe.

"Do you really think so, Mr Arabin? How very interesting."

Rolfe smiled slightly and started to cut the flap with a slow, deliberate movement. "Your concern for my welfare does you credit, but what do you really imagine we are going to find? A poisoned needle to prick my thumb perhaps? A sheet of blotting-paper soaked in germ culture? No, you are a Hungarian, Mr Arabin, and though for all I know these things may happen in your country, we are in England now."

He pulled a single page of crumpled, greyish paper from the envelope and started to read. Like the address, the writing was in that strangely childish or senile hand. He was still smiling as he read.

And, all at once, quite suddenly and without any warning, something began to happen to Rolfe's face. The smile left those carved, academic features and they went slack. The eyes seemed to glaze over, the thin mouth fell open, and a long gasp came from deep down in his body. For perhaps five seconds he sat like that, quite still and staring at the letter, and then, as though it were the hardest and most important action of his life, he reached for the cigarette-lighter. The sheet of paper curled, darkened, and glowed orange. As he watched it, he suddenly seemed to see a face in that flame. The face was his own and it was melting.

"God!" he said, quite oblivious of Arabin standing beside him. "God! God! Dear God!" Over and over again he said it. Then the room dimmed and swung sideways, something like a steel spike started to come out through the centre of his chest, and he fell to the floor.

*   *   *

Freude, schöner Götterfunken,
Tochter aus Elysium . . .

Nicholas Malendin, sometime gunner's mate on the Imperial Russian battleship *Tsarevitch,* did not believe in God, but he was very fond of classical music.

He half sat, half lay back in his big chair by the window, staring out over the Kremlin skyline, and there was a look of pure pleasure in his eyes, though he couldn't smile. By and large the plastic surgeons had done a wonderful job on his face, but there was still a certain stiffness about it when the wind was cold. From the other side of the vast room of plush and gilt, a record-player gave a surprisingly noisy rendering of Beethoven's Ninth Symphony, and Malendin's right leg beat in time to the music. His left was stretched stiffly in front of him, for it was steel and its original had been buried years ago under the rubble of Stalingrad. The highest decoration of the state gleamed on his chest and his shoulders bore the epaulets of a colonel, but these weren't the important things about Malendin. The important thing was a little plastic card in his pocket which named him head of Department Five of M.V.D., that section of the Soviet Intelligence Service dealing with Western Europe.

Alle Menschen werden Brüder
Wo dein sanfter Flügel weilt.

The chorus climbed to its final climax and the record ground into silence. With surprising agility for seventy-five years and a crippled body, Malendin pulled himself out of his chair and crossed to a telephone by the desk. The phone was fitted with a light instead of a bell, for he hated unnecessary noise, and the light had been flashing for the last three minutes. He was quite aware of this, but would never have dreamed of interrupting Beethoven. Besides, until ten seconds ago the time had been part of his lunch break, and like a good socialist he stuck to the terms of his agreement.

"Oh, it's you, Peter," he said, lifting the receiver. "Yes, I want to see you for a few minutes. Something rather interesting has come up." The scar tissue beneath his eyes forced itself into a crinkle, for his caller was an old friend and they had dropped the formal address of "comrade" years ago.

"Yes, come up right away, please. I'll look forward to seeing you—have a drink waiting as well." He replaced the phone and dragged his steel foot to a cabinet in the corner of the room. He hummed slightly as he did so, and as he lifted out bottle and glasses, he looked exactly what he was not: a jovial old gentleman without a care in the world or an unpleasant thought in his head.

The man who came into the room a moment later was medium built, medium coloured, and just approaching middle age. His hair was starting to thin and he wore a dark, rather shabby suit with leather-bound elbows. He had a wife and two children whom he adored, and he lived in a flat which he was constantly redecorating. His job fascinated him, but he would never get to the top, for he was without ambition. Men like him could be seen in any suburban train anywhere in the world, and he was the typical high-ranking subordinate, the first assistant, the right-hand man who stuck to the book and the rules of the job—any job. His name was Peter Vanin, and in his time he had killed two women and more men than he cared to remember—one of them with his bare hands.

"Ah, there you are, Peter. Come in and sit down. Family all right? Good." Malendin pushed a glass towards him and raised his own. "Well, here's luck to both of us."

He threw back the vodka in a single, practised movement and eased himself comfortably in the chair. There was a big buff folder on the desk and he picked it up, balancing it in his hand for a moment.

"This came in yesterday," he said, "from the Hungarians as it happens, which is in itself an extraordinary thing. Our loyal allies are usually so reluctant to part with any crumbs they manage to pick up. It may be of no value at all, or it could be very useful; a lever to cause a great deal of trouble in certain quarters. I'll give you the details in a moment, but first I want an opinion from you. You are said to have the knack of summing up a person's character from his face, so tell me about this man. What do you see in this face?"

"Very well, I'll have a try, Colonel, but I'm not a miracle-worker."

Vanin took the photograph Malendin handed him from the file and held it to the light. It was a very studied photograph, and it showed a tall man in a beautifully-cut suit standing before a table with a pile of books beside him. The man was smiling, and the photographer had gone to a lot of trouble to get just the right amount of strength, honesty and friendliness into that wide, posed smile.

"Yes, a very bright boy." Vanin's hand drummed quietly on the desk as he studied the picture. "He is either British or American, and nearer sixty than fifty. He is running to fat, but until a few years ago was probably very thin. He is used to power, but I should say that his power comes through people rather than over them. He is probably the possessor of some highly specialized skill. There is something I don't trust in the face; no, not exactly dishonesty, but I wouldn't rely on him. I would say that he is hiding something all the time."

"Good, Peter." Malendin's voice had the hearty ring of the schoolmaster complimenting a prize pupil. "Now, tell me something else. Could this man be broken?"

"Could he be broken?" Vanin raised his eyebrows slightly. "Yes, of course. As you know, anybody can be broken—if one finds the right pressures, that is. All the same"—he shook his head as he studied the photograph—"I don't think this man would break easily. Now, who is he, Colonel, and why does he interest us?"

"His name is Sir Martin Rolfe and you should have heard of him." Malendin pulled a sheet of typescript from his folder. "He is an economist, and if we play our cards right, he may become a very valuable ally."

"May he indeed! Yes, I seem to remember the name."

Vanin took the paper, and as he read, the picture seemed to become a living person. "Yes, as I said, a bright boy. Fellow of Blenheim College, Cambridge, nineteen twenty-five to thirty— Visiting Professor to Detroit University to thirty-eight—Civil Servant in the Ministry of Supply during the War—Permanent Secretary for five years after that. Yes, a full life. Publications include *An Approach to Economic Regeneration, The Avoidance or Cure of Diminishing Returns*. Present positions held: Emeritus Professor of Blenheim College, and Financial Adviser to the British Treasury. Yes, an important man, Colonel, but why the sudden interest in him now? I'm also curious to know why you used the term ally. A man like that could only be our bitterest enemy."

"Quite right on the surface, Peter, but only on the surface. People change, you know, and their views and loyalties alter. Well, I wonder if it might be possible to change the loyalties of Sir Martin Rolfe."

"Go on, Colonel, you're beginning to interest me."

"Thank you, I was hoping I might." Malendin's hand ran slowly across his cheek. The skin beneath it felt strangely like tissue-paper. "Now, we know that Rolfe is a very able and influential man. As an economist he is trusted by the British Government, and holds the position of Chief Financial Adviser to the Treasury. More important than that, the Minister, Lord Tremayne, is said to rely on him completely. And at the end of this month Tremayne goes to Washington for a conference concerning the pound-dollar exchange rate. Rolfe goes with him, and the British line will be exactly what Rolfe suggests."

"And so?"

"And so, my dear Peter, I've been wondering. I've been wondering if it might not be possible to sabotage that conference. Tremayne is a politician, not an economist, and he will take whatever advice Rolfe gives him. Well, suppose Rolfe gave the wrong advice—suppose they tried to push the Americans too far, and set the pound at an absurdly high figure. Then, I think, we might hit them where it really hurts: at home and in their pockets. Yes, we might hurt the British Lion very badly without anyone knowing we had a hand in it. As their own saying goes:

'There are more ways of killing a cat than choking it with cream.'
I can see some interesting possibilities, Peter."

"Yes, so can I." Vanin considered for a moment, and he saw
quite clearly what Malendin meant: the value of the pound set
far too high, and the flow of foreign money into Britain cut off
as though by a tap. He saw British production slowing down
because their goods were too expensive to sell, and the British
unemployment figures starting to grow. The rest was easy to
follow—closed factories, strikes and industrial unrest. And at the
end, a general election with a left-wing, pacifist government
coming home at a canter. The dream of the department for years:
no more rocket bases on British soil and the end of the Anglo-
American alliance, once and for all.

"But why, Colonel?" he said. "Why should Rolfe give the
wrong advice?"

"Perhaps because I ask him to give it." Malendin smiled and
suddenly he looked like a cat who knows the mouse is very near
to him. "A little bird told me something about Rolfe, Peter. He
told me that the man is frightened—he is terrified out of his wits.
And if we could learn what frightens him, if we knew that, then
I wouldn't be a bit surprised if Sir Martin Rolfe did exactly what
I told him to do."

The smile left his face, and when he spoke again he was simply
the professional policeman marshalling his facts.

"There is a man in London called Arabin," he said. "Michael
Arabin, a Hungarian traitor, who got out of the country during
the last uprising. He thought that his family had left too, by
another route, but he was wrong. They are still in Budapest, and
this makes Arabin a very unhappy man. Well, to cut the story
short, Arabin settled in England and got a job as Rolfe's secretary.
He is an economist himself, and Rolfe is the kind of do-gooder
who would employ a refugee rather than a fellow-countryman.
At any rate, he has worked for Rolfe for over nine months. Now,
those are all the facts we have been able to check on. For the rest,
we merely have Arabin's word. It seems that a week ago he called
at the Hungarian embassy in London and spoke to their security
officer. He told him that he had an important piece of information
regarding Rolfe which he was prepared to sell. The price was his
family being allowed to leave Hungary."

"I see." For a second Vanin considered his own family. He
imagined that in similar circumstances he might act very much
as Arabin had done. "What was Arabin's information, Colonel?"

"He told the Hungarians that during the last six weeks Rolfe has been receiving certain letters which might well be the build-up to a blackmail attempt. At any rate, the man is terrified of them. The first one was enough to give him a minor heart attack. Arabin's description of his opening it was rather vivid. He said he looked like a devil who had been too long in the fire. When he had read the letter he just managed to burn it and then he fainted."

"Did he indeed?" Vanin glanced at the photograph before him. "I'd be very interested to know what that letter contained. As I said, I don't think this man would break easily."

"No, but according to Arabin he is breaking now. Since the first letter arrived, there have been three more, and Rolfe is going to pieces—hardly eats at all, sleeps badly, relies on drugs to keep him going. No, there doesn't seem to have been any demand for money as yet. Arabin says he is almost sure that Rolfe doesn't even know the identity of the writer. He can't swear to it, of course, but he thinks that only the last letter could have contained an address."

"The last letter! You mean——" Vanin leaned forward in his chair.

"Yes, we have that letter all right. Arabin got his hands on it eight days ago, but he didn't give it to Rolfe. He stole it from Rolfe's desk and handed it over to the Hungarians as proof of his good faith, though he removed the address. He will let us have the address in return for his family."

Malendin pulled half a sheet of greyish paper from his folder. He looked slightly embarrassed as he handed it to Vanin.

"This seems crazy, Peter, but we have to be sure. Very possibly it's just a hoax on Arabin's part, but we must know."

"Yes, I think we should know."

Vanin grinned and took the paper. It was stained and crumpled and had been cut across the top. There were just two lines of sprawling writing and a matchstick drawing that might have been done by a child. The drawing showed a tall figure in a skirt standing before a shop window. There was a rope tied in a noose round the figure's neck, and the words above the drawing read: *I am still thinking of the gaunt woman who can blast you.*

"The gaunt woman—well, well! And this piece of nonsense, or something like it, was enough to give Martin Rolfe, the great economist, a heart-attack." Once again Vanin glanced at the photograph. "I wonder what you've been up to, my friend. I really wonder. Well, Colonel, just where are we? This is either a hoax on Arabin's part, or somebody with a rather nasty sense of humour has got his hooks into Rolfe. I don't think it's a hoax. If Arabin had wanted to invent something, he'd have been much more subtle. Have our handwriting people seen this yet?"

"Oh, yes, and I've been through their report. The note appears to have been written by an old person in poor health. The writer was almost certainly male, though they can't swear to that. They seem sure of the type of person, though. Whoever wrote this, Peter, was mentally ill. Yes, it's intriguing, isn't it, a person who is mentally sick. A powerful person, though, with something important to tell us. And if we can find him, Peter, if we can find him and make him talk—then I might hold Martin Rolfe in the hollow of my hand." He laid his hand on the desk as he spoke, and slowly flexed the fingers: a hard, strong hand that would finish a job, whatever the circumstances. "Yes, we'll get on to Budapest at once, I think—tell them we'll take over this business, and they can let Arabin know he'll be having a visitor. And I don't think I'd better involve any of our regular groups in England. The British Intelligence are rather good, and we can't afford the risk. We'll have to send out someone from here, I'm afraid. Someone who knows England well, but hasn't been there for a long time. Someone whose character is without blemish—eh, Peter? You understand me, don't you?"

"Yes, I understand you."

Vanin watched his face, and all at once the slightly cynical expression seemed to leave Malendin's eyes and he looked what he really was—a machine, or part of a machine, that had been designed in the days of violence and went on turning as its makers intended, and would go on turning like that, till it wore out or was destroyed. Policies might change, politicians alter, but the department didn't alter, and men like Malendin didn't change. His face was that of the old, unrelenting Bolshevik—the fanatic who couldn't stop, for he had sounded the trumpet which would never call retreat.

"I understand, Colonel," said Vanin, and he smiled slightly: the prim, accepting smile of the official, the professional who did a job. "I also think that you're quite right. There is no choice."

"No, there isn't any choice, Peter, though personally I'm very sorry. You see, this will be more the work for a detective than a spy, and that was once your job. Also, you were in London during the war, attached to our embassy staff. Finally, I can trust you completely."

"Yes, you can trust me, Colonel." Vanin pushed back his chair, feeling nothing but weariness and hoping that he might at least have time to say goodbye to his family. "When shall I leave?"

"Let's see." As though planning a holiday trip, Malendin opened his drawer and consulted a battered notebook. "Rolfe leaves for Washington on the twenty-fifth, which gives us very little time. All the same, I don't want to take any chances. Yes, there is a reconnaissance trawler leaving Archangel on Friday; that will do nicely. We'll have a full day to work out papers and contacts. I'll see that our people over there give you full co-operation. Till tomorrow then. I'll have everything ready for you."

He stood up as Vanin moved to the door. Just before he reached it he called him back. "Peter," he said, "you may or may not be going on a wild-goose chase, but if not, I want that information. I want it very badly, and I also want you to remember one thing: there is always a way. People lock valuables up in safes. Well, safes may be little tin boxes, or great steel and concrete vaults, but they always have one thing in common: a door, and a key to open it. And that's what I want from you, Peter. I want a key. I want the knowledge of that old and mentally-sick person which is the key to Sir Martin Rolfe. I don't mind how you go about it, but find me that key. Goodbye for the present."

He watched the door close behind the man he might well be sending to his death, and then he went back to the desk and poured himself another drink. As he did, his eyes fell on the sheet of paper and the little matchstick drawing. He smiled and raised his glass to the photograph beside it.

"Well, Sir Martin," he said, "here's to her! Here's to the Gaunt Woman who can blast you!"

CHAPTER TWO

Fog like smoke above the hills, a gun firing every ninety seconds from the cliffs, and, out to sea, a dark shape rising and falling on the Atlantic swell. Western Ireland and the Soviet trawler *Luba K* coming in against the tide.

The naval lieutenant leaned against the wheel-house bulkhead, and he was almost blind in the night and the fog, but that didn't worry him in the slightest. He trusted his navigation. He trusted his radar. Besides, the signal gun from the lighthouse on shore told him exactly where he was. The thing that worried him was the normal headache of every Russian sea-captain off a foreign coast: the constant threat of desertion. The ship was still two miles out, but already most of the crew were confined to quarters.

Once again the gun boomed out across the water, and his hand came hard down on the engine telegraph. Then he turned to the man at his side.

"All right, Comrade, this is it. A couple of miles over there is Mizen Point, where we part company." There was no trace of regret in his voice, for like all sailors he was superstitious. He had carried these people before, and he thought of them as Jonahs, bringers of bad luck. At the moment, he had just one wish: to put a few miles between the shore and the ambitions of his crew.

"You all ready?"

"Yes, I'm ready." Peter Vanin looked at the suitcase at his feet. It, and the clothes he wore, had been bought six months ago in a New York store for just such an emergency. Together with the papers in his pocket, they proclaimed him an American tourist recently landed at Shannon. He also had a wallet containing a book of traveller's cheques, and beside the wallet there rested a big, old-fashioned fountain-pen. That pen had taken several months of a craftsman's life to perfect, and if one knew its secret, one could do rather more than write with it. A slight twist on the body and the nib mechanism would slide back to show the open muzzle behind it. It fired three soft-nosed bullets and was a very horrible little weapon in the hands of a professional. These were all that Vanin had: his tools against the West.

There was also one other piece of equipment which was just as basic to his trade: a little plastic cylinder of poison, screwed to his back teeth. Colonel Malendin was a careful man, and his agents took no chances. If things went wrong one bite on that capsule would put a stop to all questions and all fear.

"Yes, I'm ready, Comrade Lieutenant," he said again, knowing that it was a lie, that he wasn't ready, that his body was soft and tired, and he'd sat too long in offices for this sort of job. All the same, it was his job, and his body would just have to make the best of it. He would have despised Malendin if anybody else had been sent. "Let's go, shall we?"

He picked up the case and moved out of the wheelhouse, feeling the fog like a blanket across his face and hearing the gun bellow again across the water, followed by a long echo from the hills behind. The signal station must be almost dead ahead, and he supposed they would go on firing till the fog lifted. With its engines cut, the trawler seemed like a little burnt-out world; a space ship doomed to drift for ever in a vacuum. It was a cramped, uncomfortable world, but at least warm, and he hated to leave it.

"You'll put a good man in the boat, won't you?"

"Yes, don't worry about that."

The lieutenant looked at the shadowy figures lowering the dinghy into the water, and his mind was on his own worry: the constant dread that, one day, enough would-be deserters might lead to mutiny. "My bos'n, Matushenko, is taking you over. He's been with this old tub since she was first commissioned, and you can rely on him all right. His main problem will be to find his way back to us when he's put you ashore." He took Vanin's case and dropped it down to a man in the boat. Then he held out his hand.

"Still, that's not your problem, Comrade," he said, feeling the slight tremble in Vanin's fingers and the coldness of his grip. Though his one ambition was to get rid of him quickly, there was a sudden pity in his eyes. "Well, goodbye now, and good luck. Lots of luck, though I hope you won't need it."

He watched Vanin swing out on to the rope-ladder, then he moved back into the chart-room to make out his log. One stuck to the rules in the Soviet service and every event had to be punctually recorded.

The fog seemed much thinner in the boat, swirling above them in streams but leaving a clear gap over the water, and Vanin could see the full length of the dinghy quite clearly. He settled himself back in the bows and watched his companion cast off and start the well-silenced motor. An old, old sailor, this Matushenko; almost ready for retirement and, like himself, a professional. He would find the beach all right, and there was nothing to worry about on that score. The only worry was who would be there to meet him. He had no illusions about the efficiency of the Western Intelligence Services, and already there might be a little group of shadowy figures standing in the fog and waiting for him. To steady his nerves, he lit a cigarette and pulled hard at it against the drag of the damp air, listening to the whine of the motor and the sough of the bows cutting across the long swell.

No, there was no need to worry yet. Everything had been planned to the last detail. An agent would meet him at the top of the cliffs and they would go to London together; it was safer that way. And in London, if things went wrong, he could get any help he needed from their office. Gregor Tanek would see to that, and he knew Tanek well: a fat, jolly, dissolute man with a taste for blonde women as large as himself, and English lyric poetry. A good man, though; one of the best they had in Western Europe. He could rely on full support from Gregor Tanek.

The real work was all his own, though. He had to find Rolfe's letter-writer and get the necessary information from him. Then he had to break Rolfe in good time for the conference and hand him over to a financial expert from the embassy. A lot to do and only five days to do it in.

He lowered his head below the spirals of mist and leaned back in his seat, thinking of his plans and hearing the gun fire again from the cliffs. As the last echo died, he suddenly looked up with a jerk and knew that something was wrong.

"All right, Comrade, this is it. This is where you get out and walk." Matushenko's hand cut the engine and the boat drifted into the trough of a wave. His words were slow and careful, as though they had been rehearsed for a long time. They had been travelling only a few minutes, and there was still a good mile from the shore.

"What's the matter? Have you gone crazy?" Vanin started to say, and then he saw the revolver in the man's hand. An old revolver, like Matushenko himself, heavy and outdated, but still lethal. It must have been treasured and hidden away for just such an emergency. "You'll never get away with it, you fool—never in a thousand years."

"Yes, I'll get away with it all right, Comrade." The man's voice was strangely indifferent, as though he were merely stating facts which could not be denied. "Apart from yourself, there's nothing to stop me, is there? No, I've been waiting for the chance to desert for a long time now, and I'm going to take it."

"But why, Matushenko? Why should a man like you want to desert? A man with your record—with your name?" Vanin arched his body for a spring as he spoke, but at the same moment he knew it was useless. He would be dead before he left his seat.

"Yes, I've got a good record, haven't I, Comrade? And mine's a famous name too. Matushenko; I should be proud of it. The same name as that Afanasy Matushenko who led the mutineers on the *Potemkin* in 1905. The man who was hanged by his own countrymen. All the same, I have reasons for what I'm doing, Comrade—I have good reasons."

"But what about your family? They're still in Russia, aren't they? You know what will happen to them if you desert." Vanin was thinking of his own family as he spoke.

"No, I haven't got a family, Comrade." Matushenko shook his head slightly. "Both my sons were killed in the war, and my wife died last voyage. The doctor told me she was going to die, but they wouldn't let me stay with her. I begged the port captain to let me stay, but he wouldn't listen. He just handed me over to a political commissar who gave me a nice, friendly lecture on my duty to the Party and Mother Russia. My wife died alone, Comrade." The big gun started to come up as he spoke. "No, I've nothing to lose, and nobody will suffer from what I do. Now, how do you want it, Comrade; in the front or in the back?"

"In the front, Matushenko, but listen to me first. Give me just one minute." Vanin struggled to put just the right plea into his voice. "I have got a family too, you see—a wife and a couple of children. Let me write to them, please—just a few lines. I'll give you the address and you could post it when you've got ashore. It won't cost you anything; only the price of a stamp. Please let me do that."

"All right, Comrade, you can write your letter. Just a few lines though, and don't try anything. If you make one wrong move I'll shoot you in the guts." As he spoke, the signal gun fired again, and his revolver moved up and down like a pointer in his hand.

"No, I won't try anything." Vanin pulled out a packet of cigarettes and took out their contents. "You might as well have these," he said, laying them on the seat and tearing open the packet to provide a writing surface. Then he reached in his pocket for the big fountain-pen. It felt like lead as he twisted the cap and felt the nib swing sideways. "I won't be a moment." He leaned forward slightly, as though considering what to write, till the pen was pointing just where he wanted it. The business was almost finished. He had only to press the switch and Matushenko would be dead.

But quite suddenly, as he looked at that heavy, stupid and rather kindly face, Vanin knew that he couldn't kill the man. He had sat too long in an office and grown too soft to kill anybody again. He was facing a deserter who pointed a gun at his heart, but he couldn't kill him, for he was a desk man without strength or courage. Whatever the book or the rules of the department said, he wouldn't shoot to kill. He began to lower his hand till it pointed at the man's wrist.

Yes, *the rules and the book!* Like a voice in his ear, like a sudden flash of inspiration, he saw how it was, and the weapon came up again. He didn't want to kill, but then he, Peter Vanin, didn't have to. Peter Vanin didn't exist as a person at all. He was just a part of the machine, a cog in the organization, and he didn't matter. Only the rules and the book mattered, and it was

they who were going to kill Matushenko, for they had sentenced
him to death. He braced his arm, waited for the next report of
the signal gun and pressed the switch. With no fuss, little recoil,
and hardly any noise, the thing he held exploded, and it was
finished. Matushenko still sat where he was, but the revolver was
lying at his feet and he looked quite different. He had three eyes
now, and one was almost in the centre of his forehead. He did
not appear to bleed a great deal.

And that was that. There was no need for reproach, though
Vanin felt slightly sick as he looked at that slumped body, which
seemed quite different in death. He had done exactly what the
book said he should do, and now he had to get on with the real
work. He moved forward and pulled Matushenko to one side.
Then he started the engine. There was a compass beside the tiller,
and he steered for the east.

The beach was exactly what he had hoped for: soft sand that
held the boat firmly, and here and there scattered rocks that
looked like small, grazing animals in the thinning mist. He took
a knife from Matushenko's belt, and very carefully cut holes in
the buoyancy tanks, then he lashed the body to the seat. When
it was quite secure, he piled a heap of stones on the duck-boards,
and removed the draining plug.

Everything was in order again, and he had done just what the
book said he should do. He was a little late for his appointment,
and Lieutenant Golinoff had lost a good sailor, but that was all.
He started the motor, threw it into reverse, and watched the boat
begin to move out to sea. She would sink in deep water and
nobody would tell any tales. He picked up his case and began
to walk up the beach.

He had made a good landfall, it seemed, and he found the path
without difficulty. It was just a sheep track winding up through
a gap in the cliffs, stepped by tufts of grass, and here and there
covered by scree falls that felt like knives beneath his thin, city
shoes. Already there was a thin glow in the east, and the fog was
breaking up fast. Beyond the piled rocks he could make out the
loom of mountains, and all around was the smell of sheep and
pinewoods and the sound of running water. When the signal gun
fired again, it sounded almost on top of him. The lighthouse
must be just round the next break in the cliffs. With his feet
slipping and stumbling on the slope, he struggled upwards, and
then paused for a moment, as the case collided with something at
the side of the track and was dragged from his hand. He bent
down and looked at the thing that had caused it: a little stone

pillar with lettering half hidden by the salt and lichens that covered it.

BRIAN CONNOR
Born 1900—*Murdered* 1922
HE DIED FOR IRELAND

Died for Ireland! In Vanin's present state of mind, with nothing but those dripping cliffs around him and the hint of low, somehow ignoble mountains ahead, Ireland seemed rather an unworthy cause to die for. He shook his head slightly and hurried on upwards to the place where his contact had been told to meet him. A few yards on, the path gave a final turn to the right, and the cliffs ran out into flat moorland. As they did so, he suddenly stopped dead, staring up at the things before him. There was a little ticking pulse in his forehead and it came from fear as well as exhaustion.

The three men hung from their crosses, and for a moment they seemed to be alive—horribly alive. He lowered the case, for he knew where he was. This was the rendezvous that had been described to him, and he knew that such things were common in Ireland. All the same, the sight still shocked him. There was something too life-like in those marble figures straining from their nails, with tortured faces turned out towards the Atlantic. He stood quite still for a moment, looking up at the Calvary, feeling terribly alone, but knowing that he wasn't alone. The only movements around him were the slight whisper of wind and, here and there, the shapes of grazing sheep—but he wasn't alone. Somewhere human eyes were watching him, as they had been trained and told to watch. He couldn't pray, but he hoped they were the right eyes.

For perhaps ten seconds he stood like that, recalling his instructions and the prepared words, then he walked forward to the most westerly cross and looked up at the face of the dying thief. Rather horribly it reminded him of Matushenko.

"Lord," he said to the damp air, and the carved stones, and the thin winter sun coming up over the hills. He felt slightly embarrassed by the passwords Malendin had given him. "Lord, remember me when Thou comest into Thy kingdom." He heard a slight movement as he spoke.

"Yes, quite correct, and almost on time too." The voice was just behind the centre cross. "Today thou shalt be with Me in paradise."

The woman stepped out from a pile of rocks behind the

Calvary, and she was tall and dark, with her hair tied back under a scarf. She wore slacks and a belted raincoat, and in the drifting mist she could have been a creature from a fairy tale. Her face might have been beautiful if there were a little less strength in it.

"Good morning to you," she said, and held out her hand. Her grip was pleasant and warm, and full of confidence. Vanin felt better for it. "My name is Kate Reilly. I hope you had a pleasant journey."

She smiled as she spoke, and though he saw the faint mockery in that smile, he didn't mind it. He thought of the roped body drifting out to sea, and he was suddenly glad that Tanek had sent a woman to meet him.

"Mine is Peter Vanin."

"Yes, I know, and I've been very thoroughly briefed about you. You are my second cousin from New York City, and your occupation is journalism. You are over here on a holiday, but you are also looking for copy. I am to take you to London and act as your assistant and general contact. That's all they told me. Would you like to give me a few more details before we start?"

"No, not at the moment." He gave a tolerant shrug of his shoulders against all female curiosity. "As it happens, I have very few details myself."

"I see. Then let's go, shall we? I've got a car parked about a mile away, and we have to catch the afternoon plane from Dublin." She watched him reach for his case and then smiled again. "Tell me, Mr Vanin—or perhaps I'd better start calling you Peter—does it worry you that I'm a woman?"

"No, it doesn't worry me. It doesn't worry me at all. As long as you're efficient, nothing will worry me." As he looked at her, he knew that the remark was quite unnecessary. Even if she tried, this woman could never be anything else except efficient.

"All the same, if we're to work together, I'd like to know a little more about you. You're not one of us, but English or Irish. Just why were you picked for the job?"

"Perhaps because I am Irish." She turned away from him and looked out towards the sea as she spoke. "I am also a landscape painter, specializing in this coast; quite a good one as it happens, and I have a cottage in the next village. That gives me an excellent reason for travelling between here and London. Does that satisfy you?"

"No, not really. I want to know *why*, Kate." Somehow the name came quite naturally to him. "Just why are you working for us? I wouldn't put you down as a keen party member, or even as a sympathizer."

"And you'd be right, Peter, quite right. I work for you for three reasons. The first is money, and the second you may be able to guess. Because of something I did when I was young and filled with an enthusiasm for political causes. I think you know, don't you, Comrade?" There was a sudden bitterness in her voice.

"Yes, I know."

Something I did when I was young. As Vanin listened, he knew exactly how it could have been done—how often it was done. Young people with a spirit of revolt following causes, almost for the fun of the thing. Causes which they would one day outgrow, which most of them did outgrow, but some were not allowed to. Some were thought to be useful, and these few were flattered and cultivated and paid. Then one day, when the enthusiasm started to die, the velvet gloves were taken off and the organization showed itself. Something discreditable, or illegal, or merely frightening would be laid at their heels, and they would belong to the Party body and soul.

"Yes, I know how it is," he said. "And what's the third reason?"

"The third reason I don't suppose you'll understand, being a Russian. It's merely because I'm Irish and because of that I feel so very, very fond of the English." Her expression altered slightly as she spoke. The look of a mischievous child discussing an unpopular headmaster.

"I understand. Yes, they are a lovable people." Vanin considered the little stone pillar on the path and the message it carried: Brian Connor—Died for Ireland.

A stupid people, he thought. A poor, foolish people, carrying on their outdated hate and following any cause, so long as it was directed against England. All the same, sometimes a useful people, for those who knew how to control them.

"Let's go," he said, and, picking up the case, began to walk forward.

The sun was already quite high above the hills now, and in the distance he could make out the winding road which would take them to Dublin. This was the real start of the journey, and he was quite satisfied. He had made his landfall, Kate should prove a reliable assistant, and the book would never let him down. Tonight he would be with his enemies, and almost every man's raised hand against him, but that didn't matter if he only followed the book. He had only to do that, and soon he would be standing before Sir Martin Rolfe with the knowledge to break him.

And he was right, of course—quite right. He was a professional who had been a long time at the game, and if he played his cards well, nothing could stop him. In a short time he would know the meaning of that scrawled letter and its childish drawing that hid Rolfe's probably very nasty secret. There was just one thing which the book couldn't tell him.

The thing was death, and if he made one mistake, one slip in the card game, it would come to him almost automatically. He walked on across the heather towards a car to Dublin, a plane to London, and the little matchstick picture that somebody with a sick mind had called the Gaunt Woman.

CHAPTER THREE

THEY hardly exchanged a dozen words in the car, but in the plane they had to talk for the sake of appearances. After a time they talked like people.

Not like real people, of course; that was impossible, for their lives only met in a world of pretence. All the same, Vanin was a good inventor, and from time to time Kate laughed with genuine amusement as he recounted the history of their American relatives. Maureen Reilly, housemaid of Boston, who had married a Polish refugee named Stanislas Vanin back in the 'eighties—the St Patrick's night after the war when Uncle Brian had missed his footing and fallen off the ferry boat from New York to Hoboken —how Aunt Tessie's saloon was doing in Jersey City——

As she listened, she seemed to get quite a different picture of this man whom she had first thought a humourless fanatic. There was a joy in him, a laughing quality hidden away under the very drab exterior. They were just coming into London Airport when she asked a question and saw the laughter switched off like a lamp.

"Tell me, Peter," she said. "I almost forgot to ask you. Is your wife well? I haven't seen her since she was a child, and I can only just remember her."

"My wife?" The good humour left his face, and it seemed to open like a backcloth to show nothing but bleakness and loneliness behind.

"Yes, Shura is well enough," he said, knowing that though the answer was true he couldn't count on its remaining so. Shura and the kids were the only things he had ever loved in his life, but they were also hostages for his good behaviour. Though he and Malendin were old friends, the rules of the department were quite clear. Let him make one bad mistake, show one sign of disloyalty, and the punishment would be automatic. It was not he who would be punished.

"And thank you for asking."

He suddenly hated Kate Reilly for her curiosity, and turned away, staring down at the approaching runway. Not till the airport bus turned into the terminal did he speak again.

"Well, Kate, here we are," he said at last, tightening his coat. "And I'd like to say how very glad I am that we've been able to meet up again."

The cousinly pretence had to be kept up, and her question had obviously been quite innocent. Besides, they were working together. All the same—the memory of his family and his little overdecorated flat was like a physical pain in his head. He watched the last of their fellow-passengers file off the bus, and then stood up.

"And now to business, my dear. I've got your phone number, and I'll get in touch when and if I need you; probably tomorrow morning. Please see that you're always by the phone till twelve noon."

He followed her out of the bus, taking his case from a porter, and stared up at the red glow of the London lights. The last time he had seen the town had been in the blackout, and they came as a slight shock—the denial of a memory.

"Well, goodbye for the present, Kate," he said. "I expect we will be meeting again very soon." As though remembering his role, and his good manners, he leaned forward and kissed her lightly on the cheek. It was an extremely dutiful and cousinly kiss and meant nothing at all, except a slight mockery. Then he turned and walked away; a very ordinary and somehow pathetic figure dragging his case through the London crowds.

Vanin took a room in a small, family hotel off the Cromwell Road, and he washed and shaved before going to work, for he was that kind of man. Besides, there was no need to hurry. British government offices didn't close till five, and the person he wanted would still be on duty. Punctually at a quarter to the hour, he went out into the street and looked for a phone booth.

"Viaduct 1122." Clear and impersonal, the well-trained voice tinkled on the end of the line, and obediently Vanin pressed the button. As he heard the heavy coins fall, he wondered how a people that prided itself on freedom could put up with the torture of British currency.

"Could I speak to Mr Michael Arabin, please?"

"Mr Ar-ab-in." The voice gave the name its full accentuation. "Do you happen to know the number of his extension, sir?"

"No, I'm afraid I don't know that, but you should be able to trace him all right. He is personal assistant to Sir Martin Rolfe."

"Oh, I see. One moment, please." The line seemed to go dead for a moment and then another voice took over.

"Could I have your name, sir, and then I'll inquire if Mr Arabin is available."

"Yes, of course; it's Vanin, Peter Vanin." He concentrated on finding a word which would get him connected, and the name of Arabin's wife seemed the obvious choice. "Would you tell him it is about the Magdalena contract, please," he said, hearing the line die again and a third voice came through.

This time he knew it was the voice he wanted: a foreign voice, speaking very slowly and carefully and struggling to hide emotion. Struggling unsuccessfully too. Even through the little plastic cap of the phone he could feel the hope, and excitement, and fear in that careful voice.

"Arabin here," said the voice. "Yes, I have been expecting your call. I would very much like to discuss the terms of our contract as soon as possible. Would this evening be satisfactory?"

"This evening would do very well indeed." Vanin glanced at his watch. "Would you name the time and place, please? Thank you. In one hour then." He made a neat entry in his pocket-book and replaced the phone.

So far, so good, he thought. He had made his second contact and everything was going according to schedule. In an hour's time he would be talking to the man who owned the address they wanted. He was also quite sure that Arabin's story was genuine. That tense, excited voice on the phone told him that. He pulled back the door and stepped out of the booth.

"Good evening." The girl came hurrying towards him across the pavement, and at first he thought she was a prostitute; though of a very curious kind. Her face was without make-up, and she wore sandals, a man's flannel trousers and a worn leather jerkin. Long black air flowed round her shoulders in uncombed tassels, and there was a big sheet of paper in her hand. For a moment he stood staring at her, considering the curious sexual tastes of the English, then he saw the black and white badge of the Nuclear Disarmament Campaign on her lapel and began to understand.

"Would you care to sign this petition, sir? It is a protest to the Government on allowing American rocket bases on British soil." She held the paper up to him. It had very few signatures but a long line of neatly ruled columns. As he looked at it, Vanin grinned and a terrible temptation to make an entry came into his head:

I am strongly against American bases on British soil— Peter Vanin, Department Five of M.V.D., Central Intelligence Bureau of the Union of Soviet Socialist Republics.

"No, I'm sorry," he said, fighting temptation. "I'm afraid it is impossible."

"But why?" The girl's face flushed with annoyance. "Why do you say it's impossible? Do you want to see our country occupied by foreign troops?" She pushed forward as she spoke. Her old leather coat smelt like a horse. "Do you think we're traitors or something?"

"No, I don't think you are traitors." He drew back, looking at the mud-stained feet, the rumpled trousers and the lank, untidy hair. "All I think, my dear, is that you could do with a bloody good wash." He touched his hat politely and walked away down the street.

The London Underground was quicker than he'd remembered, and he was early getting to the bar where he had arranged to meet Arabin. It stood on a corner at the eastern end of Oxford Street, and the doors were just opening as he reached it. He bought a paper from the kiosk beside the entrance, and then followed the procession of black-coated, bowler-hatted figures into the saloon, ordering a small whisky and carrying it to one of the alcoves that ran along the wall. Arabin would not be there for a few minutes, so he opened his paper and glanced idly at the headlines, smiling slightly as he read

KHRUSCHEV ON THE CARPET BEFORE U.N.
MR K's NEW BLUNDER

He pushed it away from him, and looked at the other occupants of the room. They seemed to be all clerical workers, all middle-class, and all in the uniform dress of black and grey. A few sat alone, bent over crossword puzzles, but mostly they stood in groups along the bar, discussing office problems, the weather, or the state of the train services to the suburbs. Vanin lifted his glass and silently toasted them.

A nice but foolish people, he thought. Mr K's New Blunder

indeed! The phrase had an almost jovial ring about it, as though it described some sporting event rather than a political crisis which could blow them to pieces in seconds. Didn't they know they were sitting on top of a land-mine?

No, they couldn't know that, any more than they could foresee the economic ruin which he, Peter Vanin, was hoping to bring against them; that if he played his cards well, and got the necessary information on Martin Rolfe, every one of them might be a little poorer before the end of next year. He sipped his drink, smiling at those well-fed, self-confident but doomed backs, and he felt slightly sorry for them. Then the door opened, and he saw the man he had come to meet walk into the room.

Michael Arabin wore the same clothes as everybody in the bar, but he looked quite different. He stood in the doorway, staring around him, and he might have been any age between thirty and fifty, and any one of ten nationalities. Only his expression was typical. That ageless, nationless face bore an expression of cynicism and weariness, and at the same time of sentimentality —of fanaticism and the complete acceptance of evil. It was the face of Central Europe.

"Mr Arabin?" Vanin started to hold out his hand, and then stopped. Something in the man's eyes told him he wouldn't take it. "Do sit down, please. What will you have to drink?"

"Oh, anything—anything at all." Arabin looked at the glass on the table and shrugged his shoulders. "What are you having? Whisky; that will do very well."

He watched Vanin move towards the bar, and then he took a case from his pocket and lit a cigarette. Somehow it seemed to be holding his face together as he dragged at it. "Tell me," he said, as Vanin sat down beside him. "I'm afraid I didn't catch your name on the phone; only my wife's name. Are you from the embassy, or did they send you from Budapest?"

"From neither, as it happens. My name is Peter Vanin, and I have come from Moscow." There was no one within earshot of their cubicle, and it was safe to talk freely.

"From Moscow! I see. Then this means that your people are interested . . ."

"It means that we are slightly interested in your story, Mr Arabin, nothing more. All the same, if we find that what you told the Hungarian embassy is true—if you can lead us to the person who has been writing to Rolfe—if we get enough information to make Rolfe work for us—then you have my word that your family will be allowed to leave Hungary without delay."

"Your word!" There was nothing but contempt in the man's voice. "I thought you just said you were a Russian."

"Yes, I'm a Russian, Mr Arabin." Vanin looked away from that set face, and he suddenly remembered London as he had known it during the war: a drab, scarred city, but a city of friends. Now it was like a great hostile trap shutting him in.

"I am a Russian, but you have no choice except to trust me, I'm afraid. I am also just a man like you, doing a job, and I have a family to think of too. Now, do we talk business or not? If not, you have only to stand up and walk out. I can't stop you." He watched the hatred in Arabin's eyes start to turn to resignation.

"Very well, I'll do business with you." Arabin reached in his pocket and drew out a scrap of paper. "Here is the address of the letter I gave to the Hungarian embassy. It is just a poste restante address, I'm afraid, but doubtless with your great organization"—his lip curled slightly as he spoke—"it should not be impossible to trace the sender."

"Thank you." Once again Vanin looked at that oddly senile or childish writing, then he folded the paper neatly and put it away in his wallet. "No," he said, "it shouldn't be too difficult to trace him. Tell me something though. Do you think that Rolfe himself knows of this address?"

"No, Mr Vanin, Rolfe does not know, and the fact that you asked such a question proves that you know very little about him. This is the fourth letter to reach the office. Rolfe has never seen it, and the other three did not carry an address. I am quite certain about that, because if they had, this one would never have been posted. It couldn't have been, you see. The sender would be dead."

"You mean——"

"I mean that Rolfe would have killed him—or had him killed. Oh, yes, Mr Vanin, even in law-abiding England he would have tried to do that. I know my employer and I saw the effect those letters had on him. If he could get his hands on to whoever sent them, he would kill that person with about as much compunction as I would need to kill a rat. Now tell me—tell me just what you know about Martin Rolfe. Then I'll try and give you a rather fuller picture."

He leaned back, listening to Vanin with a quiet smile flickering round his eyes, and when Vanin had finished he lifted his glass and drank for the first time.

"I see; and that's all you know, is it? You know the positions he holds. You know of his works on economics. You know about the commissions he has sat on. A lot of those aren't there: Financial Aid to Underdeveloped Countries in the Commonwealth; An Inquiry into Racial Discrimination in Britain. Yes, my employer takes part in a great many commissions, and he is a very influential man. He needs influence, I think. He craves for it as some people want drink or drugs or power. It's an obsession with him, this need to persuade people, to will them to follow his lead. Take that conference in Washington, for example. Rolfe knows that Lord Tremayne, the Minister, relies on him completely and he gets a tremendous kick out of it."

"I see; a form of power." As Vanin listened, he remembered his own words as he had looked at Rolfe's picture in Malendin's office: "He is used to power, but his power comes through people rather than over them."

"Yes, power is right, but only in a sense." Arabin considered for a moment. "I think it's really approval that Rolfe wants—the need to be relied on. I've only been with him nine months, but I felt it on the first day he engaged me. I could almost hear his thoughts: 'This man is a Hungarian refugee without friends in this country. I have given him a job, and it would be very difficult for him to find another. Therefore he will do his best to serve me well. He will also be grateful to me.'"

"Approval eh? That's strange." Vanin suddenly felt comfortable and secure, for he was doing the job he liked doing. He didn't feel like an agent or spy any more, but merely a policeman interviewing a witness. "Yes, that's very strange. The man is a scholar, a savant, if you like, and they are usually the most independent people in the world. Yet Martin Rolfe wants to influence people and he needs their approval. Have you reached any conclusions about that, Mr Arabin?"

"Yes, I think so." Arabin frowned, and Vanin could see that the character of his employer fascinated him. "I think that underneath everything, Rolfe is a very insecure and possibly frightened man. I think that only by holding influence over other people and gaining their approval can he get the sense of security he needs. It's as though every committee he sits on, every report he writes, makes him feel more secure; like a very rich man who works twelve hours a day to be richer, because he dreads poverty. Every share certificate in his bank, every factory he owns, is like a barrier shutting off the fear of something which will probably never happen. That's why I said Rolfe would kill his letter-writer, Mr Vanin. I saw his face when he opened the first one, and it was a killer's face all right. His security is threatened, and that's the one thing he needs in life."

"And just what do you think he is frightened of?" Vanin's policeman's voice showed nothing but polite curiosity.

"I've no idea, but it's something concrete all right. I think that at some time in his life Rolfe may have done something, or had something done to him, and the memory of it is always with him. He has tried to shut it out with work, with the approval of important people, but it is always there in the back of his mind. Then one day he opens a scribbled letter, and the terror comes into the light."

"I see." Vanin concentrated for a moment. A man is frightened, he thought. A man of influence who surrounds himself with powerful friends, and sits on committees, and advises governments. But all the time, that fear is waiting to come out into the light.

Just what could have caused a fear like that, he wondered. An imaginary childhood terror—a compulsive neurosis that started a long time ago? No, those were the obvious, *doctor's* solutions, but they didn't fit here. Those scrawled notes pointed to a real fear.

A threat of violence then—of prosecution for some indiscretion done in the past? No, nothing like that, for a man like Rolfe would have known how to deal with such threats. Vanin considered the report of the Moscow handwriting experts: "This was written by a very old and feeble person with a mental illness."

But *in the past* was probably right. Something that happened a long time ago, when Rolfe was a boy or a young man. Something which still terrified him. "The gaunt woman who can blast you."

Yes, *the gaunt woman.* Probably the words didn't refer to a person at all, but a thing. Something that happened years ago, but could still make a very hard, influential economist cry out in terror—the skeleton in the cupboard which must never come to light.

"Tell me," he said. "There were four of these letters, and since this last which you gave to us there appear to have been no more. How is Rolfe now?"

"On the surface he is back to normal, but only on the surface. Underneath I would say he is a very sick man." Arabin picked up the paper that lay on the table. "Look for yourself. This was taken yesterday."

"Thank you." Vanin took the newspaper, which Arabin had opened at the financial page. Above the market prices there were headlines reading

CITY WAITS FOR TREASURY FIGURES

and below the headlines a picture showing the same face he had studied in Malendin's office. Rolfe looked quite different now. The thin, academic features seemed even thinner, and there was no smile in the eyes. He still looked powerful and efficient, but it was a defensive power now; the face of a fallen idol—a Prussian general in defeat. "Yes, I do see," he said, "but tell me something —what do you know about Rolfe's personal life? Has he a family, for instance?"

"No, no family—no children, that is. I seem to have heard there was a child that died a long time ago, but I'm not sure. There is a wife though—I met her once."

He paused for a moment as though the memory was somehow important, lighting another cigarette as he did so.

"It was some time last winter. There were a couple of urgent papers for Rolfe to sign, and I had to drive down to his house one Saturday. That's right. About the end of February it must have been, just after he took me on. He had a house in what they call the Fens, just north of Cambridge. I remember the drive down well. It's a very flat countryside, with ditches running straight out into the horizon and big churches standing out like ships on every skyline. It was almost dusk when I got to the nearest village: a place called Heronsford; just a hamlet really, with a few houses standing round a church and a pub. I stopped for a drink and asked the way. I remember it was very cold, with patches of mist rising up from the empty fields.

"Anyway, I got my directions in the pub, and drove on towards Rolfe's house. It was about four miles from the village, down a narrow lane, and at first sight was just the kind of place I'd expected. There was a high wall running round the grounds, and a porter's lodge with a pair of wrought-iron gates beside it. The porter had to ring through to the house before letting me in.

"But the house itself—that really surprised me. It stood on a little hill which made it tower over the flat countryside, and it was very tall, with gables and spires and every form of architecture going; Victorian Gothic I think they call the style. It looked quite grotesque in the dusk.

"But this was the strange thing. Rolfe is a very rich man in his own right, Chairman of Western Chemicals among other things, but his house was in a terrible state of neglect. Oh, I know he doesn't bother about appearances, his clothes for instance are never pressed, but this was really bad; all the brickwork needed pointing, and a great line of guttering was hanging loose. It looked as though it hadn't had a workman near it in ten years.

"Anyway, I went to the door—the paint was peeling from it—and rang the bell; one of those old-fashioned ones it was, worked by wires and a handle you pulled. And the maid who opened the door was rather like the house itself. She was a very old woman dressed in a shabby apron which hadn't been washed for weeks; more like a down-and-out than a servant. She was bent too; sort of twisted—how do you say it?" He struggled for the right word.

"You mean she was deformed?"

"Yes, that's it; deformed. A cripple, and as I said, very old and dirty. She let me in, and told me to wait in the hall while she went to fetch her master.

"And that hall was brown, Mr Vanin—it was all brown. There was a faded brown carpet on the floor, and brown wall-paper with marks on it, and ugly brown furniture you couldn't sell for fifty pounds. That was the house of a man who could write a cheque for a hundred thousand any time he wanted."

"I see. You interest me. And did you meet the wife?"

"No, not really, though I saw her. Rolfe came out and signed the papers. He did it very quickly, and though they were important I got the feeling that somehow he resented my bringing them. Then just as I was leaving, I looked up and saw a woman standing at the top of the stairs. I think it must have been Lady Rolfe, because when she called down and asked him how long he'd be, she used the term 'my dear'."

"Yes, that was his wife, and like the house and the maid, she seemed all wrong; an elderly woman, in her sixties probably, but got up like a young girl, with dyed blonde hair and a dress I wouldn't let my daughter wear. Her face could have belonged to a fading street-walker. It was dead white, and the make-up stood out like red sealing-wax on an envelope."

"But you didn't speak to her?"

"No, Rolfe just let me out, and I've never been in the house since. He has a flat in London and stays there most of the time."

Arabin finished his drink and ground out the cigarette. "And that's about all I can tell you about his private life, I'm afraid. Rolfe seems to have no vices, and very few interests outside his public work."

"No, so it seems. All the same, he must have had one vice or one passion in his time; that seems certain. And you don't like him, do you, Mr Arabin?"

"No, I don't like him." Arabin considered for a moment. "I can't tell you why though. He's a good enough boss in most ways, but there's something about him—a kind of coldness which at times makes you feel you're not with a real person at all. If it wasn't for that, I don't think I'd be talking to you now. Even for the sake of my family, I don't think I would be."

"Is that so, Mr Arabin? All the same, you are talking to me, so let's have a toast, shall we?" Without asking if he wanted another drink, Vanin got up and refilled their glasses at the bar. "Yes," he said, "let's have a toast. That you may see your wife and children again."

"I'll drink to that." Arabin raised his glass, and there was suddenly hope in his face. "Does this mean that you believe my story? That you are going to let them out?"

"No, not yet, I'm afraid. It merely means that I am inclined to believe your story, because I don't think you would make up anything so very unlikely. If I find out that you have spoken the truth and this letter-writer exists, then your family will be flown to England on the first available plane. They are ready and waiting now. My department instructed the Hungarian police to hold them in the Belitza prison with their bags packed."

He drank his whisky and laid the glass down on the table. "Yes, if all goes well you will see them soon. If, on the other hand, you have been deceiving us, then I'm afraid they may stay in that prison for a very long time." He stood up as he spoke. "Well, goodbye for the time being, Mr Arabin. And don't worry, I will keep you informed of my progress."

He gave the man a final, prim and rather old-maidish smile, and without another word walked out of the room.

* * *

It was dark now. Dark and cold, with a hint of snow from the east and the street lamps glowing like oranges in the damp air. Vanin turned up his coat collar and walked forward, looking at the bright shop windows with their messages of seasonal good will and exhortations to buy—just five more days to Christmas and already the decorations looked slightly aged and tawdry: paper masks, green trees and tinsel dolls almost ready for the dustbin.

And somewhere in this vast, sprawling town was the person he had to find: the man or woman who knew why Martin Rolfe was afraid—the reason for his decayed house, his deformed servant, and his wife with that ravaged harlot's face and a dress that Michael Arabin would not allow his daughter to wear.

Arabin. He frowned as he considered the man, for his remark

had been like a blow, like a spit in his face. "Your word! But you said you were a Russian."

All the same, Arabin had been telling the truth; he was quite certain of that. Somewhere, far back in Rolfe's past probably, a very nasty event had taken place and it was up to him to find out what it was. He hadn't much time either. Three days after Christmas, Rolfe left for Washington and he had to be well in the net before then.

Place! Vanin stopped suddenly and looked at the building in front of him. He had left the shopping areas now, and for some time had been walking among empty, dimly-lit office-blocks. On the whole dimly-lit, that was. The building in front of him was a blaze of light, with flood-lamps playing on its towering stories of glass and marble. The sign over the bronze doors read:

CENTURY HOUSE
HEAD OFFICE OF WESTERN CHEMICAL INDUSTRIES

Yes, Rolfe was chairman of that company, Arabin had said, and it didn't fit at all. All this façade of wealth and power linked to a man who wouldn't even paint his own front door. It was time to start work. Vanin crossed the street towards a line of phone booths.

"Gloucester 5191." It was well after business hours, but the office he was calling remained open. It was always open to the right caller.

"Just what can I do for you?" The quiet, anonymous voice at the end of the line couldn't quite conceal its foreign accent.

"Homeway," he said. "Homeway Productions—extension 85." Almost at once the connection went through, and he heard a voice he knew well: a loud, jolly voice that made him feel much less alone. "Hullo, Gregor," he said. "Yes, Peter Vanin here. How are you, my dear chap? Good, I'm very glad. I saw your sister a few days ago. Her hair appears to be red this year." He heard Gregor Tanek chuckle good-naturedly and a chair creak as he shifted his enormous bulk to a more comfortable position. "Yes, I know that Malendin would have told you that, but I won't trouble your people more than I can help. There are just two things I want from you at the moment.

"Firstly, I want to know about the girl you sent to meet me in Ireland. That's right, Kate Reilly.

"I see. She has worked for us for three years, and is quite reliable. Good; that puts my mind at rest on one score." He reached in his pocket and pulled out the scrap of paper that Arabin had given him.

"Now I want you to send off a letter for me, Gregor. The central post offices are still open, I imagine. No, there is nothing to write down. All you need is a plain sheet of paper to be well dusted with fuchsine powder. That's right, the stain.

"Sorry, Gregor, but I'm afraid I didn't quite catch that," he said, and his voice hardened slightly. "Yes, I know it's late, but you'll just have to find some. This is very important indeed.

"Good, I knew I could rely on you. Now here is the address. The name is Smith—quite certainly a pseudonym. Yes, J. Smith, c/o Poste Restante Box 5, South Hammersmith G.P.O.

"Thank you, Gregor. Yes, it must be in the post tonight—that's quite essential. Thanks again then, and goodbye for the present."

He replaced the phone and glanced at his watch. It was exactly eight o'clock, and in twelve hours' time that tell-tale envelope would be lying in its pigeon-hole ready to be collected. To be collected by a person who was said to be mentally ill—a person who had been expecting a letter for several days now, and would probably not wait till he got home but open it in the street or the post office itself. And if that happened . . .

Vanin smiled to himself and pushed open the door of the phone box. Everything was going smoothly and according to plan. With a little luck, tomorrow would take him just where he wanted to be. Right into the sick mind of the person who knew how to frighten Sir Martin Rolfe.

All the same, he was tired now—terribly tired. He turned and began to walk quickly up the road towards the tube station and his hotel.

CHAPTER FOUR

IT snowed for six hours during the night, and at early morning the snow froze. Now it lay over London in a tight, shimmering carpet, very beautiful but quite impermanent; before evening it would have become a waste of grey, clinging mud.

Kate Reilly stood at a corner of King Street, Hammersmith, looking across at the post office. A small, unimportant building, she was glad to see, merely flattered by the name of general. She had been there for a quarter of an hour already, and at any moment the doors were due to open. The mail vans had come and gone from the side entrance, and she could see figures moving through the frosted-glass windows facing the street. Vanin had told her to get there just on the hour, but she liked to be early, for she was that kind of girl. Besides, she was very curious. He had rung her at six-thirty with his instructions, but he had told her what to do and not why. There had been no hint of explanation in that formal, precise voice on the phone. Just instructions and at the end a number, almost grudgingly given, to ring him back to report her progress. Five minutes later, she had dialled that number and rather cunningly checked the address: a small private hotel in Kensington.

But at last the doors were opening. With a sigh of relief, for her feet were like ice, she crossed the road and walked into the office, noting the layout of its counters as she did so: parcels to the right, licences and savings certificates in the centre, stamps and letters on the left. She bought four stamped envelopes, and going to a side table, pulled a writing-pad from her bag and began to compose a long and unnecessary letter to a friend. Her position gave her a good view of the door.

But whatever Peter Vanin might have told her, the person she had to follow didn't seem to be in any hurry. The office was quite busy, but the business was all routine: offices-boys buying blocks of stamps, withdrawers of savings certificates, housewives laden down with Christmas parcels. There was just one man she watched suspiciously for a moment. A tall, harassed-looking man, who came in muttering angrily to himself as though in extreme annoyance. Then he moved to the counter, parted with thirty-one pounds for National Health contributions, and went out still muttering.

Eight thirty-five. She had finished two letters now, and the clerk behind the licence counter was beginning to eye her with a good deal of curiosity. She ignored him, and tearing out another sheet of paper from her pad, started on a third.

"Dear Mary, It seems ages since I heard from you, and hope that everything is——" She stopped dead in the middle of the sentence, staring at the door, with her pen slipping forward and tearing into the paper.

For this might be it—this might be the person they wanted. She watched the man coming slowly through the doorway, and concentrated on the probable description that Vanin had given her. 'Certainly old—possibly male—may seem ill, or nervous and jittery.'

Yes, this man was old all right. She couldn't see much of the face, for his felt hat was pulled down, and a thick brown muffler covered his mouth. But there was age in that slow, stiff walk towards the counter, and the hint of sickness in that bent body wrapped in a ragged overcoat that made it look like a bundle of brown rags.

But she had nothing to go on yet, nothing at all. All she saw was an old man in shabby clothes walking into a post office. It was a poor neighbourhood, and there must be thousands of men in this area alone who looked like him. Yet, as he passed her, she seemed to sense an atmosphere, an aura round him, which was as strong as a physical smell. She suddenly felt like a book-collector, bent over an old volume he has never seen listed in a catalogue, who all at once hears a voice saying "Buy me" from the yellow pages. She was almost certain that her first hunch was right, and this was the person whom Vanin wanted her to follow.

The man walked across to the left-hand counter and leaned against the wire grill. He spoke through his muffler, and though Kate couldn't distinguish the words, he seemed to be a regular visitor. Without answering him at first, the clerk turned to a row of pigeon-holes behind him and pulled out a letter. He grinned slightly as he slid it under the wire.

"I hope this is the one you've been expecting," he said.

"Yes, I've been expecting it all right. I've been expecting it for a long time." Through the woollen muffler his voice sounded like something rotten breaking in two. He turned away from the counter and stood quite still for a moment, staring at the envelope and balancing it in his hand, as though hoping to judge its contents from the weight and texture. Kate prayed for him to open it.

But he didn't open it—not just then. For perhaps half a minute he held it like that, turning it over and over in an oddly claw-like hand, while she watched him with all pretence of letter-writing forgotten. Let him just break the flap, and she would know what to do and have the sign that Vanin had promised: transparent powders putting their mark on him and turning red against the moisture of human skin. He pushed the envelope away into the folds of his coat and began to move towards the door.

But she had to be sure. Vanin had told her that his plan was partly a gamble and depended on the man opening the letter in front of her. All she had to go on was a hunch, and this man might be anyone: an old-age pensioner collecting a long-expected present from some distant son or daughter, a boarding-house tenant wishing to conceal his mail from a prying landlady. If she were to follow him now, the person they wanted might come later and she would have failed. She stood by the counter, completely irresolute, and then suddenly her body stiffened, and she knew she was right. She was quite prepared to bet on her hunch, and she recognized the aura this man carried. It was not illness or nervousness, as Vanin suggested, but something much more simple: plain anger. For as he pulled back the door, his face turned slightly towards hers, and she looked at his eyes. A pair of old, tired and probably feeble eyes, but there was as much malice in them as she had seen on a human face. She tucked away her pad, dropped the two finished letters into a post-box, and followed him out into the street.

It was a long, slow walk, and the old man was a difficult person to follow. He moved carefully across the frozen pavements, as though fearing a fall, and he paused for a moment at every corner. In the crowded streets, with shops and hurrying pedestrians, it wasn't too hard, of course, for Kate could stop when he did and peer into a shop window. But soon they were on the long stretch of arterial road, with streams of traffic pouring into London but no shops and almost deserted pavements. She kept well behind him, walking very slowly and praying he wouldn't turn round.

They were almost to the river now. The towers of the bridge loomed high above them like fairy-tale castles, and from the opposite bank she could hear a rattle of road-drills—very faint and muffled through the frozen air. The man paused before the bridge for a moment, as though uncertain of his way, then he turned right and walked down a flight of steps leading to the tow-path.

The tide was very high, and the water reached nearly up to the lip of the embankment. As they walked along the narrow track, a tug swung under the bridge, dragging a line of barges, and from far down-stream Kate heard the distant howl of a ship's siren. The Thames suddenly seemed an unfriendly river: the colour of dull lead, with a big oil streak drifting in mid-stream and the white flashes of gulls screaming round a mooring-buoy. She kept well in against the wall, walking slowly, and all at once she felt that the world had died, and she and that muffled figure were the only creatures left in it.

For the man had stopped. He had stopped and pulled something out of his pocket, and he was looking at it. He had turned round and had started to walk back towards her. Kate crossed to the embankment and lit a cigarette, leaning out over the grey water, and watching the tug begin to swing its barges round a bend. In the road above, buses churned through the snow, and the

road-drills sounded like distant gun-fire. She was in the heart of
London and all around her were commonplace, familiar things;
so why was she afraid? Why did she stiffen as those dragging footsteps walked slowly towards her, and feel so completely alone, as
a brown arm came up and its hand rested on the parapet beside
her? She worked for one of the toughest organizations in the
world, and her training had been thorough. All the same, she
suddenly felt like a frightened child, as he looked down at her
and she felt his aura as positive as gas turning into a solid.

"Well, young lady, let's have a little talk, shall we? Just why
are you following me?" The man's thick voice brushed aside her
protest, and as he spoke the muffler slipped down to show the
face behind it. The face was without scar or blemish, but still like
something out of a nightmare, and it needed a cliché to describe
it. A rat's face, stripped of the fur which at least gave it some
concealment and dignity—an old, grey grandfather of the sewers
grinning before he started to gnaw his way into a corpse. As she
looked at it, Kate seemed to see right through the flesh and bone,
and make out the years of hate and bitterness that had turned
that face into the dreadful thing it was.

"Oh yes, you were following me all right. I saw you in the post
office, and I came down here just to make sure. Besides, I was
half expecting to be followed, you know. Your employer is not
an intelligent man, though it seems I didn't give him enough
credit." He lifted his hand and she saw that Vanin's powder had
done its job. The fingers were stained a dark, reddish-brown.

"Yes, a good idea, but we can stop playing games now. I would
have liked to keep Sir Martin in suspense for a little longer, but
it doesn't matter now—no, it doesn't really matter." His smile
grew even wider and there was no mistaking the mania behind it.

"And here is what you want, my dear. Here is the thing you
were paid to find out—my name and address. How much will you
be paid, I wonder? How much can a little secretary girl get for
helping such a great man?" A piece of paper was thrust into
Kate's hand as he spoke, and at the same time his face began to
creep closer to hers. Closer and closer it came, with foul breath
like sewer-gas around her and the stained fingers tilting her chin
upwards. And as she looked into those mad eyes, she knew quite
clearly what was going to happen. She also knew that there was
nothing to be done about it; no struggle, no running away or
calling for help, nothing at all. It was not she, but the job that
mattered, so let her once call out and everything would be
finished.

"And now you're going to pay me, my dear," he said. "I want you to tell your master that you paid for the information he wanted." There was a hand on her shoulder now, but she didn't resist, didn't even try to resist, though it was like the end of the world. She just stood there, still and passive, as the hand tightened, his face touched hers, and slowly and deliberately the grey lips found her mouth.

*　　　*　　　*

"Sorry, my dear, I really am very sorry." Peter Vanin listened to Kate's voice on the phone, feeling the nausea in it, and his own voice was very gentle. "Yes, unpleasant things happen on our job sometimes, but you must just accept them, I'm afraid. And I'm very grateful that you didn't resist him, that might have spoiled everything.

"Now, after he kissed you, he just walked off, leaving you with his name and address? Could I have it please? Thanks: John Flack, 32 Silver Pine Grove, Putney." He made a note in his pocket-book.

"And don't worry, Kate. Don't worry at all. You'll get over what happened soon enough, but I can promise you one thing. It may take Mr Flack quite a long time to forget what I do to him. Goodbye now, and thanks again."

He replaced the phone and stood quite still for a moment, staring round the empty hall of his hotel. His face was a blank mask showing no emotion at all. Then, as though reaching a sudden decision, he picked up the phone again and started to dial another number. He might be breaking orders, as Malendin had told him to work on his own as much as possible, but he was beginning to feel out of his depth. Very soon he would be dealing with a very unpleasant form of maniac, and he needed a specialist on his side. When he made his next move, it would be with reinforcements.

*　　　*　　　*

Quiet suburban streets on a quiet winter's evening, with the thawing snow lying in patches on the roofs and the pavements and the little, well-kept gardens. Well-kept houses too, with paths leading up to them, and sham Tudor timbers on the stucco, and the names of honeymoons above every door—Tintagel, Napoli, Costa Brava. Here and there curtains were drawn back from the windows, giving glimpses of Christmas trees and families settled round the fire or television set. A pleasant, respectable neighbourhood, with an air of cosiness and warmth and nice people. Men with steady jobs, women with children at private schools, a car in the garage, money in the bank, and little latticed windows to shut out the cold. And outside, in the cold, a man on his way to keep an appointment.

Peter Vanin walked slowly down Silver Pine Grove, and somehow he seemed to fit into the area: a senior clerk coming home from work to an evening by the fire—books and slippers and children and warm things. There was a slight envy in his eyes as he looked at those well-kept houses, but now and then he smiled as he read the names. A postman's job in England must need a great deal of skill and perseverance, he decided.

Thirty—Ben Nevis, Thirty-One—Sans Souci, Thirty-Two—No, there was no name by that number, no little glowing lantern in the porch, no air of careful, middle-class prosperity. The garden was choked with weeds, and the privet hedge by the wall had grown into fair-sized trees, reaching the height of the roof and giving the building the appearance of a gigantic mass of vegetation. No chink of light came from the windows, but somehow Vanin knew the house was occupied. It had the feeling of something out of one of Grimm's grimmer fairy-stories: a dwelling hidden away in the woods and waiting for a visitor.

He pulled back the rusty gate and walked across the ruin of a garden. The stucco of the house crumbled before the pressure of the bushes, leaving naked patches of brickwork exposed, and the door looked as though it had not been painted since the house was built. He pressed the switch in the porch, and very faint and far away in the distance heard a bell ringing.

For a long time he stood there, but no one came. Across the street a familiar scene was being enacted. A shiny car drew up, turned into the drive, and a bowler-hatted man got out and walked quickly and happily towards his front door—his own door which had probably been paid for, like everything else he owned. As the door opened, Vanin saw a woman come forward to kiss him, and heard the sound of music and children's laughter.

Once again he pressed the bell, and at last he heard boards creak, and heavy, slow footsteps coming towards him. There was the sound of a bolt being withdrawn and the rattle of a chain. Then the door opened about six inches, and he looked at the face of a man he had come all the way from Moscow to see.

And though he had come prepared for something unpleasant, though Kate had described it to him, Vanin drew back slightly as he looked at the face of John Flack. There was something obscene about it, something horrible in that low, hairless skull, with its skin wrinkled like old leather as it joined the sagging features. Something unspeakable in the twisted, malicious mouth and the eyes that seemed to glow in the darkness of the hall. He felt a sudden pity for Martin Rolfe as he looked at that face. Whoever he was, whatever he knew, John Flack would be a very horrible enemy.

"So my friend has sent another representative, has he?" Like his face, Flack's voice was just as Kate had described it: thick and muddy, and it seemed to come from deep down in his body. "Yes, Sir Martin has been very smart, hasn't he? He puts stain on a letter and gets a little girl to follow me. But when I give her the address and he knows where I am, he doesn't come himself. It's strange, that, and I wonder why. Is it that he couldn't come, perhaps—that he was too ill to come?" The voice broke off into a cackle of laughter.

"Mr Flack, could I come inside and talk to you? It's very cold out here." Vanin forced his face into a smile.

"Yes of course you can come in, though there's very little to talk about. I'm only talking to the person I addressed my letters to." Flack lowered the chain and pulled open the door. "Well, welcome to my castle," he said. "But don't try anything—just be very careful. I may be an old man, but I'm quite ready for you."

He raised his hand to show what it held: a big, heavy revolver, slightly reminiscent of a Frontier Colt. In his time, Vanin had made a study of guns, and he recognized the type: a forty-five calibre Webley, British Officers' Standard Pattern, First World War Issue.

"No, I won't try anything," he said, smiling at the revolver. "Not while you're holding that." He walked past Flack into the house, smelling the mustiness of it that came from old books, rotting timber and years of neglect. There was also another chemical smell which he seemed to remember but couldn't quite place.

"In here, please." Flack pulled back another door on the right of the hall and motioned him through. As Vanin entered the room, he stood quite still for a moment staring around him, for it was like something out of a nightmare.

A big, rather graceful room, probably designed as a parlour, but its builder wouldn't have liked it now. Instead of curtains, the windows were covered by sacking, and dust and cobwebs lay everywhere. An old-fashioned oil-heater glowed dully in the grate, and all over the floor there were books—hundreds of books.

Some of them lay in shelves, some were spread out on the table, but most of them were piled on the worn linoleum; one or two of the piles nearly reached to the ceiling. As they walked forward, Vanin saw a mouse regarding him gravely from behind a large, leather-bound volume. It seemed to be completely without fear.

But it wasn't the books, or the dirt, or the old, broken furniture that interested him; it was the walls—the walls and the pictures on them. Pictures that had been cut from newspapers and magazines, and pasted roughly on to the plaster; pictures of just one subject. From every corner of the big, dusty room the face of Martin Rolfe seemed to be watching him.

"No, your employer can't say I neglect him, can he?" Flack waved Vanin to the one chair that the room possessed and stood with his back to the smoking oil-stove. He still kept the revolver in his hand. "Now, let's get down to facts, shall we, Mister—thank you—Mr Vanin? Just what message did Rolfe tell you to give me?"

Vanin didn't answer for a moment. Very slowly, to gain time, he pulled off his gloves and laid them on the arm of the chair. He had to consider carefully before he made a move. His first plan had been to pose as a representative of Rolfe's, but that wouldn't work now. Every line of that sagging, rat-like face told him it wouldn't work.

"There's no message, Mr Flack," he said. "There couldn't be a message, because I haven't come from Rolfe, you see. Like you, I am an enemy of Rolfe's, and I work for quite a different organization."

"I see. Then you'd better start to tell me about it, Mr Vanin. You'd better tell me quickly." The gun began to come up as he spoke. "Just who are you, and who do you work for?"

"That doesn't matter." Vanin leaned forward, ignoring the gun. "All you need to know is that we are people who can pay you—pay you well." He reached in his pocket and pulled out his wallet. The ridge of notes showed like a blue tongue against the leather. "We know that you have certain information about Rolfe, and I have come to buy it from you."

"So that's it?" Once again Flack gave that short cackle of laughter that had nothing to do with humour. "No, you can put away your money, I have nothing to sell you. My information is very private and I need it all for my own use. Now, just how did you find out about it, and what do you know about me?"

"We know nothing about you personally, Mr Flack, except that you are a man who can help us. All we know is that during the last few weeks Martin Rolfe has been receiving letters from you, and he is very, very frightened by those letters. The first one was enough to give him a minor heart-attack." He saw a glow of satisfaction light up the man's face as he spoke. "Well, it doesn't matter how, but we managed to intercept one of those letters, and I have traced you through it. Now I want to talk business. We want to buy a share of this information which could give a man like Rolfe a heart-attack. We want to know what is the thing you refer to as the Gaunt Woman."

"The *thing*—you say the *thing*!" This time Flack's laugh was quite genuine: a great convulsive belch of laughter that echoed around the room. "No, you don't really know anything, do you, Mr Vanin? You call her a *thing*."

He laid the gun down on a table and leaned back against the mantelpiece, with his arms stretched out behind him. There was an oddly crucified look about the posture of his body, as though nails were holding it in position.

"The Gaunt Woman is not a thing, my friend, but a person—a sort of person, that is. She was born on Christmas Eve exactly twenty years ago, and she died the same day. Only a few people ever saw her, and she was soon forgotten; even I forgot her. Then one evening when I was sitting in this room, I looked at a picture in a magazine, and I saw her ghost. And as I saw it, I knew that I held the great Sir Martin Rolfe in the hollow of my hand. And that's the only clue I'm going to give you, Mr Vanin. The rest of the story you can discover for yourself."

In the hollow of my hand! As he listened, Vanin suddenly remembered Malendin's use of exactly the same phrase. He looked up at the man's evil, but not entirely mad face, and slowly he pushed the wallet away, for he knew what he was dealing with. Flack didn't want money from him. Flack didn't want anything except the infliction of pain. His first attack had failed, it seemed, and those reinforcements would be needed. Somehow Flack must be made to talk, but that wasn't Vanin's job any more. Even the department wouldn't want that, for it believed in specialists for such work. Outside, in the quiet, respectable street, one of those specialists would be waiting now, and it was he who would have to find out the story of the Gaunt Woman. All the same, there was one thing he wanted to know before he handed over.

"Tell me something," he said. "Just what did Rolfe do to make you hate him so much?"

"He didn't do anything. He just *succeeded*—like I would have succeeded if they'd given me a chance." There was a strange accentuation of the word, and in the man's face Vanin seemed to see years of pain, and emptiness, and hate which had turned to mania. Mania which made him hunt magazines and newspapers for pictures of his enemy, and paste them on his walls to keep the hate fresh and healthy.

"Succeeded? I'm afraid I don't understand you."

"No, you won't understand; nobody ever understands, nobody even tries to." The words were like an often-repeated litany, and Vanin could imagine him muttering them to himself over and over again.

"But try and understand, Mr Vanin. Try and understand what it feels like to know that you should have got on—should have come to the top; but always stayed down in the gutter.

"Oh yes, I know them, the people who succeed, the people like Rolfe. At school and university, with their nice manners and accents to please the teachers and dons. Not working any harder than I did, no brighter than I was, but always coming top; always getting the Alpha Plus, when I had the Beta Minus." The words rambled on and on like a prayer to the great god whose name was Hatred.

"And afterwards, in business, always the same people fighting to the top, and not caring who they trampled on in their way. 'Fetch this, Flack'—'You'll have to stay and work late tonight, Flack'—'Take your wages and get out.' Then they ride home to their women in big, flashy cars while I wait in the gutter.

"Yes, their women!" His tongue ran over his grey lips as he spoke the word. "They always have the best women, don't they? Women worship success, and they take their pick. I had a woman once, you know. For ten years I was married; all happy and secure till one of them kicked me out of my job, and she left me. Went off with a more successful man who could support her properly, the bitch said. A good man too, she says he is. Allows me to live in my own house, he does, his house, of course, since he took over my debts and the mortgage. I think I'd have hated the bastard less if he hadn't done that."

"Yes, I think I'm beginning to understand you." Vanin realized that though Flack had failed in everything, he would have been a great success in other ages and countries. With his two virtues of hate and envy, he would have made an excellent Christian-persecutor, witch-hunter or Jew-baiter. "Yes, I know how you feel. Your life has gone wrong, so you hate people who have been more successful. But why Rolfe in particular?"

"No, you don't understand, Mr Vanin. I don't hate Rolfe in

particular, but he's one of them; one little soldier in that huge army of the successful; one of the people who kept me down." The beads of sweat on his forehead looked slightly indecent; a disease against the grey, wrinkled skin.

"But I dreamed of getting one of them, you know. For years I dreamed about it. Just the thought of getting one of those little gold and silver soldiers in my power and making him squirm. But sometimes dreams come true, don't they? Mine did. One day I saw a certain picture and it told me something about Sir Martin Rolfe—something which could break him. I may be a failure, Mr Vanin, but I'm not a fool. I put two and two together and I made certain inquiries. Now there is one little gold soldier safe in my box, with the lid closed down on him. And when he comes out, he'll be mad, you know—as mad as you probably think I am." He smiled suddenly with the terrible sanity of the insane.

"No, I don't think you're mad, Mr Flack." Vanin forced the disgust out of his voice. He remembered what had happened to Kate, and there was nothing he would have liked better than to pull out his little pen-gun and put a bullet through Flack's forehead. He wasn't paid to do that, though. For the time being at least, he was paid to be nice to Flack. "No, you're not mad," he said. "But neither am I one of your army of the successful. So can't we do business and help each other? As I said, I'm prepared to pay well for your information." This was Vanin's last appeal, and if it failed, he would hand over to someone else. In a way he hoped that Flack wouldn't take it.

Flack didn't take it. He straightened from the mantelpiece and picked up the gun, toying with it in his hand.

"No," he said. "We can't do business, and I don't want your money. As this room may show you, I have a job. I deal in second-hand books. A runner, they call it; the lowest form of life in the trade. Still, by bringing goods to the more successful, I make a little money. Enough to allow me to eat and indulge in my rather childish hobby. You might be able to guess what it is, Mr Vanin. I play with toy soldiers. Little gold and silver soldiers who know how to die well."

He reached into his jacket and held something out in his left hand: a knight in armour that glittered strangely as though with a life of its own. Then he pushed it back into the musty prison of his pocket.

"And now, Mr Vanin, I want you to leave me alone, and I've said all I'm going to say. And don't come back either." He had stopped playing with the gun now, and it was pointing at Vanin's heart. "The information I have is my own, and I'm not selling it to anyone. But if you really hate Rolfe, don't worry about him any more. When I've finished with him, Sir Martin Rolfe will be dead—dead or insane." He turned and walked towards the door.

As Vanin followed him, he glanced back at the gloves he had left lying on the chair. A nice pair of leather gloves looking quite innocent on the worn cloth, but to him they were not just gloves, but a key. A key that would open the door to his reinforcements.

"Good night," he said, and without another word stepped out into the dark.

CHAPTER FIVE

THE man that Gregor Tanek had sent stood at the corner of the road, and there was no mistaking him. As arranged, his fawn-coloured overcoat had been left open to show a bow-tie, and his trilby hat had a little feather set jauntily in the band. There was a briefcase in his left hand, and his right toyed with a cigarette-lighter. He was very beautiful and smelt strongly of scent.

"Ah, good evening, old boy." He responded to Vanin's curt nod with a smile that lit up his whole face, and fell into step beside him. There was a certain grace in his walk, a smooth rotundity of movement that a woman might have envied. "Well, do we go to work straight away, or may I have a little briefing first?" Vanin winced slightly as he listened to his voice, and he was almost sure he could recognize the accent.

"Sind Sie Deutsch?" he said quietly.

"Am I German!" The man raised his eyebrows slightly. "Good heavens no, old chap. British—British as the flag, though I was born under a bluer sky than usually surrounds these miserable islands. I'm South-African Dutch by birth; a Boer, as some people are pleased to call us. And by the way, my Christian name is Julius. My poor dear father had a great passion for Roman history. The other name doesn't matter, does it?"

"No, the surname never matters, and naturally we must talk first."

Vanin withdrew his arm hurriedly as the man's fingers touched his sleeve, steering him across the road, as though he were a short-sighted and very valuable old lady.

"Good. Then let's do it in comfort, shall we, Comrade?" The word sounded like the insult it was intended to be. "On my way here I happened to notice a little eating-place round the corner. Nothing grand, but it looked quiet and comfortable enough. As it happens, I'm just longing for a cup of coffee." There was a slight gleam in his eyes as he hurried forward.

The café stood at the very end of Silver Pine Grove, where suburbia proper meets the main road and dies. As he had said, it was very quiet; empty, in fact, except for a solitary waitress who looked as if her sole ambition in life was to sleep. Julius beamed as she placed the cups in front of them, and then shook his head sadly over the half-empty sugar-basin.

"I wonder, my dear," he said, "if you'd be very, very kind and fill this up for us. I do so like a really sweet drink. Oh, thank you—thank you very much indeed." He shovelled four spoonfuls into his cup and stirred it to a thick syrup, grinning at Vanin as he did so. His hand looked rather unpleasant. The middle fingers were of equal length.

"I'm afraid I've got a terribly sweet tooth," he said. His age could have been anything between thirty and forty, but his face was white and unlined: a pallid wax tablet on which the years had not written a single word. A face that could be capable of anything or nothing. "And now should we get down to the sordid details? Your colleagues are always so cagey, and they told me nothing on the phone. They merely said I was to meet you here, wearing these clothes and juggling my cigarette lighter in a rather ridiculous manner. All I really did gather was that we have to make a man sing."

"To sing!" Vanin frowned and shook his head. "I'm sorry, but I'm afraid I don't understand."

"Oh dear! How very stupid of me." Julius raised his hands in self-depreciation. "Your English is so good, old chap, that I keep forgetting you are a foreigner. 'To make a person sing' is a term used largely by the British criminal classes and writers of detective fiction. It means to make him talk—to give evidence—to spill the beans—oh dear! There I go again."

"That's all right, I know what you mean now." Vanin waved aside the cigarettes he offered. They were Egyptian and had little green bands round the mouthpiece. "The position is this. There is a man in the house I came out of who has certain information my department needs. I have been unable to get it by normal methods, so I have asked for your help. Your job is to put him into the right frame of mind to give me that information. How you go about it is none of my business, but I was told you are efficient."

"Oh, don't worry about that. I'm efficient all right, and I've had very thorough training. Your people wouldn't pay me a very generous retainer if I weren't." Julius looked slightly put out: a ballerina unrecognized at the stage-door. "All the same, I'm not a miracle-worker, and I need certain information. If this chap of yours is to break, I've got to know something about him. People react to different stimuli, you see. What may work with one man may have no effect on another. Tell me about this fellow: age, character, medical history and so on.

"I see." He listened to Vanin's description of John Flack, and shook his head sadly.

"A nut case, eh? With a deep hatred of people he considers more successful than himself. Probably a psychopath, I should say, and they are always the most difficult subjects to deal with; a real passion for martyrdom at times, poor lambs.

"And old too! Old and rather decayed. Dear me, this is going to be very difficult. Physical pain would be very little use and might kill him before he spoke a word." There was a sudden sadness in that smooth, pale face, and Vanin saw that Julius enjoyed his job. "No, I'll just have to rely on drugs, and I don't like that— I don't like it at all. It's always such a gamble."

"A gamble? But I thought——"

"Oh yes, you thought they were all proved, and tried out, and a hundred per cent reliable, didn't you? Well, you are quite right, old boy, but only when a great deal of patient research has gone before—when the person in question has been thoroughly examined both physically and mentally. The drug merely lowers the powers of resistance, and then we have to persuade the subject that he wants to talk—that it is in his own best interest to talk. You're asking me to treat a complete stranger almost on the spur of the moment." Julius shook his head as though pitying the ignorance of all laymen.

"He's alone in the house, you say? Good, that's something in our favour at least. And you left your gloves behind, as an excuse for going back; very thoughtful." He nodded pleasantly. "But he has a gun—how very trying of him. Nobody can say we're over-paid, and I do so hate physical violence. All the same, we are paid, so we'll just have to do our best."

He opened his case and transferred two objects into a pocket. Then he handed it to Vanin.

"You'd better take this, if you don't mind, old boy. I'll be needing my hands free when the time comes." He stood up and looked sadly round the little, warm café.

"Ah, Duty," he said. " 'Duty, stern daughter of the voice of God.' "

But for all his effeminate, pretentious manner, Julius was efficient, and he knew his job. Vanin stood back in the shadow of the hedge watching him, and he saw efficiency in that quiet unhurried walk up to the house, the relaxed body, and the gloved hands hanging loosely at his side: the hands of an expert about to perform a task he understood perfectly. John Flack might have a dozen guns, but he wouldn't stand a chance.

It was over quickly too; so quickly that Vanin could hardly make out the details. He saw the door drag back a little against the chain, saw Flack's face peering out, and at the same moment something happened to his face. Something like a black animal appeared to leap out of Julius's hand and attach itself there, while his other hand came up with a thin steel bar in it. The noise of splintering wood was like a little sigh, and then the door fell open. Vanin gave a final glance along the street, and walked up the path to the house.

"Well, so far, so good." Julius grinned and bolted the door. "And now perhaps I'd better release our friend before his lungs are past repair."

He bent down towards Flack. The man was crawling on the floor, as though in extreme agony, but he didn't make any noise. His hands were tearing at an obscene black mass that clung to his face like a leech.

"Yes, we'll have you all nice and comfortable in a moment, old chap, but first we must protect our own interests." He kicked the gun to one side and tied Flack's wrists together with a length of wire, leaving an end loose. Then he reached for the black thing over his face. It came away with a loud sucking sound, and the flesh behind it was a bright, mottled scarlet. The repulsive mouth was wide open, dragging in great gulps of air, and the eyes were glazed like marbles.

"Now don't worry, my dear. You'll be quite all right in a moment—right as rain." He held up the thing in his hand and smiled at Vanin. "Neat, isn't it? My own invention and I'm rather proud of it. A plastic mask fitted with a vacuum bottle. Sticks to anything it touches like a limpet, and is almost impossible to take off, unless you know where the valve is. The pain is very considerable, of course, and one has to be careful. Just a little too much suction and the lungs would burst. And that would be most unfortunate, wouldn't it? Ah, so you've recovered, have you? And I must say you're no beauty either."

He dragged Flack to his feet, and neatly pasted a strip of plaster across his mouth. "No, it would never do to disturb the neighbours at this time of night. Now, where shall we take him? I want a couch or a sofa of some kind. Even a table would do at a pinch. In here, perhaps." He nodded at a door beside him.

"No, I don't think that's much use. Let's try this one." Vanin remembered the piles of books that almost filled the room, and he opened the opposite door and pressed the electric switch beside it.

"Well, well," he said, and there was a great curiosity in his eyes. "He really did play with soldiers."

The room was completely bare and without ornament, with naked plaster staring out at them. Its windows had been bricked up and replaced by air vents, and the floor was concrete. The general effect was of a military bunker, but that was not the interesting thing about the room. The interest lay in the tables and the glittering figures on them. Four long iron tables in lines, and every table supported a battlefield, with soldiers that seemed to glow with a strange, unearthly light that wasn't just a reflection from the unshaded lamp in the ceiling: Greeks at Marathon with fire on their shields; a Waterloo square standing in burning uniforms before shining French cavalry; a Roman cohort glittering as they marched. John Flack's hobby was a novel one at least; he didn't merely play with soldiers, he gave them life too— glowing light. Toys of victory for a man who only believed in defeat. It would have been funny if it weren't so horrible.

"Yes, I think this will do us very well." Julius ran his hand across the nearest table, and the armies of Gettysburg fell in heaps to the floor. Then, as easily as lifting a child, he swung Flack on to the table and secured his wrists to the top of the legs.

"Yes, very significant, isn't it? Our friend feels embittered because of failure, so he plays with soldiers. Even makes his room look like part of a fortress. Probably imagines himself to be Caesar or Napoleon from time to time. Very typical and gives us a good picture of his character.

"Rather a dangerous hobby though, I think. This lighting effect puzzles me a little. I wonder if he has produced some form of artificial phosphorescence, which he paints on his toys to make them glow." He picked up the tiny figure of a Confederate horseman and sniffed at it, looking at the bench by the wall as he did so. A big glass jar stood on it, filled with water that covered a number of pale yellow objects, the size and shape of very small cigars.

"Yes, he has indeed, the clever old devil. That's yellow phosphorus all right, and it's one of the most unpleasant substances known. Quite safe when diluted or kept under water, of course, but expose it to air and you get a very nasty reaction." He shook his little finger at the bound body on the table.

"You really should be more careful, old chap," he said, and then took the bag from Vanin and pulled out a bottle and a hypodermic syringe.

"And now I think you'd better leave me alone with him for a bit. Sorry to kick you out, but a third person in the room might distract our friend. And though you're probably a good materialist, you might say a little prayer for me. When I've given him his shots, one of three things is going to happen. It may not take at all, and we'll have to try another method. It may work and he'll be as co-operative as a lamb. Finally, it may drive him right round the bend, and we'll get nothing from him. Just wish me luck and pray that that doesn't happen.

He watched Vanin go out and close the door behind him, then he opened his bottle. There was an odd look in his eyes as he started to fill the syringe: a professional and strangely proud look. He might have been a surgeon about to save a child's life.

It wasn't long, but it seemed like hours. Vanin stood in the hall, with the atmosphere of the house all round him like a physical thing, and his body felt as cold as death. In a few minutes, if the man who called himself Julius knew his trade, he would learn Flack's secret, but there would be no triumph or pleasure in it. He was paid to do a job, and he would do it to the best of his ability, but he hated the job now. The thought of Flack's rat-like mouth reaching for Kate's, and Julius with his torturer's hands, had killed all pleasure. He even felt a slight pity for Sir Martin Rolfe; whatever the man had done, he was the victim of a monster. At the moment he had just one ambition in life: to get out of that mouldering, decayed house and walk among normal people, whatever their race, or jobs or politics. A little clock ticked noisily on the wall above him, and a mouse ran across the floor. Now and again he heard the voice of Julius through the door: a very firm, but quite impersonal voice, which seemed to have lost all trace of individuality. Then the voice stopped, feet came towards him, and the door opened.

"Well, did the stuff work? Will he talk?"

"Yes, I think so, but I'm not sure. I want him to have a few minutes on his own before I start asking questions." Julius lit a cigarette and inhaled deeply like a man who has just finished a hard piece of work. "No, I'm not certain how he's going to react, and I was right, you know. Mr Flack is a psychopath, and we can never tell which way they'll go. I've already given him nearly double the normal first dose as it is; almost enough to kill him, in fact. And that reminds me——" He raised his eyebrows slightly. "If you get what you want, do we have to kill him?"

"Yes, we have to kill him." There was no expression on Vanin's face. "You have to kill him, that is. As you told me, you are well paid."

"Oh, very well, old boy, I was just inquiring, not complaining. Now just what do you want me to ask him?" He grinned at Vanin's frown and shook his head. "No, I'm sorry, but I'll have to do the talking. That's quite essential if we're going to get anything out of him at all."

"Very well." Though Vanin hated confiding in Julius, the man obviously knew his business and was in charge now. "Flack has some sort of hold on a senior adviser to the British Government named Martin Rolfe. He has been writing him letters which at first seemed to be preparations for a blackmail attempt, but now appear to have been sent for personal spite. Whatever the motive, however, Rolfe has been terrified by them, and it is my job to find out what Flack's hold over him is. The only clue we have so far is something he refers to as the Gaunt Woman."

"The Gaunt Woman! How very romantic of him! Very well, let's see what he will tell us. Stand in the doorway, will you, and don't make any noise at all." He glanced at his watch and walked back into the room.

John Flack lay still on the table, but he looked quite different, and his face had altered. All the hate seemed to have been drained out of it, and only hate had given it life and character. It was a dead, vacant face now: the rather unpleasant mask of a puppet. Mr Punch lying in his box and waiting for somebody to pull the strings. The plaster had been removed from his mouth, but the wire still held his wrists.

"All right, old chap, here we go again." Julius stood beside the table, but he didn't look at Flack. He seemed to take care not to look at him. A few feet away from them the armies of Waterloo glowed like stars. "Now you know who I am, John, don't you? You know that I am your friend, and I have come here to help you—only to help you."

"To help me! Yes, that is right. You said you would help me." Like his face, Flack's voice was completely dead and expressionless: a sound like air being pumped through the body of a corpse.

"Yes, I'm your friend, John, and you must trust me. You must tell me something so that I can help you." Julius's voice hardened slightly. "Just what is it that you know about a man named Martin Rolfe?"

"Rolfe—Martin Rolfe. Yes, I know about him. He's the one I got, and I'm going—I'm going to break him."

"Yes, that's right, you want to ruin him, don't you? People have treated you very badly in life, John, and now you can get your own back at last. You know something about Martin Rolfe and you can break him. Now tell me about it, John. I'm your friend, so tell me what you know about Rolfe."

"I can destroy him, I can break him—any time I want to." The mouth creased a little as he spoke, and there was something horrible in the sight of that dead face smiling.

"Yes, I know that, John, but tell me how. Just how can you break him?"

"Because I've got a good memory. I saw a picture and I recognized her at last. More than twenty years ago it must have been, but I never realized the truth then. It all seemed so obvious then, because she'd done it twice before. She was standing outside that shop window, and it was snowing—snowing hard it was, and it's difficult to make out details in the snow. Very tall she looked— very tall and thin, with hair like . . ."

"Go on, John. Go on and tell me. Just what was her hair like?"

"It was like—like the things I saw in that picture. No, it's so long ago, and I can't describe it—I just can't remember."

"But you must remember, John. You have to remember, because I'm your friend, and I want to help you. I can't help you unless you tell me the truth." Julius still looked away from him, but there was a sudden urgency in his voice.

"Go on now," he said. "A long time ago you saw someone standing outside a shop window. It was snowing heavily and you couldn't see her too well, though. Later on you recognized that person from a picture: a person who has something to do with Martin Rolfe. Well, who is she, John? Is she the person you called the Gaunt Woman?" Julius brought his hand down with a crash on the table. "Tell me now, John. Just who is the Gaunt Woman?"

"The Gaunt Wooo———" The word broke off as though Flack had been gagged, and at the same moment, and without any warning, his face came alive again and it happened. From where he stood Vanin saw every detail, but he had no time to act, only to call out.

"Julius," he said. "Look out, Julius!"

But it was too late. Julius had his face turned away from Flack, and he never saw the sudden light in those mad eyes, or the body starting to swing towards him. Flack's knees caught him in the small of his back and he fell sideways, cannoning against the bench as he did so. The glass jar dropped to the floor and broke. A heap of little cigar-shaped objects lay beside him on the concrete.

It was only seconds, but it felt like a year. Vanin hurled himself forward, but it was to Flack, not Julius, that he went. Julius was unimportant now. He had made a mistake, and would just have to look after himself.

But Flack was still important. Flack was the one person in the case who mattered, and without him they might never learn the secret of Sir Martin Rolfe. Vanin's fingers tore madly at the wire that held him to the table, and as he did so he heard a little crackling noise like dry leaves in the wind, and smelt burnt garlic. He knew exactly what was going to happen, and he strained still harder at the wire, hearing the crackle grow to a roar and the smell thicken into white vapour.

A moment later the wire broke, but it was too late. The bench, half the room, and Julius were a mass of flame.

* * *

Five miles away from Flack's house there was an office whose windows were tightly closed. They were always closed after dusk, for the occupant of the office distrusted the night air. Thick curtains covered them to cut out the merest suspicion of a draught, and at the other side of the room, an enormous coke stove glowed in the grate. There was also an electric fire working at full capacity by the desk. The room was like something out of Dante's *Inferno*, but to General Charles Kirk, Head of Her Majesty's Foreign Intelligence Service, it was a near approach to heaven. Smiling like a well-fed cat, he laid down the cigar with which he had been thickening the already overpowering atmosphere, and nodded slightly.

"Yes, Igor," he said. "You've done very well, haven't you—very well indeed. Let me be the first to congratulate you."

"Thank you, sir."

The man across the desk was tall, stooping and completely hairless. His dark suit was dandified, and there was a bright flower in his buttonhole. His bored, slightly vacant expression gave him the air of a well-bred rentier, but the air was false. He worked very hard for his living, and he had been born in a

Paris slum. His name was Igor Trubenoff, chief of the department dealing with Soviet Russia, and at the moment a very self-satisfied man.

"Yes, things are going very nicely on the whole. We've got that rendezvous at Narleen in Southern Ireland completely tied up now. Nobody can go in or out without our full knowledge."

"Yes, so you've told me many times, Igor, with a great deal of pride. As I've said, I'm pleased with you. Now I suppose we'll just have to wait, and hope that before long a little mouse will come creeping in between our paws." Kirk's right hand, which lacked three fingers, drummed quietly on the desk as he spoke.

"No, General, as it happens, we don't have to wait. The mouse has already arrived. He was landed from one of their trawlers yesterday morning. Here's my first report on him." Trubenoff slid a typewritten folio across the desk.

"Thank you, Igor. I see, a man called Vanin—Peter Vanin. Yes, this is beginning to interest me slightly." His heavy, well-bred features showed no expression as he read down the page.

"Strange, isn't it?" he said as he pushed it away from him. "This Vanin seems to be quite an important man, so why should they send him over here now? They had quite a nasty jolt over that Lonsdale affair and have been lying low recently. Why should they risk a man like this Vanin now?" Once again he looked at the paper.

"Yes, educated at the Leningrad Police Academy—attached to the embassy over here in '41—chief—yes, *chief* Soviet adviser to the Hungarian secret police after the uprising. No, Mr Peter Vanin isn't one of their usual hare-brained fanatics, but a real professional. Something pretty important must have sent him over. I'd very much like to know what our friend Colonel Malendin is up to this time." He leaned back in his chair and pulled hard on the cigar. Then he pointed it at Trubenoff like a weapon.

"Well, Igor, let's have the rest of the story, shall we? All the rest. The information here has probably been in our files for years. Just cut out the secretive Slav act, and tell me everything you've learned about this Vanin."

"Very well, General, if I must, I must. I was hoping to keep it to myself till I had much more detail." Rather sadly the Russian leaned forward towards the intercom. "With your permission," he said, and pressed the switch.

A moment later the door opened, and the girl whom Vanin knew as Kate Reilly came into the room.

CHAPTER SIX

VANIN knew little about the properties of phosphorus, and when the fire came it was like nothing he had imagined, or even thought possible. A great hissing, roaring fire, with showers of sparks cracking out across the room, and white tongues of flame licking through the dense garlic vapour. The man called Julius must have died in seconds.

But Flack was dead too; that was the important thing. That last convulsive movement towards Julius had been too much for the drugged body, and the old, tired heart had stopped beating. Vanin dragged him out into the passage and looked down at the body. It didn't resemble a human being at all; the dead never do. It was like a bundle of rags with a mask stuck on top of them: a bale of rubbish waiting to be cleared away. As he looked at it, a wave of flame came belching out across the floor towards him, and Vanin hurled back the door. He didn't know how long phosphorus would burn, but the ceiling joists were bound to catch fire sooner or later. On the other hand, the walls were bare and the floor was concrete. Also there were no windows to attract inquisitive neighbours. He reckoned he had ten minutes at the outside.

Very quickly he knelt down beside the body and forced himself to tilt back the head and reach into the folds of the jacket. Flack was finished, and Flack was the one he had come all the way from Moscow to find. Only Flack knew the secret of the Gaunt Woman, whatever she might be, and the odds were piling up against them. All the same, Vanin wasn't finished yet. Flack might be dead, but it was still up to him to try and find the information they needed. The department didn't accept failure, and he was as expendable as Julius. Also he was a married man and he had to go on. His fingers ran through every pocket of Flack's clothes, finding nothing at all, then he got up and moved across the passage. Already the paint on the door was starting to blister, and burning wood was mingling with the garlic smell.

The room in the front of the house, where he had talked to Flack, seemed much darker now. Probably his eyes were suffering from the fumes, for the piles of books looked oddly unreal: heaped bricks and stones ready for the builders. He stood in the doorway for a moment, hearing the rustle of terrified mice under his feet and seeing the pictures of Martin Rolfe staring down at him. Then he walked across to the desk by the window. The boards beneath him felt soft and rotten, as though they would give way at any moment.

The desk was locked, but he opened it in seconds, his knife sliding in against the catch and the top rolling back to show the litter of books and papers it contained. Letters and accounts and sale catalogues marked in Flack's spidery hand—nothing to tell him what he had to know.

But all the same, they told him a good deal about Flack's livelihood. A *runner* was the word he had used: the lowest form of life in the secondhand book trade; one who bought from a dealer in the hope of selling quickly to another for a few shillings' profit. As he read through the papers, Vanin heard a crash of falling plaster from the next room. He hadn't very long, it seemed; already the ceiling was starting to go.

But there was nothing to help him—not yet. Nothing to tell him what had been Flack's hold over Rolfe: the thing that had made a very powerful man tremble before a scrawled note and a drawing that might have been done by a child. A man who, as Arabin said, needed security. "It's as though every committee he sits on, every report he writes, makes him feel more secure."

But here at last there might be something. Under the letters and the records of little unimportant transactions—"buy for seven shillings, sell for ten"—there was a little, flattish book bound in leather. The author's name had been pasted over, but the title stood out clear on the spine and cover: *A Short History of the Devil*.

Almost idly, Vanin opened it, and then suddenly he stiffened, for he knew he was on the way home at last. The book contained no text, for John Flack had removed the pages and very carefully sewn in fresh sheets. Like the walls of his room, they were covered with cuttings from newspapers and magazines. Not pictures but the text this time; a complete record of the man he had set out to destroy.

Peter Vanin read quickly through that book, and at every page he turned, he heard the roar of the fire increasing. The cuttings were in no chronological order and seemed to have been put in in batches. Some were old and yellowed, and some were obviously recent. Most of the earlier ones were photostats, copied from newspaper libraries. As he read through them, he saw the growth of Rolfe's career: "Appointment of New Professor"—"Statement of Treasury Adviser."

But here, almost in the middle of the book, there was something that had nothing to do with Rolfe as a public figure. Three browned and wrinkled columns, with a single heading and a date. Vanin suddenly remembered Flack's own words to him: "The Gaunt Woman was born on Christmas Eve exactly twenty years ago, and she died the same day." The date above the columns was December 29th, 1940, and the heading ran

CHRISTMAS MURDER—
CHILD KILLER STRIKES AGAIN

Yes, he had been right when he had looked at Rolfe's picture in Malendin's office. The man's face had seemed to hint at some personal tragedy then, and here was the tragedy looking out at him from twenty years ago. The story was quite clear in front of him. The last night before Christmas, with snow falling and a nursemaid wheeling a pram down a busy street. And she had left the pram for a moment. She had remembered some final card or present and gone into a store, leaving the pram and the baby outside on the pavement: the month-old baby of a senior civil servant named Martin Rolfe.

Then somebody had walked down the street and looked into that pram. Somebody had smiled probably, and wiggled her fingers at the baby, and cooed to it. Then, with a casual look through the shop window, that person had released the brake and wheeled the pram away through the Christmas crowds. A person who had already killed twice before.

But what about it? Rolfe had had a tragedy in his life. His child had been killed by a maniac, but how did that give Flack power over him? He was an object of pity, not of shame. With another crash of plaster from the room beyond, and smoke drifting in across the passage, Vanin turned the page and saw the first and only picture in the book. It showed a woman about to step into a car, and her hands covered her face. There were policemen on either side of her, and behind the police a crowd of people shouting and shaking their fists.

ELSIE GRANT GUILTY BUT INSANE

ran the headlines above it.

LIFE FOR TRIPLE MURDERESS

Vanin held the book up to the dim light, and read the account of the trial. It was fully reported, and there seemed no doubt as to the woman's guilt. Her husband had left her, and her own child had been killed in a motor accident. She had had a breakdown and was a voluntary patient in a mental hospital, but had come home for a week at Christmas. And during that week a spark of mania or resentment had started to burn in her mind, and three children had died. They had all died in the same way: suffocation, with her finger-prints clear and damning on the pram-handles. She had even admitted to what she had done.

No, there was no mystery there, but all the same Vanin read on carefully. It was his job to be sure of everything. Even with the fire racing towards him and blasts of heat spreading across the passage, he had read on. He read the evidence of the nursemaid, who had been helped, sobbing, into the witness-box. He read the medical evidence and the statement of the police, represented by somebody named Detective-Inspector George Pode. He started to read the evidence of a witness who claimed to have seen Grant wheel the pram away—suddenly he stiffened.

So that was it. That was the link between them. That was the connection that told him there was more to this story than a dead child, a tragedy for a man called Rolfe, and life in an asylum for a crazed woman named Elsie Grant.

I was standing on the opposite corner. It was snowing hard at the time, and the visibility was poor. I noticed the pram because of its colour: a very bright royal blue. I saw the woman wheel the pram away, but I didn't think there was anything amiss till much later. Yes, I saw her face, and I remember thinking there was an odd look about it. No I can't really describe what I mean, but it was wolfish somehow, and the hair was drawn down at either side, like a screen. No, I couldn't swear on oath, but I'm almost certain it was the prisoner.

The name of that witness was John Flack.

Vanin turned another page, but there was nothing further to interest him: just more accounts of Rolfe's career, and a brief story of his wife opening a new hospital wing. Nothing made sense to him, nothing seemed to fit together, but he had at least established a connection between Flack and Rolfe. Flack had been a witness at that trial, and years later he had seen a picture of someone or something he called the Gaunt Woman. Vanin looked back at the press photograph of Elsie Grant, and *gaunt* was right. *Gaunt* was the only word to describe that bent, angular body straining away from the jeering crowd of women round the police cordon. As he looked at the picture, a little germ of an idea started to grow in Vanin's head. It was just a small idea, but very horrible

--far, far worse than anything he had imagined possible. All the same it was all he had to go on, and he would follow it.

But he had to leave now. He had hoped to find much more than a book of cuttings, but there was no time to look longer. Flack might have built his room like a military bunker, but even as Vanin stared at the photograph, the whole house seemed to shake and the roar of fire redoubled. He dashed for the passage, feeling heat wrap round him like a blanket and seeing a great orange wave roll out over Flack's body. He twisted past it and just managed to reach the front door. He was on his way at last, and he had something to go on and a lot of people to see. They included a policeman who had retired, a woman who was locked away, and a rich man who was afraid. There was also another person he hadn't bargained for.

But just before he left that decayed, blazing house, he turned slightly and looked back towards Flack's body and the room where he had played with his toy soldiers.

"Goodbye, gentlemen," he said, thinking of both Flack and Julius. "I wouldn't be surprised if I don't join you before long."

It was a poor, silly joke, spoken without humour, but unless he was lucky, it could well be the truth. The date was December 22nd, the time ten o'clock. Already the hunters were moving in.

*   *   *

"Now let's see just what we do know." General Kirk leaned back in his chair smiling at Trubenoff. The papers on his desk were littered as though a bear had rummaged through them, and his ash-tray was piled high with cigar-stubs.

"And the answer, I'm afraid, is that we know very little. A few months ago you became interested in the activities of one Kate Reilly. Miss Reilly is an unsuccessful landscape-artist who had been a Communist Party member since the age of eighteen. About three years back, Miss Reilly seemed to acquire a sudden, and undeserved, affluence; bought a cottage in Eire, a new flat in St. John's Wood, and a three-thousand-pound Lancia motor-car. That was extremely foolish of her. If she'd been satisfied with a Morris or a Ford, you'd probably have spotted nothing.

"However, you do become suspicious, and a fortnight ago the Special Branch bring her in for questioning. Miss Reilly is not the stuff of martyrs, and after a few threats and the promise of immunity she talks. She talks in great detail, and it seems that she has been a very bad little girl indeed. 'Giving succour to potential enemies of the Crown' is the exact term I seem to remember. To be precise, she has been meeting agents from behind the imagined Iron Curtain at a rendezvous in County Cork, and providing them with a front during their stay here. Yes, a very naughty little girl." Kirk clicked his tongue and shook his head sadly.

"However, with your customary verve, Igor, you decide to make use of Miss Reilly. She has been in the habit of receiving her instructions from Gregor Tanek by telephone, which makes her fairly anonymous. You therefore substitute our Miss Kate Martin here for her, and sit back waiting for results. In due course a message arrives from Tanek, and Miss Martin goes off to Mizen Point, armed with a particularly blasphemous password." He broke off and frowned slightly at the girl beside Trubenoff.

"By the way, my dear, I'm very sorry about what happened this morning. I'm afraid that sometimes unpleasant things take place in our job, and we just have to accept them."

"It's all right, sir. I'll get over it." Kate started slightly at the phrase. The words were almost exactly the same as Peter Vanin had used on the telephone. As she thought about it, she seemed to picture a world of suspicion which was not controlled by countries or governments, but by departments which were always at war. She had heard a little about Colonel Malendin, and she imagined that he might be a man very like Kirk.

"Good, I'm sure you will." Kirk bent over the notes in front of him. "Now just let's see what they're after. Kate meets this chap Vanin according to schedule, and travels with him to London. She has checked that he is staying at a small hotel in South Kensington, but he has told her nothing about his business over here. He did, however, send a letter to an accommodation address in Hammersmith and ask her to see who called for it. The letter appears to have been treated with some stain, probably fuchsine powder, and was collected by a man named John Flack, who seems to be a most unpleasant criminal lunatic. By the way, Igor, you're checking on this Flack, I presume?"

"Yes, sir, the local police should be doing that now. But the point is, what do you want me to do about Vanin? Apart from what Kate has told us, we just haven't a clue to what he's up to. Should I have him followed?"

"No, I don't think so. Not yet at any rate. Remember that this Mr Vanin is a professional; quite an important man in their Department Five. The chances are that he'd spot a tail as easily as you or I would, old man. No we'll just have to wait and hope that he'll confide in this little lady before too long." He smiled at Kate as he spoke. "And what's he like, my dear? Personally I mean—a tough citizen?"

"No, not at all, sir." Kate frowned slightly, thinking of Vanin, how he had seemed to crumple up when she had mentioned his wife, and how he had looked, walking away at the air terminal.

"He's rather a pathetic little man really, doing a routine job, merely because he's paid to, I think. He also seems to be worried about his family in Russia. He looks—well, just like anybody. He might be a senior clerk, a schoolmaster, a government official; not a very important one."

"Yes, he would do, if he were any good. The good ones always look quite anonymous." Kirk reached in his drawer and pulled out a small black object resembling a button. "All the same, I'd better have a picture of him for the record; or in case we have to pull him in in a hurry. You know how to use one of these things, I presume?"

"Yes, I know how to use it." Kate took the tiny camera and slipped it into her bag.

"Good, then let's have a photograph next time you meet him. I always like to have our files up to date.

"And did I notice a slight mixture of condescension and maternal affection in your voice just now, when you described him as a rather pathetic little man? If so, you can cut it out right away. You've done very well so far, but one false move and Mr Vanin will be on to you. Whatever happens, don't under-rate him." Kirk paused for a moment, staring at the dossier before him, and his mutilated hand drummed quietly on the desk.

"Just listen to this 'pathetic little man's' record, will you? At the age of fifteen Peter Vanin was enrolled at the Secret Police Academy in Leningrad. That was probably the most important step in his life. Only the élite go there, and Colonel-General Serov was one of its most distinguished products.

"After his training, Vanin was sent to Germany for two years, attached to their intelligence branch, the Cheka as it was then, and by all accounts he did some very useful work on armament figures and so on. When Russia was attacked, he went home, and in '43 came to England, ostensibly as a minor official at their embassy. I'd be very interested to know what information he got from us at that time.

"After the war, we find him in Poland, searching out what were described as 'undesirable social elements'. You can guess what that means. The last we hear of him outside his own country is in Bucharest. He held the position of Soviet adviser to the Rumanian secret police." Kirk closed the folder and pushed it away from him. "Yes, quite a bright boy, this 'pathetic little man'. Don't underrate him, my dear."

"I won't, sir." Kate looked at his face and then turned away. On the surface it was like the face of a bluff country squire, but only on the surface. She knew it was capable of kindness and affection, but not of mercy. Mercy had no part in Kirk's make-up. He would order the death of an enemy in much the same way as a squire would tell his gamekeeper to put down vermin.

"No, I won't underrate Vanin," she said, and then broke off. She only thought the rest of the sentence: I won't underrate him, but all the same, I might get fond of him.

*   *   *

And at about the same time that she was speaking, a pleasant Christmas party was drawing to its close. The hostess had pulled her fifth cracker with false heartiness, and thrust a glass of cheap champagne into the hand of a guest who didn't want it, when she smelt burning: a stale, choking smell of burning, like garlic left too long in a very hot pan.

With a curse on all smokers in her heart, she glanced round the room and across the bright, only-just-paid-for carpet. Then she crossed to the window and pulled back the curtains. She screamed as she did.

The house across the road, belonging to a most unpleasant recluse whom the whole neighbourhood disliked, was a mass of flames.

CHAPTER SEVEN

VANIN was waiting for Kate at the Coventry Street Corner House, as they had arranged on the phone. A morning paper was spread out in front of him, open at the sporting page. He appeared to be reading the account of a football match between Arsenal and Real Madrid with marked interest.

"Ah, there you are, my dear." He pushed aside the paper and stood up smiling, as she came towards him. It was a warm, friendly smile, but she took care not to look at it too closely, for she remembered her thoughts as Kirk had read the dossier: I won't underrate him, but I might get fond of him.

She sat down beside him, ordered a cup of coffee from the waitress, and accepted the cigarette he rather shyly held out to her. As they sat there, they resembled any one of a dozen couples in the big, gilt room. He might have been a middle-aged, mis-understood, and not too successful businessman, confiding his troubles to a pretty secretary.

"Now I'm afraid I've got two more jobs for you," he said. "They are jobs which may well be—how do you say it? Yes, wild-goose chases. You see, they both concern something that happened a long time ago, and the persons involved could quite possibly be dead." He broke off, and pulled hard on his cigarette, as the waitress fussed round them with Kate's coffee.

"Tell me," he said, when at last she had left them, "does the name Elsie Grant mean anything to you?"

"Elsie Grant? Let me think for a moment. Yes, it does seem to ring a bell, though it's a very faint one." Kate concentrated hard. "Yes, of course, she was a murderess, wasn't she? I seem to remember reading about it somewhere. She killed a child, didn't she? A long time ago—during the war, wasn't it?"

"Yes, that's right. It was in 1940, and she killed not one, but three children. She was convicted of murder, but found insane. They put her in an asylum. Well, Kate"—somehow the name came automatically to him—"I'm not allowed to tell you why, or give you any details, but this woman Grant is of interest to us. I want you to find out where she is. She may be still locked up, she may have been set free, or she may be dead. But if she's alive and still in this country, I want to know where."

"Very well, I'll try." Kate made a note in her pocket-book to allow herself time to think. It didn't make sense at all. What possible connection could there be between a Soviet agent and an English murderess who was convicted twenty years ago? "And the second job?" She leaned forward with the little glass button of her jacket pointing up at his face and her hand toying with the camera switch in her sleeve.

"The second job is similar, and may also be a wild-goose chase." The phrase seemed to give him pleasure. "One of those children that Grant killed was the son of Sir Martin Rolfe—you've prob-ably heard of him—the economist."

"Yes, of course I've heard of him." Kate smiled at the question, for who hadn't heard of Martin Rolfe? It was hardly possible to open a paper without seeing a picture of that scholarly face, with an account of its activities: committees and inquiries and figures, figures so vast that they seemed incomprehensible to a normal mind. At last she felt she was starting to get somewhere. Kirk would be very curious to hear of Vanin's interest in anything to do with Martin Rolfe, the man who would speak for Britain at the coming conference.

"And so?" She pressed her sleeve and the little camera winked silently. Whatever happened, Kirk would get his picture.

"And so, I want to know about that baby, Kate—all about it. I want you to try and trace the doctor who delivered it, and if he's still alive, you must get him to talk. I can't tell you any more at the moment, as I'm still working in the dark myself. I just wanted to know everything about the child that Elsie Grant killed."

"Everything?"

"Yes, all you can get. Weight, state of health, colour of eyes, length of mother's pregnancy—everything."

"Very well, I'll do my best, though it's probably going to be difficult. Yes, twenty years ago—a long time." Once again Kate took up her pencil and made a note. The task would have been almost impossible had she been an ordinary person. She wasn't ordinary, though. With Kirk and the help of the department behind her, a lot of doors might be opened. Doors to an insane murderess, and a doctor who had delivered a child twenty years ago. It was slightly amusing that a Soviet spy should get his information through the co-operation of the British Intelligence Service.

"And is that all?" she said, smiling slightly.

"Yes, that's all." Vanin finished his coffee and pushed back the chair. "I'd like to tell you one more thing though, my dear. I'm very pleased that we're working together—very pleased indeed." For a moment his hand rested on her arm. "You know, in different circumstances I think we could be good for each other." He gave her a final, rather prim smile and folded his paper. "I'll ring you tomorrow," he said and walked away towards the line of phone booths by the door.

Vanin had two calls to make, and he took the less important first. Almost as the bell rang, that quiet, anonymous, but still foreign voice answered him.

"Homeway," he said, "Homeway Products, 85." A moment later he was giving his instructions to Gregor. He was glad to give them, for although he was a Russian, he liked to keep promises. In a few hours, Michael Arabin's family would be on their way to England.

He replaced the phone and started to dial another number—the most famous number in England.

* * *

Superintendent George Pode, formerly of the C.I.D., but since retirement the bane of his wife, the blight of the West Hampstead Golf Club, and the prize bore of the Feathers saloon bar, was only too happy to lunch with the press. He said it long and loudly over the phone, and he said it again, standing in the foyer of Moncelli's restaurant—*Internationally Known, Service Our Speciality*—pumping Vanin's hand up and down like a beer-engine.

"Good of you," he boomed for the whole room to hear. "Very good of you indeed. Always ready to help you chaps out with a story. Yes, of course, a drink or two before we eat would be just the ticket." He swaggered forward, lowered his vast bulk on to a bar stool, and took the cigarette that Vanin offered, beaming as he did so.

"Haven't been in this dump for years, as it happens, though I used it a lot in the old days; before I retired. Seem to remember that Châteaubriand was the speciality then, and they did you proud. Thanks, old chap, a large whisky would be just what I could use. Make it Black Label, barman, and just a touch of water." Like a conjuring-trick, the glass seemed to vanish in his enormous hand, and when he put it down it was empty.

"Ah, that's much better. Yes, I will have a refill, if you don't mind. Makes no difference to you fellows on expense accounts, does it?" He roared with unnecessary laughter, and struck Vanin a hard and painful blow over his left kidney.

"What paper did you say you were on, by the way? My memory is getting a bit rusty these days. Ah, yes, *The Detroit Sunday Herald*. Never heard of it, but I dare say it's all it should be. You're not American though, are you? Not by birth at least. Thought I noticed an accent just now."

"No, I was born in Poland, but I've been an American citizen for ten years."

"I see, that explains it. Had to hoof it from those Bolshevik bastards, I suppose? Needs must when the Devil drives, eh?" He had a heavy, pinkish face, a flowing white moustache, and an expression of complete self-satisfaction.

"And now, should we talk business? Scotland Yard gave you my phone number, and I understand that you're doing some articles on notable European police-officers. Very naturally you want to include me in the series. Well let's get down to the important thing. I'm not a man to be troubled by false modesty, neither am I a man who expects to work for nothing. The labourer is worthy of his hire, and all that. Just how much will your paper pay?"

"I'm afraid that rather depends on what my editor thinks of the article, Superintendent." Vanin smiled and drew out his book of traveller's cheques. "This is just a preliminary interview, of course, and I'll have to show him something in writing before he names a definite figure. At the same time, I was asked to give you three hundred dollars as proof of our good faith. Just a retainer, as it were."

"Thanks." Pode took the signed cheque and grinned—a big, wide grin that lit up his whole face. "Three hundred, eh? Fair enough for a start—very fair, in fact. Just over a hundred quid at the present rate of exchange. A bobby on the beat gets a thousand these days, of course, but all the same this will come in very handy." He stuffed the cheque away and pulled himself off the stool.

"And now, Mr Vane—sorry, Vanin, I'm quite at your disposal. Let's eat and have a yarn, shall we? I enjoy talking a great deal, and as you can imagine, I've plenty to tell. After—though I say it myself—an extremely successful career, it's about time somebody put it down in black and white." He began to walk heavily towards the restaurant, and then paused with a sudden frown on his face. "By the way, who else are you including in these articles of yours? Not Carmichael, I hope—not Inspector Willis?"

"No, neither of them, sir." Vanin noted a trace of bitterness in Pode's voice that told of petty jealousies and rivalries stretching back across the years. "As it happens, you're the only British police-officer we're including in the series. My editor felt your story should be good enough to make any others unnecessary."

"And he was dead right too. Credit where credit is due, eh?" Pode's face lit up again with good humour. "Now let's order, shall we?" He lowered himself into a chair and picked up the huge embossed menu. "Though I say it myself, I understand food." His eyes ran greedily down the card, and then he turned to the head-waiter. "Well, my boy, what's nice today?"

"Everything is nice, sir—as always." The man bore a marked resemblance to the late Pope Pius XII and he winced slightly, looking as though he were sucking a lemon and not liking it.

"Good, I'm glad to hear it. My friend here is from the United States and he's used to the best—the very best, waiter. Just see that he gets it. Now, let me think." As Pode made his selection, Vanin noticed that it seemed to be made by price as much as by choice. He obviously intended to make the most of somebody else's expense account. He shook his head sadly as Vanin ordered veal.

"Here, what's that, old boy? You've messed things up, I'm afraid. Can't drink red wine with that, and I can't have white with my steak. We'll just have to compromise with a rosé I'm afraid. Bring us a bottle of the Château Dax '55, waiter, and see that it's properly chilled. Good, that takes care of that." He leaned back in his chair, pleasurably anticipating the meal.

"Funny thing your choosing this place, Mr Vanin. I had the pleasure of depriving a chap of his liberty in here once. We arrested him at that corner table, I seem to remember. Yes, Jack Thursday it was—one of the best Con men in the business, though you wouldn't think it to look at him. Funny little beggar, less than five-and-a-half-foot tall. Started from nothing as well: doing the split-pound trick round Manchester."

"The split-pound trick?" Vanin raised his eyebrows in purely professional curiosity.

"Yes, that's right; common enough dodge before the war. You need two chaps for it. One of 'em rather nondescript, and the other imposing and obviously the soul of honesty. You and I would fit the bill to a T.

"Well, you go into a shop and buy a packet of fags—a shilling they were in those days. You pay with a pound note, and get your packet and nineteen shillings change. Out you go.

"About five minutes later I walk in. Buy another packet and pay with a ten-shilling note. Nine shillings change to come? Oh dear, no. 'Sorry, miss, but that was a pound I gave you. As a matter of fact, I can tell you the number. I always jot them down for safety's sake. Here it is—282673, and if you look in your till, I think you'll find it. Thank you.' Humble apologies from the shop girl, and ten shillings profit a time. Not bad money in the 'thirties."

"No, I suppose not." Vanin remembered the trick well. For some unknown reason it was known as a "Nikolai Rouble" in Moscow.

"Ah, here we are." Pode beamed at the approaching waiters and tucked the napkin into his collar, preparing to enjoy himself.

But between courses he talked—how he talked! After the soup, he discussed the breaking up of a gang of forgers; a most brilliant piece of work in every way. Before the steak, he told of a murderer brought to hook by painstaking attention to detail; between the maron glacé and the cheese, of a scandal regarding the sexual habits of a middle-aged statesman, hushed up by tact and self-sacrifice. Intelligence, cleverness, bravery and devotion to duty—all the prerequisites of that scourge of crime, Detective-Superintendent George Pode.

"Saint George," as he assured Vanin his colleagues had called him, "Saint George will have the blighter under lock and key" —"Put good old George on the case, and things will start to hum"—"Nah, the Super don't let no grass grow under his boots." Only at the end of the enormous meal did he ease back his chair, sniff the brandy suspiciously, as though it were not quite what he was accustomed to, and address Vanin directly.

"Well, that was very nice, old chap, very nice indeed. Can't think when I've eaten so well, though I'm sure you've enjoyed yourself too; got a good deal of material to go on already. By the way, what's your Christian name? I never could stand on ceremony. Peter, eh? Well, Pete, let's get to work. Just what kind of article had you in mind? Do you want a general account of my career, or should we concentrate on one particular case?"

"One case would be best, I think." Vanin motioned towards the waiter as he answered. Another brandy or so, and Pode would be ready to talk—to talk as he wanted him to.

"Fair enough. Though it will be difficult to select the most interesting, out of so many. What about Mason and Reade, those Brighton forgers I was telling you about, or the Croydon bank job?"

"No, I don't think so. You see, we're a Sunday paper, and our readers want something a little sordid for their morning's entertainment. The editor felt that the case of Elsie Grant might fit the bill."

"Elsie Grant!" A curious expression suddenly flitted across Pode's face as he repeated the name—a slightly guilty expression, but not very guilty: the look of a child detected in some minor naughtiness.

"Oh no, I doubt if that would do. It was all rather dull really —just unpleasant, as these nut cases always are. If you want something sordid, what about old Doctor Rankin? He was a lad, if ever there was. Cut up his wife and housemaid, and dumped them into the main sewer at Weybridge. That's a good yarn if you like, and though I say it myself, the investigation was conducted most brilliantly; threw a lot of credit on all concerned. Yes, 1946 it was. Rankin had been having an affair with the maid for . . ." He started to launch into the story, but Vanin cut him short.

"No, I'm sorry, Superintendent," he said. "It really is the Grant case we're interested in—only the Grant case."

"Very well, if I must, I must, though I think you're making a mistake." Pode took another swig at his brandy, and blew his nose with quite unnecessary violence.

"A sad little case that, concerning a very sad person. Elsie Grant was one of those girls who seem doomed from the start; almost as though the cards were stacked against them at birth. Orphanage child she was, and very plain—one shoulder higher than the other—employed as a maid-of-all-work in a slum boarding-house—no bed of roses in those days. Cinderella, in fact, waiting for the fairy godmother."

"And did she turn up, this fairy godmother?"

"Yes, she turned up all right—he did, rather. His name was Littlewood; the gentleman who runs the football pools. Elsie put her row of noughts and crosses in the correct squares, and in due course a cheque arrived. Over a thousand quid it was, but I can't remember the exact amount. Anyway, a nice sum of money by pre-war values.

"Well, Cinderella had her glass slippers now, and in due course Prince Charming came on the scene: that bastard Leonard Grant. They were married in church, she wasn't to know he had a wife already, and after the proper interval a child arrived. Two days later, Grant hooked it, taking all her money except twenty pounds. He did at least have the decency to leave that."

"And the baby died, didn't it?"

"No, it didn't die, Pete. It was killed; murdered, if I had a hand in making the laws of England. Elsie went round to the labour exchange, looking for a job, and leaves the pram on the pavement. While she's inside, along comes a drunk in a sports car, takes a corner too fast, mounts the kerb, and bang! down comes baby and cradle and all." As though to emphasize the point, Pode's hand came crashing down on the table, to the consternation of his fellow-diners. From his vantage point by the door, Mr Moncelli himself, a resplendent figure in silk-lined tails, seemed on the verge of apoplexy.

"Yes, I remember the driver got two years for manslaughter, but that didn't do Elsie any good."

"She went insane?"

"That's right, Peter. She went crazy; right round the bend. A hospital took her in as a voluntary patient for a time, but she came out ten days before the Christmas. Two days later, we got the first killing.

"Well, we couldn't get much sense out of her during our examination, nor could the doctors. Today she'd have been put down as unfit to plead, but that wasn't common then. From what we could make out, her mind had refused to accept the accident, and she was looking for her own child. She'd see an unattended pram and wheel it home: a rented house in Fulham. The children had all died through suffocation. Probably she cuddled them a little too tightly.

"And that's about all there was to it, I'm afraid. Just a nasty, sad little story, and quite uninteresting. We were tipped off by a suspicious neighbour. God bless all suspicious people, by the way." Pode raised his glass in a mock toast. "No, there was no real police work at all. We just got a warrant and searched the house. The two bodies were hidden under the stairs. Why your editor should be interested in the case I can't imagine."

"Just a moment, Superintendent." There was a sudden, eager gleam in Vanin's eye. "What did you say just then?"

"What did I say, Pete? Said I thought your editor was barmy to wish to dig it up, when there's so much better material to hand. Now the Royston murders, for instance. Yes, I'd just been promoted Inspector, I remember, and——"

"No, I'm sorry, Mr Pode, but I'm not interested in the Royston case; just the case of Elsie Grant. You said two bodies just now, though the papers reported there were three." He pulled out his notebook. "Yes, here we are: 'James Harbin, aged six weeks; Pamela Thurston, seven; the Rolfe child, one month old and not yet christened.' Just why did you say you found only two bodies, Superintendent?"

"Why, it's—it's a long time ago, isn't it, Pete? Perhaps my memory is getting rusty. As I said, the case never interested me very much." Once again that slightly guilty expression crept across Pode's face.

"All right, let's have the truth, shall we?" Vanin leaned forward across the table. "My editor will pay well for your story, but only for the full story. Just what did you really find?"

"All right, I'll tell you. I was covering up a little—in a way, that is. It can't do any harm now, and my pension is secure enough. Yes, I held something back from the press; but if you were a cop you'd understand why." Pode's smug, rather asinine expression seemed to alter, and he looked what he had been: a tough, efficient policeman who lived for the job.

"Nut cases are always the worst things we have to deal with, for two reasons. Firstly, there is never an obvious connection between the killer and the victim, as in the case of murder, for gain, for example. Secondly——"

"Secondly, they attract imitators." Vanin's words came out automatically, as he remembered his own police training.

"Quite right, Pete. They attract imitators. One loony kills a girl, say, in a certain manner and in a certain place—a church-yard for example. Well, having read the glowing reports you chaps write about it, another nut is tempted to follow his example and strike a similar blow for freedom. And if that happens, and the news gets out, then the whole thing is liable to snowball." There was a great bitterness in Pode's voice as he spoke. "And I didn't want that to happen in the Grant case. I didn't want it at all, because I'm very fond of kids."

"You mean——"

"I mean, Pete, that on my own responsibility, a slightly con-trived version of the facts was given to the press. I didn't want any more children killed, and I didn't want Elsie Grant to have anyone trying to follow her example. I didn't want it rumoured that anybody already had."

"Go on, Superintendent. So you did conceal something?"

"Yes, I concealed something all right. Oh, don't worry, Elsie Grant was guilty. She pleaded guilty to the first murder of James Harbin, and was sentenced on that charge. If she hadn't, every-thing would have had to come out in court automatically. No, there was never any doubt about it. We found those kids under the stairs."

"You found *two* of them." Clickety-clickety-click! Like a metal puzzle, the pieces in Vanin's head were starting to fit together. "But what about the third? Were you quite certain she killed that third child, the Rolfe baby?"

"The third?" Pode belched slightly, and his eyes were puffy with too much food and alcohol. "Oh yes, we were certain all right—quite certain. I talked to Elsie Grant for hours, and I'm sure she killed the three of them. She was guilty all right; as guilty as hell. All the same, in the case of the Rolfe child there was one rather peculiar feature. Yes, that's right, Pete. We never found the body."

CHAPTER EIGHT

KATE'S first job had been easy, for Elsie Grant was dead. She had died a long time ago, during the war. It took a telephone call to find that out.

A Dornier bomber, beaten back from London by fog and the barrage, had turned for home with its cargo intact. Twenty miles from the Kent coast, the fog had thinned slightly and almost overhead the pilot had made out the silhouette of a Spitfire. He had dived automatically, and as he did, a group of red-brick buildings had loomed up before him. With speed and the loss of weight his only object, the solution had been obvious. The observer's hand had tightened on a switch, and the landmine they carried went swinging down through the mist. It fell on the women's wing of Broadhurst Asylum, and twenty-three sick minds were able to sleep at last.

Her second job hadn't been so easy, however. It had taken the department a full hour even to find the name of the doctor who had attended Lady Rolfe, and when they knew it they seemed no further forward. The man seemed completely elusive: general practice in Kensington till three years ago, and then nothing—nothing at all. It appeared that he had just sold up and gone away. The National Health files could tell them little, and even the Inland Revenue Office didn't know where he was. There was just one address that might give them a lead: his mother-in-law's, a restaurant in a mid-Sussex town.

It was a lovely day, though, probably the last fine day of the year, and Kate drove slowly through bright winter sunlight, with the snow still fresh and clean on the hills. There was no need to hurry. Vanin would not be contacting her before tomorrow morning, and she wanted to think. It seemed as if she was getting somewhere at last; or at least Kirk appeared to think so. As she told him of Vanin's instructions, there had been a sudden flash of interest in his eyes, and the heavy, cynical face had looked almost boyish: young and eager, and full of excitement. The look of a terrier who doesn't know exactly where the rat is hiding, but feels that it must be very near.

"So that's it, is it? Our friend is taking an interest in Martin Rolfe, is he? In something that happened to Martin Rolfe a long time ago. And I wonder why. All very strange, isn't it? Rolfe is an important man, but what possible interest can that murder have to a Soviet agent? 'Curiouser and curiouser, said Alice.'

"As it happens, I've met Rolfe once or twice. Don't know him well, of course—not at all my kind of chap, but we use the same club, and I can tell you one thing, my dear. If Rolfe has a skeleton in his cupboard, it will be a very nasty one indeed. He's a proud man, you see, but only on the surface. Underneath, I think he feels desperately insecure, and needs power and popular esteem, as an alcoholic needs a drink. A very dangerous man, if someone threatened to take that esteem away from him.

"Well, you're doing very nicely now, little lady, and we'll just have to help Mr Vanin to find out what he wants to know. And when he's done that, when we know what he wants with Rolfe, then I'll be right behind him. Yes, I feel I'm going to enjoy this case." He turned away, concluding the interview, and once again Kate noticed the sudden cold expression on his face.

But though she drove slowly, every journey has its end, and she had reached hers now. She turned up the steep, winding hill into Saxonfield High Street, and parked the car. Before she got out, she checked the equipment that Kirk had given her: a press card and an envelope that felt flat and comfortable round its cache of five-pound notes.

The Olde Copper Kettle restaurant stood on a corner, and there was no mistaking it. The battered utensil that provided its name swayed from a wrought-iron frame, and a sign in heavy Gothic type swung below it. It was just like any of the thousand immensely genteel, completely sham and ridiculous establishments that dot the southern half of England.

Kate pushed open the bead-draped door, lowering her head beneath a wormeaten beam, and groped her way forward through the semi-darkness. The tables were low and tiled, there were reproduction Speed maps on the walls, and shapeless and inflammable objects, woven from straw, hung from the mock-Tudor ceiling. The beams on the ceiling looked as though they concealed some pretty substantial girders to hold them in position. Over the fireplace hung a poker-work motto. As her eyes grew accustomed to the light, she was able to read what it said.

> Rest awhile, traveller, and take your fill here
> Of Comfort and Kindness, and good Sussex Cheer.

Kindness might be in order, but she felt that comfort was a barefaced lie. Her knees were pressed hard against the sharp edge of the table, and the Sussex cheer seemed a long time in material-

izing. She waited a good five minutes for service, while in the
corner two grim females in masculine tweed coats eyed her
critically and then fell to discussing the wicked ways of a High
Church clergyman.

"*Father* indeed! Parading himself in the street in a cloak, and
flicking holy water in the aisle! Filling the church up with
painted images, and making the choir learn that newfangled
plain-song nonsense! A bit too plain for my taste it is, and I told
him so to his face. He didn't seem to care at all, though I've been
on the Ladies' Committee for twelve years. What old Canon
Rusper would have said I can't imagine. Enough to make the
poor man turn in his grave . . ."

There was a little brass bell on the table, and when the five
minutes were up, Kate lifted it and rang it nervously.

"Did you want something?" The waitress came out of a door
in the shadows, with a powder-compact still in her hand. She
was young and pretty, but her face was sullen: the face of an
employee who is doubtful when the next wages will be coming.
Kate ordered tea and scones as humbly as she could, and only
when they were pushed in front of her did she bring out her
question.

"Does a Dr Fenwick live here?"

"*Doctor* Fenwick? No, there's no doctor here, miss. Only Mrs
Fenwick and her mum." The girl frowned slightly. "I believe she
had a husband once, but I dunno what happened to him. Went
away, I think, and I can't say I blame him." She leaned forward
conversationally.

"I 'aven't been here long meself, and between you and me, I
don't intend to stay long either. Goin' to fold, this place is, and
I don't intend to fold with it. No, this rat's not going down
with any sinking ship; not on your nellie. Ta, miss." She took
the half-crown that Kate held out. "I'll get Ma Fenwick for
you."

The woman who came into the room a minute later was made
for persecution. She had a mild, sheeplike face, she wore bangles,
and her grey hair was tied back in faded blue ribbon. She looked
as though her only business, her one purpose in life, had been
the taking of orders. Orders from employers, from bullying
husbands, from aged and demanding relatives; any orders, so long
as they were firmly given. She bowed humbly to the two grim
females in the corner, and then hurried towards Kate, with a
nervous smile on her lips. A string of green beads round her neck
made a sharp clicking noise.

"Good afternoon, madam. Bessie said you wanted to speak to me. I do hope you've nothing to complain of." The low, gentle voice sounded as though it were very used to complaints.

"No, of course not. Everything is very nice. It's purely a personal matter that I wanted to talk to you about. You are the wife of Dr Robin Fenwick, I believe?"

"Yes, yes, I'm his wife, miss—thank you—Miss Reilly. I was his wife, that is, till——" The eyes suddenly looked as though they were about to fill with tears.

"Oh, I'm so sorry, Mrs Fenwick. I didn't know that your husband was dead."

"Dead? Oh no, he's not dead. At least I don't think so. It's just that we—that he——" She broke off, looked behind her at the two prying faces by the corner table.

"Would you care to come upstairs to my flat, Miss Reilly? It's quiet there, and we could talk. That is if you don't mind—but if you have news of Bob——" She helped Kate to move back her chair, and led the way to a staircase that lay behind the door.

The room above the café was small and chintzy and bright, but completely cheerless. Though the weather was icy, the single bar of a small electric fire was its only heating, and the chair-covers had a dead, faded look that came from too much washing. Only one wall looked rich and prosperous. A bookcase stood against it, filled with bright bindings, and Kate could read the titles on their spines: *Hood and Polinger's Surgery, Benham's Standard Midwifery, Hill and Jackson's Physiology*. To the right of the bookcase there was an opening into another room, screened by a curtain. From time to time Kate heard a creak of boards and heavy, slow movements from behind it.

"Now Miss Reilly, what did you want to talk to me about?" The woman fussed round her as Kate sat down. "Have you any news about my husband? You see, he left me some time ago, but I wondered if perhaps he'd been trying to get in touch with me. That woman who made him leave me—she might have stopped him writing——"

"No, I'm afraid I haven't any news." Kate glanced at a photograph on the mantelpiece. The man's face was handsome but strangely without character. It had good eyes, a good nose and mouth, and a good chin, but somehow they didn't seem to match, to fit together to give a personality. All the same, it didn't look the kind of face which could be *made* to do anything. "No, it's information from you that I want. Do you have your husband's address, Mrs Fenwick? Is he in England?"

"Oh, no, he's not in England. He went abroad with her. The last I heard was that they were in Jamaica."

"I see. Then I'd better explain the position to you, Mrs Fenwick. I've not really come about your husband, so much as a case he worked on a long time ago. You see, I'm a journalist and . . ." She pulled out her press card and began to tell the prepared story, just as both Kirk and Vanin had told her to tell it. She was a good, fluent liar, and it came easily: a series of crimes of the past, and, with Rolfe's present position, the murder of his child was to be included. She told it well, and when she had finished, Mrs Fenwick sat down beside her, obviously convinced.

"Yes, I see. As it happens, I remember the case quite well. I was sorry for the little boy, of course, but this Rolfe must have been a horrible man. Poor Bob was so upset at the time."

"Horrible!" Kate raised her eyebrows slightly. "Just why do you say that?"

"Well, he was so rude. A few days after the child was born, Bob went round to see him about something. I've no idea what it was, Bob never talked shop to me, but I know he was worried. Anyway, Rolfe behaved most disgracefully. He became violent and abusive, and ordered Bob to leave his house. I remember feeling at the time that when the baby was killed, it might have been some kind of judgment on him. Oh dear! That was a terrible thing to say. I'm so sorry, and I didn't mean it, of course. It's just that my husband was always such a kind, gentle man. It seemed so wrong—so unfair on Rolfe's part."

"It's all right, I can understand how you must have felt, Mrs Fenwick." Kate considered her next move and her eyes fell on the bookcase. "But I see that you still have your husband's text books," she said. "Have you perhaps his papers too? Any documents relating to that Rolfe baby?"

"His papers? Yes, I think I have them. When Bob went away, he left everything behind, except money and the clothes he was wearing. His notebooks should be in the tin trunk in the bedroom. Bob was so methodical, you know. He made notes on every case that interested him. The Rolfe baby must be there." Her face broke into a sudden look of mistrust. "But Miss Reilly, you don't mean——"

"Yes, I mean that I want to look at those notebooks, Mrs Fenwick. My agency will pay well too. A hundred pounds—in cash—now." She started to open her bag as she spoke.

"No, no, no! I really couldn't allow that. Whatever you paid me, I couldn't allow it." Mrs Fenwick's crushed, humble face took on a certain dignity in anger. "You just don't understand, do you? A doctor's reports on his patients are sacred; like what a priest hears in the confessional. And my husband was a good doctor too —a good man. He was just tired at the end, that was all. The extra paper work from that wretched National Health Scheme tired him. He had to have a change, and then that wretched woman——" She got up and pulled open the door, a servant showing out the unwelcome guest at her master's orders. "Yes, I'm afraid I want you to leave now. My husband was a good man, and I still treasure his memory, whatever he may have done."

"Your husband, my dear Lucy, was, and is, a bastard." The voice came from behind them, and Kate swung round on her heel, looking at the opening by the bookcase.

The curtains were drawn back now, and a woman stood framed between them, a big, heavy woman, dressed in black and leaning on a stick. By the features it was possible to see that she was Mrs Fenwick's mother, but there was only a physical resemblance between them. This woman had never taken an order in her life.

"Now just sit down, Lucy, and listen to me. That goes for you as well, Miss Reilly. I've been listening to what you said, and you interested me." She watched them settle themselves in front of her like guilty children, before she went on.

"Thank you. Now Miss Reilly, I'm going to tell you something. My son-in-law, Robert Fenwick, was what my generation used to call a bounder. He merely married my daughter because she had a little money of her own, and he wanted to buy a fashionable practice. Don't interrupt me, Lucy!" Her stick came down with a crash on the floor.

"But when someone younger, and richer, and more *entertaining* came his way"—there was a marked accentuation of the word—"Dr Fenwick decided to break loose. He sold his practice, because he dreaded scandal, and persuaded us to move down here. Once we had the café going, he cut and ran. At the moment, I imagine he is lying on some beach with his mistress: the half-caste daughter of a West Indian banana millionaire. One of his late patients, I may say.

"Now Miss Reilly, let's talk business. You want to have a look at Robert Fenwick's papers, and they are in my possession." She pivoted slightly on her stick as she spoke. "Well, you mentioned a hundred pounds just now, and it's not enough. Could you manage two hundred, do you think?"

"Yes, I can pay two hundred." Kate opened her bag and pulled out the envelope. Two hundred was the exact sum they had given her.

"Thank you." The woman took the notes from her and started to count them carefully. "No, Lucy," she said. "Please don't try to argue with me. I'm very sorry, but this is how I want it. In fact, Miss Reilly is like a fairy godmother, and we should be very glad of her sudden interest in Bob's career. As you know, we owe money to the landlord, to the electricity company, and to the council for rates. We owe Cook, and Bessie two weeks' wages. We owe far too much money to everybody. Miss Reilly's contribution may just carry us through till the summer, when we hope to do more business. As far as we are concerned, your husband is dead. I, however, intend to go on living. Yes, quite correct, Miss Reilly —two hundred pounds." She tucked the notes back into their envelope. "Now, will you wait here a moment, please?"

She walked through the curtains, and a minute later came back with a battered tin box which she laid on the table.

"Yes, here you are, my dear. This is what you asked for. All the good doctor's reports, written down in his own fair hand. I hope you will find what you need." She opened the lid, and took her daughter by the arm. "Come, Lucy," she said. "Miss Reilly has kept her side of the bargain, so let's keep ours. Let her examine her treasure trove in peace."

But *fair hand* was right. Whatever his faults, Robert Fenwick had kept his notes neatly and legibly. Kate laid the notebooks and clipped papers on the table and bent over them. The last book was dated just over three years ago, the first in 1933. On the mantelpiece at her side a little clock ticked above the picture of their author, and his notes ticked with them. 1934—'37—'40; January, April, November. And at last, there it was. Almost in the centre of a page was the entry she wanted.

November 23rd. Rolfe, 32, Lawrence Gdns—Today I delivered a *man* child.

There was a line drawn under the word *man*, but nothing else; no record of weight, condition, or length of mother's pregnancy —nothing to help her at all.

Kate turned a page. The next entry concerned a woman with a diseased hip bone, and the three that followed were equally irrelevant. And then she had the thread again.

Rolfe, Lawrence Gdns. Matthews gave me the result of the biological tests today, and I'm afraid there is no doubt about it. Yes, the thousand to one chance I dreaded has come off. If there is a God, then I think he may have forsaken some of us.

Below the sentences there were four words in Latin.

Very carefully Kate copied down those words, and then crossed to the bookcase and pulled out the necessary volumes of *Palin's Dictionary*. She had studied Latin at school, and she had been trained as a nurse. Already she had a slight idea of what they might mean. She didn't like it at all.

For as she thumbed through the books, she suddenly felt cold and alone in that little chintzy room. Behind the curtain she could hear a low murmur from Mrs Fenwick and her mother, but they weren't so much like voices as automatic sounds, waves lapping on a cold, deserted shore at the very edge of the world.

She turned up her coat collar and lit a cigarette. Then she began to read the final line of print that could make certainty of her suspicion. There was suddenly a great pain behind her eyes as she did so. Dr Fenwick had been right, it seemed. The chances were about a thousand to one. Two uncommon complaints had joined forces in one human child, and the sum they added up to was terror.

If it had lived, the Rolfe baby would have become a monster.

CHAPTER NINE

"AND you're sure, my dear? You checked from facts thoroughly, and you're quite, quite certain?" Peter Vanin leaned over the parapet of the Serpentine Bridge, half looking at the water, and half at Kate. "It seems almost impossible. A nightmare come to life."

"Yes, it's a nightmare all right, but still true. I checked very carefully, and I do have a little medical training." She reached in her bag and handed him a sheet of paper. "This is the exact wording I copied from Fenwick's notes, and here is a translation in simple terms. That child was born with *Morbus Crassi*, a disease which was said to affect a certain Roman family. It's a weakness of a group of nerve centres in the brain's frontal lobe. In time they would begin to shrink and lead to lunacy—very violent lunacy, if left untreated."

"And you say it couldn't be treated, because of this other illness?"

"Yes, that's right. The child was also born with Deladier's

disease. That's a condition of over-activity in the pituitary gland. The secretions would tend to cause bodily deformity, and possibly gigantism. And the point is, that though both those conditions can be treated, and possibly cured, nowadays, together you can't touch them. Interfere with the pituitary, and the brain condition would spread unchecked and probably kill the patient in weeks. Yes, Fenwick was right when he said that the chances were about a thousand to one. Two rare ailments joining forces, and together they become a nightmare."

"I see. Poor kid—poor, poor little child." Vanin stared down at the ducks floating below him like green and brown bottles: fat, overfed ducks that had grown indolent. They didn't even bother to migrate any more in the midst of London's plenty. All the same, he suddenly wished he had some bread to give them. He would have liked to do that. At the moment, he would have liked to do any commonplace, family thing. "So if it had lived, Rolfe's child would have become a monster?"

"Yes, that's right, Peter. And it was a mercy really, wasn't it— a mercy that Elsie Grant did kill it."

"Yes, I suppose you could call it that," he said, knowing that he lied, that he didn't think of it as a mercy or a blessing at all. For the department it was just a lever and a fulcrum: a way to bring pressure on a certain economist, and make him give the wrong answers at the coming conference. A way to break the Anglo-American alliance once and for all.

"And now, I think we'd better part company, my dear. You've got what I wanted, and you've done very well; very well indeed. I'll see that Gregor hears about it.

"No, I'm afraid that we probably won't meet again, not unless something goes wrong. I've only two more little jobs to do, and then I hand over to someone else and can go home. They said they'd fly me out with some of the embassy personnel: diplomatic immunity, you know." He grinned and took her hand, feeling it very soft and warm in his. Somehow its touch made him feel less alone.

"Yes, it's goodbye now, my dear, and I don't expect we'll meet again. But thank you—thank you for all the help you've given me." He watched her walk away, and then he leaned over the bridge again and considered his next move.

For he had a theory at last—only a theory, a hunch, an idea, but he had to follow it. Even though he might be completely wrong, and it was as absurd as it sounded, he had to follow it, for it was the only one he had to go on.

Take a very proud couple, he thought, and both the Rolfes were proud. He had spent two hours with one of Tanek's very reliable sources of information, and he knew a lot more about Rolfe and his wife now. She had been a Ravensburn before she married him—one of the oldest families in England. Old, proud blood which might carry a little bad seed with it.

And that couple would have been prouder still when they knew a child was on its way. An heir to Rolfe's intelligence and wealth—the direct descendant of a knight who had led a charge at Hastings. Then one day a doctor named Fenwick had walked into their house and shown them exactly what their child would become. Yes, pride would have melted like snow at his words, and Death would have seemed very attractive to that no longer proud couple.

But Death had already given its examples. Two children stolen, and probably murdered, in the neighbourhood—why not a third? If the cards were played carefully, no one would suffer; there would be no shame or disgrace for a man who craved for public esteem and a woman whose pride couldn't bear the thought that she had mothered an imbecile.

Yes, those children that Elsie Grant had stolen might have seemed like a pointer to them—a lead which Rolfe's keen, mathematical brain could easily have turned to action. Certain instructions to a nursemaid would have been the first move: "On your way back from the park, Mary, or Doris, or Jane, just stop at the store and buy me this or that. Leave the pram outside. It will be quite safe for a minute or two."

And then, while the maid was inside, another woman had come down the street and wheeled it away. A woman who had every right to, for she was the child's mother. The rest was easy to follow. Soft, gentle fingers lowering a pillow towards a face which disease would soon ravage—a little body that didn't take much earth to cover it—and at last, peace. Yes, "rest in peace, my son."

But they hadn't rested, and there was no peace. Vanin remembered Arabin's description of Lady Rolfe. A tall, overpainted woman shut away in her gloomy, neglected house, and dressed like a girl to remind her of the days when she was still young, when her husband didn't draw away from her for fear of another conception; of the time before she became a murderess; of the years when Rolfe spent some of his time with her and wasn't completely drugged by the need for power and approbation.

And then, one day, there wasn't even the delusion of peace,

and fear became a practical thing. A witness at the Grant trial had looked at a certain picture of Lady Rolfe, and the penny had dropped. To John Flack, with his hatred of success, it must have seemed like a gift from heaven, as he had stared at that picture and remembered a face he had seen through the snow, so many years ago. A trick of light, of angle, of hair-styling might have done it, anything might, but it had shown him the truth, and he could get down to his very nasty work: little matchstick drawings, with meaningless writing below them: "the Gaunt Woman who can blast you."

"No!" Vanin suddenly shook his head and spoke aloud. It was preposterous, of course. It couldn't have been like that, and there were a hundred reasons against it. He hadn't a single piece of definite evidence to support his case. All the same, as he leaned over that bridge, he suddenly knew that it was the only theory he had, and he must play it to the end—the very bitter end. He would beard Rolfe with his preposterous theory, and just hope that he had stumbled on some of the truth. Then if Rolfe broke, he could hand over to an economist, provided by Tanek, and go home.

But if Rolfe didn't break, then he would have failed, and the department didn't recognize failure. His final talk in Malendin's office suddenly came back to him.

"Goodbye, my dear Peter, and good luck," Malendin had said. "And remember something, will you—remember that we are all expendable, that not one of us matters as an individual. Only the M.V.D. and the Department matters—only the Party matters, in fact." He had grinned suddenly and raised his hand in a clenched fist salute, as though addressing a political rally.

"Yes, Comrade Vanin, the mills of our Revolution grind well," he had said loudly, and then lowered his voice. "Pretentious nonsense, of course, Peter, but the idea is true. We are not individuals, but just part of the machine. Whatever the risk, I want you to get this Martin Rolfe. I want you to get him good."

Malendin was a cynical careerist on the surface, but he at least told his subordinates the truth. He, Peter Vanin, had to take every risk in the book, and there was no coming back with a tale of failure. If Rolfe didn't break, then— The little capsule against his teeth suddenly seemed to move as though with a life of its own.

But it was time to go now. In the distance a clock started to strike the hour, and he adjusted his watch, smiling slightly as he did so. The meeting with Rolfe was not till the evening, and there was another job to do first. This time it was a job he hoped to enjoy.

* * *

"Yes, Minister. Yes, I quite understand what you say." Kirk bent over the intercom on his desk, and his face bore an expression of cynicism, boredom and rank ill temper. He hated all politicians.

"Yes, that's all quite correct, Mr Gore Williams, and there's nothing to worry about. We know all about that fire in Silver Pine Grove, and everything is under control. That's right, two people were killed. One of them was the tenant, a man named Flack, and we're trying to identify the other body now. The fire was probably started by a Soviet agent who landed in Eire last Monday.

"I beg your pardon, Minister." A dark, angry flush spread across his face. "Would you mind repeating that, please?

"Yes, that's what I thought you said. Now will you allow me to tell you something in return? In the first place, we do know what we're doing, and I'm perfectly prepared to take full responsibility for everything that happens. In the second, though you may be my indirect superior, I am still in charge of this department, and I don't want this man Vanin to be interfered with at all. When the time is ripe we'll pull him in, but not till then. Not till I say so, in fact, Mr Gore Williams." He pressed down the intercom switch for a moment and leaned back, grinning at his secretary.

"That's telling the blighter, eh, Florrie?" he said. "Give these halfpenny politicians an inch, and they start to imagine it's they, not the departments, who run the blasted country." He released the switch again, and almost at once the grin was wiped off his face.

"What's that you say? Scotland Yard told you, and they're on their way—" He listened to the voice, with his maimed hand white against the edge of his desk, and then with a gruff goodbye switched off the intercom. He suddenly looked his age.

"Florrie," he said. "Get me a line to the Special Branch at once. It seemed they've had an anonymous phone call tipping them off about Vanin. Sending a squad car to pick him up; Victoria Station at two thirty, and it's almost that now. Interfering, flat-footed fools! They didn't even bother to inform us, but told that half-witted sheep Gore Williams all about it." He watched the girl start to dial a number, and then stared up at the big electric clock on the wall. Its minute-hand seemed to move much faster than her fingers.

Two twenty-six. He very much wanted to talk to Peter Vanin, and the chances of that were small now. Unless he could get the Special Branch to stop that car in time. Unless Vanin was not merely a good professional but a real expert, this would be the finish, and they would never hear the end of the story. Kirk knew a good deal about the way top M.V.D. agents faced arrest, and there could only be one end. Peter Vanin would be dead.

CHAPTER TEN

TRAIN announcements and carols creaking hoarsely from the loudspeakers, a lighted tree glowing before the suburban booking-office, and three drunks singing their way towards the buffet. A general atmosphere of smoke, gloom and merriment, and the howl of a locomotive blowing off steam in the Continental arrival bay: Victoria Station on Christmas Eve.

Vanin paid off his taxi, somehow getting great pleasure from the man's cheerful "Merry Christmas", and shouldered his way through the home-going crowds. Big crowds, because most of the offices had closed at lunch time and the rush to freedom had already started. Crowds with a certain gaiety about them; almost an air of fiesta. He was surprised to see so many smiles on those stolid British faces.

As arranged, Michael Arabin was waiting for him near the clock, and he wore the same dark, city suit as before, though there was a bunch of bright flowers under his arm. There was still that slightly bewildered expression on his face, as though he wasn't sure which card life would turn up next, but his manner was quite different. He seemed trusting and friendly, as though hostility had left him like a long illness. He held out his hand to Vanin without hesitation.

"Well, I see that you came prepared." Vanin smiled down at the bunch of flowers. "You gave Rolfe my message?"

"Yes, I've carried out my part of the bargain, Mr Vanin. Just as you told me to. I told him I had an anonymous phone call and gave him the message, exactly as you repeated it to me: that he was to be at his house near Cambridge this evening, and you would call on him. He didn't say very much to me, but he'll see you all right. I'm quite certain about that. By the way, here's the address; take you about two-and-a-half hours by car. I've put down the directions."

"Thanks." Vanin glanced at the slip of paper and pushed it into his pocket. "And how did he react?"

"I don't know—not really. On the surface he seemed quite calm. He just listened to what I said and nodded, as though he were making a purely routine business appointment. I honestly think that during the last few weeks the poor devil has burnt up most of his emotions. As I told you before, I never liked him, but I'm very sorry for him now. All the same"—a slight smile flicked across Arabin's face—"when you get there, I wouldn't be at all surprised if he doesn't try to kill you."

"Thanks for telling me—thanks very much indeed." Vanin grinned back at him. "Now what about your family? You've checked that they were on the plane all right?"

"Oh, yes, I did that all right. I rang up B.E.A. before I spoke to Rolfe. They should have landed at Gatwick Airport about an hour ago. The connecting train is due here at half past. Yes, for once a Russian seems to have kept a promise, and I'm very grateful to you. I didn't really expect it." Arabin glanced up at the big soot-encrusted clock as he spoke, and there was suddenly an odd look of embarrassment on his face.

"Look, Mr Vanin—when we first met, you bought me two drinks which I didn't want. Well, now I'd like to buy you one back. I'd like that very much indeed."

"Thank you. So would I." Vanin smiled with genuine pleasure. "You've got twelve minutes before your train, so let's go." He turned, and together they walked towards the buffet.

The long dreary bar was crowded, but pleasantly crowded. Almost every face had a smile on it, and there was an air of gaiety, and excitement, and home-coming. Vanin looked at the piles of luggage and parcels round each family group: toys for the children, a plant for the widowed sister, sweets and tobacco for some usually neglected grandparent—good will at least once a year, a pleasant family time. Suddenly the thought of his own family was horribly close to him. He pushed it out of his mind as Arabin came back from the counter with glasses in his hands.

"Well, Mr Vanin," he said. "A very merry Christmas to you. Though I suppose you don't believe in it."

"No, I don't believe in it—not in its truth, that is. All the same, I like the story and the idea behind it. I like them very much indeed." He raised his glass. "Yes, a merry Christmas," he said. "To you and all your family." Behind his back, the drunks he had noticed earlier burst into a loud and tuneless rendering of "Silent Night".

"Thank you, then here's to both of us." Arabin finished his drink in a single quick movement and laid down the glass on a table beside him. Once again that oddly embarrassed expression flickered across his face. "Mr Vanin," he said slowly. "In a way, you're my benefactor, aren't you? You kept your promise, and, as I said I'm grateful. That's why I wondered if you would like to come and meet my family. I'd appreciate it very much if you would."

And Vanin should have known, of course. He'd been a long time in his job, and he should have seen exactly what the look in Arabin's face really meant. He should have got out while the going was good. He wasn't a fool, he should have known.

But he didn't see, and he didn't know. He just stood there, with a look of stupid, amateurish pleasure in his eyes, listening to the singing drunks and smiling at Arabin.

"Thank you," he said. "I'd like to meet your family very much. And perhaps we'd better go now. It must be almost time." He glanced at his watch and finished the drink.

Like the buffet, the platform was very crowded, with smiling groups stretched along it, waiting for friends and relatives. It was the second platform from the end of the station, and the next one to it, separated by the lines of track, was left open without a barrier. It seemed to be used as a loading bay, with cars and lorries parked alongside. Arabin bought two tickets from the machine and spoke to the man at the gate.

"Yes, this is ours all right, and it seems they'll be at the end of the train: Car Nine." He hurried forward, watching the line of numbers strung above the platform. From somewhere in front of them a bell rang, announcing the approaching train.

"This should be it, I think." Arabin stopped and looked down at his bunch of flowers, as though making sure they hadn't been broken or disarranged. Then he raised his eyes and smiled. "Well, Mr Vanin," he said. "We're quits, aren't we? We've both kept our promise. We don't owe each other anything."

"Yes, we're quits, but what about it?" As he looked at Arabin's face, a nerve in Vanin's forehead started to tick like a warning light.

"I thought I'd like to mention it for the record, that's all. I gave you certain information to work on, didn't I? I betrayed my employer, and I helped you injure the country which gave me a home. And in return for that, you released my family; a perfectly

fair business arrangement, with no hard feelings on either side."
He drew back slightly as he spoke. "Yes, we're quits, Mr Vanin.
You and I are, that is. But our countries are not quits. Our
countries never can be after what you did to us. So though there's
nothing personal in this, I've got a Christmas present for you—
a present from Hungary."

Without another word he turned on his heel and walked away.
In the distance a little green dot, which was the train, came
sliding down the rails towards the platform.

The three men moved in, one from the front, one from either
side, and Vanin knew them—at the first glance he knew them.
There was *copper* written all over those heavy, respectable faces,
the trilby hats and the belted raincoats. He drew back slightly
towards the very edge of the platform, feeling no bitterness
towards Arabin but utter disgust with himself.

You fool, he thought. You poor, incompetent, sentimental
failure. For a moment he considered reaching for the little gun
in his pocket, and then he knew it was useless. These men were
professionals like himself. They would have him before his hand
was half-way there. Only the thing in his mouth seemed real and
powerful.

"Mr Vanin?" The voice was pleasant and polite, because it
wasn't sure of itself yet. They were acting without real information at the moment; merely on what Arabin had told them on
the phone. With a little more evidence behind it, Vanin sensed
that voice would sound very different.

"Would you mind coming with us, sir? We are police-officers
and have one or two questions to ask you." To their right, the
train clicked over the points and began to run into the station.

"Yes, gentlemen, of course I'll come with you." He smiled
pleasantly and moved his tongue, feeling the little capsule slide
up into position. It seemed hard and firm, but he knew that one
good grip with his teeth would break it open. About ten seconds
it would take, he supposed. Just ten seconds, and then a single
sharp pain and it would all be over. Very easy and pleasant really;
no more worry, no more fear. If only it wasn't for Shura and the
kids. He released the capsule and felt it slide back to safety.
Behind his back came the grinding of braked wheels.

"No," he said, still smiling at the policemen, judging the
distance and knowing that he had about one chance in a hundred
left to him, but also knowing that he had to take it, that the
book required him to take it. And he always went by the
book.

"No, I've changed my mind, and I'm damned if I'll come with you!" He braced his body and flung himself sideways in front of the train.

And he very nearly made it. He felt fingers tearing at his sleeve and missing it. He heard a woman screaming as his feet left the platform. He felt his feet catch on a rail and throw him forward. Then there was suddenly nothing, except the roar of the train with its bulk looming over him, and the chassis coming at him like a battering-ram, and the wheels running towards his legs like knives. For one second he seemed to see the driver's face looking down at him, as though from the top of a high building, and then he was past it.

He was past the frame, and the coupling, and the wheels, with his feet scrabbling on the ballast towards the next platform —the platform without a barrier. For a moment he felt he had made it, and then he didn't feel anything except pain. Great waves of pain flowing over him, while something like an iron hand picked him up, carried him forward and then threw him aside, as a child throws away a broken doll.

*   *   *

He lay beneath the lip of the platform, with consciousness coming back and pain urging it on. Though it felt like a life-time since the buffer had caught him, it could only have been seconds, for behind his back the train was still moving. As though it were the last thing he would ever do, he pulled himself upright and started to climb on to the platform.

Mercifully it was deserted. He looked around him for a moment, and then crawled forward into the shelter of the parked vans, feeling the edges of broken bones grinding like files in his chest. Two ribs gone, he decided, maybe three; still, he was alive. He had a chance of getting away, and there were worse things than broken bones. He fought back nausea, and half ran, half staggered out of the station.

And his luck was holding out. As he reached the pavement, a bus was just starting to pull away. He hurled himself at it, with his right hand clutching the pillar and his feet dragging wildly in the gutter. It took every ounce of strength to pull himself on board.

"Easy, thar—jest watch it." The negro conductor scowled, and then yelped with pain and annoyance as Vanin's body cannoned against his. "That was a stoopid thing to do, sah; boardin' a bus when she's in motion. Jest you look what it says here." He pointed pompously at a notice on the panel: *It is an offence for any passenger to——*

"I'm very sorry, conductor." Vanin twisted his face into an apologetic grin, and fought back his terrible desire to vomit. "I'm a foreigner, you see, and I don't understand all your regulations. Besides, I was in a great hurry. Would you give me a sixpenny ticket, please?" He reached in his pocket for the coin.

"Well, I dunno about that." The black potentate was obviously starting to enjoy himself after the first shock. "Very dangerous thing you done then, gettin' on when we's a-movin'. Right against regulations too. Under the circumstances I'd be quite justified in turning you off mah bus." His hand moved towards the bell as he spoke.

" 'Gainst regulations indeed!" A stout lady, whose parcels seemed to cover most of the back seat, came quickly to Vanin's rescue. "'And you're a fine one to talk about regulations, Conductor!" Her voice was loud and ringing and addressed as much to her fellow-passengers as to the negro. "Yes, we know all about you busmen, don't we? Crawlin' about in convoys to save yourselves work, and keeping people waiting. Goin' on strike when you feel like it, and making my old man cycle to work, and him a martyr to rheumatism. Pullin' away from the kerb when you see somebody trying to catch the bus. Oh yes, I saw what happened, Conductor. You rang yer bell too soon, and I wouldn't blame this gentleman if he takes yer to court. What's more, if you don't give him his ticket at once, I'll put in a report to the next inspector we come across." She leaned forward and there was a glow of malicious pleasure in her eyes. "That's right, Number 87505, give 'im his ticket, or I'll shop yer." She turned a motherly smile on Vanin, as the negro beat a hasty retreat to the upper deck.

"Now you come and sit down by me, sir. Nasty shaking-up you've had just then. I saw the brute ring 'is bell when you was coming across the pavement. A foreigner too, are you? Well, at least you 'ave the decency to admit it; not like some. Who the hell do these bloody Jamaicans think they are?" Though the bus was half empty, a loud murmur of approval greeted her words.

"Thank you, madam. Thank you very much indeed. You are very kind." Vanin raised his hat and bowed slightly. "If you don't mind, I'll stand here for a little—rather winded, you see." He stared out through the rear window of the bus. Far back in the line of crawling traffic, a black car was trying to overtake a lorry, and he heard a sound which might have been a police bell.

At the same moment the bus stopped again, and he saw the welcoming sign of an Underground station.

"Thank you," he said to the stout lady, who had probably saved his life. "Thank you once again." He dropped off the bus and walked towards the station.

He ran all the way down the escalator steps, and it was like a descent into hell, with pain localized now: a sharp, biting pain in his chest, as though an animal was tearing at the flesh. Somehow he made it, though, and from now on he vowed that he would take no chances. Three times he changed trains, and at each station he looked carefully around him. Only when he was certain he had not been followed did he think of his body. He slid his right hand under his jacket and felt the damage.

Yes, it seemed that there were just a couple of ribs gone, and he was in no immediate danger. The fractures had bent outwards, tearing at the skin but keeping clear of the lungs and arteries. If only the pain would stop, he could keep going for a long time. If only he had some morphia, or even a drink, to help him! Yes, that was it: a drink. The thought of alcohol was suddenly like a spar floating towards a drowning sailor. He had to have a drink, or he'd pass out. He turned from the platform and followed a sign reading

"EXIT AND LIFTS"

Apart from a small man reading an evening paper, he was alone in the lift cage, but if his thoughts hadn't been elsewhere, the paper might have amused him slightly. It was open, with the financial page turned towards him, and the headlines read:

WILL WE FILL OUR STOCKING
AFTER CHRISTMAS?
LORD TREMAYNE'S VISIT TO WASHINGTON

But Vanin was not interested in his mission at that moment. Only pain interested him now. He stepped out of the station, staring around him through the thin, frosty air and looking for the thing he needed. Then he started to walk forward. He was in an area of narrow, crowded streets and small shops, and just in front of him was a public house. He hurried towards it, wrenching at the door and feeling the lock hold against him. At the same moment something seemed to move in his chest. No, this might be Christmas Eve, but there was no drink for him, no alcohol when he really needed it—when he needed it for the first time in his life. He cursed the British licensing laws and stumbled on deeper into Soho. The bars were closed, but there might be a chemist who would help him. Yes, if he played his cards right, a chemist might give him something.

"Hullo, darling. You looking for a good time?" The girl, or woman rather, stood in a doorway, and though the temperature was well under thirty, she seemed to be wearing nothing except a tight black dress. Her face was bloated with cold, and her smile was hard and completely automatic. To Vanin it seemed the warmest, kindest smile he had ever looked at.

"A good time? That depends, doesn't it? If there's a drink going, I'd like it. I'd like that very much indeed."

"A drink, darling?" The woman frowned slightly, looking at his face and the sway of his body. "Are you sure you haven't had enough already?" She squeezed her face back into its professional mask of welcome. "All the same, why not? It's Christmas Eve, isn't it? Everybody must have a little drink on Christmas Eve. Come on down and join our party. Plenty to drink, and lots of little girls looking for a nice friend; warm too." She shivered slightly and took his arm.

The "party" was a sad Maltese waiter behind a tiny bar, a manageress who said she had seen better days, three young whores from the Midlands and a boy named Patrick Jesus Murphy, who imagined he was tough. They smiled in different ways as Vanin came into the room: the waiter humbly; the women as though they were seeing the sea for the first time; Mr Murphy toughly, the grin of the killer in the Western saloon—Jack Palance looking at his target. The grin didn't quite come off. There were nine generations of bad food, bad housing and consumption behind it.

"Good afternoon, sir. Now just you sit down and make yourself comfortable. We're all friends here." The manageress fussed round him, seeing "drunk" and "sucker" in every inch of his body. "As it's Christmas, what about buying a drink for the house?"

"The house? Oh yes, of course, I'd be delighted." Vanin glanced round the room. It was dominated by an enormous scarlet juke-box, and photographs of film stars covered the walls.

"Would you make mine whisky, please?" he said. "A large one with no water or soda."

"Whisky, sir? Oh, I'm very sorry, but with the Christmas rush we're right out of whisky." She gave the waiter a sideways grin, and he busied himself at the bar. "We've got something else though—something very nice indeed. It's our own speciality, and you'll enjoy it all right, sir."

"Very well, anything you've got, so long as it's strong." Vanin leaned back in his chair, seeing the woman who had accosted him outside sit down beside him and arch forward. Her dress was cut very low, and there was a little pinkish mole between her breasts.

"You feeling all right now, darling?" she said. "Not feeling sick, are you? When I saw you in the street, I thought you might——"

"No, no, I'm all right." Vanin shook his head, and smiled as the waiter laid two glasses of purple-coloured liquid before them. "Just thirsty, that's all."

He knew what kind of place this was all right. Moscow was getting full of joints like it. The police closed them down every so often, but they always managed to start up again elsewhere. Supply and demand, he thought sadly. In his case the demand was purely for alcohol. The only woman he wanted was a little matchstick drawing invented by John Flack.

But at least the drink would be strong: strong and fiery. He could promise himself that. Probably liable to cause blindness, if taken in any quantity. What did they call it at home? Yes, Momma Sophie; a home-brewed and very raw form of Schnapps —just what he needed in his present situation. He held the glass in his hand, but he didn't drink at once. He wanted to hang on to pain, knowing that in a few seconds it would be dulled. He was an abstemious man, and his stomach was empty. This stuff should work quickly. He pulled out his wallet and handed the waiter a five-pound note, quite oblivious of the eyes watching him. From across the room the juke-box started to grind out a carol.

"Once in royal David's city stood a lonely cattle-shed." He giggled foolishly at the words and smiled at the girl beside him.

"I was born in a shed," he said, remembering what his mother had told him: a shack near Archangel, with the Red, White, and British Armies fighting it out over the putrid snow.

"In a shed! You are a one, darling! Don't be so silly, though. Nobody is born in a shed these days." She smiled back and raised her glass. "Anyway, drink up and let's have another round. Plenty more where this comes from. And a happy Christmas, darling. A happy Christmas to everybody."

"Yes, a happy Christmas." He raised his own glass and brought it slowly to his lips. This was what he had come for—what he wanted. The thing that could deaden pain. He tilted his head and drank deeply.

Oh no! Oh dear God, no! Oh please let me be wrong! The

glass came down in his hand to spill on the table, and he knew that he wasn't wrong, that he hadn't made a mistake. There was no power in the stuff at all, not a trace of alcohol. It was just like drinking soapy water with a slight taste of fruit-juice. He looked wildly around him, knowing that within seconds he had to be sick, and ignoring the girl's cry as the liquid slopped over her dress, he staggered towards a door at the corner of the room.

The door was marked "TOILETS", and it led into a long dark passage, smelling of cats, overcooked greens and garbage. At the end of it were three more rooms, one running out into a yard and the others labelled "HIS" and "HERS" in the heraldic lettering.

"HIS" was a gloomy little room, laid with dirty grey lino and containing two urinals, a cubicle and a wash-basin that was almost overflowing with cigarette-ends. Vanin lurched into the cubicle and did what he had to do. He did it with closed eyes and nausea as strong as the pain in his body. When he had finished he felt better, but not much better. He straightened from the pan and started to wipe his mouth. As he did, he noticed the writing and drawings on the walls, and he smiled slightly in spite of the pain. On the surface the English seemed a sane, commonplace people, but their lavatories belied them: hardly a sexual perversion had been left untouched. He pulled the chain and moved across to the wash-basin. Though it was choked with rubbish, at least the tap worked. He started to sluice his face, when footsteps sounded in the passage and the door opened.

"O.K., feller, let's have it, shall we? Let's just see that roll in your pocket."

The boy called Murphy came into the room nice and slow and easy, as the cinema and the television had shown him, but he still looked what he was—a cheap thug and quite harmless. Even though he thought he was going to rob a drunk, even with the knife in his hand, he looked harmless. It wasn't just a flick-knife that he held either, but a "genuine, hollow-ground, imported, Italian stiletto; useful for hunting and self-defence" as advertised in the *Confidential Detective Magazine*—three dollars and eighty cents in the States, thirty-five shillings and sixpence in England. He raised it slightly and began to walk towards Vanin.

"Yes, boy, I saw that roll of fivers in your wallet, so let's have it. Let's have it quickly. This baby in my hand hasn't had a drink in days, and she's getting thirsty. Do you want I should give her some of your blood to drink?" His voice was just right; hard, and cold, and cynical. A very large percentage of the entertainment industry had been paid to train it the way it was.

"Yes, come on and be quick about it. Hand over, you bloody foreigner."

"All right, just take it easy, son. You can have my wallet—you can have all I've got." Vanin twisted his face into a drunken grin. With sickness, his mind was clear again and he was almost starting to enjoy himself. Though he worked to destroy their system, he still liked the British as a people. It would be pleasant to rid them of a very nasty parasite. Besides, in a way he was a policeman himself. It was part of the job.

"Yes, take my money—plenty more where it came from. Take all I've got, but please put your knife away." He giggled foolishly and reached in his pocket, feeling his fingers tighten round the fountain-pen: a little shining charm that warded off evil.

"And take this too if you want. It's a very nice pen, if you know how to use it: probably cost more to make than you could earn in a year." As he looked at the boy's face he knew that whatever he offered him he would still use that knife; it was almost a part of him. What he did was as much for pleasure as for gain, though gain was important. This was going to be a good day: a wallet full of fivers, a valuable fountain-pen, and a drunk to be slashed. What more could one want in life?

But all the same, Vanin couldn't kill him. Whatever the book said, however strong his loathing, he couldn't kill him. He was a professional and he wasn't paid to kill louts or children. Still, he would leave behind something to be remembered by.

"All right, son," he said, and his voice was quite different now, without a trace of alcohol in it. "Let's just see if you can take me. Your police couldn't an hour ago, so let's find out how good you are. Come and get me, if you think you can. All right, you've asked for it."

He watched the tense, hating body start to spring forward, saw the knife glitter under the light bulb, and his fingers pressed the catch of the pen. As it had done before, the little gun jumped three times with hardly a sound. For a moment Vanin stood looking down at his handiwork, then he walked out towards the yard.

He had struck a blow for law and order, and he was pleased with himself. As far as crime was concerned, Mr Murphy was a back number and he would never pull a knife on anybody again; he wouldn't even be able to hold a knife. When the doctors cleaned him up, they would find that Mr Murphy had lost his right hand.

CHAPTER ELEVEN

"ARABIN—Michael Arabin? No, General Kirk, I don't think Vanin ever mentioned him to me, though he said he had an appointment with somebody this afternoon. I see." Kate bent over the phone that had belonged to the real Miss Reilly, and a little spasm of pain flitted across her forehead. "So that means it's all finished, as far as we're concerned, sir. The police were tipped off to meet Vanin at Victoria Station, and he'll either be dead or under arrest by now."

Her eyes wandered around the room as she spoke. It was a very bare room, without decoration except for its late owner's pictures hanging from the walls. There were a great many pictures, with varying subject-matter, but the treatments had all been similar, and they showed despair. A jagged mountain rising up out of the mist, with its flanks and summit outlined with black paint; a stunted tree with oddly claw-like branches stretching out across a bare moorland; a ruined cottage hanging from a cliff face. There was only moderate talent in the pictures, but they told a good deal about the artist's psychology.

And just in front of her, above the fire-place, was a scene she recognized: the three crosses at Mizen Head, where she had first met Vanin. She would remember that meeting till her dying day: the fog, the roar of the signal gun from the lighthouse, and here and there the loom of a grazing sheep. She had waited a long time behind the Calvary, wondering and dreading what kind of man she was going to meet. It was her first mission of this sort, and fear had been as thick as the mist around her.

Then, up the path from the sea, she had heard footsteps, and seen the man come out through the mist and walk towards the line of crosses. As he gave the passwords, his voice had sounded quite different from what she had expected: low, and gentle, and anxious. She suddenly knew that there was nothing to worry about, for this man was as frightened as she was, and her own fear had left her. "Lord, remember me when Thou comest into Thy kingdom." She had felt great warmth for Vanin as she listened to those words.

"No, my girl, it's not finished, not by a long chalk." Kirk's voice on the phone brought her back to the present with a jerk.

"It seems that Mr Vanin knew his job and was a bit too quick for our friends in blue. This fellow Arabin did his stuff all right —took him on to the platform as arranged, and everything was set for the bobbies to pick him up. Then, when they tried to do so, he broke off; chucked himself in front of a train. The fools! The damned, interfering fools! Just why couldn't they contact us before sending that car?"

"I see, sir. Then that means——" Once again the little tic ran across Kate's forehead.

"I'm afraid it doesn't mean anything, my dear. Vanin wasn't killed, you see. The wretched fellow appears to have the lives of a cat. He managed to make it in front of that train, climbed up on to the next-door platform and got away scot-free. Now he's on the loose, and he'll know we're after him. Yes, Mr Vanin has shown himself quite a bright boy, and it'll be the devil of a job to pick him up—probably on his way back to Russia by now." Kirk was in a vile temper, and the connection was poor. His voice sounded like a blunt saw hacking its way through soft timber.

"No, I don't think he'll do that, sir—not yet." Kate concentrated on what she knew about Vanin. "I've got the impression that he was told to finish this assignment, whatever happens. He's got a family in Russia, and he seemed to imply that there might be reprisals against them if he failed."

"I see. Yes, that's a common enough practice of Malendin's by all accounts. And let's just hope you're right. If we don't pick him up, there'll be the devil to pay. Now for the future. I'll have to put out a general call for Vanin and publish that picture you took for me. All the same, I don't think we'll get him in a hurry; not unless he contacts you again. Now there's nothing else you can tell me, is there? Only what he said about this baby of Rolfe's?"

"That's right, sir. He said he'd get in touch with me if anything went wrong, but it wasn't likely."

"Very well. Then we'll just have to wait and see. I'll put out some feelers towards Martin Rolfe, and you sit tight and pray that Vanin does get in touch with you. Goodbye for the present, my dear."

"Goodbye, General." She dropped the phone back on to its rest and glanced at the little hurrying clock on the mantelpiece: nearly five o'clock, and Christmas had started. Through the uncurtained windows, cars and buses lurched on towards the suburbs and home. Home! Home to the family—home to friends —home for Christmas! Everybody going home except one little man who had to finish his job and work late. Peter Vanin, with

the world against him, trying to find the answer to something
that happened a long time ago—something to do with a child
who was murdered twenty years ago.

She got up from her chair by the telephone and crossed to the
fire, warming her hands and lighting a cigarette to steady her
nerves. Then suddenly she heard footsteps: slow, heavy, terribly
heavy footsteps coming across the landing outside. A moment
later the doorbell began to ring.

The bell rang and rang without pause, as though something
was wedged against it, but Kate didn't answer it at once. She stood
still, staring in front of her and knowing that she'd been wrong
just now—terribly wrong. The whole world wasn't against Vanin.
He had friends all right, and one of them might be outside that
door now. A friend who probably knew the real Kate Reilly;
an unpleasant friend who would know how to deal with a spy.

All the same, she put down her cigarette and crossed to the
door. Whoever was outside had to be answered. She reached for
the Yale handle, hearing the bell like a pain in her head and
feeling the lock stiff and heavy, as though a great weight were
pressed against it. She pulled harder. Suddenly the door opened
with a jerk that threw her sideways, and Peter Vanin fell at her
feet.

Vanin loked up at her from his knees, and he didn't say
anything at all. For perhaps five seconds he crouched like that,
and his eyes swept round the room, as though looking for something that had been hidden there and forgotten. Then he started
to crawl towards a cabinet by the window. The brandy bottle
was a quarter empty when he put it down and pulled himself to
his feet.

"I'm sorry, my dear," he said at last, and it was like a corpse
speaking. "I really am terribly sorry. I have no right to come
here, but it seemed the only place. I don't think I was followed,
though." He glanced out through the window and pulled back
the curtains. With the brandy a little colour was coming into
his face.

"It's all right, Peter. It's quite all right." Kate came towards
him, starting at the lines under his eyes and the odd tilt of his
body. "But you're hurt, aren't you? That train did get you when
you jumped——" She broke off, cursing her own stupidity.

"Yes, it got me all right—got me here." He ran his hand across
his chest, but there was no suspicion in his eyes; only curiosity and
pain. "But how did you know about the train?"

"Oh, it was on the radio just now." Once she had recovered

herself, the lie came easily. "They said that a man, suspected of being an enemy agent, had escaped by jumping in front of a train at Victoria; they described him. I thought it had to be you."

"I see. They're quick off the mark, aren't they?" He leaned back against the cabinet, as though unsure of his legs. "Yes, it was me all right. I had to pay the price of a very foolish action, and the buffer of the train got me here. Nothing too serious, but I think I've smashed a couple of ribs. Give me a hand, will you? Thanks." He shuddered slightly as she helped him off with the coat and unbuttoned his shirt. His chest was thin and almost hairless, and very white, except for one place. A little below the left arm-pit there was a great purple swelling like a growth.

"Yes, you've broken two ribs." At the moment all thoughts of Kirk and her job had left Kate, and she was a purely maternal creature: a woman trying to help an injured man she had grown fond of. Her fingers ran across the swelling, feeling splintered bone under the flesh.

"They're badly broken too, Peter. I couldn't set these in a hundred years without special equipment. We'll have to get a doctor somehow."

"No, no doctor, Kate, I haven't got time." Vanin glanced at the clock on the mantelpiece. "I dare say our friend Tanek could provide a doctor if I asked him, but there's no time for that. I've got an appointment very soon, and I must keep it. Whatever happens, I have to keep that appointment. Thanks." He took the cigarette she lit for him and pulled hard at it. Even with brandy, his face was much the same colour as the smoke.

"No, you'll just have to try and fix me up as best you can. You said you've been a nurse, so get to work. Just tie me together so these ribs don't move any more. Tear up a sheet if you haven't got a bandage. It needn't be a good job, but try to make me last for another four hours. After that it doesn't matter what happens —nothing will matter. In four hours I should have done what I had to do, and Shura will——"

"Shura? Yes, she's your wife, isn't she?" Kate folded the wad of lint and undid the roll of elastic she had found in the drawer. All at once the job didn't seem important to her at all—nothing seemed important except this man with his broken body, and again she remembered her thoughts in Kirk's office: I won't underrate him, but I might get fond of him.

"Yes, Shura's my wife. I've got two children as well; a boy and a girl. If I do what I'm paid to do, Malendin will see they're looked after. Also if I fail but manage to die heroically." He grinned and then shuddered with pain as Kate started to pull on the bandage. As it tightened, she felt the ribs draw back almost into position. There was a sudden longing in her eyes as she looked at his body, though it wasn't much to look at: lean, and white, and broken; but still vital—terribly vital. Every bit of it, from the thin shoes to the Slavonic face with the lines under its eyes, was vital. If it hadn't been for Shura, she might have betrayed her country for Peter Vanin's body.

"Ah, that's better, much better." He watched her tie the bandage and flexed his arm. "Yes, I feel a new man already. This should hold me in one piece for quite a time." He started to pull back his shirt.

"Now there's just one more thing I need, and then I won't trouble you again. I think you said that you have a car in London. Good, then I'm afraid I must borrow it for a while." Once again he smiled. "Don't worry, I'll remember to drive on the proper side of the road, and you'll get it back all right. Just report it as stolen in the morning."

"Yes, of course." Kate reached in her bag and handed him the keys. "It's parked outside; a blue Lancia, and the number's on this fob." She watched him straighten his tie, and for a second her fingers brushed against his arm.

"Peter," she said, and she felt like a Judas to both sides as she said it. "Why don't you give up? Nobody could blame you now, and you haven't got a chance. They'll have your picture in the papers and someone will recognize you. Why not get out while you can? There's certain to be a Russian steamer in the docks, and if you went now you might just make it. Please Peter, I know what I'm talking about."

But he wasn't even listening. His tie was quite straight now, and he started to put on his coat. She might not have been in the same room with him, and love and hatred were very close to her.

"All right then, Comrade Vanin," she said. "Go and die, if you have to, but play it fair. Just tell me where you're going, and what is your important appointment. What is the story about Rolfe's baby? You owe me that much, I think."

"Very well, you can have it." Vanin crossed to the mirror and looked at himself: a junior executive preparing for an important client. "I'm going to see somebody about a child," he said. "A little dead child whose ghost can bring this country down like a house of cards. Here's a letter giving all the details—everything I know. You can read it if you like, but see that Gregor Tanek gets it in the morning. One of his people will have to take over from where I leave off."

He handed her the envelope and stared at her for a moment. She was a very beautiful woman, but she didn't mean anything to him; hardly anything. All the same, her lips were warm and friendly, and he needed friendship. He needed that more than anything in the world. For a second his own lips bent towards them, holding them as though they were the last warm things he would ever touch, and he felt her body respond. Then, very gently, he pushed her away.

"No, my dear," he said. "I'm sorry, but it's too late now—far too late. We might have been good for each other, but not now. Now I wouldn't be good for anybody. I'm just a poor cripple who stinks of death. Also I have an appointment to keep." He turned and walked across to the door, resting his hand on the knob. Just before he pulled it open, he looked round at her, bringing his eyes slowly up from the floor to her face and taking in every curve of her body. Kate had never felt more naked than she did under those vital eyes.

"Goodbye now, my dear," he said, "and thank you, thanks for everything. Maybe we'll meet again some day, and then——" He shook his head sadly and smiled. "But what a waste it's been— what a terrible waste, my lovely, hungry little Irish girl."

Like the last page of a book closing, the door shut behind him and Kate was alone. For a long moment she stared at the door, then she tore open the envelope in her hand and crossed to the telephone. Her fingers felt as though they were turning an enormous wheel as she dialled Kirk's number.

CHAPTER TWELVE

VANIN drove fast out of London, but not too fast. Though he had studied the map before he started, the English roads were difficult to distinguish by night, and he didn't want any police car to stop him for speeding. He crawled on through Hammersmith and Chiswick, and the sprawling wilderness of the North Circular Road: uniform houses and little factories, railway bridges and filling-stations; drive for perhaps a mile and then stop at the traffic-lights, wait five minutes and crawl on again.

But at last he was through the heavy traffic pouring out of London, and he put his foot down, revelling in the low whine of the engine which seemed to remain constant from walking pace to eighty. The Lancia was by far the finest car he had ever driven, and he envied Kate its possession, thinking of his own battered and ancient Zis. Some of these foreign agents were paid very good money, it seemed. Far better than anything the home staff could expect.

The bandage was holding well, and the dull ache in his chest hardly troubled him. If the need arose, he could rely on his body working efficiently. All the same, the effects of the brandy were beginning to wear off, and there was a stale, strangely metallic taste in his mouth. Also he was in for one of the most difficult evenings in his life—if things went wrong it could be his last evening, and he needed help. He pulled the car up before a little public house outside Cambridge, and went in, hoping for Dutch courage.

And why *Dutch*, he wondered, standing at the bar and smiling around him. He was interested in the formation of words, and the idiosyncrasies of English amused him.

Yes, Dutch courage, a Dutch uncle, a Dutch treat, not to mention Spanish fly and French letters. All slightly reprehensible things. A very strange and insular people, the British, he thought, looking at the hearty faces already almost filling the room, though it was Christmas Eve and they were allowed to drink till midnight. They are tolerant enough, but have a strange contempt for everything foreign.

A rich, happy people too, at the moment—but only at the moment. If his theory was correct—if Rolfe broke and gave the wrong answers at that Washington conference—they wouldn't be rich. Before another Christmas there might be bread-queues in England. Though he himself would be mainly responsible, the thought saddened him slightly, and he finished his drink and went out.

Flat country now, though the road still twisted and turned in respect for ancient property rights. Flat wide fields stretching away before him in the bright wintry moon, which almost made his headlights unnecessary. And, as Arabin had told him, few houses but many churches: great towering churches dominating every little slope and standing out like sails on the horizon. He remembered that this had once been a populous area, till the wool trade moved away. The people had gone now, the houses had fallen down and decayed, but the churches remained: empty monuments to a former greatness.

An endless countryside too. The sea could only have been a few miles away, but the land looked as though it would stretch on for ever. Somehow it reminded him of the Russian steppes.

And he was nearly there now. He glanced at the dashboard clock, as a signpost slid past him, and turned up a little lane to his right. Almost eight o'clock, and Heronsford three miles away. In a very few minutes he would be standing before the man he had been told to break: the man with a little guilty secret which could make him the slave of the M.V.D. for life. Only three miles and he would know if his theory was correct. The place was just as Arabin had described it to him. A high wall surrounded the grounds, and there was a porter's lodge with a pair of wrought-iron gates beside it. He rang the bell and gave his name to an old man, who checked it against a scrap of paper, muttering slightly as he did so. Then the gates were opened, and he drove on towards the loom of a big house standing back amongst the trees.

He hadn't far to go, but he took it carefully. The drive was in poor condition, with deep pits and ruts, and there was a heavy frost in the air. His tyres slipped and scrabbled on fallen leaves as they mounted the slope, but at last he drew up in front of the house. It looked enormous in the clear winter night, with crazy towers and battlements rising above the roof and not a lighted window showing anywhere. He pulled at a heavy, old-fashioned bell-handle in the porch and waited. He waited a long time, but at last a lamp came on through the fan-light, and he heard the sound of footsteps. Then the door opened and he was looking at the man he had come to destroy.

"Mr Peter Vanin. You are the person who telephoned my secretary this morning?" Martin Rolfe stood on the step looking down at him, and he was tall—much, much taller than Vanin had expected. He was thinner too, and his face bore no relation to the academic, self-confident mask that had stared out from the walls of Flack's house. His hair was still thick and dark, but the flesh below it was the colour and texture of grey paper: the face of a man who slept little and whose few dreams were nightmares.

And yet, as Vanin looked at Martin Rolfe, he knew that this wasn't quite the broken face he expected. There was great sadness in those restless eyes, but somehow no fear. Rolfe looked as though he had walked through the gates of hell and come out unbroken.

"Yes, my name is Vanin," he said, and stepped past him into the hall. A big, dark hall, with chipped oak panelling, stags' heads, and rusty medieval weapons on the walls, and everywhere a slight odour of decay. The home of a man who could write a cheque for a hundred thousand pounds any time he wanted.

To their right a staircase led up to a landing, and somebody was standing on the landing. A tall woman in a very bright dress staring down at them, and as he looked at her Vanin was reminded of Arabin's description of Lady Rolfe: "Her make-up stood out like sealing-wax on an envelope." He suddenly had the uncomfortable feeling that he was entering not a house, but a prison.

"Will you come this way, please, Mr Vanin?" Rolfe closed the door and led him to a room beyond the stairs. It was a long, narrow room with french windows, and seemed to be used as part study and part library. There were bookcases along the whole of one wall, and at the far end a big, red curtain which probably divided it from an adjoining room. To the right of the curtain was a mahogany desk with a portrait of Rolfe hanging behind it. He held some kind of silver baton in his hand, and was dressed in scarlet and gold, with a flowing cape and a cap with eagle's feathers and fur flaps. It was obviously some form of academic dress, and he made a fine sight as he stood there: dashing, and gallant, and brave, quite divorced from the grey figure who moved slowly to the desk.

"Well, Mr Vanin," he said, and somehow he managed to put a smile into his face. "You wanted to see me, and here I am. At the moment I know nothing about you, but you claim to know something about me—about a certain event in my life which happened a long time ago. You have written letters to that effect, but have now come into the open. Well, do we talk business, or do you want to prolong the agony still further?"

"We'll talk business, Sir Martin, and I don't want to cause anybody agony. I am purely a businessman." Vanin broke off and leaned forward as Rolfe opened a drawer in his desk. "But don't try anything—don't do anything silly. I belong to a big organization, and I've left a letter giving all the details I know. If you killed me, it would merely mean that somebody else took my place."

"If I killed you!" Rolfe's eyebrows came up in a bar across his forehead. "Oh, I see." He closed the drawer again, and there was a short, blackened pipe in his hand. "You thought I was bringing out a gun, did you? No, I don't imagine that would do any good, and I'm sure you've written a very comprehensive letter." He filled the pipe very carefully and struck a match. Only when it was drawing to his full satisfaction did he look at Vanin again.

"Now, as we agreed, let's talk business. During the last few months you, or some of your friends, have been sending letters which imply that you have certain damaging information against me. Well, please sit down and tell me just what you think you know, and what you want from me."

"Thank you." Vanin leaned back in the chair and crossed his legs, looking not at Rolfe, but at the picture behind him. Somehow it made it easier to talk that way.

And he told him everything from the beginning. He told him who he was, and what the department wanted, and how they had received the first communication from Arabin. He told him about Flack, and how Flack had died, and the man Julius, who had died with him. He told him what he had learned from Superintendent Pode, and what Kate had seen in the doctor's notebooks. Then he turned away from the picture and looked at Rolfe himself.

And as he did so, he suddenly felt all confidence drain away, and he knew he was wrong—completely wrong. For there was no fear or even acceptance in the man's face. Rolfe's face was as strong and arrogant as he had seen it in the newspaper cuttings, and it was smiling.

"So that's it. That's who you are, and what you think you know. That's what you will have put in the letter to your colleagues. You are to be complimented on a fertile imagination, Mr Vanin; also to be thanked." The pipe had gone out as he listened, and Rolfe picked up the matches again.

"Oh yes, I'm grateful to you, Mr Vanin; very grateful. You and your assistant killed Flack, and Flack was the one person who could hurt me. It seems that I have nothing more to worry about. No, I'm afraid your theory is quite impossible, and there's no need to take my word for that. Just check with the Queen Mary Nursing Home in Chelsea. If the records still exist, they'll tell you that for six weeks after our child was born my wife was a very sick woman, and in their care. She could no more have taken that pram than you could have done." As though changing his mind, Rolfe pushed the matches into his pocket and laid down his pipe.

"Won't you try to guess what really happened, Mr Vanin?"

"No, no, I don't need to guess." Though Vanin answered him, he had hardly heard Rolfe's last words. He was staring up at the picture again, and this time it told him the truth. The painting of a slim man with rather delicate features dressed in Tudor costume, and the plumed cap on his head had long fur flaps that framed the face like a woman's hair.

And that was the point of course—like a woman's hair. That

was what Flack must have seen: a reproduction of the picture—and it had told him the truth. It made him remember what he had actually looked at through the snow in 1940. A tall woman standing outside a shop window, and her face, her man's face, had been almost hidden by flowing hair. That was the only way it could have been, and Flack's words were very clear in Vanin's head: "The Gaunt Woman was born twenty years ago, and she died the same day."

"It was you," he said. "Just you, and you did it all on your own."

"That's right, Mr Vanin—all on my own." Rolfe had moved away from the desk and was standing with his back to the curtain.

"You know who the Gaunt Woman was now, and my wife never had any idea of how or why her son died. I planned it alone, I carried it out alone, and I've not the slightest regret for what I did." His well-bred, academic voice seemed incredibly far-off and distant, and the automatic he held looked like a stage prop in his thin hand.

*　　　*　　　*

"All right, Stirling Moss, there's no need to hurry. Just take it nice and slow and easy." Kirk leaned back in the car seat, grumbling at the driver and massaging his hands together as he did so. Though the windows were closed and a heater roared full blast, his overcoat was tightly buttoned, and under it he wore a muffler and two pullovers to protect his chest from the treacherous night air. He scowled at the dashboard clock, checked it with his watch, and then turned to Kate and Trubenoff.

"No, I don't think we want to get there too early. Unless a miracle comes up, or our friends the police let us down badly, there's no chance of Vanin slipping through our fingers this time. If he does, of course, I'll have to start applying for another job without delay.

"No, it's not Vanin but Rolfe I'm interested in now. If there really is something on him to make him a potential victim for blackmail, then he's a damn bad security risk and the Minister will have to get himself another adviser. I want friend Vanin to have plenty of time for his interview, and then I'll be very interested to hear Rolfe's account of it. And here come our reinforcements, I think." He wound down his window as the car drew up before a swinging torch, and a uniformed figure walked towards them. "Ah, there you are, Inspector. You've seen our man go through all right?"

"That we did, sir. Exactly forty minutes ago it was." The police-man consulted his notebook. "A blue Lancia saloon, registration number AVK 995, driven by a man on his own. No chance of his spotting us either. I had two constables hidden behind the bushes where the lane joins the main road."

"Good. And you've got the place surrounded as I asked?"

"Yes, sir. Ten minutes after he passed, I put my men in. There's no chance of his getting away from us—not without a miracle, that is."

"Um, well, don't be too confident about that. This joker has proved himself to be quite a miracle-worker." Kirk grunted slightly. "Just keep your wits about you, and remember he's armed. Shoot if you have to, but only to cripple him. We'll start to move in five minutes."

He wound up the window and stared at the clock again. Not one of them spoke as they waited, and its hurrying minute hand seemed the only living thing in their little, warm world. Then Kirk adjusted his collar and leaned forward.

"All right, children," he said. "Let's go, shall we? And this time it's got to be for the kill."

CHAPTER THIRTEEN

"YES, that's right, Mr Vanin, I did it. All on my own, I did it." Rolfe stood against the curtain, and there was hardly any expression on his face.

"I made the decision. I did what I had to do, and I've no regrets. It wasn't really difficult either. I was slim in those days, and I'd always been a good actor. I put on a wig and a woman's clothes and make-up, and I stole the pram. Other children had disap-peared in the neighbourhood and everybody connected my child with them. Yes, those poor children were like a gift from God to me.

"And then I killed my son." It was obviously the first time he had told anybody, and he might have been confessing to an old and trusted friend.

"And can you blame me, Mr Vanin? You came here to force me to betray my country, but as a man can you blame me? Look for yourself, and then tell me. The last book on the third shelf from the top. That's right. Now turn to Chapter Six, page eighty-nine. Oh, yes, I know the place well, and I often look at that illustration." He watched Vanin's face and smiled: a very bitter smile.

"No, it's not pretty, is it? But that's what my son would have become if he had lived. He was the victim of both a pituitary complaint and a mercifully rare condition known as *Morbus Crassi*. The Roman nobleman from whom it takes its name was put to death on the orders of Augustus Caesar. He was only sixteen years old at the time, but before he died he killed two of the six men who came to smother him."

"No, I don't blame you. I'm just very sorry." Vanin closed the book, for there was no point in looking further. The thing it showed was far worse than anything he had imagined possible, and there was no point in looking at it. No point in studying those terrible limbs and the face that needed a French word to describe it: *La Gueule*—the muzzle of a beast. "No, I can't blame you," he said. "But why not have had it put into an institution?"

"And let the world know that I'd fathered a monster?" Rolfe shook his head convulsively. "No, I couldn't bear that, Mr Vanin. I couldn't stand the shame of it. We'd both longed for a child, you know—prayed for it for years. And then one day Dr Fenwick walked into my study and told me how our prayers had been answered." Rather horribly a single tear ran down his firm, set face.

"I lost my temper and kicked Fenwick out of the house, but he'd left his notes on the table, and after I'd looked at them I knew he'd told me the truth. If he was allowed to live, my son would become like that." His eyes flickered at the book in Vanin's hand. "I couldn't let him live, Mr Vanin."

"And you didn't tell your wife?"

"No, I couldn't tell her. She was a very sick woman and the truth might have killed her. I've never told her, and the secret has been like a barrier between us ever since."

"And that's what you were frightened of when you got Flack's first letter, Sir Martin? Not of the police knowing, but only of your wife?" Vanin kept his eyes on the gun that was pointing at him, but it hardly seemed important now.

"Yes, only of my wife. With the little that Flack could tell them the police would have never reopened the case, but I couldn't risk her suspecting. She'd wanted a child so badly, you know, and she'd never have understood. No, I think it would have driven her mad." The automatic started to come up and his face tensed.

"And now, Mr Vanin, I'm very sorry, but I'm afraid I'm going to kill you. You are the only person who knows the truth, and there's no alternative. I'll get away with it too. My servants are loyal, and when the authorities find that you are a Soviet agent—when I tell them I found you going through my papers—they'll believe me all right." Rolfe almost seemed to be talking to himself.

"Yes, you're going to try to kill me, Sir Martin." Vanin's hand began to slide towards the little dummy gun, but at the same instant he knew it was useless. He hadn't remembered to reload after those shots in the club lavatory, and there was no help there. Unless he was very lucky, Mr Murphy would soon be revenged for his crippled hand.

He braced himself for a leap at Rolfe, to throw the book at him, but he saw that was useless too. The man's finger was already tightening on the trigger, and he would be dead before he could reach him. He just stood there waiting for it, and he felt no fear, but only a terrible weariness. Weariness, and suddenly——

Yes, suddenly hope. For without any warning Rolfe's face was altering again. All the determination left it and was replaced by a look of complete astonishment. The fingers slackened from the gun, and as they did so he seemed to wither. Like a fly on hot metal, his body seemed to shrink and grow smaller, and then tilt forward. The curtain behind him tilted too, and for an instant he hung from it. Then with a noise of tearing cloth the hooks came away, and he fell to the ground with the folds of the curtain covering him, nailed to his back by the handle of a rusty dagger.

For perhaps five seconds—and they felt like years—Vanin stared at the ravaged face of the woman who had saved his life, watching her kneel over the draped figure on the floor and listening to her curses.

And then he ran. He ran to the windows, wrenching them open, and it was nothing to do with the nightmare figure behind him that made him go. Outside, he had heard the sound of cars, and he knew that the hunters were out. All that mattered was getting away.

He had done all that was expected of him, and he could look after himself now. He hurled himself towards the car, and suddenly he knew he would make it. He had to make it, for he felt like a giant relieved of a great burden and beyond human injury. Three times he should have died, and three times he had escaped death. Now he was going home and nothing could stop him.

He raced across the gravel of the drive, hearing voices all around him and seeing lights come up, but he hardly noticed

them, for he was going home. He was within five yards of the
car when his knees seemed to buckle of their own accord, and he
fell forward. It was almost with surprise that he remembered that
bullets travel faster than sound and he had felt pain before he
heard the shots.

*   *   *

The room was bright and clean, and smelt of antiseptic, and
he was waiting for death. All the same, for the time at least, life
was good and there was strangely no more pain. He stared at the
blurred figure by the bed, waiting for it to come into focus, and
he smiled slightly.

I made a good run for it, he thought. Even with my broken ribs
I nearly made it. Then his eyes cleared and the smile went out.

For he knew the man all right. He had seen his picture a score
of times and read a score of reports on him. This was the man
at the top, Malendin's opposite number, though on the surface
he looked almost ineffectual. The popular caricature of an upper-
class Englishman with his tweed suit and bow tie, and the cigar
stuck out over his grey moustache. He was effective, though. Every
inch of that heavy, overclothed body would be effective.

"Good evening," Vanin said. "I led you quite a dance, didn't
I?" He had no idea of the time of day or how long he had been
unconscious, but it seemed the only appropriate greeting, for
evening comes before night and he felt night was very close to
him now.

"Yes, you certainly did, my boy." Kirk removed the cigar and
lit a cigarette, which he placed between Vanin's lips. There was
something very gentle, almost fatherly in the action. "All the
same, we got you in the end, I'm afraid." He watched Vanin drag
hungrily at the cigarette and then removed it.

"And now let's have a chat, shall we? By the way, my name
is Kirk, and I think you can guess the department I represent."

"Yes, I know you all right, and I am honoured—sir. May I
wish you a happy Christmas, General?" Vanin found the remark
amusing, but he couldn't force his face into a smile. Somehow
the muscles didn't seem to be connected with the brain any
more.

"Thank you, Mr Vanin, and the same to you." Kirk held out
the cigarette again, and then turned and grinned at the man by
the door. He was tall and dandified, with a lot of gold in his
smile, and Vanin recognized him at once as a compatriot.

"You see, Igor, my fame is world-wide." Kirk's grin swept back to Vanin, as though he were a rare and valuable possession which fate had thrown into his hand.

"And how is Colonel Malendin? In good health, I trust?"

"Yes, he was well enough when I last saw him." Vanin suddenly seemed to look right through Kirk's features and see the face of Malendin behind them. These are the people who really matter, he thought. The people who control the earth. The politicians have a little hour, but it is the permanent officials, men like Malendin and this Kirk, who shape policy. Suddenly he hated them all.

"Good! I'm delighted to hear it." Kirk might have been inquiring into the health of a friendly business rival. "And it wasn't a bad idea of his, trying to get your hooks into one of our top financial experts; might have worked, too, for a time. Yes, quite a change in your methods. The British Lion brought down by bankruptcy, eh? Ways of killing a cat.

"Now would you like to talk to me, Mr Vanin? Apart from the very end, we know the whole story, I think. We found Rolfe with a knife in his back, and the wife had shot herself. They were both dead."

"Yes, they're dead all right." Vanin closed his eyes and he knew that Rolfe had died because he was too confident. He had thought that his wife was upstairs, respecting his privacy as always, but this time she had let him down. She must have felt the tension as he waited for his visitor, and she had crept into the little room behind the curtain and listened. Like the hall, that room had been decorated with rusty, archaic weapons.

And, as Lady Rolfe had listened to her husband's confession, something in her mind had snapped, and a ready-to-hand knife had gone home through the folds of the curtain to revenge her son. Perhaps after that had come one fleeting moment of sanity, and the gun on the floor had seemed the only way out.

"No, I won't talk to you, General," he said. "You know we never talk." Nothing mattered any more, but it seemed important to keep Rolfe's secret.

"I know that you rarely talk, Mr Vanin, but it doesn't matter now. You see, you never had a chance. Whatever happened, Arabin would have given you away, and even if you'd broken Rolfe and got him to do what you wanted, we'd have pulled him in. We had all the details in your letter to Tanek."

The letter! Vanin's tongue ran against the capsule in his mouth. At least they hadn't found that. Probably they knew he was dying anyway, and hadn't bothered to look.

All the same, if he didn't die, if the hundred to one chance came off and he lived, then he might talk. One slow, accurately given injection of Sodium Pentothal would help him reveal a great many secrets. He couldn't take a chance of dying unaided.

"You got Kate Reilly then?" He hated saying that.

"Oh yes, we got Miss Reilly all right. To be exact, we got her three weeks ago, and she was one of the few who did talk." Kirk motioned to the man by the door.

"Let me introduce you to the young lady who took her place." He smiled at the girl who came unwillingly into the room. "This is my colleague Miss Kate Martin." His voice hardened slightly. "And now are you going to talk to me, Mr Vanin?"

But Vanin couldn't talk to anybody—he was laughing. He was roaring with laughter, rocking backwards and forwards on the bed, with his eyes staring up at the girl's face.

"So that's it," he said at last. "That's how you got me. May I congratulate you, my dear Kate? You did very well. You fooled a professional, and I like to give credit where it's due." Once again he shook with laughter, and then he turned to Kirk.

"All right, General," he said. "You've won this round, but don't be to pleased with yourself, for there'll be more—lots more. You can't destroy me, because I'm not a man but just a little part of a great big machine, and there's always someone to take my place." His tongue moved, and he felt the little capsule tilt into position. Then he looked at Kate again.

And as he looked at her, her face seemed to alter. It started to grow older, and rounder, and there were wrinkles under the eyes. The face of a woman who was very dear to him. A woman who would go on living if he died well and didn't talk.

"Shura, my dear," he said, but he spoke in Russian and only Trubenoff could understand him. "Shura, I love you." He gritted his teeth and prepared for death.

But those weren't quite his last words. All at once the room seemed to fade, and he was back on the cliffs above Mizen Head with nothing around him except the fog, and the grazing sheep, and the three men hanging from their stone crosses.

"Lord," he said, remembering his passwords, the words of the dying thief. "Lord, remember me when Thou comest into Thy kingdom."

The thing in his mouth burst like a blister, and the taste of cyanide was fire to burn away pain. The world tilted, and he began to swing out towards . . .

RELIGION
AND DAVEY PEACH

Robert Holles

*"Religion and Davey Peach" is published
by Michael Joseph Ltd.*

The Author

Robert Holles is thirty-seven, married, with two children, and lives in a three-hundred-year-old cottage in Essex. He joined the Army on boy service when he was fourteen; later, as an armourer sergeant, he served with the Gloucesters in Korea, and also had a tour in Nigeria. He was demobbed in 1957 after fifteen years' service. By way of recreation Mr Holles professes to play village cricket, though his inclusion in the team might well, he thinks, have something to do with his ownership of an ancient car, which is useful transport for away matches.

AUTHOR'S NOTE

All the characters and situations in this novel are purely imaginary. Garside is no specific village; yet it is every English village I have known.

CHAPTER ONE

THE reason I started writing all this down is because I happened to be talking to Bill Bradbury the artist that had the cottage on the Green. Actually he left there about eighteen months ago. He said the place put the mockers on him and he couldn't paint.

He wasn't so far out there because he let me have a shufti in this big room at the back he used to use for a studio or whatever they call it, and you ought to have seen some of the paintings. Like nothing on earth.

Anyway, I was talking to him over the Falcon one night. He was always on the piss. We happened to be talking about what goes on in places like Garside, and how the old townies would never believe it. So he said how right I was, and I said I ought to know better than most because of my being on the paper round for five year and more, and like you get to know everybody and their peculiar little habits, as well as being in line for all the bits of gossip that happen to be going the rounds.

I remember he was drinking some stuff called Benedictine that some monks were supposed to knock back in the old days. Only now it's been commercialized and any bastard can drink it that pays—even characters like Bill Bradbury that's just about the opposite end of the pole from a priest. He was a regular one for knocking back all these queer drinks like crème de menthe, vodka, and suchlike, although he's got his definite likes and dislikes, because one day I was looking at all the different bottles on the shelf behind the bar and I said why didn't he have a cherry brandy. You should have seen the look come over his face. He said did I take him for a bloody ponce or somebody?

Anyway, when I was on about Garside I told him one or two little items that surprised even him, and he reckoned I ought to write a book about it. So I asked him how does a bloke like me that's not had much of an education write a book for Christ's sake. He said all I had to do was to write it down just as if I was telling him about it. He said boy, if I could do that it would be a best seller. The only trouble was, he reckoned, that I wouldn't do it. He reckoned that if I did start putting it down I'd try and write all classy, everybody did that, and what came out wouldn't be fit for a Sunday journalist to wipe his arse on.

I don't know why I took him up on it, but it kind of stuck in my mind. I didn't actually do anything about it until about a year later, by which time he'd upped and offed quite some while, and the Purkisses had taken over the cottage.

I suppose I was waiting for something kind of special to happen to start me off. Nobody can write about sweet fanny adams, after all. Then I happened to be reading an article in some magazine I'd been stuck with because old Parker, the bloke who used to take it, decided to croak the day before it came out, so I didn't have time to cancel the order. This article was about some young bint whose old man was a lighthouse keeper, so she rowed across to the lighthouse to keep him company. Strictly against the regulations. There was another bloke in the lighthouse, a young bloke, but he was in on the secret. (I bet he was, and all.) Every time the boat came with the supplies she hid inside the lantern or whatever it is. She was there for about three years all told. This lighthouse was on an island, and there were thousands of birds on this island, and she made friends with them instead of nicking their eggs for horses' doovers like most people would have done in her position.

Afterwards she wrote a book about her experiences. According to this article she made about fourteen thousand quid out of it, and they were even going to make it into a film. I was lapping this article up, especially the fourteen thousand quid part. That evening I started on a bit of an old notebook, and before you could blow your nose a thousand times I'd filled it up and started on the next one. Once I got started I couldn't stop. It was like when you have the runs.

Well, I went on until I had as much as you'll find in an average-sized book, and then I thought I'd send it to one of these publishers. I probably will at that, one day. The only trouble is I've put down a hell of a lot of stuff about myself, and I certainly don't want every second bastard pointing the finger at David S. Peach.

I suppose I could use a false name, though. I'd have to change the name of Garside and call it Chipping something or Lower Firkin, otherwise I wouldn't be too popular with some of the people I've been nattering on about, and I'd have to change their names and all.

Still, it all comes out in the wash.

CHAPTER TWO

IT all started about nineish on a drippy old summer evening with Squidge saying, "She wouldn't! I bet you anything you like she wouldn't."

Squidge wasn't a bad kid on the whole. I mean, you could rely on him. Only he reckoned to be twice as sharp as a gnat's whisker. Occasionally he had to be persuaded otherwise. Just gently, of course.

Reggie Ferber said, "Ah, not for you, maybe."

"Not for nobody," Squidge reckoned. "Least, not unless they got a friggin' Riley or summink."

Reggie Ferber said, "Hey, see what Dave reckons. Dave, you reckon she would? Squidge reckons she wouldn't."

There were six of us that night hanging round the war memorial, which is just a big ugly cross made out of concrete stuck on top of a block of marble in the middle of a little island up at the crossroads. There's a signpost there which says: "Forbury 6: Whitmarsh 4: Garside Bottom—No Through Road."

This war memorial is what you might call a popular rendezvous for all the young tearaways in Garside. On this particular Sunday evening—I remember it exactly because it was only the second day I'd been back from my holidays—we were all on different kinds of bikes.

I was in the middle with the front wheel of my Quickly over the kerb of the island. The others were grouped around in sort of arrowhead formation with all their front wheels pointing in towards mine, except for little Piwi Grant. Piwi was riding all round the island in a circle on his racing pushbike, trying to go as slow as possible without falling off. He was always up to some kind of caper.

However. At this particular time I'm talking about I was drawing a kite in the gravel with my toe. It started off being a Maltese Cross, but when I joined the sides up it looked like a kite, so I started putting a tail on it. I was just about to make the obvious joke in connection with this, when Squidge and Reggie introduced the subject of the new piece up at the Falcon.

First off, I pretended I didn't know what they were jabbering about.

"Wouldn't what?" I said.

"Shag, what you think?" said Squidge.

"Wouldn't she? Who says so?" I was still scratching about in the gravel. I had to box clever because I'd never seen the bint in the Falcon. She was the daughter of the new landlord who'd moved in a few days after I started my holidays. Since I'd been back I hadn't been out and about much. I was too busy recuperating. Anybody who goes to the particular holiday camp I went to and doesn't get all the grumble he wants and more, can't be wanting it.

"I say so," said Squidge.

"What you know about it? S'pose you tried already?"

The way they all yelled their heads off laughing at the idea of Squidge chancing his arm with the new piece up the Falcon made it pretty obvious to me that she was away out of his reach. Anyway, he was only just seventeen, Squidge, and he was a bit of a runt with it. Whenever he went into a boozer the landlord would look at him very old-fashioned, and he'd usually have to make do with a lime and lemon. Which didn't stop him trying to come the acid.

"Well, I just reckon," he said. "I mean you can more or less tell jus' by lookin' at 'er and listenin' to the way she talks. Goes to church reg'lar, an' all."

"No kid. Does she honest?" Darkie Bowles said. He was hellish impressed. Not that it takes all that much to impress Darkie.

I reckoned it was about time I put the kybosh on the argument, so I said, "You can't tell what an apple tastes like 'til you 'ad a bite. Anyway, people as go to church are only them as 'fraid to die, an' the sinners 'cause they need it. See, that's all the reason they go for, so's they can pray to God to forgive 'em. Then they can go down the marsh again with a clear conscience."

Beetle Raynor doubled up cackling and pointing his finger at Squidge. You'd only got to mention "down the marsh" to Beetle and he was away.

Nobody said anything for a bit. They were all waiting for me to start them off on something. They're not very flush with ideas of their own. Only that night I happened to be all wrapped up in myself.

After a while, Beetle and Reggie belted off down the switchback, which is a little twisting track through a wood over the other side of the stream. You have to cross over to it by a little white bridge arrangement. The only trouble is, when they built this bridge, the awkward bastards put bars across each end to stop anyone taking bikes across, and they shoved a notice on it which says "Pedestrians Only" just in case anybody didn't get the message. So when you take a bike over you have to lift it above your head and cart it across. Talk about inconvenient.

This track is known as the switchback because it goes up and down over a lot of ridges, and twists in and out of the trees. There's a whole lot of big bony roots sticking out all over the place, so when you go flat out over it on a bike it's inclined to be a bit dodgy. I should know, because I hold the record for the circuit, twenty-eight seconds.

Actually, we'd had to pack up using it for a while about a year before, because some old girl about eighty was taking her evening stroll along the path, just when it was turning dark, and someone came round there on a bike just at that moment and knocked her for a loop. Somebody found her lying there with a broken hip about four hours later, which was lucky for her because otherwise she'd have been there until the morning, and it was a rafty old night.

A couple of days afterwards the local copper, Nobby Creighton, came round inspecting all the bikes. He didn't find out who did it, though. The old girl was up at the Forbury Orthopaedic for about six months, but she got over it in the finish.

Anyway, in the meantime I propped the old Quickly up against the kerb and squatted down on the bottom of the war memorial. I lit a fag and leaned against a little bronze plaque which had the names of the dead of two world wars on it.

I'd read these names over so many times when I was hanging around with nothing better to do that I knew them all off by heart. There were fourteen names for the first war, and six for the second.

In the first war the names were all in order of rank, with Captain S. G. Finch up top. In the second war there weren't any ranks at all, but it was easy to pick out the officers because they had their initials in front of their names, and the others had them afterwards. None of them interested me all that much except for this Ames, R. F., and somebody called Burke we used to have a laugh about sometimes. We reckoned he must have been one to have got his name on there in the first place.

This Ames, though. I used to reckon he might have been a bit like me—when he was my age, of course. He was a sergeant when he got knocked off, and a lot of people in Garside remembered him because he was a good footballer. He was captain of the village team, and he apparently used to play inside left for Forbury Athletic when their regular bloke was injured. He got his packet at a place called Cassino in Italy. His wife still lives down the Bottom. She was supposed to have been a great one for the Canadians during the war.

Not that I knew very much about what was going on then because I was only a nipper at the time. But you get some of the old people in the village, they've got very good memories. Darkie Bowles didn't know much about it either, and his father was a Canadian darkie. Old Charlie Bowles, the cowman up at Roman Farm, was in the army himself at the time. He was in the Pioneers. He was supposed to have near crucified Darkie's mother when he got back from Egypt after being away four years, and found she was up the spout.

Me, I never criticize anyone. My own mother isn't exactly virtue's queen.

I might have been in the army myself, only I just missed National Service by a couple of weeks. A lot of my mates were called up though, and none of them were highly chuffed about being chased around all day by big hairyarsed bastards who couldn't make a living in civvy street.

If there's another war though, boy, they'll have me. I'll finish up in khaki yet. It'd probably be a hell of a sight easier than being a pacifist. Anyway, all the last war conchies I've ever met are all queer-looking herberts with beards and corduroy slacks. They'd have me all right, only next time there's going to be just one socking great bonk, and after that there's not going to be anybody around to carve the names on the war memorials even. And even if there were, it'd take a lifetime. Still, there's nothing wrong with a steady old job, providing the money's all right.

It was starting to get dark. Old Ned Hoskin came creaking past very slow on his old lady's bike. Piwi yelled out "Hey up!" and pitched a stone after him. It bounced off the road into the spokes of his wheel and rattled out the other side without old Ned so much as noticing.

Darkie took a quick shufti up and down the road, then he pressed himself against the war memorial and pissed all over the pedestal. "Don't mind me," I said.

Squidge had been up the road on a recce. He came back all excited. "Tanya and the Sprat," he yelled out. "Heading this way." Darkie zipped up his flies in a hurry, then he started hollering because he reckoned to have nicked his weapon in the process. He was only kidding on.

A couple of minutes later Tanya and the Sprat came round the corner, walking very slow as if their feet were giving them trouble. Every three or four yards they stopped. The Sprat was pulling a dandelion to pieces. Bits of it were all over the front of her dress.

I sat there and watched them coming.

The Sprat was just fifteen. She's just a bundle of sticks thrown together with a smear of lipstick and pointed eyes and a dry little chuckly voice which she imagines is hell of a sexy. Tanya is a couple of years older. Her mother is a Russian, or supposed to be, and she's a bit on the hefty side. As she drew up level, I could see the loose flesh of her thighs jellying around under these tartan slacks, which were stretched so tight across the front you could almost hear the stitches gritting their teeth.

They ambled by as if we didn't exist, although Squidge stuck his fingers in the corners of his mouth and whistled them up like somebody screaming. When they were five yards past he hollered after them, "Toffee-nose! Don't wanna know!"

The Sprat turned round. "Toffee-nose yourself. Go on!" Then she what you call resumed progress. But they were both slowing down as hard as they could without it noticing.

"Haven't I seen you some place else?" Darkie yelled.

"I wouldn't know, I'm sure," the Sprat said over her shoulder.

"Wouldn't 'ave a fag on yer by any chance?" shouted Squidge. Both of them work over the fag factory in Forbury.

They were just about marking time by now.

Darkie hollered, "She fell in a machine last week, they very near put a cork tip on 'er," and laughed. Piwi leaned over his crossbar. "Don't you go too far now. Soon be time for your bed."

"You coming then, Piwi?" the Sprat shouted back. She was about a year older than Piwi in age, but a hell of a lot more in experience.

They had stopped dead by this time. The Sprat pointed to the steam coming up from the bottom of the war memorial and whispered something to Tanya. They turned inwards and started to giggle. Darkie shouted "Oy oy!" But nobody ever took much notice of Darkie. "Come on then, come over 'ere," Squidge yelled. "Or be you frit?"

"Frightened of what? You?" said Tanya. "What we want to come over there for?"

They came, though.

They were all concentrating on me, waiting to see which way I was going to jump. The Sprat came up and stood about a yard off. As far as I was concerned she might have been a mile away. She said, "Hullo, David Peach."

I didn't answer. Piwi cackled. She said it again. "Hallo, David Peach."

I just looked up at the sky and said, "Good God." Darkie and Piwi burst out laughing.

She said, "Well, so we're not on speaking terms tonight?"

I pretended I was deaf, and went on scratching about in the gravel. I was remembering the first time I took the Sprat down the marsh, and the way she'd handed it over on a platter. Didn't even have to fight for it. I wasn't the first one there, either.

It had happened about five times since. Six, maybe. I couldn't remember. Until I got sick of her possessive whiney little voice when it was all over, and the way she wanted to follow me about everywhere like a shadow. That's the trouble with women. I'd tried to pass her over to little Piwi, who was still trying to lose his virginity, but she wouldn't wear it.

As for the other bitch, Tanya or whatever her name was, I'd already wasted a couple of evenings working it over. No future there, boy. She was keeping it for company in her old age.

Tanya said, "Have you got a spare arm, Davey, by any chance?"

"Yeh—and there's summink heavy on the end of it," I said.

She was dead peeved. "You don't 'alf think you're somebody, don't you?"

"Yeh." I decided to practise my famous balancing act. I climbed on the Quickly, leaned back in the saddle, arched my spine, let my arms dangle behind me, and balanced myself with my toe points on either side. "Yeh," I said. "That's right."

"You can sit there all right. Anybody can sit there. There's nothing clever in that."

"Who said there was anything clever in it? Did I say there was anything clever in it? Look," I said, "what am I supposed to 'ave done? I ain't 'ardly opened my trap and you start on."

"It's just your attitude," the Sprat chimed in.

"Oh, go home!"

"We'll go exactly where we please, and when we please, won't we Tanya?" The Sprat was putting on her best high and mighty tone, but I could see she wasn't all that chuffed. She looked as if she might turn on the waterworks any second. She'd done it before, and I didn't want it to happen again. Not in my company, anyway.

"In that case there's only one thing to do." I leaned forward and grabbed hold of the handlebars, then jumped on the pedal and started her up. I shoved the front wheel through the middle of them and went up the village street at bat 6, which is getting on for my maximum.

The engine was kicking up a beautiful fuss. Like all the wasps' nests in creation. I looked back just before I went round the corner, and saw all their blurry faces gaping after me.

At first I wasn't quite sure where I was going, until I realized that I was heading straight towards the Falcon. Another thing I realized was that the new piece in there that everybody was raving about had been the principal thing on my mind all evening.

CHAPTER THREE

WHEN I got there, the first thing I noticed was Sydney Chubb's white Alpine among a whole lot of other cars lined up in the yard. I was thinking as I went in that she must be something out of the ordinary run, because Sydney doesn't waste his time, or his talents.

I'd never seen the Falcon so packed out. There were all the regulars, like Jim Lockhart the undertaker, Keith Ranner from up the Seagrave Garage, Teddy Paulson the builder and decorator, and even old Joe Purkiss who wasn't supposed to drink for his health's sake. There were a lot of others who normally do their boozing up at the Hare and Hounds, the only other pub in Garside, and six or seven I didn't know from jackdaws.

This bint, she was everything they said, and more.

She'd got straw-coloured hair which was very neat the way it curled round at the back. There was also a wavy bit in front which was sort of separate. She was wearing a mauvey purpley sort of dress and where it came straight across at the front it was all rucked up, only deliberately, which was very nice. She'd got all anybody could ask for up top, unless they were greedy, and a beautiful nipped-in little waist.

There's a piece something like her I've seen advertising spin driers on the television. In this advertisement she is standing in front of a split new spin drier, and some announcer comes up and asks her a whole lot of questions, just as if he's never clapped eyes on her before, and they haven't been rehearsing it all the morning. Some of the people that run television programmes, they must reckon everybody's got a brain the size of a peanut. The queer thing is, if I see some dopey advertisement on the television it always puts me off buying whatever it is they're trying to flog—if I'm buying it already, that is. With spin driers and that kind of gear it doesn't make any odds. What would I do with a spin drier, anyway?

However, this bint says yes, she's had it on appro for a few days because the one she had kept going haywire. Yes, it was simply marvellous. She'd never seen anything to touch it. Then another announcer with a very deep voice who wasn't in the picture started on about this particular spin drier in the background, about how they'd exposed it to all different sorts of temperatures without any ill effect. They even dumped one in a canal, and when they lugged it out after six months they just plugged it in and it went straight away.

Just as the announcer finished, this piece turns round, puts her hands against the edge of the sink and leans back with a little secret smile as much as to say, "It's a load of pills. Don't you believe it."

I only saw that advertisement the once. Maybe a lot of people wrote in about it. Anyway, the piece in the advert was almost the spitting image of the bint behind the bar, except the one behind the bar didn't look so experienced. She had a terrific personality, though. You could feel it. I had to fight my way through about ten or twelve of them to get to the counter.

She gave me a peach of a smile as if she'd been waiting all evening just for me to roll up. She said "Certainly," when I asked for a half of bitter. She stuck it down in front of me as if it was the millionth half-pint dished up by that particular brewery, and the brewers were making a special occasion out of it. I was half expecting her to fork over a rolled gold cigarette lighter, and everybody to start clapping. They didn't, though. I stepped back and watched her serve some pimply little bastard from the next village with exactly the same enthusiasm.

I was standing there with my eyes rolling and floating, when old Paulson tapped me on the shoulder. "You'll have to join the queue, young Davey," he said.

I wasn't too keen on Paulson. He's only got a couple of lorries and four blokes working for him regular. Three and a half really, because old Osborne's had his kidneys removed and he can only do half a day's work. But Paulson cracks on he's Sir Robert MacAlpine or somebody. He's always looking at his watch and saying, "Well, I've got to go and fiddle the accounts," or "I'd better be getting along to pay the labour, or there's going to be a strike." He reckons to pay the labour about five times a week.

"I suppose you'll be dropping in here more often," he said.

"I might be, Mr Paulson. On the other hand I might not."

"Well, I don't say I blame you," he said. "If I was your age I wouldn't let the grass grow under my feet."

I was just going to inform him that whatever age he happened to be, he wouldn't get much a look in if I was in the running. I didn't, though. You get somebody like Teddy Paulson that's spent all his life in and around the village, some day he's going to be in a position to do you a good turn—or a shafter.

So all I said was, "I bet you knocked it about a bit when you were my age, Mr Paulson."

"I did, my boy. I certainly did." He started chuckling deep down in the pit of his stomach. It turned into a horrible racking cough which nearly choked him. He had to wipe his eyes over with a handkerchief. Then he said, "There was one lesson I learned very early."

"Did you really? I wonder what it was?" I said. I pretended I was keen to know, although I never pay any attention to other people's lessons. Take old people, they always have some strange idea that if they did something in 1904, and came unstuck, everybody else is going to come unstuck doing that same thing ever after, so it's their kind of duty to humanity to go around warning everybody. Every young bloke, that is. The only thing is, that anything which applied to somebody like old Paulson couldn't possibly have applied to me.

"Come 'ere a minute," he said. He leaned over towards me and breathed his horribly stale oniony fagendy breath in my face. Then he grabbed my shoulder and stuck his disgusting little bristly tash right in my eardrum. He whispered, "I learned never to shit on my own doorstep, laddie."

He lifted up his wrist, took a quick shufti at his watch, and said, "Well, this won't pay for my holiday on the French Riviera." I was just going to say, "No, your business won't either," but I managed to check myself. He sank the rest of his pint, wiped the wet off his lips with the back of his hairy big hand, and clapped me on the shoulder. "Just work that one out, my boy, and bear it in mind." He winked, shoved his pork pie hat on the back of his bonce, and scarpered.

I wasn't at all sorry to see him go. I was having a crafty butcher's at the group around the bint. From what I could see of the opposition, there was nobody to worry about barring Sydney Chubb.

Me, I've never had to chase the skirt. All I do is hang around the places where they go, and in no time at all I've usually got one hanging on to my armpit and telling me all its secret thoughts. It's amazing the things they come out with in telephone kiosks at one o'clock in the morning.

I suppose I must be naturally attractive to women. I'm just turned twenty, pretty tall, and I've got the kind of hair they go for, dark and crinkly all over. The effect is not obtained by the use of a lot of hair gyppo, either. Just a touch in the mornings. I've usually got a quick answer, too, except when a slow one is indicated. I play football for the village and in the summer I'm the fastest bowler in the cricket team, although I don't usually get as many wickets as old Dan Bailey the spinner. He can really tweak 'em down. He had a trial for Somerset before the war.

On level terms I'd willingly chance my arm against Sydney Chubb, who is about six inches shorter than me, with a thin pale face, and isn't any good at sweet fanny bar skirt.

But in the crumpet stakes the odds were very one-sided, because Sydney Chubb's old man is Garfield Chubb up at the hall, a very rich property dealer who came to live in Garside about seven years back, in order to fiddle the income tax. So old Sydney's got an Alpine and a pukka voice and a real pigskin wallet he isn't scared of flashing in company, and the folding stuff is coming out of his pink little shell-like ears. He nearly always wears a black blazer with a striped silk scarf tucked in the neck, and he never seems to have a haircut.

I'd never actually spoken to Sydney, but sometimes when I'd be chugging home after midnight on the Quickly, he'd pass me coming the other way through the main street of the village, doing about eighty and making the windows rattle for miles with his exhaust. He'd always give a bit of a thump on the horn, and I'd sort of stick a couple of fingers up as he went belting by.

Not that I minded Sydney having a stinking rich father and a Sunbeam Alpine, etc. It was just his luck. In any case, I'd rather collect it myself than have it handed down the line. But I had to accept the situation as it stood, and I knew that the piece behind the bar in the Falcon was just a matter of territory. I don't mean anything to do with geography.

I could tell she was well over into Sydney Chubb country before I'd finished my half pint. So I drank up quick and stuck the glass back on the edge of the counter. "Goodnight," I said.

She sang out, "Goodnight," as if she really meant it.

CHAPTER FOUR

I SAID "Four'n eleven if you please, Mrs Graham."

"Davey, I've just got the kettle on the boil."

I knew it wasn't any coincidence. I said, "Just what I could do with, a nice cup of tea. But it'll have to be quick."

"Mind your feet then. I've just washed the tiles." They've always just washed something. "Look at those filthy paw marks. I'll murder that cat."

This was on the following Saturday morning. Saturday is cash day for me on the newspaper round, which I'd been running off my own bat for three years.

I started off doing it for Bert Fisher, the big newsagent in Forbury, until one day he suddenly discovered he was paying me a bit more than the profits. So I offered to take it over, and he was only too willing to say yes. It was a bit sticky at first, but about six months afterwards they started building the two big council estates down at the Bottom, which made a big difference. I was making a clear tenner a week out of the round—sometimes more. In the afternoons I knocked up another six or seven working the petrol pump up at the Seagrave Garage, or doing a bit of tractor work on Jack Tidy's farm.

Mrs Graham wasn't more than about twenty-six, and not all that bad-looking, either. I could even have fancied her, but the trouble is as soon as they get married they change. You'll see them wearing curlers in the kitchen, and they don't bother about make-up, and they're always doing something like trying to pour paraffin out of a big can into a bottle without using a funnel, and getting it all over their clothes. In the summer when they've been standing over the stove they'll often have patches of sweat under their armpits, and maybe a few stray hairs sticking out. Then they start getting chicos, which really puts the stopper on it. Come downstairs stinking of National Dried Milk and ask you if you'll try not to scrape your feet on the gravel when you go out, because they've just got little Mervyn to go off.

She said, "Did you hear about Mr Chadwick?"

"No," I said. "I can't say as I did."

She started pouring out the tea from a bluey-gold teapot with a sponge thing round the spout.

"S'posed to have left all his money to that District Nurse, Miss Merryweather, that lives down at the Bottom. She came to look after him when he had arthritis. At least, they told him it was arthritis. Not so much as a penny to his wife. I don't know how true it is."

"Wouldn't surprise me," I said. "Not the way she used to carry on at 'im."

"Did she really?" Mrs Graham was squatting on the edge of the table, stirring her tea very slowly. She must have been on about the ninety-second revolution. "Mind, she had a lot to put up with."

I just sipped away at the tea while her old curiosity got steamed up. You have to bring them to the boil. Then I said, "That's as maybe."

She latched on to this like crabs on to a bit of raw liver when you dangle it over a harbour wall. "What d'you mean by that exactly?"

"I shouldn't be telling you this," I said. "I wasn't supposed to be listenin'. Only they were shoutin' at the tops o' their voices." As I said this I took a nicker note she was holding out, and gave her change for ten bob.

"Honestly," she said, "I wouldn't pass it on." She stuck the change in her purse without looking at it. I said, "You'll have to make that a promise. I don't want to be had up for slander."

"I promise." Her eyes were like golf balls.

"Well, she used to deny 'im," I said.

"Deny 'im?"

"That's right."

"But he was an old man," she said. "He must have been nearly seventy."

"Don't make any difference, he wasn't past it," I said. "I went there one Sunday to deliver the Screws. They were shouting at each other in the passage. 'E was sayin' if she din't give 'im is marriageable rights 'e'd find someone that could. 'E said what did she think 'e married 'er for, because it certainly wasn't for 'er intelligence."

"Well, you do surprise me," she said. "I'd never have imagined. And to think 'e came over only last year to poison our rats."

I poured a drop of cold milk in the tea and walloped it down. "I've got to dash now," I said. "I never told you, mind."

Outside the gate I jumped on my trusty steed and skedaddled a hundred yards on to the next bunch of cottages. Old Mother Harpin was waiting for me on her front doorstep.

She shook out her *Daily Sketch* and stuck it right in front of her nose as if the headlines were difficult to read. She said, "What's the news today, Davey? Anyone been murdered?"

"Ain't 'ad time to look," I said. "Anyway, you don't want to take any notice o' what you read in the papers."

"They're always wrong about the weather."

"They're always wrong about everything," I said. I didn't want to waste too much time with her. She was a cunning old bag that had a lot to do with the Women's Institute, and she was knocking on a bit. Her husband was a carpenter. He was working on the big new school job over at Whitmarsh. He couldn't do David O. Peach any good.

"Just a minute, Davey," she said as I was slinging my hook. "I can't ask you in because I'm catching the half-past ten bus." She beckoned me up closer. "You haven't seen the Coopers' car recently, have you?" She said this in a very hoarse whisper, with her eyes shooting all over the place to see if anybody was listening. It was just like a couple of spies swapping information in the Casbah—wherever that may be.

I screwed my old fizz up in the way you do when you're pretending to try very hard to remember something, in order to give yourself time to make something up. I said, "Not lately, now you come to mention it." What I forgot to mention was that the Coopers' old Standard Ten had been up the Seagrave Garage for the last couple of weeks having a top overhaul. I'd even done a bit of work on it myself.

"It hasn't been outside their place for a fortnight. I'm only asking because they will keep parking it on my bit of frontage, see?" She kept folding and unfolding her spiky arms, and then folding them again the other way round. It was making me nervous.

"Well, I couldn't say. She did tell me a couple of days ago that her husband might be 'avin' a change of jobs," I said.

You should have seen her eyes light up. "Well now, fancy that, so 'e's got the push. I thought somethin' queer was going on. And 'im working in that same printing works for twenty-three years. Well, I never did."

I said, "Well, you never know your luck. As a matter of fact Mrs Cooper was on about your Dick the other day, only I can't quite remember what she said."

"Was she, indeed?" Old Mother Harpin's voice rose about six octaves.

I tapped my forehead a bit. "Can't remember what it was," I said. "Anyway, it couldn't have been very important." Then, just as I was going, I said, "Ah, I know, she was on about your Dick comin' 'ome every night loaded up with pots of paint and bits of hardboard and stuff. She said that every time 'e gets off the van 'e's got hold of somethin' off the site. She reckoned it must be costing the ratepayers a good ten quid a week, and there ought to be more supervision. Only you won't let on that I told you. She was only havin' a bit of a bind. You know what women are."

Mother Harpin was standing there like a statue, only not so beautiful. Her mug, which was normally the colour of cold porridge, had gone as pink as blotting paper.

"Anything my Dick brings back off that site is paid for."

"Yeh, well, we all know that, Mrs Harpin. Well, I'll be away."

She stood there with her gob opening and shutting nineteen to the dozen. "Anyway, what's it got to do with Mrs Cooper I'd like to know what my Dick does or doesn't do, some people have got a cheek and that's a fact, there isn't a nail from that site comes into this house that isn't paid for . . . Well I'm . . . Honestly I'm . . ."

"Cheerio Mrs Harpin." I was already ten yards away and travelling at bat four. She deserved it, the niggledy old cow. She was just as bad as the rest of them. Worse, if anything.

A lot of women in Garside look forward to me coming round with the gossip more than the papers and magazines. It's mostly the old 'uns that go a bundle on it, but plenty of the young marrieds come in after a bit. Give 'em a couple of years and one or two grubby nippers, and they're all for it.

When I first started the round I only used to pass the stuff on from mouth to mouth, because I found it was good for business. But after a while, I discovered they'd get disappointed if nothing very juicy happened for a month or so. Then I found out something else—they didn't mind whether it was true or not, they appreciated it just the same. In any case, they'd take everything as gospel. They'd look at you and nod their skulls and make little clicking noises with their tongues, and say well, it didn't surprise them, just the same whether it was fact or fiction.

That was when I started making most of it up.

The queer part was, nobody ever dreamed of calling me a liar. If they did find out that something I'd told them was all cockeyed, they'd imagine somebody else was to blame further back along the line. But what really used to get me was the fact that every silly bitch I swapped stories with used to think she was the only one in the entire village I took into my confidence. That was the biggest yell. I've often wanted to see their faces if they could have heard what I've been saying about *them* a couple of doors up the road. But they never cotton on.

Another thing I found out was that very few of the ones that were always on about what was the latest bit of scandal, were ever involved in anything themselves. It would never be them that ran off to Broadstairs or somewhere with somebody else's husband, got blind pissed in the middle of the afternoon, went bankrupt, or were seen sitting in the garden starko. Very rarely, anyhow. There used to be one gossipy old bitch down the Bottom. When her old man passed over she was informed by some solicitor that she wasn't entitled to anything he'd left because she wasn't actually married to him, and he'd got some relatives in Nottingham. These relatives came down very smartish and flogged the roof over her head, which she wasn't too chuffed about. But it's the exception, as they say, which goes to prove the gorblimey.

It definitely needs real imagination to succeed in the scandal game. When I had a really good bit of juicy rumour on the go I'd set it going at the crossroads, pick it up again on the Green, and find it there ahead of me when I got to the Bottom.

I've thought up some snorters in my time. There was the one about Ken Jeffries going to the big barbecue they held in the barn over at Roman Farm. They even had a couple of sergeants down from the Yank Air Force to supervise. I can't think why, because it wasn't as if they had bloody great sucking pigs turning on spits, like they do at real barbecues you read about. All they had was a few roast chickens you had to pay about six and nine for a leg of, and fried slingers in bread rolls which were supposed to be "hamburgers". Apart from that and being held in a barn, it was just like an ordinary dance, except that the band couldn't find the way and turned up about two hours late.

Anyway, I dreamed up this one about Ken Jeffries going to the barbecue and his wife staying behind because she had a headache, and he didn't get home until four o'clock in the morning, and when he got into bed Mrs Jeffries woke up and switched on the light, and the first thing she saw was his braces sticking out of his trouser pocket.

The best ones were always the ones when you had something that was true, and just added a bit on—such as in this case, the bit about the braces.

There was also the one about when Pauline Cross got married, which was all the rage for a long time. The story was that

Pauline's mother had got old Ma Madden to make the wedding dress on her electric sewing machine, out of some white tulle or oyster satin or whatever it is. So Ma Madden did the job and delivered the dress about a fortnight before the wedding. Then just two days before the actual ceremony, Ma Cross went round to Ma Madden's just as she was turning in for the night and asked her if she'd take the dress out another four inches round the middle.

Ma Madden created one hell of a stink because she said there wasn't enough material to take it out that much, and she reckoned it had fitted Pauline like a glove at the time she made it. She said she was certain about that, because Pauline had come round specially to try it on in her front room.

There was a terrific kerfuffle when that one got about and half the village turned up outside the church for Pauline's wedding. Mrs Cross and Ma Madden haven't spoken to each other since. It didn't help matters a lot when Pauline knocked one out about four months later.

The strange thing is, I can't remember which part of that story is true, and which part is the product of what you might call my fertile imagination. It's just as if everything actually happened that way.

CHAPTER FIVE

BY this time I'd got up as far as Tidy's farm on the Green. There was nobody in the house, but I heard a bucket clanking in the dairy. In order to get there I had to pick my way across the farmyard which was knee deep in thick slimy mud and cow dollops.

Mrs Tidy was swilling water down the middle of the concrete floor and brushing it away with a stiff broom. When I yelled at her from the doorway she turned round and came over. "Leave the papers on top of the sacks Davey," she said. "My hands are all wet. How much d'you want?"

"Three and six to you."

"Can you take it out of the overall pocket?"

I went across to a brown overall which was hanging on a nail by the door, and started sorting through a lot of floury coins in one of the side pockets. I fiddled about with them for a bit, then took out three half-dollars and put back a tanner. I knew she'd never check it. The old man would have. He was on to every last halfpenny, old Jack Tidy. He wasn't too bad in other ways, though.

She slung the broom down and rubbed her hands on a scruffy old piece of towelling. To look at her face, you'd think old Mavis Tidy was very kind and friendly, and her wearing spectacles gives the same impression. It's her wedge of a nose that really gives her away, though. The way it juts out, and the way she always tilts it up a bit when she's talking, so that you can see it coming at you like the blade of an axe.

She's really the most dangerous gossip of the lot in Garside, because she really makes a business out of it. Every time you tell her something, she'll sort of hold it up to the light in her mind, and have a butcher's at it. Then she'll try and make it tally with something else like a piece out of a jigsaw puzzle.

"You coming over next Thursday to help with the hay?" she said.

"Yep. I might be a few minutes late though, tell Jack."

She said in exactly the same tone of voice, "I s'pose you wouldn't 'ave 'eard anything about old Mr Purkiss in your travels, Davey?"

"No. What about 'im?"

She tilted her nose up about twenty degrees. "It's a funny thing, I wouldn't like to say. Last two or three times I've seen Hilda Purkiss she's been shakin' like a leaf, and looking so deathly pale, poor dear. D'you think there's anything peculiar about old Joe?"

"Old Joe Purkiss? Nah—'im?"

"Well, she never so much as mentions his name, it do seem a bit queer."

I was beginning to wonder what she was going to dig up about the Purkisses, who lived in the cottage next door to the farm. When she got her hooks into anything, she hardly ever turned out to be wrong. They say there's no smoke without fire. But old Mavis Tidy, if she ever smells any—smoke I mean—she'll find out where it's coming from, then she'll poke about until she sees what's smouldering, and blow on it until it bursts into flame.

She said, "I suppose you've heard about Mr Salt, the new vicar who moved in last week?"

I said, "What about him?"

I wasn't very well up in ecclesiastical matters, but I did know about the new vicar, who'd turned up in place of Canon Fosdick, who'd just recently retired. I'd only seen him once—the new bloke —when I'd dropped in to take his order. Actually, he looked a decent sort of character, but he wouldn't have had to be any great shakes to show an improvement on Canon Fosdick.

Old Fosdick was about ninety when he chucked in the job, and he'd been the vicar for about fifty years. There were only about six or seven people went to his services regular. Sometimes in the winter, there'd be nobody there at all. He was a cantankerous old bastard. The only papers he took were the *Church Times* and something called the *Archeological Review*, which came out about every three months. He was mad keen on digging things up, and he used to go all over the place looking for Roman remains.

I knew a bloke called Freddie Martin, who went to see old Fosdick about getting married. He had to take his bint with him and go round and have a chat with old Fosdick in his study.

He reckoned everything was buried under great piles of old papers and magazines; there was only one chair in the place and old Fosdick was sitting on that. He said there were fossils and coins and bits of old pots on every mantelpiece and shelf, and you could write your name in the dust on old Fosdick's desk.

He said old Fosdick hummed and ha'd for a bit, and then he started on about this Roman pottery. Eventually he picked up a little tiny piece of bone and held it up by the window. "Do you know what this is?" he said.

Freddie Martin said he didn't know, and then Fosdick asked Freddie's bint the same question, and she said she didn't know.

Then old Fosdick said, "It's a toothpick."

They didn't get much change out of him either, because he said as they'd never been to his church he couldn't see any good reason why he should marry them in it. He said they'd better get cracking with effect from the following Sunday, and he'd reconsider the matter in about six weeks' time.

They went straight over to Forbury and got fixed up with a special licence at the Registry Office.

Anyway, you can understand what I mean when I say that when Mavis Tidy brought up the subject of the new vicar, I wasn't all that interested.

She said, "He's supposed to be a real live wire. He came from a parish in the London docks where they're all rough dockers and people. He was on television once, Mrs Whichelow says she knew she'd seen him somewhere before. He's supposed to have been a Communist, and he's got an artificial leg, and he only became a parson when he was over thirty, he didn't even go to a proper college. D'you know what he did as soon as he walked into the church?"

"No."

"Well, he told old Frank Talbot the caretaker to take the altar to pieces, and break it up for firewood. Then he told him to fetch the old kitchen table from the vicarage that they used to chop the vegetables on, and put that in its place. He said all the incense was to be thrown away, and all the wafers for Communion, because he was going to use ordinary bread in future, just like they did at the Last Supper."

"What Last Supper?" I said.

"Don't you never read the Bible?"

"I read a bit of it once, a long time ago. I never got past the first chapter. It was all in old-fashioned writing," I said.

"Anyway," she said, "they say he just walks into any house in the village, even if the people are Roman Catholics, and starts chatting. He never mentions the word God. He was even talking to old Ned Hoskin up by the crossroads the other day. Having quite a conversation. And he's only been here a week."

I said, "Well, old Fosdick never went out of his way to talk to anybody. The only time he ever called on anyone was when he dropped in on old Ma Bassett and said he'd just caught one of her nippers in his orchard, and if it happened again 'e was going for the police. All old Fosdick ever did," I said, "was to collect bits of old Roman coins and stuff. They even used to call 'im a Roman."

"That was because he was high church," she said. "Apparently if you're high church like Canon Fosdick, you have to wear one of those little round hats, and you have a lot of candles on the go, and you're supposed to ring all sorts of little bells during the service. I don't understand it all myself."

"Well, it's no use asking me," I said. "I'm not too well up in it these days." I was backing towards the door as I was saying this.

"Hang on a minute, Davey. I didn't tell you the rest. About this new vicar, I mean, Mr Salt. He's supposed to be going to have a special jazz service every month for the young people, or so he was telling Mrs Whichelow. There's going to be a jazz band in the church and everything. Did you ever? I think that's taking it too far."

"It's not taking it far enough as far as I'm concerned," I said. "Have to bring on the dancing girls before 'e gets me in there."

"Oh Davey," she said. "You are dreadful, honestly."

"Yeh—I'm late an' all. Cheerybye," I said.

I went back across the yard like a ballet dancer.

The morning was tanking on a bit steady, so I didn't hang about at the other houses on the Green. But as I was getting near the Falcon, which is on top of a sort of rise which runs down to the Bottom on the far side, I started feeling queer.

I had a funny kind of excited feeling about the bint, somehow. I was sure I was going to bump into her when I took the papers round to the back door and collected the cash. I kept imagining little scenes with her in my mind, such as our having a very intelligent conversation about something in the paper, and me pretending to argue with her about it, and then standing back and saying, "As a matter of fact I couldn't agree with you more." Just kidding her along a bit. And then giving her a wink, and sloping. And her standing in the doorway looking after me a long time after I'd disappeared, and chewing over what I'd just said.

I was a bit annoyed because I couldn't stop thinking about her, and the nearer I got to the Falcon, the worse it was. As I went across the back yard I kept saying to myself, "Christ, she's only a stupid bint. What's the matter with you?"

I gave it the old one-two with my knuckles on the door of the scullery and after a bit she came and opened it. She was wearing a yellow apron with brown little dogs all over it.

"Oh I know, you've come for the money," she said. She disappeared and came back after a couple of minutes with a purse. She said, "Oh, and could we have a *Lady Fair* starting from next week?"

"I don't see why not," I said. I gave the old pencil a lick and wrote it down on the pad. "One *Lady Fair*."

She said, "Actually my mother takes it for the knitting patterns." Then she said, "That's a funny pencil, it's the first time I've seen a triangular one." She gave a bit of a laugh. "What does it say on the sides?"

I passed it over to her and she read it out: "The Seagrave Garage: Tel Garside 216: Petrol-Oils-Lubricants-Service. Prop. K. Ranner." She handed it back.

I said, "Keep it."

"Oh no, I couldn't possibly."

"There's stacks of 'em up the garage," I said. "I work there on and off, see."

"No, really," she said, "I only just wanted to have a look at it."

I was getting sick of the sight of the poxy pencil.

"Look," I said. "We only keep 'em to give 'em away to the customers."

"Well, it's terribly kind of you. Are you sure you've got another one?"

"Certainly." I bloody hadn't, though.

She said, "Haven't I seen you in the bar?"

"Yep," I said. She was gazing at me with these gorgeous violety lamps which were so wide open it made her look a bit surprised at everything she saw. For some peculiar reason I was feeling dead nervous.

"You're the one they call Davey, if I'm not mistaken?" she said.

"Yep." I was pretending to be hellish preoccupied with totting up some figures. "David Z. Peach."

"Honestly? What does the Z stand for?"

"Zebediah. It's biblical. What they call you?"

"Carol," she said.

"Carol? Reminds me of Christmas."

She laughed. "I've never thought of it that way before."

"That'll be two 'an eleven," I said. "How d'you like it round 'ere?"

She counted out the money and stuck it in my mitt. She didn't drop it from a height of about ten inches, either. "I think I'm going to love it. I've always wanted to live in the country."

"You come from the smoke?"

"Yes," she said. "I suppose you've lived here all your life?"

It was all very calm and natural the way she was shoving it across only for some reason I was finding it very difficult to breathe. I've never had the same thing happen to me before or since, which is why I must have started acting plain stupid.

I said to her all of a rush, "I 'spect you miss a lot of things you normally get in London though, like pictures you know and the big shops and everything, you know, just wander in and help yourself and shove everything on one o' these little trollies an' pay at the other end, and ice skatin' and watchin' the wrestlin' matches an' what-all. D'you ever watch the wrestlin', I don't mean on television? I know I would if it was me. Miss everything, I mean. As a matter of fact," I said, "they haven't got a bad cinema in Forbury. It's only been put up since the war and it's the only place around 'ere that's got the extra wide screen. I mean, any time you want to go there, see? As a matter of fact there's a good picture coming off next Thursday Friday an' Saturday. Beyond the Somethin'-or-other. Some river where the Yanks 'ad this big battle. Anyway, I 'spect you saw it before you came away."

She was looking at the tips of her fingers all the time I was natterin' on like this. When I'd finished she looked up at me and said, "It's very nice of you, but I've got to be in the bar."

Inside the house some woman's voice was hollering out, "Caa-aa-aa-rol!"

"Anyway," she said, switching on this extra big smile and getting ready to scarper, "I might manage it some day. Only you see I don't get an awful lot of . . ." She was fading away down the passage. "Coming, mother!"

"Yep well anyway . . . I'll see you get that, what was it . . .? *Lady Fair* you wanted, wasn't it?"

I was just turning away to go when I happened to catch my foot under one of those iron grille efforts they use for scraping the mud off boots, and came arse over bollocks. By the time I'd got up and picked the newspapers out of a gooseberry bush, I was so niggled I could hardly see straight.

I could just imagine her. Walking back to the pub kitchen and telling her stupid bitch of a mother all about it. "Only the paper boy. Wants to take me to the pictures. Do we want any more spuds for dinner or will these be enough?" Just passing it off. Another village swede-basher getting all steamed up for the first time he comes across a reasonable bit of grumble and grunt.

While I was picking up the Quickly I was calling myself every kind of effing stupid dense dozy idiotic sodding burk that ever crawled out of a hole in a tree. I could see her sitting snogging with Sydney Chubb in the back seat of the Alpine, and then leaning back and saying, "Hey, guess what? I'm going to make you jealous. I had an offer this morning, you'll never guess who from . . ." in that stupid Londony silly voice of hers. And it was Joskins here gave her the chance.

Not that I was interested. I knew the type she was all right, all promise and no performance. Hang it under your snitch all night, but when it came to the point . . .

Just past the Falcon there aren't any more houses. There's a steep bit going up round a curve, and then you're over the top of the hill and it's a straight run down to the Bottom. I went up the hill at a very steady bat, and switched the engine off for the run down.

Then I happened to see old Ned Hoskin pushing his bike up the hill towards me. As I came down he stopped and gobbed in the hedge. Then he bent over his handlebars again.

CHAPTER SIX

EVERYBODY in Garside knew Ned, but very few people ever spoke
to him. He was always turning up in the most unlikely places
and he was supposed to have radar ears. He was reckoned to be
always listening to other people's conversations, only I don't
believe he cared what anyone else was talking about.

You've got to look kind of insignificant to do that, and anyone
can see Ned coming a mile off. You ought to see his ears, like
two pounds of bacon rashers from behind. And the rest of his
clock is made to measure—a big squashed-in nose, dirty great
sausagey lips, a cave-like mouth full of mouldy teeth, and these
huge big black eyes set away back in his head. He was hell of a
size build with it. He was like one of these characters in a museum,
got up to represent what man looked like fifty million year ago.

Actually, Dr Lumbard once told me he was like that because
he'd got something wrong with his glands. He was actually quite
harmless, and as weak as a rabbit. You couldn't tell anyone in
Garside this, though—especially the women. Old Ned didn't look
exactly the kind of party you would wish to encounter in the
woods on a rafty old night.

Nobody knew how he managed to keep alive, especially as he
had a wife and a kid to keep. The kid was a girl of about thirty,
although she didn't look more than eighteen. They called her
Bloody Mary. She was as daft as a brush, and used to walk round
the village singing; every so often she'd rip off a fart.

Anyway, old Ned managed to scrape along on poaching and
scrounging, and doing a bit of casual work on the farms in season.
Whenever he caught anything—a hare, maybe—he'd pedal down
to the main road, park his bike in the hedge, then he'd stand in
the middle of the road swinging the hare from side to side.

Eventually he'd stop a motorist and offer him the hare for five
bob. The motorist would take one shufti at Ned's pan, and reach
for the lolly in order to get rid of him quick. Ned would take it,
then he'd go round the back of the car and pretend to stick the
hare in the boot. All he'd do, though—he'd lift up the lid of
the boot, lob the hare into a ditch on the side of the road, and
slam the lid down again. The motorist would then put his foot
down smartly, and Ned would collect the hare ready for the
next customer.

But around this particular time, old Ned wasn't too popular

with the people down at the Bottom, and I'll tell you why.

The Bottom runs along both sides of a valley, which is about a mile long, with woods on either side. Nobody lived there at all, apparently, until about 1918, when some estate agent in Forbury had the crafty idea of buying it, carving it all up into little plots, and flogging it back to the squaddies coming back from the war at the usual profit of about a thousand per cent. (All right, I'm only jealous.)

I used to go down there quite a bit after birds' nests when I was a nipper. All sorts of queer ginks used to live there. The houses were all little bungalows made of weatherboard, with red slate roofs. Little bits of fancy trelliswork round the old front door with a wooden spike on top. There was one I remember called Mon Desir and another called Seldomyn, and one called The Little Hut—which described it a treat. The people that lived there were dead keen on chickens. Everywhere you looked you could see fowlhouses with black felt roofs sticking up out of fields full of tough whiskery old grass.

There was one field down there stacked out with old motor parts. Ancient old van bodies with the sides peeling off. Rusty old back axles, big piles of rotting tyres you couldn't see the bottom of for nettles. According to some of the people that have lived there a long time, the bloke that owned it used to come down every week-end on his jack before the war and stay there overnight in an old motor-bus with curtains up at the windows. He used to keep himself to himself, so nobody ever found out who he was. He never came any more after the war was over, and they're still wondering if he's still alive, and who the land belongs to.

At one time, nearly everybody who lived along the Bottom had got something they didn't want the whole wide world to know about. It was that kind of place. Either they weren't married to their wives, or they were vegetarians, or Commies, or nutters, or they'd been inside or something of that nature. It wasn't the chummiest place in the world to live in, by all accounts.

There was a sanatorium at the far end of the valley, built by some Eytye doctor whose name ended in *otti* as far as I can remember. All the rich old bags used to go down there to get rid of their nervous breakdowns.

There was one young piece went down there. They reckon it was in all the papers at the time because she was the daughter of Lord somebody. She'd been had up for taking drugs apparently. It didn't do her a lot of good because she took a running jump off the end of a cliff a couple of weeks after they let her out. After the war the place was bought up by some rich bastard accountant from London. He converted everything into something else, and even had a miniature golf course fixed up in the grounds. Even then, he only used to come down there in the summer. He always went abroad in the winter, in case his wallet got frozen up.

Then, around nineteen fifty odd, a whole lot of people started buying up land along the Bottom and putting up little brick houses of every shape and size. There was one place about halfway along with battlements on like a castle. In the finish there was a big stink, and they held a public inquiry into it. For a long time after that nobody could shove up anything at all at the Bottom unless they greased somebody's palm well and truly.

That was before the railway from Forbury to London was electrified, and all the fresh people from up the smoke came to live in Forbury. To accommodate the surplus, the Forbury Rural District Council decided to build two big council estates down at the Bottom.

After that, Garside Bottom, as it used to be called, was considered as part of Garside proper, and everybody just called it the Bottom, as distinct from the Green, or the Village.

Stop me if I'm boring you.

Anyway, the upshot of all this was that the people up the Village have never been too highly delighted with the Bottomites, and vicky verky. A lot of the old houses in the Village have been there about five hundred years, and there's a lot of the families up there who reckon to have been living in Garside just as long, if not longer. Some of 'em claim to have their monikers in the Doom's Day Book. They reckon that all the Bottomites are yobbos and second-class citizens who are trying to poke their snouts in where they're not wanted, and they wouldn't be seen dead talking to one.

Naturally, the Bottomites aren't too keen on them, either. They reckon the people who live up the Village are miles behind the times, big swedes, turnip-heads, cretins, and snobs.

I've got to admit there's some justification for the snob part. You take Mrs Fforde-Hunter, for example, that lives at Garside Place, slap in the middle of the Village. Talk about a smell under her nose. Takes nothing but the *Financial Times*, and she can't add up sixpence nor a bloody shilling. You'll take it up the garden, and you'll find her standing on a pair of steps waving a pair of secateurs. She'll be wearing a big silly floppy bloody hat, an old pair of dungaree trousers, and the smock she bought when she thought she was preggers.

"Eau Peach, *there* you are," she'll say. "Isn't it an absolutely *gorgeous* morning. Just give me a second." Then she'll snip snip with the poxy pinchers for about twenty minutes, gassing away all the time and trying to get all the gossip out of you, at the same time pretending she couldn't care less. Cunning as a stoat.

All the while she'll be coming across with the eau Peach treatment like she's the duchess who is very good with the servants and treats them nearly as equals. Old Mother Wenborn went there once as a daily. She only stuck it for a fortnight. Said Mrs Fforde-Whatnot used to sit on a settee watching her doing the work, smoking a tiny little black cigar through a socking great long holder all the time.

And it's not as if they're loaded. They're not exactly bankrupt, mind, but nowhere near the class of Garfield Chubb in the gilt stakes. The old boy, Fforde-Hunter, is a professor at some agricultural research place the other side of Whitmarsh. He apparently does sodall else except study the life of some worm which is too invisible to be seen with the naked eye.

This worm is supposed to scoff the roots of certain kinds of plants. All these particular kinds of plants have got their own special kind of worm which won't touch anything else. Apparently, old F-H has spent the last couple of years trying to hatch out the eggs of one particular kind of worm which will only scoff the roots of sweet peas. He hasn't managed it yet, and he's done just about everything bar sit on the bastards.

Anyway, it was this mutual thingummyjig between the old Garsiders and the new Bottomites that started all the fuss about Ned Hoskin. The people up the Village used to point the finger at Ned and say he was a typical product of the Bottom. The Bottomites used to get dead niggled about this.

Actually old Ned had lived along the Bottom in a little didikai caravan for as long as anyone could remember, minding nobody's business but his own. Nobody knew where he came from, but he wasn't a true Romany. Jack Tidy reckoned he used to work the fairgrounds until he got too ugly and scared all the customers away, and after that he went on the brush wagon.

Just after they built the new council estates, a whole lot of the people who'd moved in there started kicking up a big shindy about Ned. They carried on about the way he used the road as a handkerchief, and said it was a danger to public health and all that lark. They also moaned about the way he lived. They reckoned you could smell his goats for miles, and that the soot from his fires came down on all their best Sunday frocks. Old Ned's missis used to hang out her washing on the bushes all around the caravan, and they said this was an eyesore, and spoilt the beauty of the countryside.

They also said Bloody Mary was teaching their kids bad habits.

In the finish, the Forbury council had so many complaints in about Ned, they decided to send someone down from the public health department to investigate.

CHAPTER SEVEN

THE character who came down was called Henderson. He was round about thirty, and had a nasty little tash. I know, because he stopped his car to ask me the way. I found out what happened afterwards, because this Henderson was brother-in-law to Maudie Rankin, who runs the Hare and Hounds up the Village. He dropped in there for a pint on the way back and told Maudie all about it. Naturally, he told Maudie not to tell anyone, because it was dead confidential.

But in Garside, the more confidential a thing is the quicker it goes the rounds. The best way to keep anything a secret is to hire one of those megaphone things that blokes holler through at boat race crews when they're practising on the river, go up to the crossroads, and bawl it out at the top of your voice. That way, you can be almost sure nobody'll take any notice.

Actually, if I was sweating my guts out rowing, and some mouthy bastard kept on at me from the shore, I'd feel like giving him big licks when I got to the bank. But that's by the way.

According to Henderson, he stopped his car on the road opposite Ned's caravan, which was hidden behind a whole lot of young trees and bushes. But he could see where it was by a few puffs of smoke coming out.

He got out and walked up a little twisting path. When he got round the bushes he saw the caravan. There were about eight goats tied up all over the place. As soon as the goats saw Henderson they stopped munching, lifted their heads up, and looked at him very old-fashioned.

Henderson could see that the situation was very dicey. He would have to go very near the goats if he was going to get to the caravan, and most of them had big curly horns. One of them, which looked like the king goat, ran towards him and started straining at the cord. Just as he was trying to make up his mind whether it would be too undignified to make a sudden dash, or if he ought to make a big detour round the bushes, he noticed someone watching him from behind a water butt at the back of the caravan.

It was Bloody Mary, wearing an old flannel nightdress. She suddenly whipped round the front of the caravan, shouted something in the door, then disappeared round the far side.

Then a woman—Ned's wife—came out of the caravan, and walked down the steps. Henderson said she was just like a Red Indian squaw. She'd got black hair drawn right round her forehead and pinned up at the back. Her face was very brown and sharp as a hawk's. She was wearing a black dress which finished up at her ankles. There was a big tear in the skirt in the shape of a letter L.

Henderson said to her, very official, "Are you Mrs Hoskin?"

She didn't say a dickie bird, just stood there staring at him as if he was a visitor from outer space. So after a bit he began to get niggled. He said to her, "In the absence of a denial, I shall be obliged to assume that you are." He'd got all the lingo off pat, this Henderson.

Then she said, "We don't keep any dogs 'ere, Mister."

Henderson said, "I'm from the public health department and I've come to inspect your living accommodation."

She still didn't understand what he was on about, because she said, "Yes, it's a lovely day, but you see if we don't 'ave some rain afore tomorrow."

"I'm afraid we've had a number of complaints," said Henderson.

"What did you say, Mister?"

Henderson had to shout. "A lot of people have been complaining."

"Oh yes, I expect they will," she said. By this time Bloody Mary had crept back and was standing the side of her.

"You did get my letter, I presume?" said Henderson.

"Letter?" said Ned's missis. They were both looking at him, he reckoned, as if he was a half-wit. Then Bloody Mary suddenly went off into fits of laughing.

So Henderson said, "Well, we'd better get on with it." With one eye on the goats, he nipped smartly across to the caravan and went up the steps to have a butcher's inside. There was a tame jay sitting on the top step, and it squawked and shuffled sideways as he stepped over it.

Inside, a sick goat was lying on a pile of sacks in front of a paraffin stove. It looked up and gave a feeble bleat. Henderson reckoned its eyes were bright yellow. A tin kettle was singing away on top of the stove, and thick black smoke was swirling up over it and flattening against the ceiling, which was caked with soot.

Everything else was a jumble of blackened pots and pans, old army blankets, and tatty old togs. In the middle of the floor was this chipped enamel bowl with a screwed-up wedge of Maggie Ann inside. But Henderson reckoned he couldn't take in everything because his eyes were smarting from the fumes. Apart from that there was a funny smell around which made him feel queer, like the smell of boiled rabbit, he said, only very strong. He decided to get a breath of fresh air a bit smartish.

When he got outside he started making some notes on a pad. The two women seemed very interested in all this, he said, as if they'd never seen anyone writing before.

After he'd finished, he said, "I wonder if you could show me how you manage as regards the disposal of sewage?"

Ned's wife gave him a smile. "We live here a long time, now," she said. "Lovely weather."

Henderson said, "Where's the lavatory?"

She suddenly seemed to understand when he said that. "Yes, I show you," she said.

She took him to a place made out of sacks against a tree at the corner of the woods. As they got near it Henderson noticed that she started hanging back; then she turned round and started walking back towards the caravan. He shouted out, "Wait a minute," but she didn't take much notice.

He took a shufti behind the sacking, and saw this antique old lavatory bucket with handles on the sides, underneath a cut-out packing case. Then he went back to the caravan. On the way he nearly walked into a big cluster of brambles growing through a great heap of rusty tins.

The old girl gave him a really friendly smile. He was just saying something like, "Look here, I'm afraid I . . ." when she tugged at his sleeve and said, "Never mind, the kettle is nearly boiling. You want to drink tea?" He reckoned she went through the motions of drinking a cup, as if she thought he wouldn't know what it was. He didn't want to offend her, so he said, "Well, all right . . . if you insist."

He stood outside the caravan and lit up a fag. There was a lot of activity going on inside, and every now and again Ned's wife or Bloody Mary would come to the door and give him a kind of encouraging smile. They were jabbering away all the time, according to Henderson, only he couldn't make out what they were saying—it sounded like a foreign lingo. Bloody Mary came out after a bit with a jug and started milking one of the goats into it. The jets hit the inside of the jug with a kind of hollow *plunk*, going higher and higher up the scale. Henderson said his stomach started to feel very dicey.

After about twenty minutes, the old girl handed him a pint mug full of this steaming yellowy stuff. It had a strong, bitter tang to it. The two of them drank with him. He reckoned they couldn't take their eyes off him, even when they were having a sip.

However, the stuff wasn't quite so nasty as he'd expected, and he managed to get through about half of it. Then he put the mug down on the step, looked at his watch, and said, "Well, I've got to rush off now. Thanks for the tea."

Bloody Mary ran down the path in front of him. Just as he turned round the corner of the bushes he looked back and saw the old girl waving to him from the steps of the caravan. The jay was perched on her shoulder.

He said that Bloody Mary was leaning against a tree stump. Just as he was getting into his car she ripped off a cracking great fart. Then she started pissing herself laughing.

Naturally, when this Henderson character came to write his report, he really put the bubble in, and the upshot of it was that they gave old Ned six weeks to up anchor and away out of it. But just around that time, a council house on one of the estates down the Bottom fell vacant, and they decided to hand it over to Ned.

Just in case he couldn't pay the rent, they got Dr Lumbard to sign a certificate to say that he couldn't do any normal work owing to his condition, then they fixed him up with six quid a week from the National Assistance Board.

Of course, he wasn't allowed to keep any goats, and they gave him strict instructions not to light any fires around the place except in the fireplaces provided.

You'd think everybody would have been satisfied. Naturally, everybody up the Village was highly delighted, but the people down the Bottom who lived on the same housing estate weren't at all chuffed about having Ned as a neighbour. Every day, just after he moved in, he used to get letters—unsigned, of course—telling him to sling his hook, and inferring he wasn't exactly welcome. Not that it worried Ned much, because he couldn't read or write any more than his missis or Bloody Mary, and he used to ask Alf Sparks, the postman, to read anything that turned up in the mail. Old Alf used to keep the letters afterwards, and he showed me one once. It said:

Why dont you go back where you come from you ugly face barstard we're all respecktible peeple on this estait we dont want no dirty gippos living here so if you knows whats good for you you'll scram out of it for good and all and take yore dirty stinkin wimmin foke along with you.

A frend.

Alf being a decent old stick, he used to read the letters over to himself first, then he'd pretend to read them out loud to Ned. But he used to make them up as he went along, so it sounded as if they were from people living round about who were highly chuffed about Ned and his family coming to live in their midst, and wanted to make him welcome and wish him all the best in life and what-all. So for a while old Ned went round with a big smirk on his pan, and when somebody put half a brick through his front window one rainy night he thought it must have been an accident.

It wasn't long before the people on the estate got up a petition to the effect that Ned and his family ought to be removed forthwith, and sent it to Forbury council.

The council didn't take any notice, though.

As for me, I didn't see what all the fuss was about. My motto is "Live and let live, because twenty hoggin equals one nicker, and the devil take the last bastard up the ladder."

If there is a devil which I doubt.

CHAPTER EIGHT

WHEN I went over to help Jack Tidy with the haymaking the following Thursday afternoon, I walked into the kitchen and there was Mavis Tidy mixing the chickenfood and smiling right down to her armpits. She didn't say anything for a while, so I knew she was on to something big. The ordinary stuff they come out with straight away.

She waited right until I'd finished pulling on my overalls, then she said, "Davey, you know what I told you the other day about there being something funny about old Joe Purkiss? Well, I was right. Hilda came over here yesterday and sat down in that chair you're sitting in, and poured out her heart to me, poor soul.

"Did you know that Hilda used to live in this village when she was a young girl? We were very friendly in the old days. Then she qualified as a schoolteacher and went up north to take a job, and that's where she met old Joe and married him, I was ever so surprised when I heard, because he must be twenty years older than her, and she was very attractive when she was younger, I mean even now she's only fifty and she's very well preserved although I know her hair's not its natural colour."

I said, "What's this, a history lesson?"

"We used to have a lot in common, Hilda and me. We used to go to dances in the old days together when we were young, oh it was so different in those days Davey, with all the socials we had, and all of us going to the Coronation celebrations in Forbury, riding in a hay cart, and going for picnics down the Bottom when there weren't any houses there at all, and everybody going to church on Sundays in their best clothes and the men all going to the pub after for a chat . . ."

"Yeh, well," I said. "I 'spect old Jack'll be waiting." I wasn't going to sit there and waste half an hour while she got to the point.

"Hang on a minute, Davey. I was just telling you about old Joe. Do you know he had a heart attack on Tuesday—at least Dr Lumbard said it was a heart attack. Anyway he was lying there on the mat in her kitchen, and she came in from the garden and found him. Naturally, she got into a proper state. So she rang up Teddy Paulson, because Teddy is an old friend of hers. In fact they were very sweet on each other years ago, I think they were going to get engaged, but they had a quarrel over something or other and that's why she took this job up north.

"So anyway, Teddy Paulson came over. You know his wife's been bedridden all these years? Well, he came over right away and the first thing he did was to send for Dr Lumbard, which she ought to have done straight away, only she was in such a dither. Then Dr Lumbard came over and he said Joe would be all right because he'd only had a mild stroke, and he must have knocked himself out when he fell down and hit his head against the fireplace. So Dr Lumbard and Teddy Paulson lifted Joe on to a couch, and then Dr Lumbard examined him, and he told Hilda that she'd have to be careful with him because he'd got a dicky heart, and might go off any time. 'After all,' Dr Lumbard said, 'he's had a life and a half of it if you was to measure mortality with a spirit level.' Old Joe was always a one for the brandy, apparently. So Hilda started crying a bit, and they were both telling her not to worry, and then she suddenly turned round on them, and said, 'I've always been a God-fearing woman, but do you really think I'll mind when he's gone, after all I've had to put up with?' "

"Tell me the old story," I said.

"So with that, she pulled up her sleeve and showed them all the purple bruises where he kept creeping up and pinching her when she wasn't looking, and she pointed out of the window to the flower beds, and the flowers which were just stalks because Joe had pulled all the heads off. And she picked up the cat and showed them where he'd snipped off the end of its tail with the garden shears. She told them that Joe used to put holly leaves under the sheet on her side of the bed, and once he even chased her with a bread knife, and she thought he was going to kill her, but he was only pretending. Yes, it was terrible. She said he was always searching for Bibles in the house, because he knew she always read from the Scriptures on a Sunday night, and he didn't want her to. So she had to read them when he was out at the pub, and sometimes he'd creep back and catch her at it. Then he'd snatch the Bible out of her hands, and burn it page by page in front of her.

"So then Dr Lumbard made her sit down and they all had a drop of sherry which she said she had to hide in a vinegar bottle, and she started telling them all about Joe, and how they'd lived quite a happy married life for years up in Duxford, where she first met and married him, except he was always a bit on the childish side, what with his pranks and practical jokes, but she said she always forgave him at first because he'd had shell shock very bad in the first world war, and she thought it was something to do with that.

"This was up until a year ago when he retired and sold his business. He used to carry horses and cattle to market in special lorries. But after he retired he turned very strange, she said.

"She said he'd buy bags of sweets and give them away to children. And sometimes he'd wrap up a stone in a toffee paper and put it in one of the bags. She said he'd keep taking things out of the house and burying them in the garden, and then pretending to help her look for them. He got worse and worse, and one day he took and went down to the town, walked up behind an old lady, poked her hat off with his umbrella, and started twidding it round just out of her reach. They had him up for that, and he had to pay twenty pounds damages. He kept sending removal vans to people's houses who didn't want to move, and once he sent the fire engine to a place six miles away where there wasn't any fire. When the firemen got back they found two hayricks burning just outside the town, but they were too late to do anything about it.

"She said he once ordered a three-tier wedding cake to be sent to the manageress of the laundry, although she'd been married fourteen years. Another time when the Duxford football team had a big match on, he rang up the opposite team and cancelled it. All the spectators were there and everything. Isn't it dreadful?

"She said there was this detective who followed Joe every time he left the house, but the detective was a big daft chap who always acted as Santa Claus at the toddlers' Christmas Party in the Town Hall, and you could pick him out anywhere because he was six foot five. Joe was much too cunning to get caught anyway, she said. Once they summoned a man for putting a live rat in the letter box at the post office, but it was really Joe that did it. Damaging Her Majesty's mails or something they had 'im up for—the other man I mean. He said he'd only gone there to post some football pools for the lady next door because she had bronchial asthma, but they still fined him two pounds. Hilda said she was certain it was Joe, because the day before he'd come back from a walk with something in his pocket, and later on he'd emptied everything out of her sewing basket, and made little holes in it with a gimlet. She said she was going to look inside, but she was afraid to because she could hear something scrabbling about.

"Anyway, the long and short of it is that mercifully for Hilda, old Joe had a slight stroke, and he couldn't move one side of his face for a long time. They took him into hospital, and while he was there a police inspector came to see Hilda. She said he was very nice about it, considering. He told her that the last thing in the world he wanted was to hurt anyone's feelings, but he had a duty to the people in the town, he said, and if he ever managed to put the finger on Joe he was going to get him put away for a long time. He said he was fond of a little joke himself, but there was a limit to everything, and he thought it wouldn't be a bad idea if Joe was to play his little pranks somewhere else. He said anywhere would suit him, except Duxford.

"So Hilda took the hint. Unbeknown to Joe she sold the house, which was in her name, and bought the cottage down here which had just become vacant after Mr Bradbury left. She said she wanted to come to Garside, because she had so many old friends here who could help her in her troubles."

I said, "What did old Joe say when 'e found out?"

"He didn't make any objections, because he had to be kept quiet for a long time, and he didn't know what was happening until he found himself settled in the cottage. But he started getting better very soon, and after about a month he started drinking again, and Hilda said he started to get the same old crafty look in his eye.

"Anyway, she told all this to Dr Lumbard and Teddy Paulson, and Dr Lumbard said, 'Oh, so that's what he's been up to, the old scallywag.' Then he told Hilda he'd be giving Joe a course of injections for his heart, and he said he'd drop in and give him a jab every other day, and he'd slip in something else while he was at it, which would keep him quiet. He said that all Joe would want to do would be sleep most of the time, and she'd have nothing to worry about. He also said that he wouldn't give him much more than six months for this world, but not to place too much reliance on that statement, because whenever you said that about anybody they usually lived to be a hundred.

"Hilda was very thankful when he said this, and she told him she'd been very frightened. Teddy Paulson told Dr Lumbard that just as a precaution he'd drop in himself every so often and have a chat to old Joe, just to keep him happy and make sure he didn't go off the rails again. Doctor Lumbard said he thought it was a very good idea.

"What d'you think of that, Davey?" said Mavis Tidy. "Wasn't I right after all? And to look at him you'd think he was just a nice, kind old country gentleman."

"Well, it just goes to show, don't it?" I said. "Anyway, he might 'ave 'ad good reason, 'e might 'ave been jarred off with bein' nagged at."

"Oh Davey, how can you say such a thing? I've never known such a kind, good-hearted little body as Hilda Purkiss."

"Yeh, I know. They pour it over you like treacle," I said. "Well, I 'spect old Jack'll be wonderin' what's gone wrong wi' the works." And with that I walked out of the door backwards. I was right about Jack Tidy. By the time I got up the field with the Ferguson, he was just about gnawing his fingers down to the knuckle joints. "I've just been having a bit of tongue pie with your good lady," I said. "You want to watch it with her or they'll be shoving her on the B.B.C., she can talk just as fast as Lady Barnett, and nearly as good looking. Okay, where d'you want me to start?"

CHAPTER NINE

THERE was this podgy little bastard sitting in the Wagon and Horses in Forbury. He'd got a very unhealthy-looking fat sort of whitey face and a fat neck, and he was wearing a brick-red jersey in colour with a rolltop neck. You ought to have seen his eyes, though. Real little porker's.

"Now you take the Yanks," he was saying. "You take the Yanks as an example. What do they know about international politics? Sod-all. Do you know why? Because they haven't got the experience. Not like us. Finest diplomats in the history of the world, the British. Old Eden, for instance, he knew what it was all about. Winchester and Oxford University. Very clever. Got it here." He tapped his bonce. "He knew how to handle the Russians—old Kruschev, the lot. Best Foreign Secretary this country ever had. Better than Palmerston. And what's he doing now? House of bloody Lords, I ask you!

"The old Yanks, mind, they never listened to Eden. You know what they did? They even sent an ambassador to Ceylon that didn't even know they grew tea there, because somebody asked him as soon as he stepped off the plane, and he said he didn't know, fella, because he always drank coffee himself. Actually, they produce forty per cent of the world's tea on that island. Forty per cent!"

It was the following Saturday. I was squatting on a bar stool next to little Porky, who was yapping to some clapped-out looking character wearing a hacking jacket and corduroy trousers who was sitting on the stool the other side.

"Course, you know what the trouble is over there in the States. The women are the guv'nors. Yes indeed. Did you know the women in America own four-fifths of all the property? And they always leave it to their daughters instead of their sons in order to perpetuate the system.

"You take old Kennedy. He doesn't run that country. He might *think* he does. He's just a figurehead. The real people who run the States are a bunch of women called 'The Daughters of the Revolution'. They have all the say over there. Did you know that whenever the Yank army goes into action they're not allowed any liquor, just because the Daughters of the Revolution think it's immoral? All they get is ice cream. The old tooty-fruity. They control most of the votes, you see, and nearly all the money.

The women over there outnumber the men by five to four—and they know it, boy, they know it.

"As a matter of fact I was born in the States. Yep. I actually saw the first light of day in liddle ol' Boston, Massachusetts. Now you take Boston. You've heard people talk about class distinction in this country. Well ..."

I was trying very hard to get this bint Carol off my mind. I'd been thinking about her on and off ever since the time I'd taken the papers round. Since then I'd stayed away from the Falcon, and I'd only seen her once in the previous week, in the front seat of the Alpine next to Sydney Chubb.

This I wouldn't have minded so much, except that she leaned out and waved as they went past, and gave me this very wonderful smile.

The only trouble was that thinking about her made me feel very dissatisfied with *myself*. After all, I kept thinking, what was I? Just an odd job man in a crummy little dump like Garside, a poxy cornerboy, the Romeo of Chalkpit Lane.

Why should a bint like that—or any other class bint—take any notice of me?

Normally, when I went to Forbury of a Saturday night, I'd be wearing the Italian electric-blue drape jacket, the old black stovepipes, and winklepickers. This time, though, I'd shoved on a really posh blazer, almost black and made of very good cloth, which I'd picked up at a collection they'd organized in the village a few months before on behalf of the refugees in the Congo or somewhere. Actually I'd been delivering papers one morning when I'd come across Mrs Wellard, the local secretary of the refugee business, sorting out a big pile of togs in her front room, which people had sent in from all over the place.

I'd noticed this blazer and tried it on, and it fitted me a treat. Then Mrs Wellard looked up and wanted to know what I was doing, so I said I was just thinking what a nice blazer it was, and how bloody queer it would look on a nignog.

Mrs Wellard said I mustn't call them that, I must call them "coloured people". But she said she'd let me have the blazer provided I popped into the village shop for her and picked up a bottle of cider vinegar. She said I could drop it in on the way back. She also said would I mind stuffing the blazer under my jacket as I went out. Apparently the people in the new bungalow opposite had got eyes like stinking eels.

She made me promise faithfully that I'd remove the badge on the breast pocket before I wore it, because it was the badge of some very famous public school—she didn't exactly know which one. But she did know the gentleman who'd handed it in, and she reckoned he might not appreciate it if he saw me sculling around the village in his blazer, with the badge up. As a matter of fact, she said, he'd sent it in with a little note saying would she please see the badge was removed before she sent it on to the Congo.

When I got the blazer home I had a good old shufti at this badge. There was a castle tower with crossed oars over the top and a scroll underneath which said, *Te Digna Sequere.*

This castle was picked out in red, and the rest in silver and yellow, and I thought it was real classy. I was so fascinated by the badge I couldn't bear to tear it off. I wrote down the bit of writing from the scroll on a separate piece of paper, and asked one of the kids at the village school to take it to the headmaster and ask him what it meant.

I didn't hear anything for a fortnight, although I kept reminding this kid. Probably the headmaster didn't speak any Greek, and had to send it to the British Museum or somewhere. Anyway, eventually I managed to find out that it meant, "Follow Things Worthy of You".

I thought this was very appropriate, because I've always been very fussy about skirt.

However. I was sitting on this bar stool and my mind kept wandering, and I'd keep thinking back again to Carol, and then I'd come back to reality and old Juicy would be nattering on: "Just think what we've spent on Defence since the end of the war. Billions and billions—the actual figure is astronomical. And what's it all for? No empire to defend. We've given it all away. And the Yanks are miles ahead of us. The Russians are miles ahead of us. What's the use of trying to compete? Apart from that we've got Yank air bases all over the country. Polaris submarines. All we've got to do is turn round to the Yanks and say, 'Look, you want this country as a base. All right, we don't mind that, just as long as you don't drag us into your quarrels with the Russians.' See, nobody's going to get stuck into us while we've got the Yanks here. Then, instead of spending all this money on defence, we use it for research, and higher education, and raising the standard of living.

"Take higher education. You've got to have the technicians. This lot that's in now. Old Selwyn Lloyd and company. Butler. They just don't twig it. Old Macmillan. Walks around with his eyes shut all the time. They want to bring back the birch all right —just to tickle up the bloody Cabinet. You wouldn't think this was supposed to be the New Elizabethan age, would you? You've only got to look around. The Swedes could lick us at cricket if they tried, but they don't. They're just not interested. Now you take the Swedes. Highest standard of living in Europe, and d'you know why? Because they keep their snitches out of other people's arguments. Too bloody crafty, see. N.A.T.O.? They just don't want to know. Do you honestly blame 'em? They don't chuck their money down the drain, the old Swedes . . ."

I walked out of the bar in disgust. Outside, I turned the corner and went through to the bog in the back yard. There was some middle-aged bloke in there. "This the place where the nobs 'ang out, cocker?" he said. Then he started buttoning up his flies. "Jus' goo right through yer, dunnit?" he said. "Aaa-rah, 's'er waste er money." I didn't say anything, not feeling in a very witty mood.

It was a very ancient bog which stunk of about three centuries of urine, mixed with this very sharp smell from a couple of big cubes of disinfectant they'd stuck in the gutter to melt. The wall was built of sort of black slate, and the surface was very rough and broken. In places there were kind of layers of grey and green and rust-coloured scum. I don't often notice these things, but in this particular case there wasn't much else to look at, bar a few lines of writing scrawled on the wall in indelible pencil slap in front of my eyes.

> *The Three Ages of Love.*
> *20-35. Tri-weekly.*
> *35-50. Try weekly.*
> *50 and over. Try weakly.*

I wasn't much looking forward to the rest of that evening. I couldn't even get hopelessly pissed, because I'd got to get back to Garside on the Quickly. Anyway, getting hopelessly pissed isn't all it's cracked up to be, what with laying in bed all the day after, feeling like death and spewing your ring up every five minutes.

Just as I was turning away from the wall, and thinking these dismal thoughts, I was joined by some elderly bloke with a shiny blue suit and a red scraggy neck who was wearing the badge of the British Legion.

"What goes in gotta come out," he said. His voice was wobbling about all over the place. "It's one o' the laws o' nature."

"Yeh," I said. "That's right, Pop."

CHAPTER TEN

As the town hall clock was striking nine I was beetling along the High Street with my hands stuck in my trouser pockets.

Nothing ever changed much, I was thinking, in Forbury.

Even if it did, there was such a lot of yap about it beforehand that when it happened it was history already. Such as this espresso bar they opened two or three years back that people had been on about for ages, and when it did open the place downstairs where they had the big juke box was much too small, and it's always crammed out with Grammar School kids that get a short haircut and reckon to be Adam Faith. The only skirt you ever see there is young teasers, the pony bloody tail brigade, always babbling on about this boy and that boy. That's what education does for you.

I was beginning to grow out of Forbury just like I'd grown out of Garside a while back—I realized that. I knew every pub and every shop and petrol pump and slot machine, and I knew which clerks in the post office were bastards and which ones weren't. The coppers the same. I knew I was going to the weekly hop at the Town Hall—the one big dance in Forbury—and I knew that I'd come out of there after the last dance, or maybe just before then to avoid the crush at the cloakroom, and I knew that I'd be with one of the pieces that get there regular. And I knew I would take it home and somewhere on the way, in a shop doorway or an old air-raid shelter, or maybe in the bushes back of the town cemetery if we happened to be going past it, I'd try it out, and maybe I'd get it easy or I'd have to fight for it, or I might not get it at all. And I knew it didn't make much odds one way or another.

I knew I was growing out of Forbury all right. Only growing out of a place and actually *getting* out of it are two different cups of cocoa.

So I let my legs carry me up the steps of the Town Hall, through the big oak doors, and I paid my three and a kick to this little gnome that is always sitting there week after week dishing out the tickets.

I went straight to the bar. It's best to get in there early because there's always a hell of a crush later on, and you're lucky if you manage to get anywhere near the counter without being involved in a punch-up. The bar itself is in a very old-fashioned room with fancy panelling on the walls, a high ceiling with patches of damp all over it and a couple of dirty big chandeliers hanging down. There's also these long old browny-looking pictures of ex-mayors and aldermen and what-all. Nice bastards!

I sort of burrowed through to the counter and bashed half a dollar on it, trying to attract the attention of Buller, one of the barmen. Every time he'd serve somebody he'd go back to the cash register and tip the gilt into it very slow, then he'd amble back to the counter with about a dozen of them bawling the names of drinks at him, and he'd just rest his hands on the counter and kind of cock his ear at somebody and say, "Next?"

Eventually he worked his way down to me. "Pint of bitter," I said.

He whipped up a half-pint glass, stuck it under the tap, and slopped it down in front of me.

"Buller, you deaf? I said a pint!"

"Sorry, chum," he said, "only 'alf-pints at a time. New council regulation. 'Ad too much trouble 'ere already, some o' you youngsters. Can't 'old it, that's the trouble. Sixty quid's worth o' damage in the last month, apart from people complainin' about the foul language."

"Okay, Buller, make it two half-pints," I said.

"For two people?"

"Yeh—me and my mate."

He gave me a nasty look. "Ain't got time for muckin' about. Where is 'e, this mate o' yours?"

"Comin' in a minute. Just gone to take the dog for a walk."

"All right," he said, "take your word for it. I ain't got time to muck about." He grabbed another glass, filled it up and forked it over, then he belted the old cash register, whacked down the change, and cocked his old lug at somebody about two yards farther along. "Next?"

I picked up the two glasses, wandered into the dance floor, and shoved them down on one of the tables scattered around the edge. Then I dropped into a chair and had a quiet shufti round.

The way I was feeling, though, the prospects weren't any too bright. The place itself was just like a huge big vault. All over the ceiling and walls was a lot of manky old flags and bunting which had been shoved up about two years since for some New Year's Ball and never taken down again.

The band was sitting on a stage at the far end and one of the saxophone players was making a lot of little tootling noises, just as if he was practising a tricky bit for the next number. Very professional. A couple of the others were leaning forward and talking to bints on the dance floor. They always looked hellish earnest. Ronnie Dodd and his Cosmopolitans, never been outside bloody Forbury.

It was this Ronnie Dodd himself that really turned me over. He was a thin, round-shouldered character with a straggly bit of beard. He was always saying, "Well now, my children, this time we're coming up for a bit of a treat from away back, featuring Nick on the drums, so hear this!" And the special treat would be the band making a proper balls-up of "Big Noise Blew in from Winetka" with Ronnie Dodd shouting "doom doom doom doom doom doom doom doom" into the mike. And he'd got this habit of standing up to announce the next number and looking from side to side about six dozen times without saying anything, just as if everybody was killing themselves wondering if it was going to be a slow foxtrot or a general excuse-me quickstep. Every time the band came to the end of a number he'd sing out, "That's all, boys and gir-hirls!" A real personality!

I decided to concentrate on the doorway. It was about time to start weighing up the talent.

The dance usually starts officially at eight, but hardly anybody turns up till nine, and from nine to half-past is the critical period for sorting out the crumpet.

The bints are normally outnumbered about two to one, so you've got to get a rift on if you want to pick up anything reasonable. Most of them—barring the ones that come in with somebody—collect around a group of tables in one corner. You have to keep a crafty eye on the door and spot them as they come in. Then, after you've sorted out the one you want, you have to be just strolling past the bints' corner when the band strikes up. You have to grab it quick then, before anybody else does, and get on to the floor with it.

One dance is usually enough for experts like me to find out whether a particular piece is worth persevering with or not. If it isn't, you have to dump it fast and grab another. This is a bit dicey, because the collection is getting smaller and smaller all the time, and the best lookers are always the first to go. Four on the trot is about all you have time for, and if you haven't got fixed up by a quarter to ten you're either unlucky, or you have to latch on to one of the dozen or so freaks that get left in the corner all night, until somebody gets pissed enough to ask one of them for a dance.

Either that, or you have to chance your arm with somebody else's piece—which is rather dicey because some of them will stay with you all evening and then go back to the bloke they came with—or you can hang around the doorway around half-past ten as a last resort, in the hope that something a bit decent will drift in after the pictures turn out.

As I'd been going to the dances in Forbury on and off for years, and the bints who came there were more or less the same bints who came week after week until some silly bastard got all serious and married them, I had a pretty good idea of the form already.

The best thing was when some piece that had got married and stopped coming suddenly turned up on its own after about a year away, because then I'd know it was only after the one thing, and there was nothing I liked more than snatching something which belonged by rights to somebody else that didn't know how to look after it properly. Whenever a married bint turned up, I'd always drop whatever I happened to be with, and make a beeline for it.

Of course, I occasionally came unstuck. There was the time I snapped up a gorgeous little married piece I'd never seen before in my natural. About thirty. Very good dancer, too, and pressed herself up against me as if she couldn't wait to get outside.

She was asking me all sorts of personal questions such as whether I'd got any regular girl friends, what I did in my spare time, and if I was in favour of couples that were going to get married having a regular nibble just to make sure they suited each other, before it was too late. I said I was all in favour. It wasn't until halfway through the middle of the last waltz that I found out she was a welfare officer, making out some kind of a report on youth.

But this particular night, I just couldn't bring myself to make the effort. I sat there feeling like a pork chop in a synagogue, keeping myself to myself and watching them all swishing and swirling around in disgust. The collection was getting smaller and smaller, and I just watched the bints I'd normally have been interested in getting whipped on to the floor, steered round it a few times, and then marched off to get warmed up in the bar. None of them were a patch on Carol, I was thinking.

Once when there was a "ladies' excuse me" quickstep, some very young piece with a sort of stiff flared skirt which was supposed to make her look very available underneath but I knew she wasn't because I'd taken her home once, this young bint came up and asked me to dance with it. "Who with, you?" I said. "I got too much respect for my feet." She looked hellish annoyed, but they soon get over it. A couple of minutes later I saw her belting past with somebody else, nattering away like a machine-gun into his earhole. Probably about me.

I watched the collection get less and less until only the frumps were left. One of them was the District Nurse, Mabel Merry-weather—the one who was supposed to have been left a stack of money. I'd never seen her at the dance before. She was on her jack, and all. Didn't stand much chance of a pick-up either, what with her pasty owly face and her thick-lensed goggles and her legs which were the shape of sausage balloons bent in the middle. She must have been cracking on forty, at that.

I'd never thought I'd have seen her out after it. Still, maybe she was making out a report like the other bitch. Maybe she was inquiring into the circumstances in which so many young tarts in Forbury got into the pudding club before they were married.

If she was doing that, she had certainly come to the right place.

Anyway, just at that moment someone clapped a hand on my shoulder and said, "Watch it, Davey." It was Jock McNeil.

"Jock!" I said. "How goes it, boy?"

"This one for me?" he said. He sat down the other side of the table, and started knocking back one of the halves of beer. He sank it in one swallow, then shoved down the glass empty, licked his lips and said, "Gah, like gnat's piss!"

You could tell Jock was one of the most famous characters in Forbury, by the way everybody looked at him as soon as he walked into a place. One of the coppers that normally stand in the outside passage was now hanging around in the doorway keeping a crafty eye on him. Not that Jock was the kind of bloke it would be difficult to pick out in a crowd. He was big enough for a start, and none of it was blubber. Then he had a beard—a proper full set and black as the ace of spades, not a nine-days wonder like Ronnie Dodd's—and he always wore a kilt although his family had lived in England for several generations and he didn't have anything like a Scotch accent.

He was about three years older than me and he'd already had a couple of years in Borstal and six months in the nick. I used to see him around the town on and off, and he always used to stop and have a natter.

"What's the score in Perfidy?" he said.

"Where the bloody hell's Perfidy?" I said.

"Here. In this very place." He jerked his chair around and had a shufti round the hall. "Ugh! It's about time they sent this consignment back and got some replacements," he said. "Talk about the Chamber of Horrors." Then he happened to see a couple of herberts talking to their bints in a little group a few yards away. These herberts were trying very hard not to notice Jock, and they were yapping away in very toffy voices and saying "Ectually" about every other word, and they were both wearing these cavalry drill trousers. So Jock looked straight at them and he said, "Hi-yi, watch your pockets, watch your pockets!" in a very loud voice. They looked round very sharp when he said that; you could see they were dead niggled, especially when Jock roared out laughing.

He turned towards me again. "Well David, tell me all about it. How've you been going on for tail?"

"Not interested," I said.

He laughed. "Coming from you, Davey, that's the shock statement of the year. We'll have to get it properly mounted and shoved up on the main gates of Buck House. 'Davey Peach wishes it to be publicly known that he is no longer interested in kyfer.' " He leaned over and started fingering the badge on my blazer. "Hey, that's my old school crest. Where d'you get that?"

"I was there an' all."

"Were you? Were you? Really? Peach? Can't say I remember a Peach, ectually . . . you bloody liar, I'd 'ave seen you coming out the headmaster's study."

"Yeh," I said. "Backwards."

He started laughing again, right out loud; he never held anything back.

Most people in Forbury reckoned Jock was a bit of a nutter, but he had his bonce screwed on all right. When he was a nipper he passed the eleven-plus and went to Forbury Grammar. He was supposed to have been one of the brainiest kids they had there, until he suddenly started going haywire when he was sixteen, and got himself expelled. Not long after that he was picked up on a screwing job in London, and got a dose of Borstal. After he came out, he started work on the building as a brickie.

He'd work on some job for three or four weeks at a time, slogging away as long as the daylight lasted, whamming them down about three times as fast as anyone else, and knocking up about five quid a day on piece rates. One day when he was bashing away on a new housing estate, some official of the brickies' union came up and started asking him questions. He said did Jock know that he was exceeding the official quota for laying bricks, also did he know that he was supposed to stop for a tea break every so often, and was he aware that he was doing too much overtime. He said if everybody did what Jock was doing there'd be mass unemployment everywhere, and he wanted to have a shufti at Jock's union card. So Jock laid his trowel down, turned round, and lifted this herbert a real snorter. Then he started whamming down more bricks. They reckoned the union bloke was still stretched out on the deck when Jock packed up for the night.

After he'd done a few weeks' work, Jock would suddenly up anchor and disappear—maybe in the middle of a job—and he wouldn't turn up again until a month or six weeks later. Nobody ever knew where he got to, except once, when he was in Brixton for assault and battery. Everybody knew about that because they really made pigs of themselves over it in the local rag.

"What you been doing with yourself lately?" I said. It was the first I'd seen of him for about three months.

"The campaign," he said. He was just lighting up a dirty big cigar.

"What campaign?"

"Nuclear disarmament." He pointed to this little badge on his lapel. "Ban the horrible bomb."

"You believe in that?" I said.

"Certainly I believe in it. Better than the Masons. I used to be in that mob until they rumbled me. I've been through the issue in my time, Davey boy. Commies, Fascists, Moral Rearmament, Empire bloody Loyalists, People's League for the Defence of Freedom, the lot, but this one is a real doddle. All you do is stick the old badge up, and you're quids in."

"No bull?" I said.

"I'm supposed to be the district secretary in Forbury, see. I've been to three different places in the last month and stayed the week-end. One of them was a bloody lord up in Durham, dirty great mansion, butler, moat full of trout, everything laid on. The others were a Labour M.P. and some old actress, Dame Laura somebody. They were all stinking with it."

"Don't you have to go on all these big marches and what-all?" I said.

"Yeh, but it's dead cushy. Most of 'em only do the first day. Then they all jump into their Ford Consuls and charabancs and they're away with the mixer. They join in again just before the column gets to Trafalgar Square. There was about eight thousand turned up for the start of the last one. After the first day we were down to about five hundred. The march itself is a snip. If you get cheesed off all you got to do is start limping, and sit out on the side of the road. Then somebody comes along in a Land Rover, picks you up, and takes you on to the next town. Then you just find the nearest boozer and put your feet up until the mugs arrive.

"All the time you're marching there's blokes running up and down the column dishing out little pamphlets and sticks of rock that 'ave got the old badge down the middle instead of Brighton or Margate. Every couple of hours you fall out for a mug of char and a sausage roll. The only thing you have to watch is getting stuck with a banner. Last time out I got lost on the way."

"How d'you manage that?"

"Well, I got talking to this young piece from Whitechapel. Jewess, she was, bloody lovely. Anyway, we got as far as some place called Maidenhead Thicket. There was never a place so well named as that, boy. She reckoned she couldn't go any farther, so I suggested us kipping down for the night in the open. She was all for it. Actually she wasn't all that fussy about banning the bomb either, she'd only come because some television producer was going to be on it, and she was after a part in his next play. The trouble was, as soon as he heard his name was down for the march, he shuffled off smartly to the States."

"Didn't they twig when you didn't turn up next morning?"

"No, they don't keep any track. We got a lift on a lorry as far as Hammersmith, and joined up again as they came through. When we got to the Square I was livelier than any of 'em, see, because they were shagged out from the march. In fact I was a bit too lively. I finished up in the nick for obstructing a copper."

Just as he finished saying this he looked over my shoulder and started getting up. "Hang on a minute," he said. "I've just seen somebody I want to talk to. I'll be back in a bit." He started pushing his way through the crush.

I watched him go straight up to a blonde who was standing talking to three blokes, very cool and sophisticated—she was the big attraction there, all right—and start talking to them. I could see the three blokes weren't at all chuffed about Jock barging into the conversation, from the look on their mugs, as much as to say, "look here, how dare you have the brass neck to address a high-class piece of crumpet in our presence, aren't you aware she belongs to us, my man?" They had something else to think about before long because Jock suddenly grabbed the blonde before she could move a muscle and gave her a big passionate kiss.

He didn't give a monkey's for anyone, not Jock. Not the law, nor the gaffers, nor the trade unions nor anybody. They couldn't put the mockers on him.

Take this bint, Carol, I was thinking. If he wanted her he'd just walk in and grab her like he was grabbing the blonde, and waltz off with her right under the nose of Sydney Chubb and his poxy Alpine. He didn't care if you had the arse hanging out of your trousers, or if you were somebody that mattered like Lord Flumdunkum or some actress. It was all the same to Jock.

CHAPTER ELEVEN

AROUND this time I was gradually finding out that there are people in this country that matter, and people that don't matter. There's a very distinct barrier between them, boy. I know which side of the fence I was on, and all.

I was getting very sharp at recognizing the people that did matter. Money was a lot to do with it. Not everything though. It was a mixture of money and what kind of school you'd been to, and the way you talked and dressed, and what you did for a living, and who your bloody uncle was on your mother's side.

You could always tell them by their cars. They'd have Jags and M.G. Magnettes and Rovers and sports jobs with hoods—even very old ones—and usually they'd have a whole lot of badges plastered all over the front of the radiator. You wouldn't find one of them dead in a Ford Popular.

There wasn't anything written down about the barrier but it was there all right. It certainly was. There's a pub along the Whitmarsh road, right at the end of my round. When I finish up there on a Sunday morning I'll very often have a quick one in the bar.

This pub is called the Boar's Head and the old stage coaches used to stop there. It's reckoned to be one of the oldest boozers for miles around, and it certainly looks it. Cobwebs everywhere. The bar is full of ancient old pistols and stuff and instead of ordinary lights they've got these old stagecoach lamps with electric bulbs inside. On Sunday mornings it's always six deep in people that matter.

Sometimes I'll get into conversation with them. Last Sunday for instance I was standing next to a couple of them, fairly old blokes about forty. Rough old sports jackets they were wearing. Posh drawly voices. Haugh yes old boy, I was absolutely furious. Striped ties. They noticed the bag over my shoulder and asked me if I'd got a buckshee *Observer* and I had, as a matter of fact. So then they got on to asking me about the newspaper trade, and how much I made out of it, and what was the most popular rag, and if people stuck to one paper all the time, or did they chop and change, and so on.

After a bit I asked them to drink up and have one on me, but they said no, thanks very much and all that, but they'd got to be pushing off. Then I grinned at one of them—the tall one—and said to him, friendly-like, "And how do you earn *your* living, if it isn't a rude question?" He winked at his mate and said, "That's a bit of a trade secret, isn't it Charles?" Haugh yes, no comment, old boy. And then the other one, Charles, turned away a bit and said in a sort of low voice, "Well, I wonder what old Stephen's up to? I suppose you heard he'd put down seven thousand for that new place of his?" Then they turned away and went on nattering between themselves. Not long after I heard the tall one say, "Well, I suppose we could just about manage another, don't you?" and Charles said, "Yes, I think that's a splendid idea."

I just stood there for a bit, jugging up and listening to their conversation.

You can always tell the people that matter by listening to them talk. They always know somebody's kid who's at some public school. If they say, "I'm thinking of taking Susan over to Stratford next week," they mean they're driving down in the Jag with the missis to see some play by William Shakespeare. They're always going up to town for a show, or to this place called Glyndebourne where something or other goes on. If they say so-and-so is in the army they mean he's an officer, because if they did happen to know somebody who was an ordinary bucko they'd keep quiet about it.

They might be on about somebody and they'll say, "Of course, he's red-hot Labour," but you'll never hear them say somebody is red-hot Conservative. Then there are the people they talk about, like this Froyd, and Peter Ustinov, and the bloke that does the drawings about St Trinians. And Ian Esko or somebody. They are always mentioning somebody on the films, or the television, that they know personally. They might say, "Have you ever met Harry Secombe? Used to live in the flat below us before we moved. Amusing little chap. Exactly the same in private life as he is on the stage."

There were plenty of things they *never* talked about, such as bint, and who was going to win the world cup at football. If they talked about sport it was always ruggah or cricket or tennis or the horses. If ever they talked about a fish they'd caught it'd be a trout or a salmon, and if they were on about shooting they'd never say how many partridges or pheasants they'd got. It'd always be so many brace.

And they'd always be drinking either pints of bitter, or short drinks with stuff in them like olives and bits of lemon and quite often they'd be scoffing little tiny cucumbers. I was getting so I could see them coming, and I could even pick out those who were just pretending, like for instance the fat little bastard who'd been on about the Yanks in the Wagon and Horses.

Anyway, while I was chewing over all this, there was a waltz on and they'd turned off half the lights. Hellish romantic. I happened to look out on the floor, and noticed that up the far end half of them had stopped dancing and were trying to look over each other's heads at something that was happening in the corner. So I got up and walked down the side of the floor to see what was going on.

There were a lot of people standing around Jock and another bloke—one of the herberts who'd been talking to the blonde in the first place. Jock had got hold of the front of the herbert's shirt, all scrunched up in his fist, and he was saying something, and the other herbert was saying something too. The blonde was hanging on to Jock's arm and shouting, "Let go, please let go."

The copper was standing next to Jock and looking straight into his eyes with a hell of a serious expression. I heard Jock say, "I'm not worried. You think I'm worried about that?" He still kept hold of this herbert's shirt.

A lot of them at the back started jeering and shouting and somebody hollered out, "Well, don't stand there jawing about it all night—let's have a bit of action."

The blonde put her hand on Jock's shoulder. She was still pleading with him. He suddenly smiled and let go his grip. Then the herbert said something, and Jock grabbed him again and started shoving him towards the door, with the copper hanging on to him like a leech. I heard Jock say, "All right then, outside, if anybody wants . . ."

After that they talked a bit more, and the other copper came back with a sergeant, but Jock seemed to get tired of all the talking, and he gave the herbert a sudden push that sent him flying into a table. It happened to be the one table that the skivvy who was collecting the glasses and bottles had chosen to shove them all together on, so there was quite a mess when matey picked himself up out of the ruins. The sergeant and the two coppers grabbed Jock then, and marched him out of the door, with the blonde following.

A bit later I had a shufti out in the passage, and saw Jock and the blonde talking to the sergeant. They weren't arguing, just having a quiet chat. Then I saw the sergeant shove out his hand and tap Jock on the chest and say, "All right Jock, I'll hold you to that, remember," and Jock said, "Anything for a quiet life, is that what you mean, George?" and the sergeant said, "That's the ticket, Jock." Then Jock said, "Well, good night, George, my regards to the old woman," and the sergeant said, "See you again some time," and Jock laughed and said, "Not if I see you first," and the sergeant was laughing as Jock went out with the kilt swinging round his knees and the blonde hanging on to his arm as if he was likely to get blown away any second.

I don't know why I stayed after that, but I couldn't seem to drag myself away. I was feeling very hot and considerably jarred off, and completely clapped out into the bargain. I knew I wasn't going to latch on to anything, and I wasn't even going to try. The place was putting the mockers on me more and more the longer I stayed. But the only other thing I could do was jump on the old Quickly and go tanking off home to my pit, which was even more depressing. So I just kept getting two halves of beer from the bar and knocking them off, and when the bar closed I just sat there.

Once I had a butcher's at the collection. There were just five or six left—the real no-hopers. Miss Merryweather was sitting bolt upright in the middle. I saw a character called Boozy Bancroft go over there. This Bancroft is a gangling specimen of about thirty with specs, who is supposed to be very intellectual. He works for the Electricity Board. Every Saturday he comes into the dance after getting cut down town, but they always let him in because he's harmless. He wandered around the collection like a praying mantis asking them to dance, but they all refused as if he was insulting them, until he got to Mabel Merryweather. When he got to her she got up with a sort of glassy smile and marched out on the floor, with Boozy lurching after her. He got hold of her the wrong way round, and she tried to put him right, but before they got properly sorted out the music stopped and that was all boys and gir-hirls. Then Ronnie Dodd announced the next dance—the last waltz. "So just close your eyes and make the most of it, my lads and lassie-ohs!"

CHAPTER TWELVE

AFTER that I just couldn't hang on any more, so I barged my way out through the middle of the floor, cut through the queue outside the cloakroom and scarpered. There weren't a lot of people in the streets, only the odd drunk, but the fish and chip shop was still open opposite Tibby and Tibby's, so I went in and ordered plaice and nine. This I scoffed in the doorway of a tailor's shop with all the old dummies looking on and licking their chops behind the plate glass windows. There was also a couple snogging in there, but they didn't take much notice of me; maybe they were preoccupied or something. Even when I offered them a chip they didn't answer, which I thought was a bit ungrateful.

By the time I got back to the car park back of the Wagon and Horses, where I'd left the old Quickly, it was coming on to rain. I unlocked it, got in the saddle smartly, and batted up the high street like a bomb. At the traffic lights I got a red just as I was coming up to cross, but I didn't see any coppers so I went straight over. A big Wolseley coming the other way nearly didn't miss me, and the bloke trod on his anchors and stuck his bonce out the window.

"What's the matter?" I yelled out. "You colour-blind?"

"You dangerous young lunatic, etc. . . ."

"Stuff it, uncle."

Four miles outside the town the engine packed up on me. I got off cursing and started to fiddle around with the plugs. The rain was belting down and I hadn't got my oilskin. I checked all the leads, then I happened to glance at the petrol gauge, and noticed that the indicator was leaning right over on the "zero".

It had never happened to me before. I slung the contraption into the grass on the side of the road, and kicked it. "You bloody whoring gitting animal thing," I yelled. "Why didn't you tell me you were out of juice? Oh Christ!" I knew it was the bint on my mind made me forget to fill up that morning. Carol! The stupid cow. Well, the next time she gave me a mouthful of teeth I was going to spit in her eye.

However, I started walking along the side of the road back towards Garside, and the bloody pawni was giving it big licks and no messing. Before I'd got a couple of hundred yards, my old pickers were saying yes and no to each other like newlyweds that can't get out of the habit.

It was coming down so fast I felt like jumping in the deep end of Watford Baths just to get out of its road. I couldn't do that very well because Watford is a fair distance from where I was, and I didn't reckon it was worth making the effort to get there, with not having much transport to speak of. Apart from that I'm not too sure they've got any baths down at Watford. Swimming baths I mean, not the domestic variety. It would have been a right old sell hiking all the way to Watford, I was thinking, only to discover on entering the city gates that there weren't any. I suppose there must be, though, because Watford is a fair old size. They've even got a public baths in Forbury.

Well, when I say public baths, it's just about the size that any reasonable film star would use to keep tropical fish in. You go there in the summer boy, and it's standing room only. In any case, by the time I got to Watford it'd probably have stopped raining.

In the next mile I was soaked, and after that it didn't matter. I was marching along there in the pissing fornicating rain like a guardsman, yelling out a dirty song I'd picked up from somebody in the Navy. *"The captain's wife was Mabel, whenever she was able, she gave the crew their weekly screw upon the kitchen table . . ."* They didn't have kitchens on ships. Galleys, they had. *"Upon the galley table . . ."*

The posh blazer I'd got on wasn't posh any more. Especially the crest. All the red of the tower had run into the yellow of the letters and vicky verky, and the oars were taking a real bashing. I wasn't too chuffed about this when I saw the result next morning. Just like a scrambled egg. Now if I went to one of these really natty schools and I had to have a badge on my blazer, I'd make sure I got hold of one that didn't go cock-eyed in the first shower of rain. On the other hand, I don't suppose the herberts that do go to natty schools ever get the rain on 'em all that much.

There's always some chauffeur or somebody hanging around with an umbrella at the high port, and one eye on the sky. Some flunkey or somebody outside the hotel just to see they don't stop a drop as they climb out of their Armstrong-Siddeleys. After all, the character who'd had the blazer before me must have hung on to it for nigh on thirty year, and the badge was perfectly okay when it came into my possession.

In the next half mile three or four cars went swishing by. I was only waving at them like a lunatic, but they didn't let it worry them too much. Naturally, I can understand bints on their own in cars not stopping to pick up stray herberts at one o'clock in the morning on a lonely country road, but only one of them had a piece of skirt driving. One of the others had a bloke in it driving very slow, with a piece next to him in the front seat. He was driving with one hand, and what he was doing with the other I couldn't see because I'm not nine foot tall, but I'll bet it wasn't on the gear lever.

Not that I blamed him for not stopping, either, because I wouldn't have done in the same circumstances. But the other jobs were being driven by blokes on their own, and when they went tanking past the only thing I could think of was hoping their back axles would break in half before very long, the mingy bastards.

Eventually a car did stop. I heard it slowing down before even I'd got my arm up to wave, and lo and behold it was Miss Mabel flipping Merryweather in her little pre-war Austin Seven.

I jumped in before she could change her mind. I slammed the door after me about six times but it wouldn't shut, so she put her arm across and gave it a bit of a jerk. "You have to pull it upwards and a bit to the left," she said. "It's having the knack."

After that the conversation what you might call flagged a bit until we got to the Garside turning. For one thing, I was too busy wiping the water out of my eyes to say much, and for another, she wasn't exactly my cup of cocoa. She might have been if she'd got a different pan and a different figure and was about fifteen years younger, but as they say, you can't have everything. Actually she wasn't a bad old stick, always very cheerful. She was what people call a "person". "That Miss Merryweather," they'd say, "she's a nice person." Or a pleasant person, or a busy little person. When anybody—any bint I mean—gets called a person, it means everybody can relax. At least, I've never in all my born days heard a real cracker called a "person".

Then she said, "I saw you at the dance. Did you have a good time? You didn't look as if you were enjoying yourself."

"About average," I said. "I saw you and all. Did you get what you wanted?"

She looked at me a bit sharpish when I said that.

"What d'you mean, did I get what I wanted?"

"Well," I said. "I thought you were probably making out some report for the council or somebody. You know, 'The Youth of Today', and all that caper."

"Oh no. I was there in a purely private capacity, I assure you."

"You keen on dancing, then?" I was just making conversation, I didn't really want to know.

She thought about it for a bit. Then she said, "Not terribly. I used to be when I was younger."

I said, "I suppose you like the old-fashioned stuff, you know, like the St Bernard's Waltz, and the Valeta, and the Dashing White Oujamaflick."

As a matter of fact they have this old-time Scotch dancing business every Thursday fortnight in the Village Hall. All the old biddies get down there and they have the radiogram going full blast. They all dance with each other, and believe me, they really give it a pasting. Like a herd of bloody rhinos. None of the men from the village ever get there at all, and no wonder. Who wants to get trodden to death, these days?

She said, "No, it's much too energetic for me, I'm afraid."

Just as she said this I noticed she'd passed the turning off to Green End Cottages, which is where I live, and was bashing on up through the Green. So I said, "Would you mind dropping me off here, Miss Merryweather?"

"I wouldn't want you to arrive home in that state, Davey," she said. "Why don't you come along to my place first? You can dry yourself out in front of the fire and I'll give you a drop of Scotch before you go. We don't want you to catch pneumonia. I can easily run you back."

"Well, that's very good of you, Miss Merryweather," I said, "but I don't want you to put yourself out on my account."

"Oh, that's all right, Davey. It's no trouble."

Confidentially she was still travelling flat out, which was about forty-five, so I didn't have all that option. In any case, the way I was feeling just then, if anybody had offered me a stiff dose of arsenic I would no doubt have fallen in with the suggestion. On top of everything else, I was just about bursting for a slash.

She lived on her tod in a little wooden bung about halfway along the Bottom. She went belting up a rough old drive made out of ordinary ground and very bumpy, and slammed on the anchors so hard we nearly finished up on the bonnet. "Sorry," she said.

I'll say one thing for these little old pre-war jobs. They certainly made the springs.

However. We got out and made a dash for the door. She turned the light on in the living-room. "I'll switch on the electric fire," she said. "Would you like to go to the bathroom and dry your face with a towel?"

I nipped in there smartish, but what I was hoping to find wasn't there. All there was, was a bath and a sink. I've known some hairy characters would just as soon use the latter in an emergency; apparently it's a regular habit in Her Majesty's Forces. But this particular sink was too high anyway, and there wasn't anything to stand on. So I resisted the temptation, gave myself a steady old rub with the towel, shoved a comb through the curly locks, and went back out there with my eyes rolling.

"There's just one other place I'd like to visit if you don't mind," I said.

"It's round the back. Turn left as you go out and you can't miss it."

I probably couldn't have done in daylight. As it happened, it was jet dark and raining pitchforks, and I finished up in the coal hole. It was about ten minutes before I got to the right place, and even then I had to tear the bloody latch off to get in. By the time I got back I was soaked all over again.

She was just pouring out a couple of big tots from a bottle of the Pope's. "Sit down, Davey," she said, "and make yourself comfortable. I should take your things off if I were you. I'll hang them up to dry."

I took off my blazer and laid it down in front of the fire.

"What about your shirt and trousers?"

"I think they'll dry quicker on," I said.

"Please yourself. But you don't have to worry about me, Davey. I've seen plenty of human anatomies in my time, male and female."

"Yes, I 'spect you must have, Miss Merryweather . . . well, anyway, I don't think I'll bother." I was feeling a bit queer. I mean, it was the casual way she came out with it. "Anyway, we'll see how it goes."

There was a hell of a lot of furniture in the room. In one corner there was one of those very ancient television sets with about a four-inch screen—a sort of little bubble arrangement. B.B.C. or nothing. I just about fell into a long settee affair. It wasn't all that comfortable though, because one of the springs was sticking into my duff, and I was too tired to move over.

"The cup that cheers," she said. "Do you take any soda with yours?"

"Yeh—not too much."

She squirted a bit in and lobbed it over. Then she had a bash at her own and just about drowned it. "Cheerio, Davey."

"Cheers!"

"The infants are safe from the storm," she said.

"The witch watch?"

"The infants. Safe from the storm. You and me."

"Oh yeh—I get what you mean."

"Are you warm enough? If you like I'll switch the other bar on."

"I'm all right actually," I said. "Don't you worry about me."

"How's the newspaper trade these days?"

"Bearing up."

"Heard any decent scandal lately?"

"Nah—never listen to it."

There was this dirty great clock ticking away like a bastard on the mantelpiece. It seemed to get louder every time there was a gap in the conversation. And there were plenty. I was just about Harry Flakers by this time, and I didn't feel much like coming across with the sparkling old Peach repartee any more. All I felt like was caning the pillow, to tell you the truth.

"Don't you think you ought to take your shirt off? It's soaking."

"No thanks. I don't think I'll bother."

"Are you sure? You could easily catch a nasty chill."

"Not me. Never had a day's illness in me natural."

"Oh, Davey, touch wood! You never can tell. There's always got to be a first time."

She jumped up, grabbed hold of the clacking old clock, and whipped it over for me to touch. I was just putting a finger on it for the sake of peace and quiet, when it started chiming all over the place. Gave me a real turn.

"Davey! I'm sure that's an omen of some sort."

"Yeh. It's just reminded me I've got to get going," I said. "Got to be up early in the morning." I knocked off the Scotch.

"Well, you'll have another one before you go." Before I could reluctantly refuse she snatched the glass out of my hand, stuck about half a pint of Scotch in it, and shoved it back.

"Well, all right, if you insist."

"I definitely prescribe it for you, Davey," she said.

She sat there for a bit watching me drink it with a kind of gloating look on her pan that I wasn't all that highly delighted about. She had this very owly round face with specs on, and she had what might have been a very useful pair of Bristols on somebody else. But with her you couldn't tell where they ended and the part underneath began; she didn't have what you'd call a waist, it was same all the way down. She was wearing a sort of tweedy costume, and she was leaning back in her chair with her hands clasped at the back of her neck. Her skirt was stretched very tight across her knees, and she had this socking great pair of chubby legs sort of coming out of a big dark hole at you.

Not exactly appetizing. Especially at that time of night.

"I hope the light isn't too glaring," she said. Then she said, "You're very tall for your age Davey. How old are you?"

I remember saying something about feeling a hundred-odd. After that I don't remember anything for a bit. I must have drifted off. Christ knows how long I was away, but the next thing I remember she was hunched up next to me on the settee like a dirty great crab, and she'd got her mitt round my waist. She was pretending to come the old nursing touch, but David Q. Peach knew better.

"Are you all right, Davey? I do think you ought to take more care of yourself. You'd better finish up the rest of this." She held out the glass again. It was as full as when I'd started on it.

"No thank you very much, Miss Merryweather." I was wide awake now, boy. "I really think I ought to be on my way."

"Why don't you call me Harriet?" she said.

"I always thought your name was Mabel."

"That's what a lot of people call me. I suppose they think it suits. My real name is Harriet. I think it's much nicer than Mabel, don't you?"

"Yeh, I suppose it is, now you come to mention it."

I took my hand away as if to scratch my nose, then tucked it under my armpit.

Then she said, "Davey, have you got a regular girl friend? You know, somebody you'd like to marry?"

"Well, I wouldn't say that, exactly . . ." I was trying to think what was the best way of getting out the door without any trouble. I'd have to walk home, but I wasn't too worried about that. "I can't think of any offhand," I said.

"I've never had a lot of boy friends," she said. "I've always been too ugly, I suppose."

"Oh no, I wouldn't say that, Miss . . . er, Harriet. I've known a lot of girls that are much . . ." I decided to have a bash at the whisky after all. I needed it.

"It's very nice of you to say so," she said, "but it's no use running away from the truth. I'm as ugly as sin. Anyway, I've always been too independent to want to get married. I should think I'd be quite impossible to live with."

"Yeh, I suppose you would in a way," I said. "Well, thanks for the hospitality and everything . . ."

"There's only one regret I have, though." She was staring me straight in the eye. I daren't move. She said, "Davey, if you could have anything in the world just for the asking, what would you choose?"

"I don't really know," I said. "I s'pose a million nicker'd do me, at a pinch."

She grinned a bit when I said that. "Money, of course. What a dreadful young materialist you must be. Still, I suppose there are worse ambitions. But how d'you know a million pounds would bring you happiness?"

"I'd just have to take a chance on that," I said. "Anyway if I had all that amount of gilt, I wouldn't worry whether I was happy or not."

"D'you know what I'd choose? Above any sum of money, or anything else for that matter?"

"No, I don't."

"A sweet little baby of my own. Either sex. It wouldn't matter to me."

"No, I don't suppose it would . . . well . . ." I knocked off the rest of the Scotch in such a hurry I near bit a piece out the side of the glass. "O' course, we're all different," I said. "We all got our different likes and dislikes." I was going to jump straight up and scarper then, but she put her hand on my thigh and pressed it down.

"There are all sorts of things money can't buy, Davey. I had quite a large sum left to me by a patient not long ago. Did you know that?"

"I did hear something to that effect."

"Yes, I expect you did," she said. "It's all over the village. Do you know, Davey, I've nursed the people of this district for the last twenty years—ever since I got my S.R.N. certificate—and that was the first real gesture of appreciation that anybody . . . anybody . . ." She took a real deep slug out of her glass.

"That's a hell of a long time," I said. I half sort of got up.

"Sit down, Davey. Surely you're not scared of an ugly, middle-aged spinster like me?"

"No, of course I ain't." I tried to give a chuckle but it came out so queer I had to start coughing to pretend something was tickling my throat.

"I've brought more than three hundred babies into this world. Lovely, bonny children. Three hundred. And some of the mothers, Davey . . . I wouldn't give you that much for them." She snapped her fingers in front of my snitch. "Some of those mothers shouldn't be allowed to keep a dog, never mind a child. I mean it! You haven't seen what I've seen." She was looking hell of a fierce.

"No," I said. "I don't suppose I have."

"That's what I'd choose. My own baby."

"Couldn't you kind of . . . well, adopt one? I mean, if you want one as bad as all that?"

"No, they're not all that keen on single women adopting babies. Anyway, I want one of my own flesh and blood. I want to go through the agony of bearing it."

"D'you reckon it's still raining?"

"In about three years' time I shall be too old for child-bearing," she said.

"Yeh," I said. "Well, none of us are gettin' any younger, are we? I honestly must start makin' tracks, otherwise the people in this village ain't going to get any papers tomorrow. Today, I mean. P'raps we could continue this conversation some other time, okay?"

"If I was going to have a child, d'you know what I'd do?" she said. "I'd go right away from here. Nobody need know. After it was born I'd settle down somewhere and get a part-time job in a hospital."

"You wouldn't have any trouble there," I said. "Not with your experience and everything."

She suddenly jumped off the settee.

"All right, you want to go, don't you? You don't have to tell me."

"Well, there's no hurry, only I got the round to do, see, and . . ."

"I shouldn't have kept you all this time. I'm sorry, Davey. You'll just have to write it off to experience. Just put it down to the stupid vanity of a dumpy little toad of a district nurse who just happens to be a little lonely in life. Come on, I'll take you back."

It was still coming down in vanloads. On the way back she said, "If you do happen to catch a chill, drop in at the surgery before hours on Tuesday and I'll fix you something up." When we stopped outside my place, she just sat there looking straight in front of her, and she said, "Good night, Davey," without looking round.

I had a quick shufti at her, and I noticed these whacking great tears rolling down her cheeks. She wasn't making a sound, either. It was bloody weird.

"You all right?" I said.

"Yes, I'm quite all right. But thank you for your solicitude."

"Don't mention it. Good-bye," I said, "Harriet."

That ought to have been the finish of that, by rights. Only when she turned the car round the stupid cow went too far into the bank and got stuck in a ditch. It took me half a bloody hour to get her back on the road, by which time we'd woken up half the neighbourhood. Which naturally pleased me no end.

After that I staggered in, set the alarm for three hours later, and went spark out on my pit.

CHAPTER THIRTEEN

How I managed to crawl out that morning, bike up to the Seagrave Garage, unlock the pump, fill a half-gallon can with petrol, pedal on to where I'd left the old Quickly, and then collect the papers from Forbury and carry on with the round, I shall never know.

Anyway, I did it. Or it may have been somebody else for all I knew or cared at the time. All I know is, if somebody had started shouting the odds at me about not getting the right paper I'd have poked them straight in the snout, man, woman or child. I was in that kind of mood. Fortunately nobody did. When I got back home I snaffled half a pork pie, then climbed right back on the pit again to catch up with all the kip I'd been missing.

It must have been just after six o'clock in the evening when I woke up again. For a minute or two I laid there wondering where I was. Until I heard the church bells walloping through the window. Just by the side of the bed was a cold cup of tea with a scum on it, which Doris must have brought in whilst I was in kip.

I call her Doris now. Once I used to call her Ma. Only one afternoon a couple of years back, while she was down the village, I happened to be rooting about in a drawer for something, and I came across a stack of old letters and documents. So I started having a shufti at them.

There was a birth certificate in there with the name of David Marks on it, which caught my attention, seeing it was the same Christian name as mine. I had a look at the mother's name, Sheila Marks. Underneath it, whoever had made out the certificate had written, "A variety artiste". In other words, case explained. It was dated the day I was born.

That was when I started feeling a bit dodgey. Doris had always told me she'd lost my birth certificate, and couldn't get hold of another one. When she came back I stuck the piece of paper under her snitch and asked her where it came from. She nearly went off into hysterics, wanting to know why I was ferreting about in her personal papers, etc. I just waited for her to calm down, then asked her again.

She turned on the old waterworks properly then, and she said, "Oh Davey, if only I'd told you before, but I kept on putting it off. I'd rather have anything happen than you finding out for yourself like this."

"That's me then?" I said. "David Marks?"

"Yes, it's you."

Then it all came out in a rush. About how Doris used to be a dancer, and about how during the war she was in one of these E.N.S.A. concert parties, travelling around the country entertaining the squaddies. This Sheila Marks, Doris, and another bint were all part of the same act, singing and dancing. The Ingram sisters they called themselves. Until Sheila started taking her duties a bit too seriously, and some army officer shoved her in the spud queue. When the bloke in charge of the party found out, he told her to take her charms elsewhere—he was probably narked because he hadn't been getting anything.

So when she finally had the kid—me—she was pretty desperate, because the officer—my old man—had done a smart about turn in the meantime and got himself posted.

By this time the act had broken up. Doris couldn't get any work on her own because she was putting on a lot of weight, and the other bint got cheesed off and joined the A.T.S. Doris got a job in a factory, but she still kept in touch with Sheila, and she offered to look after me until Sheila found herself another job and was able to make proper arrangements. Then after a bit Sheila got fixed up with a team of acrobats somewhere up north. She was the one that got slung from one to the other, apparently. Every week she sent Doris a couple of quid out of her pay. But after a couple of months the money wasn't coming regular, and soon after that it stopped coming at all. Doris made inquiries at the halls where Sheila had been performing, and she eventually got in touch with the acrobats, but they said she'd left them some time ago, and they didn't know where she was because she hadn't left any address.

While she was telling me this, Doris dug a photograph out of an album and showed me it. There were the three of them in this photograph, with little sailor hats perched on top of their heads, black stockings, and kind of sailor shirts which came down just far enough to avoid showing everything they'd got. It wasn't all that much, anyway. They had their arms linked together, and they were winking their heads off, standing there with their legs crossed and one toe balanced as if they were just waiting for someone to clap hands three times and start them off on "Stop your ticklin' Jock". The big cuddlesome one in the middle was Doris, and Sheila was the little frizzy-haired bit on the left. Nice little china-doll's face and everything. Peaches and cream. Gin and tonic. Call me curly, mother dear, for I'm to be Queen of the lay.

It's queer, but all the time Doris was nattering on, I was looking at her and wondering how I could ever have believed that she was my mother.

Not long after Sheila disappeared, Doris married a bloke in the R.A.F., Jack Peach, and they passed me off as their own kid, ration books and everything. But Jack Peach got posted out to Burma, and he was knocked off in 1944. When the war was over, Doris moved down to Garside to live with her mother, who croaked when I was twelve year old. A pernickety old party she was.

All the time, Doris was passing me off as her own nipper. She had another bash at trying to find Sheila, and even went up to Somerset House, but no dice. Maybe she'd been killed in the blitz.

After her mother passed over, Doris married Stan Lennard, who's always worked on the gardens up at the Hall—he's been head gardener there for some time, with two blokes working under him. He's about fifteen years older than her, and walks with a bit of a limp, but even without it he'd have his work cut out to keep up with Doris. I haven't got eyes in my head for nothing, boy.

When I discovered all the historical details, I decided to go on calling myself Davey Peach. Naturally, I had a good think about it. I went up to my room and looked in the mirror, and I said to myself, "Davey old lad, officially you're nobody, you don't even exist, you haven't got any relations, you're not even a proper bastard."

After I thought about it a bit I had a good laugh to myself, because I suddenly imagined I was a millionaire, going to some big reception as the guest of honour, and jugging up the old champagne, and then somebody, the Lord Mayor or somebody standing up and saying, "My lords, ladies and gentlemen"—like they do at the big fights, with a fanfare of trumpets and all—'pray silence for our guest of honour, the Right Honourable

David J. Peach." And I'd stand up very slowly in my midnight blue dinner jacket, bow tie, diamond cuff links and what-all, and I'd sort of look around the table and I'd say, "Ladies and gentlemen, I'm going to let you into a little secret. There is no such person as Davey Peach. You won't find that name anywhere in Somerset House.

"I'm not Davey Peach," I'd say. "I don't know what my name really is because I've never met my father to ask him. I'm just the consequence of a bit of a rough and tumble in the long grass behind the car park," I'd say. "And if you don't like it you can stuff it," I'd say. "But you will like it, because if you don't you won't get any nice fat contracts."

As a matter of fact I felt a lot better when I found out about Sheila being my real mother. I felt kind of free, as if I need never be beholden to anybody any more. I went on living in the same room, but I'd just come and go as I pleased, and I paid for my bed and board like any lodger. Doris didn't like it for a bit, but she soon got used to it. As for old Stan, he hardly even noticed the difference. The only time we ever had anything to say to each other was when he'd be doing his football pools of a Thursday evening, and he'd ask me if I thought Everton was going to beat the Villa. He used to creep in and out like a snail and he always looked half asleep.

He wasn't all that dim, though. One night he came back early from a whist drive and caught Doris snogging with Ken Jeffries behind the rainwater butt. He didn't say a dicky bird, but she didn't get any housekeeping money for a fortnight, and old Stan took all his meals in the kitchen up at the Hall. I had to lend her a fiver to stop her from starving. At twenty per cent interest, of course.

CHAPTER FOURTEEN

ANYWAY, I was lying there very peaceful apart from all this racket from the bells, wondering whether to try and find the energy to get up and make myself a fresh cup of tea, or just lie there stinking. Eventually I did get up to shut the window.

There were all sorts of people shuffling past on their way up to the church. Also quite a few cars. There seemed to be a terrific lot of folk going to church that evening. I suddenly realized that it was the night for this jazz service arrangement.

Then I saw *her*. Carol, I mean. On her jack, and all. Wearing a greeny-black costume, sort of loose-fitting with a fairly wide skirt, and a hat made of white feathers curling round. Her face looked very serious. Black high-heeled shoes she'd got on and . . . well, I won't bore you by going into details, but she looked bloody gorgeous.

By the time she'd gone out of sight round the bend, I'd come over very religious all of a sudden. I reckoned that what was good enough for Carol was spot on for young Davey. So I started shoving on my respectable suit—the slate-blue one with the pinky flecks—and before the old clappers had stopped I was beetling up through the boneyard where all the old parish fathers lie with their bastardries neither forgotten nor forgiven, and all their earthly goods and chattels nabbed smartly by the dear ones left behind.

There were cars and motor bikes all over the place. Old Frank Talbot was standing in the road waving his arms, and trying to sort out the parking. There were even a couple of charabancs there, all the way from London.

I hadn't been inside the church since I was a kid, and it certainly looked dead strange, especially with so many people in it. I stood in the doorway for a bit having a shufti round to get my bearings.

At one side there was a raised bit with a long table on it. About six blokes were sitting on a form behind this table. One of them was Jerry Podmore, the chief reporter on the *Forbury and District Examiner*. He's the actual bloke that does this business about "Question and Answer" every other Friday. What he does, he gets hold of some big pot in the locality and asks him a whole lot of questions, such as, *"Q. In your capacity as chairman of magistrates, you must come into close contact with much of the sordidness and evil which infests society. What would you say is the principal thing which you call upon to sustain you through the disillusionments of this world?"* And underneath it you'll get, *"A.* A natural and quite incurable optimism, I should say, allied to a fundamental belief in the basic *goodness* of human nature, and last but by no means least the comfort of coming home to my dear wife at the culmination of a hard day's endeavour."

I wish he'd ask me some questions. I bet the editor wouldn't print the answers, though.

There were also one or two other local reporters on the form that I knew by sight but couldn't put a finger on their names, and a couple I'd never seen before, only I reckoned they must have come down from the big papers in London because they sat apart at the end with little grins on their pans, and they kept whispering to each other. Every now and again one of them would go through his pockets as if he'd forgotten something. You could see they were trying to give the impression that this was just a bit of a lark, and normally they'd be writing about something much more important, like Mr Duncan Sandys arriving at some airport.

Up the front, just under the pulpit, four blokes were sitting in a little group, all with their Sunday best suits on and instruments in their hands. A couple of saxes, a trumpet and a clarinet if I remember rightly. They were tootling away at this tuning up caper, just like Ronnie flipping Dodd and his Cosmo doofers on a Saturday night.

While I was standing there taking everything in, Mrs Wellard appeared from nowhere—I swear she must have been walking about on tip-toe—and bunged a prayer-book in my fist. "Well, well," she said. "Davey Peach of all people. You *are* a stranger." She was speaking in a hoarse whisper, so I said, "Excuse me, what did you say?" She looked a bit niggled at having to repeat it. "You *are* a stranger." I switched on a lovely big fake smile. "Yeh—I suppose I am. How's everything in Babylon these days?"

She must have thought I meant somewhere else, because she said, "Oh, much the same as usual." She was looking at me all pink and rosy, enough to give an archbishop the bellyache, and I haven't got a very strong stomach. "Won't you take a seat?" she whispered.

"You got anything left in the two and nines, up front?"

There were about twenty people queueing up behind by this time, so I thought I'd better get sat down before all the seats went. But just at that moment I saw what I was looking for. I just caught a glimpse of the white feathers about eight rows up. The pew behind her was just about full, but I reckoned they could squeeze in a little 'un like me. So I walked up there and started to work myself in.

I had to say "excuse me" a lot, because all the folk in that pew were on their knees, saying a little prayer before the fireworks started. I got to behind Carol, and squatted down between two old dames of around eighty, both dressed exactly alike. Maybe they were twins—any rate, they didn't seem to appreciate being separated. I near had to prise them apart.

I thought I'd better say one of these little prayers like the rest of them, so's not to be conspicuous, so I got down on the old mat and leaned my elbows on the shelf in front. Another three inches, and I'd have been touching her hair with my forehead.

It might have been this—I mean her being so near and everything—which upset my concentration. Anyway, I couldn't think of anything to pray about. "Christ Almighty . . ." I kept saying to myself. "Christ Almighty . . ." Eventually I said, "Let everybody that's ill get better quick, hoping this finds you as it leaves me, yours sincerely, Davey Peach, for ever and ever, Amen!" Then I sat back in the seat again.

The place was just about packed out by now. The bells had stopped clanging and there was a kind of big hush everywhere, except for some of them clearing their throats. I had another crafty butcher's around before anything started. A couple of rows behind me I saw Mrs Purkiss, siting there very prim and proper, with old Joe the side of her. He was looking straight at me with a glassy kind of stare, and he didn't move a muscle when she leaned over and tightened his tie. Ned Hoskin had just come in, and all. He was standing just inside the door in his rough old clothes, looking around him in amazement. What looked like a pair of rabbit's ears were poking out from under his jacket. I saw Mrs Wellard go up to him and say something, and he turned round and shuffled out the door.

Just then the Rev. Johnnie Salt came out from somewhere up front in his ecclesiastical togs. He stood on this little kind of platform effort with a fence in front—not the proper pulpit—and said, "We'll begin with hymn number one hundred and sixty-seven."

With that the band struck up and we were away. It went something like this:

> "Oh worship
> The King (boop-a-doop)
> All glorious
> Above. (yeah man!)
> Oh great fully
> Sing
> His power
> And his love. (yeah, yeah!)
> Our shield and
> Defender
> The ancient
> Of days (boop-a-doop)
> Pavilioned
> In splendour
> And girded (yeah, girded)
> With praise."

At first it sounded very queer, I'll admit. Not many people joined in. But when they got into the swing of it they really started giving it big licks. You could have heard the last verse halfway to Whitmarsh.

After that there were a whole lot of prayers and stuff, and every so often this pop singer who'd come over with the band would jump up in front of the pulpit and sing little bits like:

> "*As it was,*
> *(Yeah) As it was*
> *In the beginning,*
> *In the beginning,*
> *Is now and ever shall be.*"

In the middle of all this Johnnie Salt stood up at the place with the fence in front and started reading a bit out the Bible. It was all in proper English, too, not the old-fashioned variety.

The bit he was reading was all about some character who went away to be crowned king. He must have been next in line for it. Before he left he gave all his servants a nicker and told them to get cracking while he was away, and see how much profit they could make on it. When he came back he had a check up. One servant had made ten nicker profit, so he stuck him in charge of ten cities. Another had made five nicker, so the king made him the gaffer over five cities.

Another character was dead scared of losing his nicker, so he just wrapped it up in his handkerchief. This king said to him, "Well, the least you might have done was to shove it in the Post Office and got the interest back." Then he took the nicker back off him and gave it to the bloke that had made a tenner. He reckoned that people that take the risks and make plenty of gilt will always make stacks more, whereas those who are more or less skint will always remain that way. Which is fair enough. You take old Garfield Chubb for example.

Anyway, that was the gist of it.

There was a good deal more praying after that, and a couple of psalms which I couldn't make head nor tail of, although they were all jazzed up. While all this was going on I was having a shufti round the place.

It was a hellish old church, built in around fourteen hundred and something. It must have taken a fair amount of graft, too, when you consider that the blokes in those days didn't have a lot in the way of tools. Take this big stone arch, for example.

Carvings all the way up. Whoever knocked that out must have had some patience, and no messing.

Right next door to me was a big thick round pillar going right up to the roof. About ten foot up were some initials—C.H.L. 1846 —chipped out of the stone. I kept wondering what old C.H.L. was doing with himself lately, apart from pushing them up, and what kind of a bloke he must have been when he was sculling around in Garside. He must have been a crafty herbert to get them up that high. Probably nipped in with a ladder after closing hours. Bit risky, and all. Only got to get caught by the vicar and old C.H.L. would have been on the boat for Botany Bay. Talk about the good old days!

Over at the side were a couple of little stone staircases built into the walls, and I wondered if anybody ever went up them. They were so narrow there wasn't room to spit hardly. If you met somebody coming down when you were going up, you'd be in a right old two and eight.

Most of the time, though, I couldn't keep my eyes off Carol.

Actually, I suppose any body reading this might come to the conclusion that I'm a bit of a bastard on the quiet. In the accepted sense of the word, I mean. I don't reckon I'm any worse than anybody else, though, when I take a shufti round. I don't claim to be a religious maniac or anything. But I'll say this much. I agree with everything old J.C. ever said. You can look it up in the book of words, and I'll swear by anything that's there in black and white.

The only trouble is that it runs directly opposite to human nature. You got to live in this world, not die in it of malnutrition. What's the use of handing everything to the shysters on a platter?

How many millionaires give all their gilt to the poor? And why don't they? Because the poor would immediately stick it all on the pools, and a third of it would go straight back to the poxy government.

This business about do as you would be done by is all cockeyed. In my opinion, that is. You've got to do as you *expect* to be done by—as you bloody well *know* you're going to be done by. And you don't have to stand on a hedge to get done in this world, Charlie.

Sure, I sometimes fiddle the change on the paper round. You know why? Because I've lost count of the characters in this village that have suddenly moved while they happen to owe me a month's papers.

However. We had a stab at "Onward Christian Soldiers" and

then Johnnie Salt walked over and climbed up in the pulpit. He didn't look like a proper parson, even with all these togs on. Quite a little bloke, with a narrow kind of face and this limp. He didn't talk like a priest, either. You know, he didn't kind of half sing the words like a lot of them do, as if everything that comes out of their mouths is holy or something. No, he just talked as I'd talk to you, only a bit louder, naturally.

He started off by saying, "I'm not going to preach a sermon today. I'm just going to tell you something about the condition of your church."

Then he said, "This church has been standing here for five hundred years. There's nothing special about that. Most of the churches in England are very old. It's not particularly sacred, either. No church is sacred. You won't find God in a church any more than you'll find him under a flowerpot in your garden. It's just a convenient place for us all to get together for the purpose of worship.

"But it's not going to be convenient for much longer, because it's falling to pieces. We've had the architects in," he said, "and they tell us that a large section of the roof will have to be replaced, and the bell tower needs repairing. This will have to be done very soon, because in six months' time the church will be too dangerous for us to use.

"The repairs will cost about four thousand, five hundred pounds," he said. "We have been promised about eight hundred from the bell fund. We have another six hundred in the parish fund. So we shall need to raise a further three thousand pounds if we want to save our church. If we don't raise that money," he said, "the bishop has decided to close the church and cancel the living.

"So I'll tell you what we are going to do. Every family in the parish will be given a pound note from the parish fund. You will be asked to use it, like the king's servants in the parable of the talents, to make more. If, in six months' time, each family has been able to increase the money by five times, all our troubles will be over. But if we fall short, we shall lose our church, and by doing so we shall have proved ourselves lacking in the faith which inspired our forefathers to build it, and maintain it safely throughout the last five centuries."

After he said that he climbed down from the pulpit and walked back to the place with the fence. It just about bowled everybody over. There was a big murmuring noise at the back, and some of them even started clapping. I mean, I was a bit shook up myself, because although I knew he was a bit out of the ordinary run of padres, I was still expecting him to waffle on about original sin and what-all. (Not that there's anything very original about that, in any case.)

I was thinking about it all the time we were supposed to be singing the next hymn. I had a bit of a laugh to myself at the time. "Catch the people round here raising three thousand quid," I thought to myself. I was remembering when the Women's Institute tried to raise fifty nicker for a bus shelter about five year ago. You wait for a bus in Garside on a rainy day when you haven't got a mackintosh—you'll soon find out what success they had in that quarter.

Soon after that we had another hymn, and a prayer for the Royal Family and all its heirs and successors, and then we came to this bit about all those who are set in authority under them and I said, "The bastards," and one of the old girls next to me turned round like a startled faun. That was the issue. Everybody sat around for a bit, then they started moving. I was right behind Carol all the time. When somebody stopped her on the way out and started nattering I had to hang around and pretend I was looking something up in the prayer book. Johnny Salt was waiting by the door, having a word with the customers as they filed out. He had quite a serious little conflab with Carol, holding up the works, then he smiled and she smiled, and went out. Then he got to me.

"Hallo," he said. "Davey Peach, I believe. I've heard a lot about you."

"Don't you believe a word of it," I said. "It's all lies." I was trying to wriggle past in the crush, with one eye on Carol. "Good night."

He grabbed hold of my arm. "How did you like it? The service?"

"Oh, I thought it was terrific," I said. "I'll have to come again some time." He didn't let go my arm though. He'd got a grip like a thousand volts. "Look, I wonder if we could have a little chat some time?" "Sure, any time you like, only . . ." "All right, what about Tuesday?" "All right, any time's all right only . . ." "Well, let's say half past two then if that's con . . . yes certainly see you then all right then I'll look forward to seeing you okay only I got to rush I see well good night and thanks for com . . . 'night." I was away. Outside I could just about see the feathers disappearing through the gate at the far end of the churchyard.

I didn't want it to look as if I was hurrying. But boy, did I stretch my crutch down that path. Not for me the mellow yew-tree's shade. Caught up with her just by the cattle crossing. "Excuse me," I said. Panting like a fiend, I was. "I couldn't help but notice . . . haugh haugh haugh . . . you in church as a matter of . . . haugh haugh . . . fact I was sitting right . . . haugh haugh . . . behind you and I . . . haugh . . . thought what a good singing voice you . . . haugh haugh . . . had."

"Oh, were you?" she said. Surprised as hell. "Well, that's very kind of you, as a matter of fact my mother wanted me to have my voice trained once, but I didn't think it was good enough." Then she flashed over this very sympathetic smile. "This is just between the two of us" kind of lark.

"You should have," I said. "You'd have been Chris Barber's vocalist by now."

"Well, I wasn't actually thinking of going in for that sort of singing. I was really going to train for the opera, you see, only I decided it would be a waste of time. Anyway, what did you think of the service?"

"So-so," I said. "Not bad for a first attempt."

"No, I suppose not. But it's a good idea, don't you think? Having a jazz band and everything?" She turned round to look at me again with her surprised eyes and I said, "Yeh, yeh." I was trying to stop myself looking at her dills all the time. "A very good idea." We'd just about reached the gate of Doris's place and I was wondering if I ought to wander in, or if I could risk pretending I was going up the Falcon anyway. I risked it.

I liked the way she just accepted the way I beetled up and started chatting to her. Most of the dozy bints you see around, you walk up to them and come across with the old conversation technique they get dead nervous. They look at you with the old, "Yes, what can I do for you?" sort of business. Dead from the neck up.

I said, "Yes, I've always thought religion is a very good thing for people, don't you? I mean, it makes you sit up and think occasionally, don't it?"

"Yes, of course," she said. "Except for the unlucky ones."

"Unlucky?"

"Yes. There are lots of people who haven't any religious beliefs at all. They've got nothing to fall back on."

"Oh yeh, that must be terrible," I said. "Anyway, I 'ope they manage to raise all that money. I wouldn't like to see the old place fall to pieces. It's a hell of a lot, though. Just think what you could do with three thousand quid. You could have your own place for that money, and a second-hand Jag standin' outside."

She seemed to get all worked up when I said that. In a nice way, of course. "But we've got to raise it somehow. That lovely old church. It would be dreadful to just let it crumble away to dust."

"Don't worry," I said. "It'll be a long time before that happens. Them places is very solidly built."

We just walked along without saying anything for a bit. Confidentially I was caning the old bonce for something intelligent to come out with. Then we got to Elm cottage right on the corner of the Green. "That's a pretty little place," she said. "The windows look like eyes. D'you know who it belongs to?"

"Yeh," I said. "Miss Sparrow. She teaches down at the school. She *has* got a glass eye as a matter of fact. She always used to take Standard Three. Old Pincher Watson was the headmaster then, old bloke with a ginger moustache, retired now. She couldn't stand 'im. He used to come into the classroom when she was teaching, and he'd open a window and sort of hold his ear as if he couldn't catch what she was on about. Then he'd suddenly butt in and say, 'Aha, think what you're saying, Miss Sparrow, think what you're saying.' "

"I shouldn't think anyone could stand that."

"She nearly got engaged once to the bloke that came to do the boilers," I said.

"Why only nearly."

"They 'ad a bust-up. He used to spit the dust out, see, an' she said she couldn't bear anyone spitting, so 'e said it was better than a dose of T.B., and anyway he could 'ardly be expected to change the 'abits of a lifetime."

"I suppose you must know just about everything that goes on in this village?"

"Well," I said, "I've got my ear to the ground, as you might say."

She looked a bit serious. "What d'you think of Mr Salt, the new vicar? Tell me."

"Seems a decent enough bloke," I said. "Wants me to go round an' see 'im on Tuesday, 'alf past two. Don't know what it's all about."

"Does he honestly?" she was really bowled over. "He asked me to go round too, at the same time."

"Well . . ." I was highly intrigued at this bit of intelligence. "What a coincidence. Wonder what 'e wants us for?"

"I've no idea. We'll just have to wait and see."

We were just passing the Tidy's farm by this time, and I saw old Mavis chop us off a look from round the corner of the dairy.

I could see the old Falcon looming up on the landscape, and it was looming a bloody sight too fast for my liking.

"Anyway," I said, "he was married already."

"Who? The vicar?"

"The bloke that cleaned the boilers out. Always used to wear a black hat, summer and winter. His wife left 'im, though. He was the bloke that always lit the bonfire on Guy Fawkes' night, when we were kids. Nobody else used to do it."

"Why not?"

"I don't know. It was a sort of tradition. Only they eventually stuck 'im inside."

"What for?"

"Pinchin' turkeys." I couldn't stop talking, boy. I was a mine of information. "From up Whiteacres Farm. Forty-six altogether, only a fortnight before Christmas, and another nine he asked them to take into consideration from somewhere else. That was when Tiny Ferber was up at Whiteacres. He used to lie in bed until twelve o'clock every day, then he'd get up and knock off a full bottle of gin before dinner. Eat an' all, he could. Think nothing of putting away a whole leg of pork at a sitting, and four big apples for dessert. Les Roach was working up there at the time, he reckoned they put him on the scales once in the barn, and he made twenty-three stone five and a half. Actually his sister used to run the place—Tiny's sister I mean, not Les Roach's —she's just like a man, very short cropped hair and a deep voice and always wears combination overalls. Always having big rows, they were. Once she said Tiny ought to go and sleep with the pigs, so just to spite her, he did. Old Roachy said he found 'im there in the morning when he went round with the swill, snoring away in the corner with a couple of empty bottles for a pillow, and the old sow doin' 'er tank. Eventually 'e fell over one day just after he'd eaten a big meal and they sent for the ambulance, but he was dead meat inside two hours, only thirty-eight an' all. Something to do with the liver, they said."

We'd got right up to the pub by this time, and we stopped in the entrance to the yard. "How awful," she said. Then she started laughing, but put a hand up and stopped herself. "I know I shouldn't really laugh, but it was the way you came out with it. Just as if it's the sort of thing which happens every day."

"You'd be surprised," I told her. "It's fantastic some of the people you bump into in this place."

"Yes, it must be. Well, it's very sweet of you to walk all the way back with me. I have enjoyed listening to your description of . . ."

"Yeh," I butted in. I'd come over nervy again, the way she was looking at me. "Well, actually I was going to nip down here for a jar, anyway, so I thought as we were both goin' the same way . . ."

"That reminds me," she said. "I expect we'll be getting quite a crowd in tonight, after the service. I'd better go and change. Daddy will be wanting some help in the bar."

"Yep, well okay," I said, "Carol. Anyway, I'll mos' probably see you Tuesday up at the vicarage."

"All right," she said, "Davey. Bye-bye." She said "bye-bye" very low and soft. Then she turned away and scarpered quick, but I watched her in the back door and she looked back and gave a bit of a wave as she went through.

I walked into the public bar like the Duke of flipping China. Her old man was in there. Dapper little cove he was, brown suit, octagonal glasses, always looked a bit harassed, and no wonder with a daughter like Carol. I ordered a pint of best. It went down without touching the sides.

CHAPTER FIFTEEN

HE wasn't a bad old boy, this vicar, Johnny Salt. I'll say that for him. He was kind of human.

All the priests and clergymen and people I'd met up to that time had fallen into what you might call two categories. Not that I'd met too many—I didn't make it a habit. But either they'd be right up in the clouds as if they were too good for this world, and sort of hanging half in and half out of the next, or they'd be supercilious bastards that had the impression a lot of ordinary people have, that the sun shines out of their jacksies. Like old Fosdick for example, and another one I bumped into on a train in Wales a year or two ago.

I'd been on one of these "Outward Bound" courses, where you have to shag about in the mountains, and walk across rivers, and live under canvas for six weeks, and I was just coming back. Boy, I could have eaten a chief constable before breakfast. Fit as a tuning fork. Could I have done with a woman, or could I have done with a woman? Give 'im the money, Mabel! Anyway, there were the two of us in this compartment, me and an R.A.F. bloke that had been on the same course.

The train stopped at some little village and this parson got in. Black togs, dog collar, the lot. Face like four pounds of putty with holes in. The R.A.F. bloke looked at me and sort of nodded.

After we'd been going for a bit, this R.A.F. bloke said, "Excuse me reverend, but seeing as how you're a member of the cloth, I wonder if you'd mind me asking you a few questions about the Bible?"

This parson looked as if he'd swallowed a wasp.

"Certainly, my dear fellow," he said. I don't know if he meant certainly he minded, but anyway the R.A.F. herbert got dug straight in. "Well," he said, "you know how it reckons in Genesis that Adam and Eve had two sons, Cain and Abel? And Cain went and killed Abel? Well, how did Cain manage to carry on with the human race if there weren't any women around?"

Old white-chops gave a sort of snigger. You could see he didn't like it, though. "Yerse," he said. "That old chestnut again." Then he said, "After all, what does it matter? I'm here, and you're here, so the problem must have resolved itself in some fashion."

So the R.A.F. bloke said, "Yes, I know, but that doesn't exactly answer my question. Anyway, we'll skip that one for a minute. What about old Noah? Have you ever stopped to think what size ark he'd have to build to get in two of every kind of animal, not to mention all the birds and insects and whatnot? Even then he'd have to have a hell of a lot of storage space to carry all the grub for them. It'd have to be about six times the size of the *Queen Elizabeth,* at least."

He got all snarky after that, this parson. He kept saying, "Why don't you tell me what's troubling you, my dear chap? I should be only too willing to help you, if I can."

But the R.A.F. bloke kept saying, "There's nothing troubling me. I've just got an inquisitive mind."

Eventually we stopped at another station and the parson got out. "Well, I have to get off here," he said. "I'm very glad we've had our little chat, and I hope I've been able to dispel some of your doubts. If I were you I'd have a nice long talk to your padre when you get back to your unit."

He got out then. I stuck my head through the window, and saw him get back on the train again lower down. I told the R.A.F. bloke and we rolled all over the seats cackling like maniacs.

Of course, I'd probably never have bothered to go round to the vicarage on the Tuesday if I hadn't found out that Carol was due to make an appearance. When I got there, smack on the dot of half-past two, Johnny Salt was frigging about under the bonnet of his car, a 1946 job that looked as if it was the first one they made after the war when they were still in the middle of switching over from tanks.

He looked up when he saw me coming up the drive on the Quickly. "Hallo Davey," he said. "D'you know anything about cars? Or should I say motivated junk-heaps? No, this one isn't even motivated."

"Mind if I have a shufti?" I said.

"No. Go ahead."

I leaned over and peered at the works. "What's the trouble?"

"Just can't get a spark out of her."

"Can you switch her on?"

He went round and switched on the ignition. After a bit he shouted, "Have you found anything?"

I said, "You can't expect 'em to roll for ever. Even cars get tired."

"You don't know this old sow like I do," he said.

I was reaching around inside, gritting my teeth like all garage blokes do when they're on the job.

"Look," I said, "I bet you're very keen on this old crate. I bet you wouldn't part with it for anything. There's a bloke up the far end of the village, name of Frank Diamond. He's got a 1928 Flying Nine, calls it Dulcie, polishes it up every week-end. Even buys it flowers on its birthday. It wouldn't get 'im to the station."

He got out and put his hand on the radiator. "Did you hear that, you bitch?" he said. "You won't get any flowers out of me. I'll take the first offer."

"I know a bloke as might give you fifty bob for the scrap value," I said. "Only he'd probably sting you three nicker to tow it away." I was still frigging about with the engine. At least, I was pretending to, because the first thing I noticed was that one of the battery leads had juddered off, and that was the first thing I fixed. "Try and start her up now," I said.

She started at the first attempt. He came over all chuffed and excited and clapped me on the back. "You must be a mechanical genius. What did you do to it?"

"Ah—nothing much," I said. "Just a bit of trouble with the old differential, that's all."

"The what? Differential? Oh, I see. Well, it's all a mystery to me," he said. A few seconds later, while we were leaning against the bonnet wiping the grease off our fingers with a rag and nattering about cars in general, Carol arrived.

"Ah, there you are," he said, all jovial. "Now we're all complete. I assume that you two know each other?"

"Yes, we are acquainted," she said, looking a bit coy. She wasn't, though, she was only looking it. "I'm sorry if I've kept you waiting."

"Not at all," said Johnny Salt. He had these thick black eyebrows that met in the middle. "Davey has been performing technical miracles on my car. Come on, let's go and have a chinwag." We all walked across to the vicarage, which is a tall grey-looking place about half a mansion in size. He opened the front door, which must have weighed about half a ton, and went through into a big kind of hallway. Very dark and gloomy. Then he pushed open another door and said, "Pile in and make yourselves comfortable. I'll just go and see if I can raise a cup of tea and a biscuit."

The room itself was cosy enough. There was a desk in one corner with those arm things you have to pull out, and these very deep leather-covered armchairs you sink right down into and don't see the light of day for twenty-four hours. One of the walls had glass cases full of books all the way up it.

"Well," I said, "here we are again."

"Yes," she said, and switched on a bit of a smile to go with it. But I could see she was six hundred and ninety miles away. Then I remembered I hadn't seen Sydney Chubb's Alpine cluttering up the drive-in outside the Falcon lately, and I wondered if that was anything to do with it.

Johnny Salt came back and shut the door. "Well, that's fixed," he said. He plonked himself down in the chair in front of the desk and swivelled it round so he was facing us. "Now," he said. "Let's get down to business. I'll tell you why I've asked you along. You were both at the jazz service on Sunday. D'you remember the parable about the servants and the pounds they were given— the parable of the talents?"

"Yeh," I said. "I remember that bit."

"Well, I expect you'll also remember what I said about the money we need for restoring the church, and the way I suggested in which we might raise it."

"The same way," I said. "By giving everybody a nicker to start off with."

"Exactly. That's where you come in."

"Us?"

"I wondered if I could enlist your help."

Carol said, "I'm sure we'd do anything we could. Wouldn't we, Davey?"

"Yeh, I s'pose so."

"That's very generous of you both. You see, what I want to do
—what I'm very keen on doing—is to get some of the younger
generation working on this. Like yourselves. Young people with
vitality and initiative. Particularly as you both come into contact
with most of the people in the village in the course of your work."

"Yeh, I see what you mean," I said. I was getting a bit fidgety
all of a sudden.

"What would you like us to do, Mr Salt?" Carol said.

He sat there for a bit on the edge of the chair, crossing his legs
and swinging the tin one from the knee. It was making little
squeaking noises like a hinge.

"Look. I hope you don't think this is too much of an imposi-
tion. I'd like you to take over the organization of the scheme.
Davey as secretary, you Carol as treasurer. Davey, you've got a list
of the addresses of every family in the village which takes newspapers. That covers just about everybody. I'd like you to start
by sending out the envelopes with the pound notes in. Carol will
handle all the money as it comes in, and pay it into the bank. You
could both work out possible ways and means of putting the
money to work, and make suggestions to the people you meet in
the course of the day. Keep them up to it. Make sure they don't
put the envelope in a drawer and forget all about it. Between
the two of you, I'm sure, lies our only hope of saving the church.
What d'you say to that?"

"Ain't you takin' a bit of a risk?" I said. "Maybe most of 'em
will just take the nicker as a gift from 'eaven."

"That's a risk we've got to take. You see, Davey, if the people
of this parish aren't prepared to work for their church, they don't
deserve to have one. It's as simple as that."

Carol was just bursting with it. "I think it's a lovely idea," she
said. "I should be very pleased to be the treasurer, and I'm sure
Davey will make a very good secretary, that's if he'll do it, of
course." She gave me the full benefit of her lamps, all fizzing and
sparkling. "You will, won't you, Davey?"

"Yeh, well, as a matter of fact I . . ."

There was no stopping her. "Wouldn't it be wonderful to see
the money gradually mounting up. We could have a meeting
every fortnight just to see how it was going . . . Oh, Davey, please
say you'll accept."

They were both looking at me. Johnny Salt said, "Well, we
don't want to press him, do we? If you don't think you can spare
the time, I should quite understand. Why not think it over for a
day or two?"

I was turning it over in my mind. First of all, I was thinking about my reputation. Davey Peach working for the church? And not even getting paid for it? It just didn't sound natural. On the other hand, there was this item that Carol had just mentioned, about meeting every fortnight to check the accounts.

"Okay," I said, "when do we start?"

She came flying across, slung her arms round my neck, and kissed me on the cheek. Very chaste and whatnot. "Oh, Davey, I *knew* you would." Johnny Salt sat there grinning, taking it all in. At that very moment old Ma Talbot, who was doing the house-keeping at the vicarage, charged in with a trayful of teacups.

You ought to have seen her pan! Eyes like acorns. Especially when she realized who she'd been warming up the old teapot for. She nigh broke the saucer, whamming it down in front of me.

As it happened, I'd always got on all right with Ma Talbot until about a year before when she and Frank had a niece of theirs staying with them for a fortnight. She was a pretty warm piece of snicket, aged about seventeen, this niece, long honey-coloured hair. Sometimes she'd be on her own in the cottage when I came round with the paper; Ma Talbot was looking after old Fosdick, who was sick of the palsy or something at the time. So we'd have a bit of a natter. A couple of days before she was due to go back, I volunteered to show her round the marsh, so she slipped out one evening and we joined up by the war memorial. Anyway, somebody must have seen us and put the bubble in smartly, because we'd only got as far as the bridge when Ma Talbot came swooping down after us on her sit-up-and-beg bicycle. Not a very trusting nature, I must say.

After she'd gone we started on about ways and means of getting this scheme on the old assembly line. Very merry we were. At the same time I kept having this peculiar feeling that old Fosdick, or his ghost, was suddenly going to lurch in and turf us all out, Johnny Salt included for not wearing a dog collar, not talking as if he'd got a mouthful of prunes, and not acting as if he'd got a halo round his bonce.

After about half an hour he stood up and Carol stood up, and I got the message and stood up too. "Well," he said, "it's been very invigorating talking to you youngsters. I feel ten years younger myself." He couldn't have been much more than thirty-five, actually. "And I'm very grateful to you for helping out." He ambled across to the door. As we were going out he gave a funny little grin and said, "I suppose I ought to add that I haven't mentioned any of this to the parochial church council. I'm meet-

ing them tomorrow night, so you'd better keep it dark until then.
But I don't think we've anything to worry about on that score."

He saw us out on to the drive, still chattering away about one
thing and another, then he gave us a sort of shabby old salute
and said, "Cheerio, then. Keep in touch."

I picked up the Quickly and walked up the drive with Carol.
She was still all steamed up about this fund-raising caper. Give
a woman the chance to cover herself with a bit of the old glory
nonsense, and she'll spend the rest of her life eating out of your
lily-white palm. "Davey," she said, "there's a little room at the
back of the pub that used to be the private bar, but we don't use
it now. Perhaps we could take it over for our conferences?"

"Certainly. I think it'll be the ideal place," I said. I reckoned
that any place would be ideal if there was only her and me sharing
it, but I didn't say so. I was thinking that as the scheme was going
to last for the next six months, we were going to have at least a
dozen chances to get better acquainted. Which was quite a fair
bit of gravy for Davey.

So when we got to the front gate, I fixed up to see her the
following week, then I jumped on the Quickly and went up to the
Seagrave Garage at bat 9, which is way past my maximum.
Actually I once did bat 10 coming down this hill they call Fidler's
Cut the other side of Whitmarsh, only I don't count that because
there was a full bloody gale right behind me at the time, and I
nearly finished up in the council paddling pool.

CHAPTER SIXTEEN

ALL this business about the talent scheme was the talk of the
village, especially when it went round that I was involved. Everybody was asking me about it on the round. "Is it true you're
helping to organize it, Davey? I didn't know you were religious-
minded. When I first heard about it I said to my Bert, I said,
'There must be somebody else of the same name in the village.'"

"No, it's me," I'd say. "There's only one Davey Peach."

"Well I never . . ." etc. I knew what they were all thinking but
I didn't give a monkey's. If I couldn't raise any money for the
church, I thought, I wouldn't stand much chance of making a
lot for Davey.

So I looked at it as a kind of big test. I'd take any challenge as
regards money. There's something I'll always remember from
school. There was this kid called Raymond Allbright. His old
man owns the big electrical goods store in Forbury. He's always

had plenty of dough. I never had two halfpennies to rub together. Doris was hard up at the time, what with having to support her old girl. All she used to give me for pocket money was threepence a week, which was always gone by the Monday.

Raymond Allbright was a real little porker. He used to have to take special exercises two evenings a week, and he was always on a diet. He used to give me little tests, for money. Like at dinner time he'd fill a glass with water, empty the salt cellar into it, and pass it over to me. "Drink that, and I'll give you a tanner." I'd drink it, and feel like spewing. He'd spin the tanner across the table so it would roll off the edge and I'd have to pick it off the floor.

"You see that swallow's nest," he'd say. About thirty foot up a drainpipe it'd be. "Get me an egg out of there and I'll give you a bob." So I'd shin up and find it full of young 'uns. I'd bring one down. "That's not an egg, is it? I said an egg." He'd give me twopence compensation.

Once he offered me a penny for each shoelace I could bring him, so I went straight up the changing room and half-inched forty-two from the gym daps lying around. He tried to back out, and said he'd offered a penny for each *pair*, and in any case they weren't proper shoelaces. I nearly slotted him one then, but I didn't dare, for fear I wouldn't get shyce. I had to take the one and ninepence in the finish.

Maybe that's what started me off wanting to be rich. If I ever do make a fortune, the first thing I'm going to do is walk into Allbright's electrical stores. Old Allbright will have snuffed it by then, and Porky will be standing in the middle of the shop like a barrel of lard. Of course, the business will be going downhill fast with him running it.

I'll have this big coat on with an astrakhan collar, and he won't recognize me. I'll buy up every item in the shop, and then I'll sign the cheque, and watch his face as he reads the name on it. And all the time I'll pretend I don't even *know* who he is.

There was a bit of barney at the parochial church council meeting when the vicar broke the glad tidings about me and Carol. I heard all about it from Mavis Tidy, who's got a very strong contact there, Mrs Whichelow.

Apparently Mrs Fforde-Hunter got on her hind-legs and said, "Does the vicar seriously consider that Mr Peach is quite the most suitable person to be associated with an enterprise of this nature?" Johnny Salt said, "Yes, I do think so, otherwise I shouldn't have asked him." Then Mrs Wellard said, "Well, they're both very young, and Mr Peach isn't a regular church-goer." Johnny Salt shot her down in flames, and all. "I selected them because of their youth and enthusiasm," he said. "If we try to discourage the younger people from working for the church, the church will die anyway. Raising money isn't dependent on regular churchgoing—nor is Christianity." He gave it them hot and strong, old Johnny Salt.

After a bit of to-ing and fro-ing, old Ma Pinches started. A real narrow-minded old cow, she is. If she lived two hundred years ago, boy, they'd either burn her for a witch or make her president of the witch-burning committee.

"Is the vicar aware," she said, "that the young lady whose name has been put forward as treasurer is actually employed in a public house?"

So old Johnny said yes, he thought that would be a great advantage.

Eventually Mrs Wellard turned to old Commander Findlater who's about seventy-six and has to wear a hearing-aid, and asked him what he thought of the idea. He hadn't got the thing switched on or something, because he didn't seem to know what they were all gabbling about. All he said when Mrs Wellard asked him was, "Absolutely first class."

Mrs Wellard more or less had to agree with him because he owns the meadow where she keeps these two old horses which she saved from the knackers, and he lets her have it for free. But he can be a dicey old customer when he's roused. One time I made out his monthly account and left the O.B.E. off the end of his name. I didn't do it purposely either, but the way he carried on about it you'd have thought he'd caught me watering his geraniums.

In the finish only Ma Pinches voted against it, and nobody was too worried about that, because if Ma Pinches *does* vote for something, it's usually enough to put the mockers on it for a start.

So we had all these forms printed explaining all about the scheme and what it was for, and a week later I went round to the Falcon with all the addresses, and Carol and me spent a whole afternoon writing out envelopes. There were five hundred and forty-eight altogether. I even included one or two that didn't take newspapers, such as Ned Hoskin. I came back that evening when Carol had collected all the gilt from the vicar, and we put a nicker note with one of these forms into every envelope, and licked it down.

The next morning, I delivered them with the papers.

You'll probably find this hard to believe, but all this getting involved with the church caper soon began to have a subtle effect on me. It sort of came up behind and belted me over the bonce while I was looking the other way. I suppose Carol had a lot to do with it and all. I started to get respectable.

To be quite honest I started growing up a bit. Weight of responsibility and all that lark. What I mean is, being secretary of the talent scheme and whatnot, I couldn't very well go teararsing round the village as I used to do, and hanging round the war memorial of an evening with the lads, whistling up every bit of passing crumpet. I realized I was getting too old for that kind of caper.

All these togs I had for instance. I turned out my wardrobe one evening, and laid everything out on the bed.

Six suits I had. Stovepipe trousers, flaps, vents, lavender lapels, drapes down to the knees, pillows in the poxy shoulders. The shirts and all, every colour of the rainbow and a few more, some of them all in one lump. There was one in particular I got from Warbey and Deedes in Forbury when they had a sale on. It started off at the neck bright purple and finished up bottle green at the tail, nor could you twig where one colour ran into the other. And the ties the same.

Eleven pairs of torpedoes I had, from ordinary black patent leather pumps to shell-pink suede brothel creepers and yellow snakeskin strapless sandals. All the shapes of trowels.

I stretched myself out on the bed on top of all the gear and had a bit of a think. I was wondering if I ought to get myself something a bit more what you might call conservative. Then I wondered if I wasn't turning a bit soft. "Before you know what's what, young Davey," I said to myself, "you'll finish up like the rest of 'em."

It was just like the wasp jar, I was thinking. Old Doris isn't too keen on wasps. Whenever one buzzes into the kitchen she starts flapping and waving her arms and shouting, "Shoo!" but the wasp don't take a blind bit of notice. Nor would I if I was carting a hypodermic and a stiff dose of poison around in my duff.

But Doris is a lot more clever than the wasps. She's got a couple of big glass jars standing just outside the back door, both half full of jam juice. These jars have got paper covers over the top with just one little hole poked through that's big enough for a wasp to crawl through and no more. Well, you'd think they'd appreciate this wasn't just generosity on Doris's part and keep out the road. But they don't. I've watched 'em time and time again. They'll catch a whiff of the juice, light on top of the jar, and in they'll go. I've never see one come out yet, boy.

You'd think they'd have the common to take a shufti through the glass first and see all their muckers drowned in the juice, and one or two of the more recent arrivals struggling about on top. But no. The lure of the juice is too strong.

I was thinking that life is like that. Just one big lovely jar of jam juice. I mean, getting spliced and having a steady job in some factory, and having kids and that.

It's nearly always a bint is the bait. You get interested in a piece of skirt, normally because you can't get what you want out of it, and she gets her hooks into you, and before you can turn round and holler there's one in the oven and the clappers are ringing. And that's you in the jar, friend.

After that you spend all your hard-earned gilt on getting a place to live and a motor on the h.p. and a washing machine and curtains and a perambulator, and transistor radio sets and insurance policies, and then you find you've got to flog yourself to death just to keep going. By the time you're forty-five you're Harry Flakers and you might as well be in your box.

Except for one or two crafty characters who can see it coming. What they do is, they have a rare old time until they're about fifty, no responsibilities or nothing, and then, when they've got plenty in the bank they latch on to some luscious young piece of about twenty-four and marry it. Just so they got somebody to look after them in their old age. And the piece concerned doesn't dare to come the old acid, because otherwise there won't be anything juicy in the last will and temperament, except for the dogs' home down the road.

After all, why jump in the river when you only need a drink? That's how I see it, anyway.

Of course, there might be the odd wasp that sniffs the old juice and flies right on past. I wouldn't know. I suppose it's possible. But if you ever do see one doing that very thing, that wasp is me, boy, Davey Peach. And what's more, you won't find *me* finishing up as a stain on the back page of the *Radio Times*.

CHAPTER SEVENTEEN

ABOUT a week after the distribution of the pound notes I was sitting against the bar in the Falcon having a quiet natter to

Carol. It was about half-nine in the evening, and there weren't more than six in the bar all told. All the optimists who'd crowded in when Carol had first put in an appearance had begun to drift away after a while, when they found out about her being religious.

We were on about the scheme, when old Joe Purkiss wandered in, called for a double Scotch, and sat himself down in the corner.

Actually, it was very strange about the scheme. Ever since I'd dropped the envelopes through the letter boxes, we'd been expecting everybody in the village to start running around in circles. Nothing of the kind. Nobody had said so much as a dicky bird. Just as if they'd swallowed 'em whole. I was beginning to wonder if the five hundred and forty-eight nicker wasn't just going to disappear into thin air without anybody bothering to mention the subject.

Carol was saying, "Well, we've got to give them time to digest it, Davey. It'll probably come as quite a shock to a lot of people."

"Yeh," I said, "I'd give 'em a shock. Some of 'em want a charge of dynamite up their backsides. That's what they need in this village."

"What are you going to do with your pound?" she said, to change the subject.

"Me? I haven't decided yet."

"There you are. You can't condemn other people."

"Well, they might *say* something," I said. "After all, we're supposed to have free speech in this country, so it wouldn't cost 'em anything."

"Anyway," she said, "I've decided what I'm going to do with mine. Shall I tell you? I've changed it all into pennies and I'm going to start building a stack on the counter. I shall ask everybody who comes in to add to it with their spare coppers."

She shook out a nicker's worth of copper, and I started helping her to build the stack. She'd printed a little card to go with it: *Add your spare pennies to the stack and help to save the church.*

"I think it's a very good idea," I said, "but there's only one snag."

She looked up sharp. "What's that, Davey?"

"It's going to take you a month to count 'em." I was just kidding her on a bit.

All this time I was keeping a crafty eye on old Joe. I knew he wasn't supposed to be out on the booze, owing to his condition. After a bit he stood up and ordered another double. Then he sat down and started knocking it back. He was just staring in front of him with his sort of sad eyes, moving his lips a bit every now and again as if he was saying something to himself. He was getting very red and fiery in the puss. He'd got a rolled umbrella propped against his knees.

Carol gave a nod over in his direction. "D'you think Mr Purkiss is all right?"

"Yeh," I said. "He's slipped the chain for a couple of hours and he's making the most of it."

The pub was having a pretty quiet night, and one by one the others beetled off until there were only the three of us left. It was about ten minutes to closing by that time, and old Joe had sunk two more doubles in between. He was still muttering to himself, and the side of his mug kept twitching. There were these tufts of black hair sprouting out of his ears. Eventually he got up all of a sudden, catching his knees on the table, and staggering a bit. Then he took hold of the umbrella, turned round, and swiped his empty glass clean off the table. It broke into about fifty thousand pieces.

As he went out I said, "G'night Mr Purkiss." But he didn't answer.

Carol said, "Davey, don't you think you'd better see him home? He might come to some harm." She was looking hellish worried.

"Ah, he'll be all right," I said. "He's only got a bit of a skinful." As a matter of fact I was just working out that when the bar closed she'd have to come to the front door and close it behind me, and it was pretty dark in the passage. But just as I was saying that there was a big clatter as one of the window panes came through from the outside, and Joe's umbrella poked into the curtain.

"Looks as if he's breaking up the 'appy 'ome," I said.

"Please go and see what he's up to. He must be ill or something. He's always been such a nice old chap." I didn't tell her what I knew about old Joe. But I could see I'd have to do something about it.

"All right. I'll go and put 'im to bed."

I went and stood in the doorway for a few seconds, trying to get my eyes used to the dark. All I could see up the road was a few patches of light from the windows of the cottages on the other side of the Green. Then I heard his footsteps up towards Tidy's farm, and I started running in that direction.

After a bit I saw him walking up the middle of the road, rolling a bit, but fairly steady on his legs. He walked right past his own cottage, and I noticed there weren't any lights on. I was wondering what had happened to Hilda Purkiss.

I put on a bit of speed and caught him up. I walked along the side of him for a bit, down towards the village. He didn't say anything. He didn't seem to notice I was there until I said, "Hallo Mr Purkiss. Don't you think you'd better be gettin' in? It's a bit late y'know."

He stopped then, pulled a box of matches out of his pocket, and lit one in front of my face. It flared up and then went out. "Why, it's the young Hinckley boy," he said. "How are you goin' on, son? I used to know your father, Bill Hinckley. He was in the trenches with me in the war," he said. "We was in the old Bucks Yeomanry."

"No, I'm Davey Peach," I said. "You know me, Mr Purkiss. I deliver the papers."

"Can't say I know anybody name o' Peach," he said. "Let's see now . . . Peach. You'd better ask in the post office, I 'spect they'll know in there. I'm a stranger meself."

He started trotting on again.

"I'm not looking for anyone," I said. "Anyway, the post office is shut. Don't you think you'd better make your way 'ome, Mr Purkiss? You wouldn't want your wife to worry."

"I'm not married," he said. "I've got a brother that's married, I 'spect that's the one you mean."

He walked on down into the Village. I was walking right beside him but he didn't say anything else. It was the day before they emptied the dustbins. Quite a few people had got them standing just behind the front gate ready for the cart in the morning. Every time old Joe came to one he'd pick it up from over the fence, empty it on the pavement, and stick the bin in the middle of the road. I kept saying to him, "I shouldn't do that if I were you, Mr Purkiss. Someone'll only have to clear it all up again." He didn't answer. There was this hell of a cunning look on his mug, and he kept chuckling as if it was all a game. Charlie Bowles came along the other side of the street while Joe was turfing out the rubbish. He stopped and looked for a bit, and then walked on. I suppose he reckoned it was none of his business. A couple of cars came through the Village. They slowed down when they picked up the dustbins in their lights, and squeezed round them without stopping.

Old Joe tore down all the posters on the big board outside the general stores: *It's a Man's Job in the Regular Army; You can Retire at Fifty-five if you invest With the Life and Legal; Come to the Whitmarsh Cancer Carnival; This is what Liberalism offers You*, the lot. When he came to the telephone kiosk he went in and started making some calls. He filled in the time he was waiting by poking out all the little windows with the end of his umbrella. He came out again, walked up as far as the crossroads, and pushed the signs round so that Whitmarsh was down the Bottom and Forbury over the marsh. Then he turned round and came back up. I stood in a doorway as he passed. He was a bit wobbly on his pins, and he was making these weird little cackling noises.

I followed him back through the Village and up to the Green. He stopped on the way to sling a couple of big stones at old Fforde-Hunter's glasshouse, which stands about fifteen yards off the road. The first one missed, but the second made a terrific clatter. I half expected old F-H to come belting out of his front door. He didn't, though. He was probably listening to some music by old Ian Esko or somebody on the Third Programme, and they were probably playing the bit that sounds like three hundred and seventy yobbos turfing bricks at somebody's glasshouse. Either that, or they'd gone next door to watch the T.V. The old Fforde-Hunters are too snobby to have a set of their own. Whenever there's anything on they want to see, they have to watch it on somebody else's.

I followed him up to the Green. He turned off up towards the church. I reckoned it was about time I did something, if only for Carol's sake, so I decided to get hold of Dr Lumbard. At first I tried to phone him from the box, but Joe had yanked all the bloody wires out. So I ran all the way through the Village to his place which is just opposite the Hare and Hounds.

His missis opened the door. I knew she must have been just about to hop into bed, because I saw the light on upstairs when I knocked. She had a dressing-gown on and her hair was sticking up like a porcupine. She'd got some kind of grease all over her face. "Yes, what is it?" They bloody hate it when you catch 'em looking natural.

"Is Dr Lumbard in?"

"No. He's out on a case. What d'you want him for? Is it important?"

"Yeh—I reckon it is."

"Well, I can't say when he'll be back. He's been out nearly all day. I don't think he'd want to go out again when he does come back unless it's an emergency."

"All right, forget it," I said. I started to scarper.

"Don't you want me to give him a message?"

"Not particularly."

I was thinking of going round to old Nobby Creighton, the village copper. The trouble is that Nobby happens to be as thick as a plank. Apart from that he's got a nasty suspicious mind. He's the kind of bloke, if anybody sent him a Christmas card he'd take the prints off the inside and file 'em for future reference. Not that anybody sends Nobby Christmas cards, but you'll appreciate what I mean. In the end I decided to knock up Johnny Salt.

I went round the vicarage and battered on the door. He came out in his shirt sleeves with a cup of coffee in one hand, munching a slice of toast.

"Well, it's you Davey. What a pleasant surprise. Come on in."

"No, I can't come in," I said. "It's old Joe Purkiss, I thought you ought to know. 'E's gone barmy."

He stopped chewing. "Gone what?"

" 'E's wanderin' round the village smashin' everything up."

"Is he? Well, in that case we'd better try and stop him. Hang on while I get my jacket." He nipped in smartish and came back pulling on a sports coat. "Jump in the car, Davey. Where did you last see him?"

" 'E was on 'is way up to the church."

On the way I told him about Joe. He just kept nodding his napper and taking it all in. We nearly ran into a flock of Jack Tidy's sheep that old Joe must have driven out on to the road as he went by. We stopped at the church gates and hopped out. "We'll have a look inside, first," said Johnny Salt.

The doors were wide open. Johnny Salt went across to a bank of switches and put on the lights all up the middle of the church. I had a quick shufti round. "'E's definitely been 'ere," I said.

"I'm afraid so."

There were prayer books scattered all over the place, and a couple of big vases of flowers smashed to smithereens on the floor. We went in and walked up the aisle. This old kitchen table Johnny Salt was using for an altar was turned over on its side. In the middle of the steps just below it old Joe had left his trademark. It looked hell of a strange thing somehow, this sad little old turd sitting there in the middle of the church on its tod, and I suddenly saw the funny side of it. I all but burst out laughing, I could hardly help myself. Johnny Salt didn't take much notice though. He just said, "Well, he's not here now. Let's have a look round the churchyard."

When we got outside again, he said, "You take the left-hand side of the path, I'll take the right."

"Okay." I went across the boneyard, dodging in and out of the

graves in the dark, and nearly breaking my neck on one or two
occasions. Joe had been there, all right. There were flowers
scattered around, and I kept treading on bits of broken urns and
jamjars. The tap which they used to fill the vases was full on. I
went across to turn it off, and then I saw him lying stretched out
across a grave. The gravestone was at a slant, as if he'd been
trying to heave it over. I shouted to Johnny Salt and walked
towards old Joe.

Johnny Salt bent down over him and started loosening his
collar. "He's just breathing," he said. Then he got up. "Davey,
we'll have to get him to hospital. Jump in the car and nip down
to the vicarage. You'll find a telephone in my study, and you can
call the ambulance from there."

"Right you are," I said.

I looked back as I went out the gate. Johnny Salt was kneeling
down the side of Joe and he looked as if he was praying, although
I wouldn't like to say for sure. I started to shiver, first because
it was getting a bit rafty, and second because I'd just realized how
bloody spooky it was in that boneyard.

Just as I was pulling into the vicarage, I happened to notice
an ambulance coming up behind. So I jumped out and started
waving like an octopus. The bloke in it stopped.

"Anything the matter, mate?"

"Yeh—there's a bloke been taken queer up at the church."

"What's 'is name? Paulson?"

"No, Purkiss."

"That's funny. We got a call to pick up somebody name o'
Paulson, but when we got to 'is address 'e warn't in an' 'is missis
didn't know nuffin' about it. Blind O'Reilly, this is a queer do."

"Well, what you moanin' about, you got a customer," I said.
"'Ang on and I'll take you up there." I jumped in the car and
tanked off back to the churchyard. The ambulance pulled in
behind. There was another herbert in the back. We all took a
corner of Joe and rolled him on to the stretcher. One of the
ambulance blokes—the one out the back—said, " 'E don't look
any too bright, do 'e, Johnno? Looks like a cardiac to me."

"That or the bottle," said the other one. "Watch where you're
plantin' your great feet."

They shoved him in the back, and the driver climbed back into
the cab. He took his cap off, smoothed his hair, and shoved it
back on again. "Any o' you relatives o' the dec . . . er, I mean
patient?"

Johnny Salt said, "No. I'm going to inform his wife, then I'll be getting in touch with the hospital. You'd better push on."

"Right you are, guv'nor," the driver said.

Johnny Salt dropped me off home. "You sure there ain't nothin' else I can do?" I said.

"No. There isn't much more we can do except to call on Mrs Purkiss and tell her the news. Anyway, you've done enough for one night, Davey. If it hadn't been for you I expect the poor chap would have been lying there all night."

"Yeh, well, I suppose there is that to it," I said.

"Good night, then."

"Good night, Davey.'

CHAPTER EIGHTEEN

MAVIS TIDY told me about the rest of it a few days afterwards. I'd gone up the farm to build a bit of a wall for Jack, to keep the pigs out of his kitchen garden.

"She was terribly upset, Hilda, when she got back and found Mr Salt waiting outside her front gate with the news about Joe. Actually she asked me round there the next morning and told me how it all happened, poor soul, her hand was really shaking when she was pouring out the coffee, I had to take the saucepan out of her hand. She said Mr Paulson had asked her to go over with him to his houseboat and pick the curtains to go in it, you see he only bought this houseboat a few weeks ago, it's over on the canal at Stanningford Basin, and he's doing it up so that he can take his wife Lily over there for holidays during the summer. She doesn't get out at all, being bedridden, and he thought she would just love to lie on the deck and watch the barges and the little sailing boats, especially when they have these regattas. Only of course Teddy had to do all the decorating himself, and he said he was quite hopeless at curtains and things and it needed a woman's touch, so Hilda said she'd go down and see over it just for poor Lily's sake, but they decided not to tell Lily because she's got a bit of a jealous nature, and they didn't want her to lie in bed and stew over it."

I started laying down a fresh course of cement, and I said, "Yeh. Sounds just like this divorce case I was reading about in one o' the Sunday papers. Carry on."

"So anyway, Hilda said she'd better get a bus to Forbury and Teddy could pick her up on the way through, otherwise you know how people talk, she said. The trouble was that Joe was supposed to have his injection that morning. So Hilda rang up Dr Lumbard and she said she had to go and visit a relative who was ill, and would he let himself in and see to Joe if she wasn't there when he arrived, and Dr Lumbard said he would, so Hilda caught the Forbury bus and Teddy Paulson picked her up there in his car."

"Would you mind chucking over that little trowel?" I said.

"Well, what happened was that Dr Lumbard was called to an emergency case that morning, some woman having a baby only it was upside down and they didn't find out until it started coming, anyway he was there all day trying to turn it, but unfortunately it died, and he didn't get home until very late, and by that time he'd forgotten all about Joe's injection.

"Hilda said Joe was very drowsy when she left him, but he must have woken up properly later on, and he went through the house looking for drink and money, because all the drawers were turned out and everything was in a terrible mess. She still hadn't finished clearing it up, she said.

"It wouldn't have been so bad if they'd got home when they expected to, at tea time, but she said they went to the houseboat and measured up the curtains, and then they went into Stanningford, and she had to go to five shops before she found anything suitable. After that they went back to the boat, and Hilda was feeling a bit hot and tired. So Teddy said why didn't she have a lie down while he was measuring up for the linoleum, so she did, on one of these bunks. She said she must have dozed off because when she came to it was half-past six. Teddy said he hadn't wanted to disturb her because she looked so peaceful. Then they started off back, it's about an hour's run normally, only all the cars were coming back from some rally, and they got in a dreadful jam. Then Teddy got a puncture of all things, and found he'd left his jack in the garage. Well, he had to walk nearly three miles to one of these A.A. boxes and phone for one of their patrolmen.

"It was another hour before the patrolman arrived, and Hilda said he was very casual about it even then. She said he was very tall and thin, he was just about the tallest A.A. man she'd ever seen. Teddy was furious about it, and when the A.A. man put the spare wheel on, he didn't even tip him anything. Hilda said the A.A. man gave Teddy such a look.

"So it was nearly eleven when they got back and Joe was already in hospital. She rang up at once and they said it was heart strain and he was in a coma and there was nothing she could do but they'd let her know how he was in the morning. She said that what really shocked her was the fact she religiously hadn't left any money in the house except for the pound for the talent scheme which she'd put in a little box and forgotten all about. But old Joe found it all right. He went down the pub with it and spent it on drink, and Hilda said it was the drink which must have turned him evil."

"Yeh," I said, "that's a likely bloody tale, an' all." I looked up from dunking a couple of Fletton half-bats and there was dear old Mavis with her mouth open and her ears flapping.

"What on earth d'you mean?"

I was away, I just couldn't help it. Old Mavis had kind of sparked off what you might call my creative instincts.

"I'll tell you what on earth I mean. For a start, Teddy Paulson didn't leave no jack back in the garage. Teddy bloody Paulson's got one of those big new Vauxhalls with the jack built in. I noticed it a couple of weeks ago when 'e shoved it in for servicing up the Seagrave Garage."

"Ooooh, are you sure about that, Davey?"

"Positive. And I haven't got eyes in my bonce for sweet fanny adams." Mavis Tidy was licking her old chops with anticipation. She was so excited she nearly leaned on the bit of wall I'd just finished. "Hey, steady there," I yelled.

"Have you seen anything then?"

"Yeh," I said. "It would be about a week ago. Tuesday I think it was. Yeh, Tuesday, I remember now because that's when *Woman's Wealth* comes out."

"What happened?"

"I was delivering, see. I was a bit late that morning, and it was rainin'. Well, I usually shove the papers under the door knocker except when it's wet, then I shove 'em through the lavatory window. But it was shut last Tuesday, so I went round the side to the sitting-room window, but that was shut an' all. I could see old Joe lying back in a big armchair in there, snorin' away. Anyway, I was just goin' to nip round and knock on the back door when I saw a bedroom window open a bit farther along. So I nipped across and shoved the papers in there. Teddy Paulson and Hilda Purkiss were sittin' on the edge of the bed. They weren't just having a polite conversation, either. When they heard the paper drop in they both jumped apart like a couple of grass-hoppers."

"You mean they were . . ."

"Look, I never said what they were up to, did I? So don't go jumping to conclusions."

She said, "Well, I never did." She was always never doing, don't ask me why. "Good lord, I'll have to be getting back to my wash."

She couldn't scuttle back to the house and get on the blower to Ma Whichelow fast enough. Or maybe she'd just bought some new kind of soap powder like this old bitch on the television, the one that buys a packet in the High Street, rushes out the shop, jumps in a taxi, belts home, tears through the garden gate (without paying the taxi, hi-yi!), and starts frantically sticking all the family's scruffy old togs in the washing machine. Then they switch to this very smooth announcer: "I say Mrs Smedley, what's the hurry?" And old Mrs Smedley turns round, and a right old harridan she is too, and leers all over the place. Probably one of the technicians is holding up a five-bar note in the background. "All my neighbours say that Poxo washes whiter than anything else, and I just wanted to find out if it's true," she says. I'll leave you to guess what the answer turns out to be. Anyway, you've probably seen the advert. Lucky you!

Joe Purkiss snuffed it about five days later. There was a big funeral. Old Hilda didn't just get old Keith Lockhart round to fix it up, she had some very big firm from London on the job. The four blokes they had to carry the coffin all looked like toffs themselves, and their gaffer—the one that walked in front of the hearse—might have been Old King Cole in person.

Quite a few of Joe's relations from up north turned up. Johnny Salt did his stuff, and Joe was shoved under the proverbial sod with the appropriate pomp and circumstances, as they say.

Mavis Tidy was invited round there afterwards, and the next day she gave me all the griff, about how Hilda Purkiss looked very sad and dignified and didn't shed a tear and about how everybody said how brave she was. Apparently she'd done the thing properly and laid on quite a spread; there were some very nice ham and tongue sandwiches which went in no time at all, and sardines on bits of toast, and some bought chocolate cake which Mavis Tidy reckoned was a bit sickly. Before this lot was brought on they all had a glass of sherry, and one of Joe's relatives said something about what a pity it was old Joe couldn't be there sitting among them knocking off the sherry and enjoying the joke, it would be right up his street, etc., which Ma Tidy thought was a bit tactless under the circumstances.

After they finished off the scoff Teddy Paulson got up and made a bit of a speech about Joe. He reckoned that although their acquaintance had been regrettably short, he would like to say what a fine old chap Joe had been, and what a lovely character he was at heart, and what a great gap it would leave in the lives of everybody that had been lucky enough to know him.

Everybody clapped when Teddy said this, and then some brother-in-law of Joe's jumped up and said what a sad loss it was to all of them up north, and how happy he was to know that Joe's last few years, when his health hadn't been so hot, had been spent in the care of such a grand little woman as Hilda, and last of all he wanted to mention what a lovely spread she'd put on for them. She really must have put her hand in her pocket, he reckoned, that is if ladies had pockets, which he understood they didn't.

They all laughed a bit over that and then Hilda Purkiss got up and thanked them all, particularly Teddy Paulson who she said had been such a great comfort to Joe during his last illness. She said it was very unfortunate Joe having to suffer at the end of his life, but in the end it was a merciful release, and she could only say what a great privilege it was to have shared twenty years of her life with such a fine and upright man as Joe had been when he was in possession of all his faculties. After all, she reckoned, you married someone for worse as well as for better, and her only regret was that she hadn't been able to comfort him in his last few days before he went to his eternal rest.

There was just one more thing she'd like to do for him, she said. As he'd always been a man of religious principles, she wanted to make a contribution of £50 in his name to the church restoration fund. Although she wouldn't be left very comfortably off, she thought this was the least she could do, and she knew that Joe would have approved.

Just as she finished saying this, and everybody was nodding and yessing and saying what a wonderful gesture it was, there came a knock at the door, and Hilda went to see who it was. Ned Hoskin was standing there.

"Yes?" she said. "What do you want?"

"Sorry, missis," he said, "but I 'eard as 'ow your maister 'ad 'is accident, an' I thought as 'ow 'e might not be needin' some of 'is old clothes, so anythin' you could let me 'ave I'd be very much obliged."

All this time, old Ned and his family were still living on the council estate, and all the neighbours up there were still thinking up ways and means of getting them out from under. Old Ned didn't know much about it because he wasn't on the grapevine, and any letters he got used to be opened and read by Alf Sparks, who'd cut out all the nasty bits.

Nobody actually interfered with Ned, but they didn't actually take him to their bosoms, either. He used to come and go exactly as if he was living in an igloo in the frozen North. But as he'd always been used to living on his tod—apart from his missis and Bloody Mary—he hardly noticed it.

About a fortnight after I'd dished out the talent money, I happened to be talking to Alf Sparks. We often used to cross paths by the Hare and Hounds—he'd be just finishing his round and I'd be starting mine—and if we'd got a bit of time to spare we'd sometimes have a natter.

"Was that you give ol' Neddy that 'yer pun' note, Davey?" he asked.

Alf is one of the few characters in the village who still talk in the old Garside lingo. There aren't many left. What with the Canadians being stationed in the place during the war, and all the townies who've poured in since, and all the Yank stuff you get from the pictures and the telly and the comics, it's hardly surprising that most of the young folk around talk as if they were born on some island in the middle of the Atlantic.

"Yeh," I said. "That's right, Alf."

"Oi wish Oid been there at the toime, 'at Oi do." He'd just got back from his holidays.

"What's the trouble, then?"

"'E didn't know what 't'was for, see, 'cos 'e couldn't read the writin', an' 'e couldn't ask me to read it for 'un, 'cos I warn't thar. So 'e opens the envelope, sees the pun' note inside, an' thinks somebody sent it to 'un out o' kindness o' 'eart, y'see."

"So what did 'e do with it?"

"Do wi' it? 'E took it straight down to the shop an' spent 'un."

"Well, it don't matter," I said. "What's a quid note between friends?"

Alf shook his white old bonce. "Ah, 'at's the trouble, ol' Ned's worrit, see, 'cos 'e told 'em up the shop 'an they told iviry bugger else, an' now they're all be laffin' at 'im everywhere 'e goo."

I soon found out old Alf was right. Everybody in the village was talking about Ned spending his nicker up the shop, and one moment they'd be laughing conkers, and the next they'd be tut-tutting and saying how disgraceful it was.

It must have somehow got round to Bloody Mary in the finish, because one morning she got her shopping bag, took the bus to Forbury, walked into Marks and Sparks, and started filling up

her bag from the counters. Of course, they nabbed her and sent
for the coppers. Not long after she was up in front of the beak,
who remanded her for a medical report. She didn't say anything
in court apparently—they reckon she was singing and trumping
all the time—but some policewoman who'd questioned her said
that Bloody Mary had told her she was going to take the stuff
home and flog it, so that she could give old Ned the quid back
and stop him from worrying.

CHAPTER NINETEEN

Up to now I still hadn't made up my mind what to do with my
own nicker. Not that I hadn't got any ideas. I had plenty. But
none of them came to anything. Either they involved too much
hard graft, or they were too dodgey on the legal side. Then one
Thursday morning I happened to be having a shufti at the racing
page in one of the papers, and I noticed this horse called *Talent
Money* which was running in the 2.45. The race was being tele-
vised, and all.

This horse was a two-year-old, and it'd won five times out of
six starts. None of the other nags in the race had won more than
twice. I went straight out to the phone box and stuck the nicker
on it with Ricky Richards, the bookie over at Forbury.

When it was time to go over to the races I was parked right in
front of the set. There were all sorts of preliminaries first, which
got me all nervy, especially as Doris had decided to start hoover-
ing the carpet and I just about had to press my ear to the bloody
gogglebox to understand what the commentator was on about.
First of all he read out the list of runners. *Talent Money* was
running, all right. Then the commentator said, "Now we'll take
you over to the enclosure where Gerry Enwright has found someone interesting to talk to."

This Enwright was a big comedian with a curly tash and one
of those big cloth caps which clip down over the peak. All
muffled up in a scarf and everything. "I want you to meet Mrs
De Mesta," he said, then he turned round and said, "Mrs De
Mesta, I believe you have a runner in the next race?"

"Yes, that's absolutely c'rrect," she said. This Mrs De Mesta,
can you imagine a human-sized louse with four chins in a fur
coat? This Enwright said, "And what would the name of it be?"
and she said, *"Riley's Portion"* in this very deep throbby voice.
"Picked him up myself at the Newmarket sales," she said. "Got

him jolly cheap as a matter of fact. Only eight hundred guineas as a yearling."

"D'you think he'll build up into a useful sort?" said this Enwright.

"Oh, I do indeed, when he's settled down y'know. Jolly good bone structure. I've always liked the stock."

They nattered on for a bit about this horse's sire and what it came out of, and some other cowing horse she half owned with somebody else that had been second at Catterick or somewhere. Dead interesting. There was a scruffy nipper of about ten standing just behind them and listening to the yap. He turned round and gave a terrific yawn at one point. In the finish Enwright said, "And what sort of a chance would you give *Riley's Portion* in the next race, Mrs De Mesta?" "Oh, we're not expecting too much," she said, "but he's been going well in training, and he should enjoy the gallop, although it's probably a bit short of his best distance, and the going's a bit hard. We'll just have to hope for the best." She tried to cross her fingers, but a whole lot of dirty great rocks got in the way. Frightfully jolly, what?

Then the first commentator—the bloke in charge—came on again. "And now over to Claude Ridgewell in the parade ring." They switched on to the nags going round in a big circle. About ten all told. They all looked the same to me. But this Claude character reckoned to be a real expert. "Number six," he'd say, "that's *Midnight Music*. Not a bad type of filly, a bit short in the wind, and probably needs this race. That's number eight, *Aquamarine Dandy*, a bay colt by *The Red Bandit*, last time out beaten only a short head at Thirsk by blah blah blah. Very fresh-looking, beautiful runner this one, but maybe a little out of its class in this company, blah blah." Then he came to *Talent Money*. "A good sort of colt, won five times this season out of six starts, should do well later on." Then he switched right over to the next nag.

After matey had finished in the parade ring, they went over to somebody else for the latest odds. "Well, we've got a clear favourite in *Riley's Portion* at seven to four, then they go threes *Pride of Gilburny*, four to one blah blah, sixes *Midnight Music*, tens blah blah, a hundred to eight blah blah and *Talent Money*."

I sat up a bit straight when he said that. I reckoned he must have made a bloomer. He hadn't though. When the race started *Talent Money* was still well out in the betting and *Riley's Portion* was even money.

The race was over five furlongs. They frigged about getting into position. When the tapes went up the commentator—the chief one—hollered, "They're off!" as if everybody didn't know. Then he said, "*Talent Money* was almost left, but *Riley's Portion* got a flyer, and is a length ahead as they come to the four furlongs from home marker."

About halfway down the course some other nag, the *Aquamarine Dandy* one, was in front by about two lengths. When they had about a furlong to go, I could see the jockey on *Aquamarine Dandy* looking round as much as to say to the jockey on *Riley's Portion*, "Come on, you slow bastard, I can't hold him in much longer, I'm pulling his head off as it is." The commentator was getting really worked up. "It looks as if young Duckling may have left it too late with *Riley's Portion*."

Young Duckling must have heard him. He lifted his stick and started flogging the arse off *Riley's Portion*. It didn't make much difference, but the one in front, *Aquamarine Dandy*, started dropping back a bit, and just on the post *Riley's Portion* got its muzzle in front.

The commentator sounded very chuffed and relieved. His voice was full of five pound notes. "A brilliant piece of riding by young Duckling, who's having a wonderful season." He didn't mention anything about the brilliant piece of riding by the bastard on *Talent Money*.

After the race, I saw some of the jockeys riding in. The swivel-eyed get on *Talent Money* was jogging along next to another jockey, both of them smirking and laughing all over their pans. *Riley's Portion* was walking along very droopy, covered in sweat and lather, and completely clapped out. All the other nags were trotting along tossing their old nappers and pawing the deck as much as to say, "Okay, we had a bit of exercise. When does the race start?" Then the commentator said, "Before we get the starting prices, we've just got time for another word with the lucky owner, Mrs De Mesta."

I jumped across to the set and kicked the screen in, right in the middle of Mrs De Mesta's juicy face. Dead centre. Then I yanked all the valves out, ran upstairs, and dropped them out of a window, laughing like a bastard to hear them explode. That's what I'd have *liked* to do, anyway. The only snag was, the insurance people might come round with a few dicey questions.

I was dead peeved with the whole business. Particularly when I imagined Ricky Richards using the nicker as a tip the next time he dined out in some swank restaurant up town. I was still stewing over it later on in the afternoon when I went up to the

Seagrave Garage to put in a couple of hours on the petrol pumps. But by the time I'd finished, I'd made up twenty-five bob of the nicker on the side, and I was feeling a bit more cheerful.

There are three types of motorists. Those who watch the clock every time they fill up, those that watch it some of the time, and those who never watch it at all. Anybody can pick out the first type. It's not so easy to pick out the other two, but it comes with experience. And once you can do that, you're quids in. The biggest laugh is when somebody you've just twisted out of a gallon offers you a couple of bob on the side for your trouble. And it's queer, but the blokes who are easiest to twist are always the ones who are generous with the gilt, and vicky verky.

I was just about to knock off when Teddy Paulson pulled in with his new Vauxhall. "Couple of gallons of best, Davey," he said, "and a bit of air in the tubes if it's no trouble."

I didn't try to fiddle him on the juice—you got nothing to play with on a couple of gallons, and anyway old Teddy watches the clock like a hawk. But when I was checking the tyres I couldn't help thinking about him and his puncture. Of course, I knew he hadn't got a built-in jack. But I did have a good shufti at the spare wheel in the boot. The tyre was as new as the day it came out of the factory.

On the way home I bumped into Squidge by the war memorial. He was bending down and doing something to the works of this ancient old Tigress of his. So I stamped on the Quickly's anchors and pulled up within a couple of inches of his front wheel.

"Hallo, Snodgrass. How's it goin', mate?"

He looked up and said, "Well, if it ain't the reverent Davey. Said your prayers lately?"

"Stuff it, shortarse!"

"Was that you sittin' over the marsh the other night, readin' the Bible?"

"Look, if you don't stuff it I'm going to kick your teeth down your little ol' froat. Are you receiving me?"

"I am receiving you loud and clear, lootenant."

This was more like old Squidge.

"Then hear this, you son of a bitch. We are now approaching Saturn at ninety degrees centigrade. Over."

"Check. Hey, lootenant, there's summink wrong with the landin' gear. It won't operate. Over!"

"The trouble with you," I said, "is you been readin' too many packets of cornflakes."

"You're only jealous," he said.

"Where's Darkie?" I said. "Where's Beetle Raynor and Piwi and the others?"

He looked disgusted. "They don' come down any more since you packed up comin'. Beetle's s'posed to be after some bint, lives over at Sidwell, 'e goes there reg'lar to see 'er. I reckon she's got 'im by the short and curlies. The others just sit round the telly all night. Except on Thursdays me and Piwi goes over to the Y.M.C.A. hall at Whitmarsh for the badminton.

"Seen anythin' of the Sprat lately?"

"Nah—'er? Wouldn't touch it wi' yours, let alone mine." Which meant he hadn't had the chance.

"What's the matter with your old scooter?" I said. "Won' it go?"

"'Ad a lot o' trouble with it lately," he said.

"Want to let an expert take a shufti?"

"Gerraway," he said. "I wouldn't trust you with a bicycle pump."

"You know what's wrong with that," I told him. "It's clapped out. You want a new engine."

He was getting a bit narked. "You think you're funny, don't yer?"

"Yeh—I can't 'elp it if I was born with a sense of humour, now can I? I tell you what." I'd suddenly had this wonderful idea. "Why don't you turn that thing in and get a new one? Only cost you another fifty nicker on top o' what you'd get for it second 'and."

"Where'm I goin' to get fifty nicker? Maybe you can show me the tree where it grow?"

"I could tell you how to pick up fifty nicker with no trouble at all," I said.

"Aaah, why don't you take a runnin' jump?"

"No, I mean it," I said. "Listen. You know that nurse down the Bottom, Mabel Merryweather? She wants a little job doin' for 'er, see? Only she can't get anyone to do it. She'd fork over fifty nicker like a shot. She's got stacks of gilt, old Chadwick left 'er a couple of thousand when 'e died."

Squidge was starting to get interested. "What she want doin', then?" he said.

When I told him he went a bit pale. "Hey, what you take me for? Old Mabel? Give over, for Christ's sake."

"What you cribbin' about?" I said. "I give you the chance of pickin' up fifty quid just like snappin' your fingers, and all you do is moan."

"Yeh, why don't you do it then?"

"Me? I don't need the money, see? Anyway, I thought I'd pass it on to you as a favour."

"Some favour," he said. "Anyway, 'ow d'you know she'd cough up, even if I did take 'er on?"

"She'd cough up all right. I know old Mabel. She don't go back on 'er word. I tell you what I'll do, I'll write you out a bit of a note, see? Then you can nip up there tonight after it gets dark. There won't be anybody else there."

I always carry a pencil and a notebook, on account of people stopping me any old time of the day and wanting some new magazine or other that's just come out. I sat down on the war memorial and wrote the note straight away:

Dear Miss Merryweather, (*Confidential*)
The bearer of this note would be quite willing to undertake that little job you mentioned to me a few weeks ago. He is a personal friend of mine and I can guarantee his services because there was a little matter of a young girl of seventeen in Whitmarsh last Christmas, but she got married to somebody else. The fees for my friend's services will be £50 payable to the bearer, plus a further £50 payable to the church restoration fund, if and when the result is to your satisfaction.
Yours Faithfully,
David Y. Peach.

I handed the note over to Squidge and he read it through. "Hey," he said, "what's this about some young bint of seventeen in Whitmarsh? I never . . ."

"I know. Keep your face on. Only you got to have some kind of what they call a reference for a job like this."

Then he got to the part about the other fifty nicker going to the church, and he didn't like it a bit.

"All right, listen," I said. "Old Mabel's a bit on the religious side, see? If she thinks that the church is going to get something out of it, that'll make it all right with her, see? Otherwise she might have second thoughts or something. You know what women are."

He still wasn't satisfied. "I don't know, though. Imagine having to climb in with that old boot."

"They're all made the same way," I said. "Anyway, you don't 'ave to look at 'er. You can do it blindfold, she won't mind."

"I still don't reckon . . . I mean, it's not right," he said.

"Yeh—it'd be all right if it was Miss Great Britain or somebody, wouldn't it?" I said. "Look, Squidge. The old girl wants a chicko, see? She don't want to get married, and in any case she's not everybody's cup of chocolate. All right, that's not her fault, is it? But she still wants a nipper. Is that a crime? So what's wrong with somebody fixin' 'er up? I mean, it's not as if she's expectin' anyone to do it for nothin'. All right, so you get your whack out of it, and the church gets a whack, and old Mabel gets what she's always wanted. So everybody's happy. I honestly can't see anything wrong with that."

CHAPTER TWENTY

By this time I'd already had a couple of sessions with Carol in the private bar up at the Falcon, and not made any progress to shout about.

It was quite a cosy little nook with frosted glass windows and a gas fire, two or three chairs, a table we used to sit round, and a nice big settee I'd had my eye on from the start. The rest was a bit dodgey, though. Most of the time I was in there with her I could hear her Ma creaking about in the upstairs room, and once or twice she'd open the door and ask how everything was going, and whether we'd like a cup of tea and so on. Not that she had much to worry about.

Carol had got this talent scheme on her mind all the time. She was getting all steamed up about the ackers not coming in. When we counted up after the first six weeks, there was only about ninety-six nicker in the kitty, including the fifty from Hilda Purkiss.

"At this rate, we're not even going to get the first thousand pounds, Davey," she said.

"We'll have to liven 'em up a bit," I said.

"Yes, but the question is, how?"

"Listen. I've got a suggestion to make."

"What's that?"

"We start keeping two separate lists. One for what we collect up the Village, the other for down the Bottom."

"What difference is that going to make?"

"Well, see, the people up the Village don't go much on the people down the Bottom, and the people down the Bottom aren't exactly in love with the people up the Village. So all we do is to turn it into a competition—see who raises the most."

She wouldn't see it for a long time. I had to use all the celebrated Peach powers of persuasion.

"But, Davey," she said, "even if it worked, we'd be encouraging the wrong kind of spirit."

"Not encouraging it. Just makin' use of it for a good cause."

"We'd just be cashing in on their petty jealousies."

"We've got to cash in on something," I told her, "otherwise we're going to be right up the Swanee."

"I can see your point, but I do wish we could think of some other way."

"Yeh, so do I," I said. "I'm like you, I wish everybody in the world was all nice and friendly and lovey-dovey. I wish it was just one big happy family arrangement. But you try doing somebody in this village a good turn and they'll turn round and call you an idiot—or else they'll wonder what you're making out of it on the side. When you've been in this place as long as me, you'll begin to think the same way. It's catching."

"What a depressing prospect. Surely there are some good people among them, Davey?"

"You get the odd one or two occasionally, but they don't stop long. It's too lonely for 'em."

She had to agree in the end. Just before we broke it up I said to her, very casual. "Oh, by the way, I was just wonderin' if you'd like a trip over to Thurrock Forest one day if you can spare the time. It's one o' those National Trust places, about twelve miles away. It's s'posed to be the best bit o' country around these parts, actually. They've even got deer roamin' around, very tame they are, nobody's allowed to shoot 'em bar the wardens. There's a bit of a lake, an' all. I could borrow a car, see. It wouldn't take us long to get over there."

"I'd love to come, Davey," she said.

"Okay then. When d'you think you could manage it?"

"Saturday's my best day," she said. "I could get away about eleven and we could have a picnic lunch, but I'd have to be back in the bar before six."

"All right, that's laid on. I'll pick you up as soon as I've finished the round."

Myself, I'm not all that fussy about this country business. Take nightjars. Nightjars give me the willies. Cuckoos the same, they bore me silly. Honeysuckle and all that caper, well, I mean I was all for it when I was a nipper. I was always scrattin' about in the woods. I used to come home in the summer with dirty great bunches of wild flowers, all different, and give them to Doris. All she'd say would be, "All right duck, just shove 'em in the sink." And the next day I'd probably find the stalks sticking out the dustbin. Of course, when I got older I had other fish to fry.

Beech trees and owls and jackdaws and kingfishers. All that junk. They're all right in small doses. But you get so you don't worry about it. Nowadays I don't even notice the scenery unless it's got stockings on. I could live on top of a gasworks if the money was there.

There's a bit of poetry I learnt at school. Something about, "the swallows twittering in the straw-built shed". Whoever wrote that, I bet he's never lived under thatch. If he had of done, he'd have kept a four-ten handy, and he'd have written his bits of poetry about something else.

I was dead keen on this Thurrock Forest though. There's something about trees, long sweet-smelling grass, and the blue sky above, which seems to take women by surprise. Give them a basinful, and they'll do anything for you in return. I'd already been over there with four really stubborn cases, and never had a failure. Well, actually, I'm a liar. One failure. But that was only because I happened to pick the wrong time of the month.

Not that I ever take anything for granted. I've had too much experience. For instance, the previous week I'd gone over with the cricket team to play at Little Borthwick, a village about five miles away. They play on the vicarage meadow there, and in the next field there's a big old bull which must weigh the best part of a ton. Paddy, they call it.

Well, they always reckoned old Paddy wouldn't hurt a fly. Even the little nippers in the place used to stroke him and pull his tail. He always looked half asleep. Whenever Little Borthwick had a game on he'd wander over to the fence, rest his head on the barbed wire, and watch.

Anyway, Little Borthwick went in to bat first, and they got about eighty-four. We went in after tea, and they had our first four out for sixteen. Then old Norman Makepeace went in.

He's a big built bloke is Norman, works on a farm, hasn't got a lot of science, but once he gets his head down he can really cane 'em. Well, their slow bloke was bowling his tweakers at the time. He was the one who was doing all the damage. But he pitched one a bit short, and Norman went about two yards up the wicket and caught it on the up. The ball went so high we nearly lost sight of it. When it came down, it caught old Paddy straight in the middle of his chops. Mind, it must have been going a fair tickle.

There wasn't any more cricket that evening, boy. Old Paddy came straight through the fence with his chain and anchor flying in the breeze. Talk about blood, sweat, fire and snot! We had to give 'em ten quid afterwards towards a new pavilion.

CHAPTER TWENTY-ONE

For the next week I went around in a bit of a daze, thinking about the trip to Thurrock Forest and trying not to think about it at the same time, so that the days would go quicker.

Eventually it came round Saturday again. I didn't stop for any gossip that morning. I was in such a hurry collecting the cash that I was fourteen and ninepence down when I checked the books.

As soon as I'd finished the round I whipped up to the Seagrave Garage. Keith Ranner was lending me his open tourer for the day. She's a big old pre-war job which he keeps there in case of emergencies—say the breakdown wagon happens to breakdown or something—and he lets me have the lend of her occasionally provided I pay for the juice. You can get eighty out of her at a pinch, but she burns a fair quantity of oil in the bottom gears, and there's a sort of high-pitched hum in the back axle when you're going a good lick which'll have to be inquired into one of these fine days.

In spite of getting up an hour early, and running around all morning like a blue-arsed fly, it was nigh on quarter to twelve before I pulled into the back yard of the Falcon. I gave it a couple of toots on the button, and after about five minutes she came flying out the back door.

She was looking a real treat in a pair of skin-tight green and white pants and a yellow sweater. She'd got a picnic basket under one arm, and in her other hand she was carrying a green parasol and a white handbag and a dog lead with a pooch on the end of it.

"Am I very late? It's been a bit of a rush."

"No, we got plenty of time," I said. I went over to take the basket off her and stick it in the boot. Directly this pooch clapped eyes on me it started barking its head off.

"I thought we could take Jixie along with us," she said, "if you wouldn't mind. She won't be any trouble, and she loves having a run in the country."

"Course not," I said. I did mind, though. I'd seen this Jixie before, and we weren't all that palsy-walsy. It was a fat black and white mongrelly-looking thing with a patch of brown over one eye, something like the one they use in this business about "His Master's Voice", only it was a bitch. Jixie, I mean.

I bent down to pat its head. All the time I was cursing the thought of having to take it with us, and thinking as how I'd like to make it a present of six laceholes. It must have known what was in my mind, because it twisted away out of reach and started yapping all the more.

"Now Jixie," she said, "stop being silly, it's only Davey." She looked up at me then and said, "It's only because she doesn't know you. She's always a bit suspicious of strangers. I'm afraid she does sometimes kick up a bit of a fuss."

"Ever thought about 'avin' 'er debarked?" I said.

"How d'you mean?"

"Well, they give 'em an operation. Just make a kind of tiny slit in their throats—they don't feel any pain—and whenever they try to bark after that it just comes out as a little whistling noise. It don't cost much, either. I know several people that 'ave 'ad it done."

"Oh Davey, that would be cruel. Poor Jixie!" She bent down to stroke it, and it started whining and carrying on. Then it looked across at me with daggers drawn and gave a sort of low growl.

"All right," she said. "We forgive him, don't we Jixie?"

We spent another quarter of an hour trying to get Jixie to sit quietly in the back seat, but she wouldn't wear it and kept jumping out. "I suppose it's because everything's so strange," Carol said. "She normally loves riding in cars."

I was beginning to think we weren't ever going to move away from the pub. In the end Carol said she'd take Jixie on her lap. "Just until she gets used to the motion."

We started off then. Just before we turned off on to the Whitmarsh road we passed Squidge, coming towards us on his brand new Tigress. He nearly went into the nearest ditch when he lamped who I was with.

I had to stop after a bit, because the poxy animal was wriggling about on Carol's lap and she couldn't hold it. "Jixie," she said, "if you don't behave yourself, Mr Peach is going to turn round and take you straight back home." I was all ready to take her up on that statement. She didn't mean it, though.

We stuck the dog in the back and tied the lead to the door

handle. Going through Whitmarsh it was jumping up from behind and scrambling all over my shoulders.

"Jixie, stop it! I don't know what's come over you."

She quietened down a bit after that. Then Carol happened to turn round and found her chewing a bloody great hole in the upholstery.

I was glad when I drove through the gate of this forest and forked over the entrance money. Up to that time the only conversation we'd had was Carol apologizing for Jixie, and me telling her not to worry, it didn't matter a bit.

As a matter of fact, Saturday isn't exactly the best day of the week for taking a piece of skirt over to Thurrock Forest.

It's been there all the time, but nobody knew about it until five years ago, when the National Trust had the bright idea of making people pay to go in. When that happened, everybody from as far away as the outskirts of London started charging up there, especially on Saturdays and Sundays. The trade got so heavy that they had to put up the price of admission and start laying on some facilities such as ice cream stalls and a putting green and a tea garden with those big striped umbrellas.

This particular Saturday was near the end of the season—it was about halfway through September—and the forest closes down for the winter. It was a pretty warm day though, and it definitely looked as if plenty of people had turned up to make the most of it. There must have been nigh on a thousand cars in the field just inside the gate, not to mention motor bikes and scooters. And even then you had to take into account the shysters who'd parked on the grass verge up the road and come in through the hedge; which would have included me if I hadn't been taking Carol.

I drove about half a mile up a bumpy old track through a big stretch of parkland where the cars had started thinning out and it didn't look quite so much like the outskirts of Clacton on August Bank Holiday. I stopped under a tree. Carol said, "We'd better have lunch straight away, Davey. Are you feeling peckish?"

I was feeling something else every time I looked at her, but I didn't bother to mention it. I laid out the groundsheet I'd bought to bring, and Carol brought the picnic basket over and started pouring coffee.

"Well," I said, "this is the life."

"Yes. Isn't it gorgeous?"

"You look pretty gorgeous yourself in that rigout. Suits you down to the ground."

"Oh, d'you honestly think so?" She flashed over this terrific smile. Dimples in every corner. "Actually they're just a few old things I dug out so that it wouldn't matter if I messed them up." She stretched herself, then laid back on the groundsheet. It was a double-sized, heavy duty one I'd picked up at this army surplus place in Whitmarsh.

"God's in his heaven, all's right with the world," she said. "At least, it feels like it, just at this moment."

I said, "Yeh, I see what you mean. What d'you want? Ham, chicken, marmite—or cold sausage?"

"I think I'll have one of those little fish fingers. My mother made them specially."

As soon as we started pushing back the scoff the bloody pooch came sniffing around. "Jixie," she said, "I know what you want." She started scratching it in the middle of the back. It was wiggling about and snarling with ecstasy. I knew what Jixie wanted, all right. As it happened all it got was half a chicken sandwich and a cold slinger. Then it sat there and started barking for more. "No, Jixie," she said. "You had a whole plate of Dogomeat before you came out. You've got to think of your figure." Then she gave it another chicken sandwich and the best part of a pork pie. Talk about the starving masses in Asia! No wonder they're getting stroppy out there.

"Have you been here very often before, Davey?" she said.

"Once or twice."

"What a lovely place. Isn't it wonderful that so many people can come here and enjoy themselves in the open air, instead of it just belonging to some duke."

"I'm not so sure," I said. "Most of 'em just don't know how to enjoy themselves. They haven't had the experience, see? They'd be just as happy pushin' a mower round their bit of lawn at 'ome, or takin' the kids for a game of rounders in the park. If I owned this forest," I said, "I wouldn't let anyone in. I'd just sit up in the biggest tree and take pot shots at the deer passing by. Or maybe I'd send up a couple of kites."

"I didn't know you liked flying kites, Davey."

"No, not that kind, I mean these 'awks, like falcons only a lot bigger. I'd ride around on a big black stallion that nobody else could touch without getting kicked to death. I'd gallop back to the old mansion at night, and some servant would bring me in a dirty great boar's head on a silver tray, with an apple in its mouth and one of those frilly things round its neck like Sir Walter Raleigh used to wear, we had a big picture of him in our geography classroom at school. Then after I'd scoffed it I'd sit up half the night knocking back Napoleon brandy."

She was quite amused when I said this.

"Davey, you are funny. I can't imagine you as a feudal baron. What would your wife be doing?"

"I shouldn't bother about gettin' married. I'd just keep six or seven concubines."

I was hoping she was going to ask if she could be one of them. Then I'd say, "Certainly," and she'd say, "Which one?" and I'd say, "Number two," and she'd say, "What would I have to do to become number one?" and I'd say, "Do you really want me to tell you?" Then the conversation would be getting on to the right tack.

Only she just laughed and said, "Well, I suppose we'd better be clearing away the débris."

We stuck the basket back in the boot and then she said, "Shall we go for a little stroll?"

"Good idea," I said. "D'you want to have a dekko at the lake?"

"I'd love to."

I started folding up the groundsheet. "I'd better take this along," I said, "just in case we get tired and feel like squatting down somewhere."

The lake was just behind a clump of trees across the way. Actually I wouldn't call it a lake; it's about the size of a skating rink. The putting green and the tea garden and the ice-cream kiosks are all situated around the lake, and it's very peculiar, but you'll find eighty per cent of the people that go to the forest concentrated around that little area. Maybe they're scared of getting lost.

They were as thick as woodlice round the banks of this lake. Wandering about, laying under the trees snoring, the kids running about playing tag and munching ice-cream at the same time, old girls with great fat white arms, Teds strumming guitars, thousands of 'em. Some of them had even managed to get their cars down there in between the trees, so they wouldn't have to walk anywhere.

A lot of the old dears had got their knitting with them. There were even three herberts slinging darts at a dartboard stuck to a tree. About sixty transistor radios were blaring like stink, all playing the same bit of music. Massed brass bands, it sounded like.

We stood on the bank for a bit watching a couple of swans and their young 'uns cruising around in the middle. You couldn't get too near because there were blokes fishing round the sides, and some of 'em weren't too fussy about where they were casting their hooks. They'd got all the gear—little stools, wading boots, landing nets, gaffs, the issue—but all I ever saw anybody catch were little roach about three inches long. I saw one bloke just below us pack up for the day. He pulled up his keep net, and all the little blighters were leaping about in the bottom. Then he weighed them on some scales, and counted them as he tipped them back into the water. About forty of them there must have been. He wrote it down in a notebook, then he packed everything up very carefully and went off as merry as a little pig.

We didn't stay there too long. To tell you the truth I was feeling a bit embarrassed standing there next to a really nifty piece of crackling like Carol, with this groundsheet over my arm. I kept noticing people pointing us out and having a bit of a laugh and a joke about it.

Anyway, we buzzed off after a bit, and then a rather dicey situation arose. Just as we were walking through this clump of trees, a couple of Teds came round some bushes towards us. One of 'em was a pretty tall bloke with a pasty complexion and red spots all over his puss. The other was a young kid of about fifteen. This Ted—the big one—stopped when he saw us go past and gave Carol the eye, just as if she was stuck in the middle of a shop window, no messing. Then he clapped eyes on the groundsheet, and as I passed him—we were walking in single file along this narrow track at the time—he dug me in the back with his boney elbow, and said, "Two's up, mate."

It wasn't as if he'd whispered it, either.

Naturally, I couldn't very well let that pass. So I grabbed hold of his jacket. "What was that you said, cocker?" I asked him.

"I was just asking arter you wiv a nibble," he said. "Surely you don't wanner keep it all to yerself, mate? Share an' share alike, tha's what it says in the Bible."

He was quite a bit taller than me, this Ted. Only he was very skinny with it. A real streak of piss and wind. I reckoned I'd pretend to go for his throat, and just as he put his hands up I'd bring my knee straight up in his goolies. Then I'd give him a real clobbering while he was on the deck, and after that I'd grab hold of his manky little friend and tie him up in knots—if I managed to catch him. While I was what you call summing up the pros and cons of the situation, Carol came pushing past me.

"Are you trying to be funny?" she said to this Ted.

He sort of leered at her. "Well, it depends what you . . ." He didn't get any further than that because she brought her arm over and caught him a smart wallop right across the gob. Actually she meant to smack his face, only he turned his head just at that split second. I've never seen anyone look so surprised before or since.

"Caugh, 'blige! Ey, I was on'y 'avin' a bit of a joke," he said.

"Well, you can keep your nasty, smutty little jokes to yourself. Come on, Davey." She turned round and trotted off up the track as calm as you please.

I said to matey, "You want to watch that tongue o' yours, china. It's goin' to get you inner trouble one of these days." Then I caught up with Carol. I said, "You shouldn't 'ave stopped me. I was goin' to do 'im a good turn." The track had got a bit broader by this time, and there was room for the two of us to walk side by side. She suddenly reached out and clutched hold of my hand, which shook me considerably. "I know, Davey," she said, "but it was just as well you didn't. I wouldn't want anything to spoil such a lovely day." Confidentially, I was inclined to agree, although I didn't tell Carol. What I mean is, some things are inclined to work out different from the way you expect. Before I'd got a knee in his knackers, matey might have got his nut under my chin. Of course, I'd have done him in the finish, but I might have had to spend the rest of the afternoon trying to stop my snitch from bleeding, which is apt to put anybody off their stroke. But as it was, with honour satisfied all the way round, and me walking along the side of her, holding her mitt and getting in the odd tickle at the middle of her palm, everything in the old duflick was splendiferous. Until we got to the putting green.

CHAPTER TWENTY-TWO

SHE got very excited when she saw the putting green. "Oh, Davey, let's have a round, shall we? I haven't played for ages."

I went and got the clubs and balls off an attendant in a little white hut. This attendant would be about seventy odd, and he looked as if he hadn't washed for a fortnight. Also he could have done with a clean shirt, with a collar to it. It's peculiar though—have you ever noticed that whenever you come across an attendant like that in a public bog, or at the swimming pools or the point-to-points or any of the places they usually do have attendants, all rough and scruffy I mean, that they'll treat *you* like dirt if you let 'em? The clean ones are normally all right.

"You played this game before?" he said.

"Yeh. I was runner-up in the Open Championship up at St Andrews last year. Didn't you know?"

"You can only go round the once. Don't try'n go round twice because I shall be watchin' yer."

While I was standing there waiting for him to fork over the gear, he took out a rusty old tin, took a few pinches of tobacco out of it, and dropped them into a bit of rice paper—it wasn't even proper fag paper. He licked it down the edge, then stuck it together and put a match to the result. But when he tried to smoke it there was a queer crackling noise and then half the baccy dropped out the end.

"You want a scorecard?" he said.

"Well, it's better than just tryin' to add it up in your bonce."

"Ain't no need to be cheeky, young 'un."

When we got out on to the first hole Carol said, "We'll have to take it in turns to hold Jixie. Would you like to go first?"

I hit the ball pretty wide first time. Then I held the lead while Carol had a bash. She took quite a time over it, and finished up about four inches from the hole.

"You didn't tell me you were an expert," I said.

"I used to get quite a lot of practice," she said. "There was a green right next door to where we used to live."

I took five strokes getting down that first poxy hole. Carol did it in two. When she polished off the next couple in three apiece, the situation was getting a bit dicey. What I'd intended to do was to play around a bit and get about the same score as Carol, and then arrange things so as we got to the last hole dead level. In the finish I was going to let her win by one stroke. She'd have known I let her, of course. But as it turned out I was getting all nervy and fidgety and taking fours and fives. Having to hang on to Jixie between shots didn't help matters exactly. After about six holes she turned round and said, "Davey, I hope you're trying. You don't have to let me win, you know." I just grinned across, dead what's known as enigmatic, as much as to say, "Just wait and see what's coming up any minute now."

What did come up was my old friend, the attendant. He came walking across the green with his head sort of cocked to one side and this very important look on his face as if I was the Prime Minister and he'd come over with a message from the Cabinet to say somebody had declared war on the Chinks, and what were they to do about it. When he got up to us he started shaking his bonce. He said, "No dogs allowed on the green. Can't you read the notice?"

"All right," I said. "Keep your 'air on." I turned round to have a butcher's at Jixie. She was just doing a lovely big crap on the little arrow which said, "Hole No. 7". Carol came over. She said, "I suppose we'd better tie her up." Then she bent down and spoke to the pooch in question. "It won't be for long, Jixie darling. Only while Mummy and Uncle Davey finish their game."

I took Jixie over to the side of the green and tied the lead to one of these young trees which had been planted all round the edges. Flowering currant or something, they were supposed to be. This one had got little pink flowers all over it.

After that we got on with the round. Not for long, though, because after we'd played another couple of holes we got jammed up behind a foursome in front. Two townies and their horrible wives.

I reckon it must have been the first time any of 'em had been near a putting green. They were all taking double figures for every hole, and every now and again they'd have a terrific giggle about it. Especially the one they called Fairy. She wasn't anything like a fairy actually. Anything but.

"How many's that, Fairy?" they'd say.

"You're supposed to be counting."

Then they'd piss themselves laughing, and not only that; they'd look round at me and Carol at the same time to see if we were sharing the joke.

Old Fairy was really lapping it up. One of these nylon blouses she'd got on. You could see about ten straps crossing each other underneath.

"I'm sure the holes ought to be bigger, Frank. Wherps! Oh dear, is that fourteen already? I should 'ave brought my glasses. Oh Madge, I think I've hit your ball, does it matter? Frank, don't just get out of the way, why didn't you stop it? You are awful. Anyway, I'm going to get it in if it takes me all night."

Then they'd go off into hysterics again.

While we were all hanging around and listening to this because we didn't have any other option, I happened to notice Jixie tearing towards us with the tree in tow. Highly chuffed, she was. When she got to Carol she started prancing about, wagging her whole body. Fairy and Co stopped playing—if you could call it that—and started cackling like hyenas. There were about six or seven other couples on the green, and they all joined in.

"Jixie, that's very naughty! Davey, quick, what are we going to do?"

I had a quick shufti over at the hut. The attendant was just inside the door with his back turned. Making another fag, maybe. I unhitched the lead from the tree, took it back, and planted it back in the place where it came from. I had to do a quick job on it, and most of the roots were sticking out of the ground.

After that we decided not to play any more, which was just as well. I was about eight strokes down at the time. I took the clubs and balls and handed them back in at the hut. The attendant went over them with a fine-tooth comb in case we'd done any damage. While he was inspecting the balls the tree fell over. Which only goes to prove that you should never look for the obvious in this life.

I didn't tell him, though. You've got to let people find out these things from their own experience.

After we packed in the putting lark she suggested us having a bit of a stroll through the forest. This was right up my alley. We started off on a long track through the woods with her hanging on to my mitt, and Jixie treading on our heels.

"What's that?" she kept saying. "Is that a blackbird?"

"Looks more like a starling to me."

"Oh, do look, there's a squirrel. D'you think it's got a nest?"

"S'pose so."

"I wonder if we're going to be lucky enough to see a deer. D'you think we shall?"

"You can never tell."

"I'd love to go camping in a place like this. Can you imagine lying awake in your tent at night and listening to the badgers?"

"Yeh." I was imagining something quite different.

"I've always wanted to be a naturalist."

"A what? You mean like those people who walk around starko?" I was beginning to get interested.

"No, you mean naturists. Naturalists are people who go around studying the habits of wild animals. But I'm afraid I wouldn't be clever enough for that."

"You don't need to be clever with looks like yours."

"Well—thanks for the compliment. But I think brains are much more important than looks, don't you? Listen! D'you hear that funny grating noise? What sort of bird d'you think that is? There it goes again."

It went on like that for a couple of miles or more. All the

while I was trying to think of something to say which would sort
of bring the conversation round to the subject of what we were
there for. Only I couldn't.

With skirt, you've always got to find something in common,
apart from the obvious business. You've got to find something to
lead up to it. That's what takes all the finding. Everything else
is cushy in comparison.

Say her brother's motor-bike's got teledraulic forks, like one
bint's brother I knew. I mean I knew the bint, not her brother.
Well, that's what we started nattering about, believe it or not. Of
course, women are usually interested in different things, which
is half the trouble.

I knew Carol was interested in religion. But it's not a thing
you can actually *talk* about. Everything which there is to say
on that subject's been said already. After all, it's been sacking
along with the same set of rules for a couple of thousand years.
Even longer if you count the Old Testament.

Since I'd got involved with Carol and Johnnie Salt I'd been
having the odd shufti at the Old Testament now and again when
nobody was looking, just to keep up the form. There's some
characters in there that couldn't have been all that religious.
Kipping around the place with all and sundry, and what-all. And
you take this character, I read a bit about him not long ago,
Elisha. About how he was passing by some town or other, and a
gang of little kids came out and started yelling at him and calling
him "Baldy". Any ordinary bloke would have taken it in his stride,
dished out a few thick ears, and gone his way. But Elisha got dead
narked. He started cursing these nippers left, right and centre.
While he was calling them everything he could lay his tongue
to, a couple of she-bears came out of a neighbouring wood and
proceeded to tear these kids apart. Old Elisha just stood there
looking on, without lifting a finger. He reckoned it served them
right for their brass neck. A nice old party he must have been.
These bears knocked off forty-two nippers all told.

I don't say they're all like this Elisha character in the Old
Testament, but wherever you like to open the page, you'll nearly
always find someone mixing it for somebody else, and very often
there's a woman at the bottom of it.

Still, I should think things have changed considerably since
then. You wouldn't expect people nowadays to go by what the
old Jewboys did all that time ago. I mean, they had a different
kind of approach. You take this bit of poetry I came across the

other day, I wrote it down as a matter of fact. It goes something like this: *The lips of a strange woman drop honey, and her mouth is smoother than oil. But her latter end is bitter as wormwood, sharp as a two-edged sword.*

Well, that's all arse about face to my way of thinking. It should be her mouth is as sharp as a two-edged sword. And the other job which is smoother than oil. But maybe I'm prejudiced, or maybe women have changed a lot recently. I wouldn't know.

To tell you the honest truth, I wouldn't be surprised if a lot of this religious stuff was invented by the priests in the old days. I mean, you've only got to look at it logically. Just suppose I go out one night, get tanked up, pick up a married bit and finish up carving it off a slice. Well, that's supposed to be against the book of rules. Okay? Right, well the next morning, being a Sunday, I go to church. I go along to the church and the old padre gives me a drop of wine and a bit of biscuit which I'm supposed to believe is old J.C.s body and blood. So, I scoff this, get back to my pew, and say a couple of prayers. Okay, finish. Then I go back home, I don't have to worry any more because I've washed away all my sins. It's just like you're supposed to say, "Okay God, I'm sorry," and God turns round and says, "All right, we'll forget about it this time, but don't let it happen again."

Well, you can stick that for a game of soldiers straight away, because I just know it wouldn't make an atom of difference. Not to me, anyway. The only people it affects are the Bible punchers who queue up there regular every Sunday—and they're just the kind of characters who are scared to do anything to forgive. And if you try to argue with them about it, they'll just give you a pitying look as if you must be puggled for not believing it the same as they do.

What I reckon is, old J.C. just came along to kind of set an example, and tell everybody how they *ought* to carry on. I don't reckon he was all that fussy about what they did afterwards. I mean, he'd given them the old chapter and verse, it wasn't any fault of his if they didn't take a lot of notice.

Eventually we came out of the wood into a big stretch of parkland.

"Shall we find somewhere, and take the weight off our feet," I suggested. I meant it. I really needed the rest.

"All right."

I nipped off in the direction of a whole lot of clumps of bramble and stuff, and did a bit of a recce. What I was actually looking for was a little bit of nice soft grass with bushes nearly all the way round to give us a bit of privacy. But there was always a snag. Either the brambles met in the middle, or there'd be a gorse bush in the wrong place, or somebody had been successful there in the recent past and forgot to conceal the evidence. The only places that hadn't got anything wrong with them were already full. There was one couple in particular that were making good use of the conditions.

When I got back to Carol I said, "There's nowhere round here. P'raps we'd better move on a bit."

We were standing in this big open chunk of field. She said, "Why not let's sit down here, Davey. It seems a very pleasant spot."

"Not exactly sheltered, though, is it?"

"Well, the sun's out, and there's hardly any wind."

"All right, I'm cushy," I said. I started spreading out the groundsheet.

"Do you know what happened just now while you were gone?" she said.

"No."

"I saw a woodpecker. At least, I'm almost certain it *was* a woodpecker."

She sat down and hugged her knees for a bit. Then she laid back. I was lying right there beside her.

"When you look up at the sky, doesn't it make you feel insignificant?" she said.

I said, "Yeh, I suppose it does. Did I tell you they've got this big picture about Jesus Christ coming to the Forbury Rialto at the end of this month?"

"Have they? I don't suppose it'll be very true to life, will it? They just alter things to suit themselves. I could almost go to sleep, lying here."

"Yeh, so could I."

I was thinking I'd let her go to sleep and I'd sort of drop off too and we'd kind of accidentally roll up together, and by the time she'd woken up again . . . But she suddenly turned over to face me, and grabbed hold of my hands.

"Davey, it's very sweet of you to bring me here. I have enjoyed it."

"It's a pleasure. Honest."

"I only hope I haven't disappointed you too much."

"What d'you mean? You haven't disappointed me at . . ."

"Oh yes I have. I'm sure I must have. You know what I mean."

"No, I don't know what you mean."

She was only about six inches away, and looking straight into my eyes. Boy, it was bloody torture, never mind frustration.

"Well, when a man asks a girl to come to a place like this, and she says she'll come . . . well, they usually . . . you know what I mean. Only, well . . ."

"Only what?"

"Well, I wanted to come with you, because I'm so fond of the country and everything and I do like you very much, you're always saying such funny things only, well . . . you see I could only do anything like that with anyone if I really . . . well, you see the two things would have to go together, I mean I'd hate you to think I was prudish or anything . . ."

"Oh no, I don't think that," I said.

"Well I mean it'd be only natural if you did expect . . . I mean after I said I'd come . . . oh dear, I'm not putting it very well, am I? What I mean is, I'd hate you to think I was just a . . . a . . ."

"Yeh. I know what you mean."

"You don't really think I'm one of those, do you? I mean we haven't really known each other all that long, have we?"

"Yep. I mean no."

"Oh dear. You don't look very happy about it. Have I said the wrong thing?"

"I'm just g'n'ave a weed if you don't mind."

We didn't discuss the subject any more, because Jixie decided to sit down. There were at least fifty acres lying around where she could have planted herself, but she had to pick the six inches between me and Carol.

We both tried to shove her over a bit, but dogs when they don't want to move can weigh half a ton. After a bit Carol jumped up and said, "I know what's wrong with you, my girl. You need a bit of exercise. You're getting fat and lazy." Then they both went leaping off into the trees, and Carol came back with a hunk of wood which she started to sling around for Jixie's benefit. This went on for a quarter of an hour, then Carol came back all out of breath.

"Davey. Could you take over for a bit? My arm's aching."

So I took the hunk of wood off her and started tossing it around. There was one thing I noticed. When Carol was pitching it, Jixie would run off and fetch it back and lay it at her feet so she could pick it up and throw it again. But when I was lobbing it, the poxy animal would run and get it, then bring it back to about five yards away, and lie there growling over it. I'd have to walk up very slow and make a quick grab before Jixie could pick it up again and run off another few yards with it.

Every time I did manage to grab it first, she'd hang on to it with her feet, growling and grunting for bloody dear life.

I'll tell you something else I noticed after a while. There wasn't just one dog chasing this hunk of wood, there were three. Well, actually Jixie was after the wood, and the other two were after Jixie. They weren't getting much joy out of it though, because every few yards they kept stopping to bite chunks out of each other. I chased them off a couple of times, but they just hung around and kept coming back for more, until I accidentally on purpose caught one of them across the backside with the hunk of wood. They both scarpered after that, but as soon as they disappeared three more took over.

Carol came running across then.

"Jixie! Come here! Let's have a look at you. Oh dear, I thought as much. I suppose it must have been all the excitement. I think we'd better be taking her home, Davey." She had a shufti at her tiny little gold watch.

"Good heavens! I'm going to be late as it is."

She put Jixie on the lead and we started walking back to where the car was parked. On the way we were picking up dogs of all shapes and sizes, and I was walking along in the rear trying to keep 'em at a distance. Jixie knew what was in the wind, all right. She was kind of scuttling along in a sitting position.

I still kept the hunk of wood in my fist and waved it every time a pooch got a bit too close. They were running along each side of us, circling round, and having little two- and three-handed scraps now and again. There was one big lop-eared alsatian that looked as if it didn't intend to take no for an answer. I wasn't too keen on forcing the issue, either. It was just padding along about two or three yards to the rear, and a bit to one side. Now and then it'd stop and scrape each paw in turn on the ground, just like somebody flexing his muscles when there's a punch-up just around the corner.

I wasn't too sorry when we got to the car. Carol picked Jixie up. The alsatian got a bit excited when she did that. "Quick Davey, open the back door. I'd better get in and hold her."

This alsatian nearly got his nose trapped in the door as I whammed it shut. Then, as I jumped in the front and started her up, it was leaping up behind with its dirty great grey tongue lolling out a yard, and trying to get in the back. Carol wasn't looking any too merry about the situation.

We bumped up the track to the gate and out on to the road. The alsatian followed us for about a quarter of a mile. I'll say one thing for that breed—they don't give up easy.

On the main road I was doing eighty. Carol leaned across and yelled in my lug-hole.

"Davey! We didn't see any deer after all."

CHAPTER TWENTY-THREE

WE got to the outskirts of Whitmarsh in under ten minutes, then I had to stop behind a terrific long line of cars. I turned round to Carol. "Bit of a jam up front somewhere."

"This would happen to us. I'm going to be awfully late. It's after six now."

"All right," I said, "I'll try and squeeze past."

There wasn't anything coming the other way as far as I could see, so I pulled up and went beetling up the line. All the other drivers were giving their horns big licks for some reason, but I wasn't too worried—I knew they were only jealous because they hadn't the brass neck to do it themselves. Just as we got into the town I passed a police car, then a line of old vintage jobs all polished up to the nines, creeping along at about 4 m.p.h. I noticed the police car pulling out to follow me, so I trod on the old pedal a bit.

In front of the vintage jobs there were about a dozen blokes with old-fashioned togs on, fake mutton chop whiskers and so forth, riding along on ancient old penny-farthing bikes. They all started hollering and shouting as I went past. The police job was still coming up behind.

Anyway, I pressed on past a big Sneddon & Son's fruit lorry which was all rigged up to look like a castle, with characters dressed as Robin Hood peering over the battlements. In front of the castle was another lorry full of bints in Dutch bonnets squatting on milk churns next to the tits of a dirty great cardboard cow, and in front of that was another lorry which just had things like stocks and gallows on it, with some big blubbergutted herbert standing the side of an execution block with a massive great chopper in his claw. When we turned into the High Street I could see masses of people lining the pavement, and I suddenly twigged. I looked round at Carol. "Hey," I said, "we've got mixed up with the Whitmarsh flipping Cancer Carnival."

I nipped smartly past another half-dozen wagons all tricked

out to represent something or other, but the crowd was so thick farther up I had to pull in amongst the procession. Just behind us was a big brewery truck with a notice on the front which said, "Whitmarsh Amateur Dramatic Society presents, *An Inspector Calls* by J. B. Priestley." The back of this truck was full of people acting their heads off, although nobody could hear a bloody word they were saying. In front of us was a big carriage affair with the Carnival Queen stuck up in front on a throne with her attendants squatting down all round. Waving and smirking in all directions, she was. She turned round and looked back once and boy, she wasn't a patch on Carol. Which gave me the big idea.

Carol leaned forward just then. "Davey. Won't we get into trouble?"

I said, "Listen. Shove up your parasol and start wavin' to the crowd. They'll think you're some sort of visiting beauty queen from Margate or somewhere."

So that's what she did. Going up the High Street we were getting more cheers than the real Carnival Queen. After a bit I actually started to feel as if we ought to have been there in the first place, with all the people yelling and clapping and the old guards' band giving it big licks up the front. The only snag was I was having to crawl along in bottom gear, and the old bus was burning up oil by the gallon. You could hardly see these people acting behind for exhaust fumes, and they were all coughing and spluttering and rubbing their eyes instead of concentrating on the matter in hand.

I was really having the time of my life. Only a bit farther up a real inspector called. On me. He popped out of the crowd and started walking along the side of us. He'd got a lump of paper in his fist.

"And who are you supposed to be, may I ask?" he said, dead sarcastic.

I told him the first thing I could think of.

"Modern Times."

"Modern Chimes?"

"Modern Times!" I yelled at him.

"What number?"

"They didn't give us a number," I hollered. "We came in as a late entry, see. Mrs Thingummyjig knows all about it."

"I thought I couldn't see you on my list," this inspector shouted, "I suppose you're top of the glass."

"Top of the what?"

"Topical class!" he screamed.

"Yeh—that's right."

"You ought to be about six places back, in front of 'Istory down the Ages. Better stay where you are now."

With that, he scarpered back down the line. I wasn't too keen on keeping his company, either, although I'd got nothing against him personally, apart from him being a copper I mean. I kept trying to slip out along a side street, only there were people stretched right across. We got nearly as far as the bottom of the High Street when Jixie, who'd been whining and carrying on all the time, managed to slip her collar, and hopped over the side.

The first I knew about it was Carol thumping me on the back. "Davey, stop! Jixie's jumped out!"

"I can't stop."

"You must stop. Oh Davey, please, please stop!"

I stopped. Carol nipped out and disappeared. The poxy engine stalled. When I yanked the doofer it wouldn't answer. There was a horrible stink of petrol.

I jumped out and had a bash with the handle. No dice. Then I climbed back in again. I could see the cart containing the beauty queen just disappearing round the corner.

It was funny, but there was about ten thousand people on the side of the road. They were all shouting advice, or sniggering, or just gaping. Not one of 'em offered me so much as a peppermint cream, never mind a shove. The bloke driving the brewery lorry behind was just standing on his bloody horn, which was a great help. So I went back for a couple of words.

"You'll break that, cocker, if you don't leave off," I said.

This driver wasn't one of the regular brewery drivers. He must have been one of the actors who hadn't got a part in the play. Funny little bloke with nasty sort of poached eyes and a sharp little beard. Queer as a 6½d. stamp, I wouldn't mind betting.

"Well," he said in this whiney voice, "you should never have brought that car into the procession in the first place, should you? You ought to have known better. I wouldn't have taken a car in that condition . . ."

"Look, what about doin' somethin' constructive, instead o' just sittin' there yappin'?"

"What can I do? I haven't been blinding everybody with a lot of filthy, stinking fumes, have I? I haven't . . ."

"Look, stuff it. Just give me a bit of a bunt in the back, that's all I ask."

I went round and stuck her in gear. Miladdio came up behind and started shoving with five ton of lorry. The unfortunate part about it was he'd got one of these fixed starting handles sticking out the front, which was the first thing that made contact with the back of the old bus. But I managed to get started again, and I whipped round the corner of Station Rise and straight up a one-way street. The wrong way, as it happened, but I wasn't fussy. The last thing I noticed when I left the High Street was Jixie going like the clappers past the Mac-Fisheries, with a hairy big sheepdog in hot pursuit.

I managed to park in somebody's drive, and spent the next hour and a half looking for Carol. But there were people milling about everywhere, and I couldn't see sight nor sign of her.

In the finish I decided to go back on my tod. When I got back to the old bus there was this character in a tweed suit, looked like an army officer, standing there. Apparently it was his drive, and he'd been waiting to get his own car out for the last hour. He was dead snotty about it. I wasn't feeling too bright myself, and we had quite a lively little discussion. I managed to keep my temper, though.

I drove back to Garside then. On the way through I called in at the Falcon; I reckoned I'd better notify Carol's old man of what had occurred, in case he thought she was being raped or something. Standing outside was Sydney Chubb's Alpine.

Sydney Chubb himself was leaning against the bar in the corner, chatting away to Carol. Very confidential. They stopped when they saw me, and Sydney Chubb grinned and gave a sort of slight nod.

"Oh, there you are, Davey," said Carol. "I was beginning to wonder where you'd got to."

"I was beginning to wonder the same thing," I said.

"Wasn't it awful, Jixie getting away. It was a miracle I found her really, she was right up by the stocking factory sitting on a window ledge, the silly woman. Anyway, I got hold of her and then I started looking for you, only lucky for me Sydney came along in his car and saw me looking lost, so he gave me a lift back."

Sydney Chubb was kind of laughing to himself while she was saying this, only not making any sound.

"Yeh, that was very lucky," I said. "Well, I better be gettin' up the garage, else ol' Keith'll be creatin'."

"Aren't you going to have a drink, old boy?" said Sydney Chubb.

"No thanks. I better be gettin' along, see?"

I took the old crate back to the Seagrave Garage. Keith Ranner was standing by the petrol pumps, looking up and down the road.

"Where the Jesus Christ have you been, you bloody dozy half-wit? I thought you said you'd be back at six. I been hangin' around here for an hour, waitin' to lock up."

"I got held up at Whitmarsh. They got some stupid carnival on. It's murder."

"I'll bloody well murder you. Go on, shove it in the garage and look sharp." Just as I was doing that small thing he yelled out, "Hey, hang on a minute!"

He came up behind. "What's this sodding great dent in the boot? What the hell have you been up to?" He started looking all over the car then. "Christ Almighty, look at this!" He pointed to this big rip in the upholstery, with all the stuffing hanging out. "That was never like that when you went out."

"All right, we had a bit of an accident."

"You wouldn't chuckle you've 'ad a bit of an accident. What's this bloody dog's spew doing all over the back seat?"

"What dog's spew? Oh, that. Don't worry, I'll clean it up."

"You're damn bloody right you'll clean it up. And you'll mend that hole. And you'll knock that dent out. I want you up 'ere first thing tomorrow afternoon, young Davey. And don't you ever dare to ask me for the loan of a shagging car again!"

I stuck the car in the garage, grabbed hold of the Quickly, and went tanking back home. When I got there I went straight up to my room without a word to Doris or any bastard, and climbed in between the sheets. I didn't even bother to take my clothes off. I just didn't want to know, any more.

CHAPTER TWENTY-FOUR

I WAS so busy with this talent scheme business during the next couple of months, I hardly had time to spit. Because turning it into a competition, the Village versus the Bottom, was more successful than even I had bargained for.

Everybody was killing themselves making something or other —fudge, hand lotion, calendars, lace d'oyleys, table mats, hearth-rugs—and trying to flog them to their neighbours.

There was an insurance bloke came round one day to collect the subs at the end of the month. It was the first time he'd worked the territory, because the bloke that usually did it had just gone inside for a couple of years for sticking his fingers in his satchel.

By the time the insurance bloke had got from one end of the village to the other, he'd got a car full of raspberry jam, cuddly toys, picture frames, and photograph albums.

They got so keen down the Bottom that two women—quite young bints they were—both made about fifty jars of marmalade. They couldn't get rid of them, so they finished up flogging 'em to each other. Neither of their husbands would touch the stuff, and the kids soon got cheesed off with it for breakfast, dinner and tea, so in the end most of it had to be dumped.

Old Wainwright up the Green stuck his nicker in a tin and buried it in a plot of land in his front garden. Then he put up a little notice to say that anybody who cared to pay a shilling could stick a little peg in the plot with their name on it, and whichever peg was nearest to the tin would get the nicker. He was making four or five quid a month out of the deal.

The paper round was taking twice as long as normal. I'd go round in the mornings, and all the old crones would be stuffing a couple of half-dollars in my fist. "Will you add that to my lot, Davey," they'd say. "I managed to sell two pots of tomato chutney yesterday to the man that comes round with the laundry. I suppose you couldn't do with a pot yourself? I could let you 'ave it sixpence cheaper."

"No thanks all the same."

Then she'd lean forward, this old crone, and whisper in my lug-hole. "Who's winning up to now?"

If the old crone came from the Bottom, I'd say, "Well, up to yesterday morning, the Village was seven pounds thirteen and eightpence in front."

"Are they really?" And the old cow would sneak away and start bashing out more chutney.

Naturally, if it happened to be one of the old crones up the Village, I'd say the Bottom was a little bit in front.

And this wouldn't be happening just once or twice every morning, it'd been happening every other door. All told, I must have been picking up more than a hundred nicker a week.

It was just like a wrestling match, with no holds barred. When old Commander Findlater heard the Bottom was in front, he grabbed hold of his Parker 51 and signed a cheque for fifty guineas. Wham! As soon as they got to know about this down the Bottom, somebody went along to the place which used to be the sanitorium, and touched the accountant that lived there for twenty-five. He couldn't very well refuse because he was in the middle of a round of golf at the time with one of his toffee-nosed chums on the miniature golf course. What you'd call an expensive round. Wham!

Then Ma Whichelow from down the Bottom started up Bingo sessions every Thursday night in the village hall. She spent the original nicker on tickets. She was pulling in three or four quid a week. Wham! Then Mrs Fforde-Hunter got cracking with a cheese, wine and frolic party. The idea was, she had tables all over the place with plates of different kinds of cheese on, and bottles of vin rouge and whatnot. You just had to help yourself— not me, because I didn't get an invite. She only invited the people she knew had got stacks of gilt. The frolic part was some old geezer playing stuff like, "When I grow too old to dream" on a piano accordion. I happened to meet him at the bus stop, and told him the way. Reckoned he used to play for Geraldo or somebody until he retired.

When everybody was scoffing the cheese and knocking back the vino and having a good old natter about what have you got in your garden this year, I've got absolutely nothing in mine, Ma Fforde-Hunter very craftily stuck her nicker on a big silver tray, and sent it round. Of course, after that nobody could put *less* than a nicker on the tray, and one or two of the really flush characters dropped in a fiver. She finished up with sixty-three quid.

Wham wham!

We passed the first thousand quid mark and were well on the way to the second. I was beginning to get quite famous. One morning, just as I was checking the newspaper accounts in my room, Doris came flying up.

"Davey, there's two men at the door. They say they want to see you. They say they're from the *Forbury and District Examiner*."

I was dead niggled with Doris at the time because that same morning the catch on her fridge door had busted and when I'd got back from the round I'd discovered she'd used the bottom half of my fishing rod to prop it shut.

"I'm a bit busy at the moment," I said. "Tell 'em they can come up in about ten minutes. I'll give you a shout."

"Davey! You can't keep them waiting."

"Can't I? You want to sit 'ere and watch me?"

She went out clucking like an old hen. I hung around for a bit, then I hollered downstairs and they came up. One of 'em was this Jerry Podmore. He came in the room with his hand stuck out in front of him. "Ah, Mr Peach. Mr David Peach I presume.

Glad to meet you. Podmore's my name, *Forbury and District Examiner*. This is my photographer colleague, Dennis Blades."

"Pleased to meet yer," I said. "Take a pew."

He sat down on the end of the bed.

"Now we're just—Dennis and I—doing a little—erm—what you might call a piece of prose, about this remarkable scheme concerning the—erm—concerning the church in which I am given to understand by the worthy—erm—worthy vicar of this parish that you are so closely, and if I may say so—erm—praise-worthily involved. Am I correct?"

"S'right," I said.

"Right now—erm—while we're talking, I wonder if you'd object if our estimable friend Dennis took one or two pictures of you, because we like—erm—we like the informal study if you see what I mean."

"No, I don' mind."

"Excellent. Excellent." Then he started on asking me a whole lot of questions about the scheme, how much we wanted, how much we'd got so far, how much different people had raised and how, and what-all. He wrote it all down in little squiggles on a pad.

"Now then," he said, "about yourself, Mr Peach. Would you say you feel a better person for doing all this?"

"Well, not really. I've always enjoyed very good 'ealth, see."

"Yes but I mean, deep down inside, do you feel—erm—do you feel a better man for what you're doing for the church? Does it give you what you might call a glow of . . . well, shall we call it a kind of glow of inner spiritual satisfaction?"

"Yeh, I s'pose it does. Put down yeh."

"Would you—erm—would you recommend it for young people generally?"

"Recommend what for young people generally?"

"Well, you know. Taking a hand in local affairs. Erm—working for the—erm—working for the benefit of the community as a whole, so to speak."

"Yeh, I suppose you could say that."

"Would you say that you've learned anything since you've been doing this particular job?"

"I can add up a lot better than I could when I started."

"Yes, but I don't mean that. I mean—erm—what I mean is, have you learnt anything about yourself, or people generally?"

"People generally. Now let's see. Well, I s'pose you could say it's amazin' what they get up to," I said.

"You mean you're continually being amazed by the—erm— let's say you're continually being amazed by the inventiveness and resource of ordinary men and women once their interest and imagination has been—erm—shall we say stimulated?"

"Yep, that'll do."

"Well, I think that's all we need. Thank you very much Mr Peach. Now we'll be having a few words with the—erm—with the young lady in the pub. Might even take in a little refreshment while we're at it, eh Dennis?"

"Good idea," said this photographer. He'd been popping his flashbulb all the time we'd been nattering. "Just a minute though. I think I'd like one of Mr Peach just holding the list of contributors to the fund, and sort of pretending to check through."

Actually I hadn't got the list—I'd sent it round to the vicar the day before. So I grabbed hold of the newspaper account.

"Like this?"

"Lovely. Just look across towards my left shoulder. That's it."

You ought to have seen the stuff they printed. A picture of me on one side, and one of Carol on the other. "Youth takes a hand," and all that caper. Enough to make you want to throw up. Still, they say all publicity is good publicity.

A couple of days after it came out I happened to be delivering down the Bottom. When I got to Mabel Merryweather's place I was just slipping the *Daily Mail* under her knocker when the door opened, and Mabel stood there. I was a bit surprised, because normally she's never there at that time of the morning.

She was looking dead smart in this new tweed costume she'd got on. "Hallo Davey," she said. "I see you're in the news."

I said, "Yeh, these reporters, I just can't get rid of 'em. There was a couple hidin' under the table when I came down to break-fast. There ought to be a law against it."

"Now, now, I know you're becoming quite a celebrity, but you mustn't exaggerate. How's the scheme going?"

"Quite tidy, thanks."

"Oh yes, I forgot to give you my contribution." She handed over a thick envelope. "And I just wanted to say that I'm very, very grateful." With that she leaned forward and gave me a socking great kiss on the chops. Boy, it was like stopping a wet orange at fifty paces.

"Well," I said. "Anything I can do, any time. I got to get going now or I'll never be finished."

"All right, Davey. Good-bye."

"Cheerybye, Mabel. Harriet, I mean."

Up the road a bit I had a shufti inside the envelope. There were ten fivers in there. I peeled off a couple for commission and stuck them in my inside pocket, then I put the others back.

The Bottom was leading again.

CHAPTER TWENTY-FIVE

On the whole, I was feeling reasonably chuffed with myself. It's nice to be Mr Peach occasionally, even to the wrong people. Of course, it's got its drawbacks, having to be respectable. Pretending to be polite to people you happened to know were right bastards, for instance, and opening doors for old bints to go through first, even though you happened to be in twice as much of a hurry as they were. Naturally, I more or less had to turn up for church at least once a month, which was beginning to brass me off.

I mean, when you've been to church once you've been a thousand times. The trouble is, they never change the picture. The only interesting thing was Johnny Salt's sermons. He used to natter about everyday things like sex, and people doing different kinds of work and not knowing what to do with their spare time, and about what would happen if nobody wanted to do the washing up—it just wouldn't get done, etc. He was even on about something the Pope said on one occasion. He reckoned it was all cockeyed.

He was always giving some queer example. For instance, he might get up in the pulpit and start off with a question: "What would you do if you didn't smoke, and somebody offered you a dirty great Havana cigar? Would you be honest and refuse it, or would you stuff it in your pocket and say you'd have it after lunch, just so's the other herbert would think you were just as accustomed to smoking cigars as he was?" Or words to that effect. I forget what the answer to that one was, but anyway that was how he'd start off.

But like with everything else in this life, you've got to take the rough with the smooth. At least, when I was in church I could sit and look at Carol. And usually I'd walk back with her after. I hadn't given up hope there, boy; as a matter of fact I couldn't hardly think of anything else. The more you can't have a thing, the more you want it. I'd actually been a virgin since I'd first clapped eyes on her, which was getting on for five months—easily my record.

We were still having our fortnightly sessions. I've got to admit that after the day at Thurrock Forest, relations were a bit strained for a while. Our conversation was strictly on business lines. She didn't mention Jixie, and I didn't bring up the subject of Sydney Chubb. But after a month or so, she was so chuffed at seeing the money rolling in that things began to get friendly again.

I was due to see her a couple of days after I'd said good-bye to Mabel Merryweather. All the morning I was thinking about it, and wondering if anything was going to happen.

I reckoned that something had better happen soon, because the scheme would be all over in another couple of months. By the time I was ready to go down to the Falcon, I was all stewed up thinking about it.

I'd almost decided to try my hand with her and risk the consequences. All the way down on the Quickly I was telling myself that if I didn't make a move that afternoon I never would. Was I in love with it, for Christ's sake? Did I intend to marry the bint? Well, if I hadn't got any such intention, what the bloody hell was I afraid of? I remember that day specially because it was the first day which was really rafty that autumn, with a lot of fog hanging around, and also it happened to be my twenty-first birthday.

On the way up through the Green, I noticed Mavis Tidy standing with her arms folded at the farm gate, and I could tell something was brewing even before she saw me and started waving for me to stop.

"Anything up?" I said.

"Oh Davey, I wasn't expecting to see you."

Her old snitch was really carving it up, and the way her eyes were glittering you'd imagine old Jack had got eight draws up out of only eight on the coupon. Not that he'd shell out a lot in her direction if he had. Although there's a piece of crumpet about forty years old but still bashing it, that lives in a caravan along the Forbury road—she might have got a fur coat out of the deal. She used to get all her eggs at the farm until Mavis started wondering why anybody had to come four miles twice a week for a dozen fresh eggs, especially a trim little blondie in skintight slacks, and why old Jack had to take her on a personal tour of the chickenhouses every time when there was always a couple of buckets of fresh henfruit standing in the dairy. Still, I suppose we've all got problems.

"Did you see the ambulance go up?" she said.

"No, why? Somebody snuffed it?"

"Haven't you heard, then?"

"Nope."

"It's poor Mrs Hoskin—you know, old Ned's wife."

"What's the matter with her?"

Ma Tidy tipped her spectacles, then she bent her head down to look over the top.

"She's dead!"

"What did she die of?"

"She committed suicide, they only found her an hour ago, it was Mr Salt actually found her, apparently she'd been in a very nervy state ever since they took that daughter away from her and put her in Lexbridge Asylum, what was her name?"

"Bloody Mary."

"That's right. Well, you remember they said she'd have to be certified after she went and stole all those things in Forbury, and she wasn't fit to plead? Well, apparently Mrs Hoskin was very upset because they'd always been company for each other, so anyway..."

"Just hang on a minute," I said. "You say the vicar found 'er?"

"That's right, you see he went round to see her just before twelve o'clock this morning, apparently he's been going there two or three days a week ever since the daughter was taken away, and just sitting there talking to Mrs Hoskin and old Ned. There's been quite a lot of talk about it according to Mrs Whichelow, there's a lot of them been saying that if Mr Salt was really doing his job, he wouldn't be able to spend so much time with just one family.

"Well anyway, I was just going to tell you. Mr Salt went down there this morning, and nobody answered the door, so he thought they must be out, and he was just going away when he heard this goat bleating, well it's only a kid actually, and it's the one that all the trouble was about."

"What trouble?"

"With the council. You see, old Ned brought it home a few days after they came for the daughter and gave it to his wife as a pet, just to take her mind off things. But a lot of people on the estate complained, and some of them wrote to the council to say that Ned was keeping goats, which was all against the regulations. Anyway, about a week ago they sent a man down from Forbury Council, Mr Henderson his name was. Of course, he saw the kid running around the house, and he said as far as the Council was concerned it was a goat, and Ned would have to get rid of it within a fortnight, otherwise they'd be turned out of the house. Well, as I was saying, when Mr Salt heard ..."

"How did she do it?"

"Do what?"

"Do herself in?"

"I'm just coming to that." You can never put old Mavis off her stroke. "Where was I? Oh yes, Mr Salt heard the kid crying and he looked up and saw its head poking out of the bedroom window, and he thought it might fall out any second. So he went round to the back door and found it unlocked, and he thought he'd better go upstairs and shut the window. When he got up the stairs he opened the bedroom door and my dear, there she was, lying on top of this old iron bedstead which didn't even have a mattress on it. Stone dead. Mmmm. Poisoned herself, they say. Nobody knows what she must 'a took, deadly nightshade most like. These gypsies, they know all about that sort of thing. Been brought up to it."

"Yeh, they know all the tricks of the trade," I said.

"Well, let me tell you the rest of the story." There wasn't any stopping her. "The vicar sent for Dr Lumbard and he came, and of course they called in the police as well. Just after the inspector got there from Whitmarsh old Ned himself came in, and when he saw the police there he ran off, but they chased after him and Mr Salt told him what had happened. D'you know what he did then? He went up and had a look at his poor wife lying there, then he came downstairs, took hold of an old fork with one prong missing, and started digging over a piece of ground. Not so much as a word to anybody."

"Ah, they're different from us, the old didikais," I said. "They don't see things the same as we do."

"I shouldn't think they do, from the looks of it. They're all still up there now, waiting for the ambulance, that's why I wondered if you'd seen it. I wouldn't have known anything about it only Mrs Whichelow happened to slip in just now for some milk, she's got her eldest son coming to stay with the three young children, she says it always wears her out. Only she lives quite close to Ned's place, and she got to hear of it."

"She's got ears like a bloody ferret, that woman. She can hear the grass growin'."

"Davey! She's not as bad as some I could mention. Anyway, she was saying that old Ned'll have to move out of the council house now he's on his own. You're only allowed to live there if you have a family, it says so in the regulations."

"Well," I said, cocking my leg over the Quickly and getting ready for the off, "nobody seemed to want 'im there. Maybe they should never 'ave shifted 'im in the first place."

"Anyway, there it is," she said. "Well, I mustn't stand 'ere jawin', I've got the chickens to feed and Hilda Purkiss is coming round this afternoon. She's having a proper time of it, poor dear."

"Why, what's up with 'er?"

"It's Teddy Paulson's wife, Lily. She's taken a turn for the worse, terrible pains in 'er stomach so she says. So Hilda's been going round there nearly every day to cheer her up a bit. She says it nearly always upsets her, but considering what Teddy did for old Joe just before he went, she doesn't think she can hardly do anything else. Even Dr Lumbard doesn't know what's wrong with her."

"Well, you never know," I said. "A bit of competition might do 'er the world of good."

"It's nothing to joke about, Davey."

"Well, be seeing you."

She said, "Oh, by the way, you heard about Miss Merryweather, I suppose."

"No. What about her?"

"She's gone. Just packed up and left without telling a soul. She didn't even tell Dr Lumbard until the day before she left. I can't understand it, can you?"

"No."

"It wouldn't surprise me," said Mavis, "if there wasn't a bit of funny business goin' on *there*."

The old air-raid siren over at Whitmarsh was giving the peace a pasting when I got to the Falcon and stuck my Quickly in the yard. They only use it for fires nowadays, so the firemen will hear it, drop whatever they happen to be doing, belt across to the fire station, and get to the fire in time to piss on the dying cinders, but there was a fire in me that afternoon, boy, coming up from below and turning my eyeballs to cinders. When Carol opened the back door and let me in she was only adding fuel to the flames.

"Come on in, Davey. We're all on our own today."

"How come?"

"Mummy and Daddy have gone over to Hocking in the car to visit my grandmother. She's in hospital over there. I'm afraid she's been taken very ill."

"What time will they be back?"

"Oh, in a couple of hours' time, I should think. Why?"

"I was just wonderin'."

I was thinking, "This is it, Davey boy." I was also feeling a bit nervy, like a general on the eve of some important big holocaust or whatever they call it. Battle, anyway. She led the way through into the private bar and switched on the gas fire full blast. "We'll soon warm the place up," she said. I walked across to the fire and stood there warming up my duff, watching her as she went round the room blowing a bit of dust off here, arranging a curtain there, jiggling the flowers around in their vases and all the other little bits and bobs that bints do whenever they take anybody into a room. She was wearing one of those sloppy woollen dresses that are supposed to make women look as if they haven't got any figure, but it didn't work with Carol. Come to think of it, only women that have got really cracking figures ever wear that kind of dress.

Then she sat down all very businesslike at the table and opened this big accounts book that she entered all the names and money in.

"Well," she said, "how much have we got this time?"

I yanked wads of money from every pocket, and shoved it in a stack in front of her. "A hundred and eighty-four pounds six and fourpence, all told," I said.

Her eyes went all big and round. "As much as that? We are doing well."

I started reading out the names of the people then, and how much they'd raised. She was putting the Village down in black ink, and the Bottom in green. When I got to Mabel Merry-weather, forty pounds, she said, "That's a lot. How did she raise it?"

"I wouldn't know. She just stuck it in my 'and. She was in a tearin' 'urry at the time."

Right at the very end of the list I said, "You can put me down for eight quid." I'd made this in the last month out of fiddling on the pump, and believe me it was a real strain parting with it.

"That's wonderful, Davey. How did you manage it?"

"I've been flogging Christmas annuals, see."

"And you didn't tell me a word about it. You are secretive." She gave me a smile I could have cut out and framed.

She started adding up the figures then. "Davey, we're only seven pounds short of two thousand." She was all breathless with excitement.

"Yeh, but we still got a long way to go. How does the Village stand against the Bottom?"

She started counting again. "The Bottom is drawing ahead. They're about eighty pounds in front now."

"I thought as much."

She put down the pen, blotted the book, and closed it.

"D'you know something, Davey?" She shifted round so she was looking straight at me. "I think you're a very nice boy."

"Well, it's decent of you to say so an' all that."

"I do say so. D'you know, I was only thinking about it this morning. Out of all the boys I've ever known, I don't think there's one of them who'd have done what you're doing—not for the same reason, anyway. They'd only do it if they thought they'd be getting something out of it."

"What kind of reason d'you mean, exactly?"

"Well, just for the sake of the church, I mean. That's the trouble with people these days, they only think about themselves, there's no . . . well, no feeling for anything. No sort of . . . compassion. D'you see what I mean?"

"No."

"Oh dear. I'm hopeless at explaining anything. Well, you take the people that come into this pub every night. You just stand behind the bar all the evening like I do, and listen to their conversation. What do they talk about? Just trivial things. It's nearly always something to do with money, you know, such as how much more they earn when they do overtime, and how much a tin of distemper costs, and how they manage to avoid paying their income tax. Either that or they're pulling somebody to pieces. There doesn't seem to be much love left in the world, Davey."

"I wouldn't go so far as to say that."

"I don't mean sex or anything." She was getting properly worked up. "There's plenty of that about. I mean *real* love. You know, love between man and man, and between woman and woman. Everybody loving each other and trying to help other people. All different sorts of loving."

She was standing with one foot on the chair, and she was leaning forward and looking dead serious, only the effect was lost on me because I could see right down between her dills.

"You do see what I mean, don't you Davey? If you come across somebody who's, well, blind or something, and you stop to say a kind word or invite them to your house. Very few people would invite a blind person to their houses because it's too much trouble. That's the kind of love I mean, or if you help an old woman across the road or try to cheer anybody up because they're lonely or miserable, I don't mean a relative, it could be a complete stranger, but the trouble is, everybody seems to be governed by self-interest these days. They don't want to get involved in anything that's not going to be to their own advantage. Whew, it's stuffy in here. Shall I turn the fire off? Are you too hot?"

"No, I'm just about right, thanks. I know exactly what you mean, though. There was a bloke like that used to live along the Bottom, a bit older than me, name of Robin King. I'm not kiddin', 'e was a real pig's nephew. If 'e saw you 'anging over a cliff and 'ollerin' for 'elp, 'e'd come and stick lighted match stalks under your fingernails. His old man was the same; the whole family was the same. They nearly shoved his old man in jug once for kickin' some 'unchback in the froat. Always 'avin' fits in the road, the father was, they used to call 'im Fitty King. The mother ran off with a corporal in the Military Police about five year ago. I don't say I blame 'er."

"How awful."

" 'E used to work in a little sweet factory in Forbury, Nickols, Rye and Bentley's, this Robin King . . ." I had to keep on talking just then because I'd hardly had anything to eat all that day what with thinking about Carol, and my guts had started rumbling like distant thunder. " 'E was in the separate part at the end where they make the Turkish Delight until they gave 'im the push, you know what for? They caught 'im gobbin' in the vats. After that 'e got a job in this big tyre repair depot. You know what 'e used to do whenever they gave 'im a slow puncture to mend? Well, 'e'd take this sharp little penknife . . ."

She was running a finger round the inside of her mouth. "I seem to have got a jagged tooth. I suppose I ought to go to the dentist. Only I hate going to the dentist. I'm an awful coward."

"If you do so," I said, "I should keep away from the bloke over at Whitmarsh. Chappelle, his name is. Herbert Chappelle. He's got a surgery just opposite Boots."

"Why? Isn't he very good?"

"Yeh—'e's all right as a dentist, only 'e's got a bit of a reputation with the women if you understand what I mean. There was a young girl went there only a few months ago, nineteen she was. Old Chappelle sat 'er in the chair and gave 'er a whiff o' gas while 'e did an extraction. She didn't feel a thing. Only when she got outside in the street she realized 'er brassiere was undone. Her mother went down to the surgery an' kicked up a hell of a stink, they even had to fetch the police in the finish. She couldn't prove anything though."

"Oh dear. Well, thanks for telling me."

"I just thought I ought to mention it."

"It just goes to prove what I was saying just now," she said. She suddenly took her foot away from the chair and leaned against the table. "Good heavens, isn't it getting thick in here— d'you mind if I open a window?"

I said, "Don't move, I'll do it for you."

But she'd already started walking across to the window. I was just behind her. "You see Davey, nobody seems to have any . . ." As she was saying this she was reaching up towards the catch on the window. I couldn't stand it any longer when she did that. I just came up from behind and brought my hands up underneath her armpits.

". . . loyalty towards . . ." She just stood there, she didn't seem surprised or anything. Then I turned her round and kissed her. ". . . anything except . . ." She pressed her hands against my shoulders. "Davey, you're squeezing me to death."

"Sorry," I said. I kissed her again only very kind of soft and gentle. It lasted a hell of a long time, and at the end of it she wasn't pressing against my shoulders any more.

Then she said, "Davey, I was beginning to wonder if you were ever going to . . ."

"Yeh, but I thought from the way you were talkin' . . ."

"I'm not all that old-fashioned," she said.

"Don't you remember what you said that time we went over the forest? About 'ow the two things 'ad to go together or some such thing?"

She was messing around with my hair. "Well, they were beginning to go together even then, but I wasn't quite sure. Anyway, you can't expect a girl to make all the running."

After she said that, it wasn't very long before we found ourselves on the settee, and about a couple of hours later—or it might have been only five minutes, I always lose track of time— we were getting stripped off.

That was the way it was, boy. That's exactly how it was.

While I was taking off her stockings she said, "Davey, d'you really think we ought?"

I'll say one thing. All this stuff about heaven and hell they're always pumping down your throat. Well, I've got a pretty good idea what heaven's like, boy, because I was there that afternoon on the bloody Axminster with Carol and two cushions. I've been there several times since, and I reckon to be paying a few more visits before I snuff it.

And when that day comes, I'll take my chance on the other place.

You can pass me the pitchfork. I'm cushy.

CHAPTER TWENTY-SIX

I WOULDN'T expect anybody to actually believe this, but it's true. All the time I was raking in the spondulicks for the church, I never once got the itching finger.

It sounds very peculiar, I know, and as a matter of fact I've regretted it many a time since. There's plenty of doddering old cows in the village that've got as many gaps in their minds as hedgepigs have got fleas, and no more chance of getting rid of 'em. They can't even remember what day it is, some of 'em—either that or they don't want to. They certainly wouldn't have known how much cash they'd handed over from one day to the next. I could have knocked up a fair little stack out of it. I can't think why I didn't when I look back; I keep thinking I must have had a hole in my bonce.

I suppose one reason was that there was so much of it, and it came from so many different places, it didn't seem like money at all, somehow. It was just like filling your pockets with Bingo counters and empty packets of Smith's crisps for all the difference it made. I was reading an article once about millionaires. Apparently they hate to handle money. They think it's dead crude. They never keep any cash on their persons, and they hate spending any, which is why their wives are always getting their handbags nicked while they're waiting at bus stops. All the really big multi-millionaires are as tight as ducks' arseholes which everybody knows are watertight.

But the other reason is more peculiar, and demands a more careful analysis. (Hi-yi, I got that last bit out the *Sunday Times*.) All my life there's been a sort of big Voice inside me saying, "I bet you!" When I was a nipper it'd be saying things like, "I bet you can't run up to Roman Farm and back without stopping," or, "I bet you couldn't fill up a kitbagful of Canon Fosdick's William pears from his pear tree, which is right underneath his bedroom window."

When I was a bit older it dared me to poke the biggest boy in the class right in the snout the next time he gave me a shove in the shoulder as we were going out the classroom. Actually this was one of the few things I didn't take it up on, but only because I heard his parents were moving to Ludlow at the end of the term. It was the Voice that dared me to have my first shag when I was fourteen, standing up against the wall in this little alley behind the big ironmonger's in Whitmarsh. The copper station was only just around the corner, and on the other side of the wall was the rack where the coppers stuck their bicycles.

Just this side of Whitmarsh there's a place called Cumber's Meadow where the railway line goes through. There was a gang of six of us used to get up there of a Sunday afternoon. We used to each put a bob in the middle, and we'd play this game of standing in the middle of the track when the train was coming, and seeing who'd be the last to get out of its road. It was the Voice that always dared me I wouldn't win the kitty, and I always did. And when some pasty-faced little bastard got into conversation with me in a pub in Forbury—I was only sixteen at the time—and offered to drive me back to his place where he said there were a couple of lush bints in the flat upstairs who were just begging for it, the Voice told me what he was really after, and bet me I wouldn't make him stop the car just outside the town, drag him out in the road, knock skittles of shit out of him, then sling his ignition keys in the nearest ditch.

When I first walked into the Falcon and clapped eyes on Carol, the Voice told me she was away out of my reach, and bet me I'd never take her cherry in a million years. And when I got the job organizing the talent scheme, which gave me the chance, the old Voice was right behind me, betting me I'd never raise so much money, I hadn't got the brains to do it.

Naturally, I accepted. I never refuse a bet from the Voice, and up to now I've hardly fallen down on anything. Just one or two items like this biggest boy in the class effort, and the time the Voice bet me I couldn't swim across the River Thames and back one time I went to a place called Bourne End with Doris, who's got a cousin or somebody that lives there. Only I happened to get cramp on the way over, and it was very nearly my chips. I had to get somebody to take me back in a boat.

The strange part is that the Voice never minds when I succeed. But it's always horribly narked when I don't make it—whatever it's asked me to do—and won't speak to me for weeks. I've always regretted I didn't smack Ron Beddowes on the snitch before he went to Ludlow, and if our paths ever cross again he'd better watch his bloody step. I haven't been to Bourne End since that last time, but if I'm ever passing through that way I'll take a pair

of swimming trunks with me and get across that river and back.
I don't care if it's the middle of February.

Liar!

"That's why, after I'd got there with Carol, I started getting
worried about the scheme. It's like when you put a nicker on
the Autumn double—it's no use getting one leg up without the
other. I imagined myself saying to the Voice, "What was that
you said about not bein' in Carol's class? I didn't quite catch what
you said." And the Voice turning round and saying, "All right,
I'll give you that. So what? That was the cushy number. But you
didn't manage the tough bastard, did you? That one about raising
the three thousand nicker. You and Paul Getty! Don't make me
laugh! You and my arse, you mean."

The way I looked at it, we were going to finish up a few hundred
quid short. Although the cash was still coming in at a fair rate
it was already dropping off, and I knew that all the big stuff was
finished. Nearly everybody had forked over something, apart from
one or two puritans up the Village who'd sent the original nicker
straight back to Johnny Salt with a little note to say how sinful
it was to make money, and half a dozen shysters down the
Bottom who'd spent it up the Falcon, and claimed they'd never
had it in the first place.

Apart from that, the news had got around that the Bottom was
well in the lead, so there wasn't the same what you might call
incentive.

There was still one character left in the village that still hadn't
coughed up or said a dicky bird, and that was Garfield Chubb in
person. Which explains why I marched into the call box the
following Friday night and dialled Garside 81.

I was shivering a bit while I was listening to the old brr-brr, on
account of they still hadn't put in the windows that Joe Purkiss
had knocked out, and the breeze was fair whistling through.

After a bit somebody picked up the receiver at the other end
and said, "Garside hate-won?" It sounded like a man's voice at
first, then I realized it must be Garfield Chubb's secretary, Miss
Lucking, the one that lives up at the Hall. He's the kind of bloke
that always has to have a secretary hanging around to tuck his
shirt in, etc.

This Miss Lucking was a real "person". I'd seen her up the
Hare and Hounds several times. About fifty, she was. She could
toss it back, and all. Always wore these flyaway specs, very hoity-
toity. I pressed the button firkin.

"Put me through to Mr Garfield Chubb," I said.

"Who's that speaking?"

"The secretary of the Garside Church Restoration Scheme."

"Sorry, but would you mind repeating that more slowly?"

"You 'eard me the first time," I said. I was getting a bit niggled.

"I'm aw'fly afraid Mr Chubb isn't heah."

"That's funny," I said. "I could have sworn I saw 'im turning into the drive in 'is Bentley about twenty minutes ago."

"Well, actually, he's just come in, but he's aw'fly tied up at the moment."

"S'all right," I said. "I'll 'ang on." She whanged down the phone with a terrific clatter. About twenty minutes later, she picked it up again.

" 'Allo," I said. "I'm still 'ere."

"Look, would you mind getting off the line. Mr Chubb has an important call to make."

"I won't keep 'im long."

"What is it you want, young man?"

"I just wanted to ask 'im for an appointment, that's all. Old lady."

I heard her go, "tssk tssk." Then she said, "Just a moment."

She came back after a couple of minutes. "Mr Chubb says he can see you for ten minutes only next Wednesday at seven in the evening. Will that do?"

"Ta ever so much. I'll be there at seven sharp," I said. I put the telephone down like a ton of bricks and chipped a bit off the rest. Still, I reckoned they could fix it up while they were doing the windows. I believe in keeping people fully employed. Especially these layabouts in the Post Office.

CHAPTER TWENTY-SEVEN

HARDLY anybody in Garside had ever seen Garfield Chubb except through the back window of the Bentley. Nobody knew much about him, either. Miss Lucking would occasionally drop bits and pieces at the Hare and Hounds when she was tight as a tick, but she never gave much away. Stan Lennard hardly ever clapped eyes on him, apart from when he was at a loose end, and he'd take a stroll out into the gardens just to see if the gardeners were doing their whack. He lived in this big Tudor mansion place just past the crossroads on the way to Whitmarsh, and he was supposed to have one room in there with all long shelves around the walls containing the biggest collection of miniature booze bottles in the world, all different. His missis was a big fat bag with long yellow hair, but she wasn't too keen on the country life, and spent most of her time up in this big flat of theirs in London.

The house itself is about three storeys high, and sort of narrow. It's the kind of place you wouldn't be surprised to see the front door open, and a knight in armour come prancing down the steps on a filthy great charger. It was just turning dark when I went along there on the Wednesday. As I was turning to go up the drive I noticed old Ned Hoskins parking his bike in the hedge about a hundred yards up the road. He'd got a big bundle over his shoulder, wrapped in an army blanket. I stopped to see what he was up to. He climbed over a gate and started walking across a field of stubble, making for the edge of a wood.

Well, it wasn't any business of mine, I reckoned. I went on up the drive. Sydney passed me going the other way in his Alpine. He gave me a queer look. I bet he was wondering what I was doing, invading his territory. I parked the Quickly in the courtyard, ran up the steps, and rang the old Westminster chimes. Mother Finn, the housekeeper, answered the door.

She looked dead scared when she saw me. "Davey! What is it ye want?" she said. She was almost whispering, for Christ's sake. Mother Finn is Irish, I'll say no more. She must have thought I'd come to collect Stan Lennard's bicycle pump or something. "Why didn't ye come round the back? Mr Chubb's here."

"Yeh, I know. That's who I've come to see."

She looked really terrified when I said that. "Ye can't see Mr Chub widout ye have an appointment."

"I got one."

"Ye mean Mr Chubb has asked to see ye?" I could see the old bag didn't believe it.

"That's right."

"Ye'd better wait here a minute. Oi'll go an find out."

I stood there cursing until she got back. "It's all right, ye can come in," she said, which was big of her. I got inside the door and she bolted it. "Miss Lucking'll see to ye," she said. Then she scarpered as if she wanted to wash her hands of the whole business.

I hung around in this entrance hall for a bit. Hats and coats in all directions. Then Miss Lucking came out. She always walked with one leg crossing right over in front of the other. A lot of virgins do that, especially when they're knocking on a bit, to signify they've still got something to guard.

"Aren't you the young man who telephoned the other day?"

"'S'right."

"Something about some local charity or something, wasn't it?"

"Yup."

"I see. I'm aw'fly afraid Mr Chubb's rawther busy at the moment. Would you like to take a seat?"

I squatted down on this sort of throne arrangement which was about ten centuries old and as hard as iron. She disappeared, and came back after about twenty minutes.

"Mr Chubb can see you now."

I followed her through a big room where everything was in red and gold stripes, even the wallpaper. There were a lot of pictures on the wall that looked as if they were meant to be bits of street after a road accident. In one corner was the biggest television set I've ever seen, with a radiogram and a frigging cocktail bar built in.

At the far end was another door which I knew led to the inner sanctum, because Miss Lucking sort of stiffened up and started walking on tiptoe as we came up to it. She stopped outside, and patted her hair. "I didn't quaite ketch your neem," she said.

"David S. Peach."

She opened the door, put her head round it, and said, "Mr Peach." I bowled in. She shut the door behind me. It didn't make a sound.

It wasn't the room where he'd got all these little bottles of booze around the walls. No fear. I bet they keep that bastard under lock and key with Miss Lucking around. It was quite a small room actually, with black old beams all over the place and a massive big fireplace at the end, in the middle of which was one of those electric fires which is supposed to look like a big stack of burning logs.

Garfield Chubb himself was sitting on the far side of a massive big yellowy desk with a white telephone on it, and bits of paper cluttered all over the top. There was a bottle of Vodka right next to his elbow, and a glass. All I could see of him was his socking great bald dome bending down over the desk, with a couple of tufts of black hair sprouting out from each side. He was a big bastard. He was working out something on a pad. All he said when I came in was, "Plonk yerself dahn, cock."

I sat down. He went on writing figures on the pad. Every so often he'd grunt and cross something out. He kept picking up a cigar and taking drags, and once about an inch of ash fell on what he was doing. He just blew it away. After about another ten minutes he said without looking up, "Well now, what can I do for you guv'nor? Only make it snappy, 'cos I got things to do, see?" He said it in this shocking old cockney voice. Dead common.

"Well, I'm the secretary of the, er hrrrm, Garside Church Restoration Scheme you see Mr er hrrrrm, Chubb . . ." I had to keep clearing my throat to get my voice down to normal—it sounded like a poxy choirboy when I started off. "We're trying to raise a lot of money for the church, er hrrrrm."

He stuck up a big fat hand. "Don't say any more, cock. So you thought you'd come along and see if you could sting me for a few nicker. All right, that's fair enough. Mind you, I don' go ter church meself, don't believe in it, never did. Biggest bunch o' moneygrubbers . . . never mind." He grabbed a cheque book and scribbled in it, then ripped the top cheque off and slung it across the desk.

"There y'are, son. That do yer? Orf yer go, then. Tell that bloody secretary o' mine to come in on yer way aht."

I picked up the cheque and had a quick shufti at it. I said, "Excuse me, Mr Chubb."

"Whassermadder nah?"

"You made this cheque out for five quid."

He looked up again. "Yeh, tha's right. Whassermadder with that? It won't bounce."

I took a hell of a deep breath.

"Well, there ain't nuthin' the matter with it, Mr Chubb. Only I was expectin' a bit more."

He gave me a startled kind of look and stuck his cigar in the ashtray. Then he smiled out of the corner of his big juicy gob and started to sort of nod.

"So you was hexpectin' a bit more, was you? And how much was you hexpectin', may I hask?"

"Well, about five 'undred."

When I said that he sort of flinched as if somebody had belted him across the ear with the flat of an axe.

"Five 'undred," he said, very quiet. He started pressing the tips of his fingers together in front of him. Then he said, still very quiet, "What did you say your name was, cock?"

"David Peach."

"Well, listen to me, Mr Peach. David. You got all sorts of bloody neck, I'll give yer that. But I'll tell you summink for nuffink, Mr Peach. You jus' take that cheque and git aht of 'ere inside ten seconds or you won't git buggerall? Got it?" He bawled

out, "Lucking!" She came prancing in; she must have had her
mitt on the door handle.

"Show this gennleman out."

"Excuse me Mr Chubb," I said. "I got a proposition."

"You got a what? You 'eard what I said, you cheeky young
bastard. Git aht!" Miss Lucking was going tsssk tsssk again.

I got up then and I said, "Listen Mr Chubb, if I can tell you
'ow you can make five thousan' quid, would you give five 'undred
to the church?"

"What's that?" He cupped one hand to his earhole. "Say
again?"

I said it again.

"All right, son. Siddown. Now you jus' tell me 'ow to make five
fahsan'. I'm listenin'. Only make it sharp."

"I'd rather talk about it in private if you don't mind."

"All right, Lucking."

She gave me a look as if I was the purple death in person, and
pranced out.

"Come on then, cock. Get weavin'. I ain't got all night."

I said, "All right. You got a five-acre field in the middle of the
Village, Mr Chubb—the one they use as a recreation field for the
kids. That right?"

"That's ker-rect."

"I s'pose you know you could get a thousand quid an acre for
that field if you flogged it as building land? It's the best building
site in the Village."

"Yeh, I know that. I ain't stoopid," he said. "Only I'd never get
plannin' permission from the council to develop that site, see? Not
while it's the recreation ground. They got it marked down for
that when I bought it, see? Anyway, what's it got to do wiv you?"

"I was just thinkin'," I said, "as 'ow you might get plannin'
permission for that field if you went about it the right way."

"You were, eh? Well, you just tell me, 'cos I'd be innerested ter
know."

"Okay," I said. "You got another field of about six acres down
the Bottom. That right."

"Yeh, that's right."

"Only you couldn't build on that because it's too low-lyin'.
There's a spring down one end, and it's liable to get flooded in
the winter time. It's a proper ribby ol' field; it ain't even any
good for grazin'."

"Go on, cock."

"Well, if you could get that field down the Bottom accepted as the recreation ground, you could go ahead and build on the other one."

"Ah, there's a big snag there, cocker. First off, the people in the Village'd never wear it, see. They wouldn't want a whole lot o' new buildin's slap in amongst 'em."

"Yeh, I know that. But the people down the Bottom'd be all for it, because their kids don't use the recreation ground anyway. It's too far for 'em to walk. So they'd be all in favour of gettin' it moved up to their end, even if their kids did get wet feet occasionally."

"You got a point there, cocker."

"So all you got to do is write a letter to the parish council before their next meeting which is on Friday week, and offer them the field down the Bottom instead of the one up the Village. They'll 'ave to call a public meeting to vote on it, and it's sure to get passed, because there's twice as many people down the Bottom as there is up the Village. Then as soon as you get it passed, you apply to Forbury Rural District Council for permission to build, and they're bound to approve it because building sites are very short in this area anyway."

He sat back for a bit, lit a fresh cigar, and rolled it all round his big slobbering lips.

"Not bad, not bad," he said. "Only between you an' me, cocker, I've seen these little plans come unstuck before."

"O' course, there's somethin' else you could do, just to make sure," I said.

"Whassat?"

"There's a bloke in the village name of Paulson," I said. "'E's the local builder. 'E's also the chairman of the parish council, and 'e also represents Garside on the Forbury R.D.C. Now if 'e thought 'e was goin' to get the contract for buildin' those 'ouses, I'm sure 'e'd want to assist in every possible way."

"D'you smoke these fings?" Garfield Chubb said. He lobbed over the box of cigars. I caught it and forked one out. "Thanks," I said. I lit up. Then he took a big swig of the Vodka and poured some more into the glass. I thought he was going to offer it to me but he didn't.

"Five 'undred nicker, you said."

"Yep."

"For the church dahn the road?"

"Yep."

"And you don't reckon to make anyfink aht of it for yourself?"

I said, "Anything you like to give me, over and above the five 'undred, is up to you, Mr Chubb. If it comes off all right."

"Ar, if it comes off," he said.

Then he said, "All right, we'll 'ave a bash, cock." He scribbled something on a pad. "O' course," he said, "I won't be able to say nuffin' to this—what's 'is name—Paulson?"

"I was thinking I might 'ave a word with 'im myself on the subject."

"Tha's up to you," he said. "I don't know nuffin abaht it, see? And I don't wanna know."

"You never told me," I said.

"We ain't even discussed the subject. Unnerstand, Mr Peach?"

"I understand, Mr Chubb." I was having a bit of trouble with the cigar. The bloody thing was burning all down the underside. I tried turning it round but it didn't make any difference.

"What you do for a livin'?" he said.

"I got the local paper round."

"Is it a good one?"

"Not bad," I said. "Keeps body an' soul together."

"Yeh, an' I s'pose it gits better every time a new 'ahsin estate goes up, innit?"

"It don't get no worse," I said.

"You ain't all that simple. Are you cock?"

"People got to make a livin'," I said.

"Y'know what?" he said. "I wish my son 'ad got a bit o' your commonsense. Only I dropped a big bollock, see. I sent 'im to one o' these public schools. You know what they went an' did wiv 'im? They turned 'im into a fuggin' numbskull."

Then he said, "Hey, I got work to do. Go on, piss off. Don' fergit what I tol' yer." He bent his bonce over the desk again.

I picked up the five-bar cheque and walked across to the door.

"Cheerio then, Mr Chubb," I said.

He didn't even look up. He just stuck a hand out and wagged it.

CHAPTER TWENTY-EIGHT

I'D just finished my round the next morning, and was beetling back along the Bottom, when Nobby Creighton stopped me.

If anybody was to ask me to write out a list of my favourite people in Garside in strict order of merit, the first name would be Davey Peach and the last would definitely be Nobby Creighton, the local copper.

Not that he's ever done me any harm—he's much too stupid to

be dangerous. But it's not for lack of trying. The trouble with Nobby is he's got such a small mind. If you was to cycle through the village at three in the morning wearing a striped jersey, with a sack over your shoulder and a jemmy between your teeth, you'd be all right with Nobby providing your rear light was showing. And the way he sucks the arses of the local gentry, boy, is something hard to believe in this day and age.

But the worst thing about Nobby is this funny idea he's got, that whenever something happens in Garside, Davey Peach is sure to know something about it. So the day after he'll stop me in the road and start asking a whole lot of questions—such as the time when somebody ambled into the village post office and nicked about ten quids' worth of stamps while nobody was looking.

There was also the time when Professor Fforde-Hunter's Aston-Martin went missing, and they found it about a week later in the middle of some gorse bushes up Whitmarsh Common, minus the battery and the back wheels. And there was also the little matter of the two herberts in the black van who parked up at the Green one evening. The following morning, about fifteen people in the Village couldn't find their cats anywhere. Nobody could find the black van, either, or the two herberts that were in it. That was around the time when moggies were fetching about four quid apiece for vivisection, although I believe the bottom's fallen out of that particular market since.

As it happened, I had nothing to do with any of these little bits of devilment. Even if I had of done, I certainly wouldn't have appreciated old Nobby coming round looking for me the day after as if I was suspect number one. You've got to admit he's dead subtle, though, is Nobby. He'll usually start off by saying, "Now, Mr Peach, I'd like you to give me a full account of your movements starting from six-thirty yesterday evening, the twenty-first."

"Yeh?" I'd say. "What for? What's been 'appening?"

"Never you mind what's been 'appening, my lad."

So you can imagine I wasn't too delighted when Nobby Creighton suddenly stepped out from the side of the road just past the council estate, and started waving for me to stop.

When I saw him doing the old semaphore stuff I made a beeline for him so he had to jump out the way, then I turned a neat little circle in the road and finished up behind him.

"Hey, you be careful, you dangerous young lunatic."

"I didn't do it," I said. "I swear."

Then I noticed there were a couple of other people with him; a bloke and a tart. The bloke was a big dozy-looking oaf, but the tart wasn't so bad. She was about thirty-five, and looked as if she knew what it was for, or had known. Sort of experienced. She had a very useful pair, set pretty wide apart, which you don't often find.

Nobby said, "'Ave you seen anything of old Ned 'Oskin on your travels?"

"Old Ned? Why, what's 'e been up to?"

This woman said, "Oh, it's not for anything he's done. We're from the Hinchcliffe Memorial Hospital for the Aged, and Mr Hoskin has signed an application to become a voluntary patient. We've come over specially to fetch him, but he doesn't seem to be at home." Very brisk and businesslike, she was. Obviously she was the gaffer over the other one, who'd just been brought along to hold Ned down, if and when he got stroppy.

I said, "How could old Ned sign a form, I wonder, when 'e can't read or write?"

She gave a patient sort of smile. "In cases of complete illiteracy we normally take the patient's thumb-print as a signature."

I scratched my bonce. "I do seem to 'ave seen 'im recently, only I can't remember exactly where," I said. I was kind of playing for time while I worked it out. I'd heard of this Hinchcliffe Hospital before. It's away over the other side of Forbury, and all the oldies in the district who have gone a bit dippy, or are too ancient to look after themselves and haven't got anyone to do it for 'em, go there. One or two other people from Garside have gone there in the last few years, and nobody's ever heard anything of them since.

I didn't exactly want to be responsible for sending old Ned to the place. On the other hand, he was being kicked out of the council house, and there wasn't anywhere else for him to go, so maybe I'd be doing him a favour. Not that it was any skin off my nose. I thought of saying nothing at first, and having a quiet word with Johnny Salt about it; then I remembered he was away at some big religious conflab in London.

This hospital tart could see me trying to make up my mind. "We're rather worried, you see," she said. "The old chap's been under a great deal of strain recently, and he might have taken it into his head . . ." She thought for a bit, then she said, "We wouldn't want him to suffer."

Nobby Creighton piped up, "Now look 'ere, my lad, if you've seen this man I want to know the full details, otherwise . . ."

I was just turning the wheel of the old Quickly round ready to scarper, when the hospital tart laid a hand on Nobby's arm. "Just a minute, constable," she said. Old Nobby didn't like the "constable" part at all. She looked at me with this very sort of sad, weary smile. "If you have seen him, in the last day or two, please try to remember, for his sake. We're very anxious about him, you know."

She gave me a really nice, slow smile, just between her and me, as if Nobby and the other bloke didn't exist.

I said, "Yeh, now I come to think of it, I do remember. I saw 'im about a quarter to seven last night."

"Whereabouts?" Her eyes went all sharp.

"Up the road to Whitmarsh. About a mile away from 'ere. 'E was just going into a wood. Got a bundle on 'is back."

Old Nobby got his pencil and notebook out. "Are you sure about that?" he said.

"No, I just dreamed it up," I said.

"What did you say 'e 'ad on 'is back? A bundle? I s'pose you don't know what was in it?" I was just about to start swearing, when this hospital tart said, "I don't think we need to bother about the details, constable." She turned towards me. "D'you think you could take us to the exact spot?"

"Yeh, I reckon so."

"Well," she said, "in that case we'd better start searching for him straight away." She turned towards Nobby. "Don't you think so?"

Nobby said, "Just a moment, ma'am. I don't think we'd better do anything until I've notified my 'eadquarters about the new evidence that's just come in. Excuse me a minute." He nipped off and went into one of the houses to get on the blower.

While he was away the hospital tart was coming the old buttering-up caper about what a lovely sleepy old village Garside was, and how charming all the people were that she'd spoken to, etc. She said she'd always had to live in towns because of her work, but she'd always wanted to settle down in a nice little spot in the country like Garside, where everybody knew everybody else's business. She wanted to know if I knew Ned very well. I said, "Nobody knew 'im all that well except for maybe the vicar. They just sort of knew 'im from seein' 'im around."

"Oh I see," she said. "Well, he seems to have had a rather tragic life, but we'll look after him. He'll be very happy over at the hospital. He'll have everything done for him, and nothing to worry about."

Nobby came back after a bit looking highly chuffed with

himself. "I've just been on to the Chief Superintendent," he said, "and he agrees with me that we ought to get a dog down 'ere to pick up the trail."

"A dog?" The hospital tart wrinkled her nose up a bit. "Oh, well, I suppose it would help, but we don't want to alarm the old chap, do we?"

Nobby said, "They're sendin' Sergeant Wallbanks over straight away. 'E's bringing Boadicea."

For the next half hour we hung around by the side of the road while Nobby Creighton kept on about this dog Boadicea, and how it'd tracked down about sixty dangerous criminals and whatnot, and won about a dozen medals at the tracking trials. "She shouldn't 'ave much trouble pickin' up old Ned," said Nobby. "I reckon I could sniff 'im out myself at a pinch." He kept looking at his watch and saying, "They ought to be 'ere any second."

Eventually this blue police van came round the corner and pulled up in front of us. Sergeant Wallbanks jumped down into the road. Little bloke he was, very energetic. He looked too small for a copper, but I suppose they stretch a point if you can handle dogs. "Mornin'," he said. "Nice day for a bit of trackin'. No wind, 'eavy atmosphere, no rain. Who we 'sposed to be lookin' for, anyway?"

This hospital tart started telling him, with old Nobby butting in now and again with odd bits of useless information. Then he went to the back of the van and opened it. As soon as he got the door half open, a socking great hound jumped out and started fawning round his ankles. "All right, all right," he kept saying. "Goo'bitch!"

He clipped a lead on the brute and brought it round to the front. The hospital tart said, "What a beautiful animal. It's a Doberman, isn't it?"

The sergeant said, "That's right, ma'am." She put her hand down to pat it, and I could see its gums wrinkling up over its choppers. The sergeant grabbed her wrist. "I wouldn't touch 'er ma'am, if I was you," he said. "She's strictly a one-man dog."

He said he'd have to have something belonging to Ned for the brute to smell, so we walked across to Ned's house. There were faces peering out from behind the curtains of every window in the estate. Nobby Creighton didn't worry about fiddling with the lock or anything; he just took one charge at the front door and we were in.

There was a terrific stink hanging around the place, like rancid butter. We had to step over a heap of coal in the passage. There was a chest of drawers on its side in the front room that had been half chopped up for firewood, and empty cans were scattered everywhere.

I had a quick shufti in the bathroom. The bath was half full of water which had got a green scum over the top. Going up the stairs, I nearly fell over the best part of a loaf of bread which was as hard as a brick. I had a gander in one of the bedrooms. There was an old iron bedstead in there with about three army blankets all screwed up on top. By the door was a pisspot lying on its side, and what had been in it was lying in little pools all over the floor.

In one corner I noticed a big heap of sacks, so I went across and lifted the top one off. Underneath was a dead goat with all the skin stretched tight over the bones. I went downstairs in a hurry. At the bottom, I picked up a pair of old woollen socks with big holes in the heels and toes. The bottoms were as stiff as a board.

They were all standing around in the kitchen. I heard the hospital tart say, "Heavens, how sordid," as I went in.

I tossed the socks over to the sergeant. "These do?"

He caught them, and held them up with one hand, holding his snitch with the other. "The very thing," he said.

"They look as if they're more holy than righteous," said Nobby, grinning all over his stupid pan.

The hospital tart was holding a little lace hanky to her nose, and dabbing it. "We'd better get a bit of fresh air," said the sergeant. So we all filed out again, and the sergeant said, "If you like to jump on your bike and go down to the place you last saw 'im, we'll follow along be'ind."

So the hospital tart jumped into her car with the big dopey-looking bastard, and the sergeant climbed in the van along with Nobby, and we started off. When we got to the place, they stopped behind me and pulled in off the road. I showed them Ned's bike in the bushes, and the sergeant lugged it out and gave his brute a sniff of the saddle, as well as waving the socks in front of its snout. The hospital tart said to the dopey-looking bastard, "I think you'd better stay here, Parkin. We don't want to be too many in number."

The sergeant took the dog over the other side of the gate and walked it up and down. He kept saying, "Goo'bitch, goo'bitch." It suddenly cottoned on to one particular spot of ground and started snuffling, then it was away across the field with the sergeant on to it, and the rest of us trailing behind. The hospital tart said, "It's lucky I thought to bring a pair of sensible shoes."

We went into the wood and out the other side, across two more fields of stubble, then about a mile up an overgrown lane with bits of branches whipping against our faces. After that, we squeezed through a hole in the hedge, and crossed a meadow into another wood. The brute was tugging so hard on the leash that the sergeant kept having to break into a bit of a run.

We hit a track running through the wood and followed it for another half a mile, then we came to a dead stop. The brute was walking around in little circles, snuffling under the dead leaves.

"That's queer," the sergeant said. "He must have left the track somewhere around here." He started leading the brute in and out of the trees, trying to pick up the trail again. The hospital tart sat down on a bank and started emptying the rubbish out of her shoes. She was just about shagged and there was a dirty great ladder in one of her stockings. She looked hellish determined, though. Old Nobby said, "Well, he's certainly made a nuisance of 'imself this time."

I was leaning up against the trunk of a tree, picking a red and white toadstool to pieces. I took out a weed. "Any of you ladies or gentlemen got a light?" I said.

CHAPTER TWENTY-NINE

It was just at that moment I remembered old Gascoyne and the chalk pit. This Gascoyne was the hermit who lived along the Bottom for years. I'd only actually seen him once, when he came up the Village to get some stores, like he did once in a while.

I couldn't have been more than five or six at the time, but I'll always remember it. He was a tall, rough-looking bloke with a ginger beard, and he wore a kind of scoutmaster's outfit only dead scruffy, with a scout hat and bare knees. The thing that impressed me most were his bare knees which were caked with about six months' dirt, because Doris, and all the other grown-ups I knew at the time were always getting on to their kids about washing their knees.

I was with about four other kids when I saw him, all older than me. We all danced around him yelling but he didn't take a scrap of notice, not even when one of the other kids pitched a big chunk of flint after him.

According to Mavis Tidy he'd come from quite a high-class family and he had a very good job in the high-ups of the post office at one time, until he decided to chuck it all up and went off to live in the woods on his jack. I can understand it in a way because I've often felt the same, only I don't reckon I could stick it more than a fortnight without seeing so much as a piece of skirt, so it wouldn't be worth the money for the tent.

But the funny part about old Gascoyne, he wasn't skint or anything. Pots of ackers he was supposed to have in the bank over at Forbury. He'd disappear for a couple of months every summer, and Ma Tidy reckoned he used to go off to the Alps in Switzerland to act as a guide. She reckoned he was very famous out there. He knew the mountains like the back of his hand, and had even written a couple of books about how to climb the bastards. I don't know how true it is.

When he was down at the Bottom, old Gascoyne used to live in an old canvas shack in the woods at the back of the valley, but it used to get a bit rafty for that in the winter, especially as he was cracking on in years, so one year he took himself off to an old chalkpit over at Thursday woods, on the Whitmarsh side of the Bottom, and hacked himself a big cave out of the chalk. He lived in the cave every winter after that until 1947, when there was this terrific freeze-up. A couple of months later, when the snow cleared away, some of the folk down the Bottom realized they hadn't seen him lately, and somebody went up to the cave to see how he was. Mavis Tidy reckoned that when they found him he'd been dead quite a while.

I'd been inside the cave myself when I was a bit older. There was a kind of round hole at the entrance going back about six feet, and then curving round to the left into a big open space about four yards across. Naturally, I didn't hang about in there, because old Gascoyne was supposed to haunt the place. It was hellish dank and gloomy in there, even in the daytime. None of the kids I knew ever went near the chalkpit after dark.

We waited until the sergeant came back round a clump of bushes. "No luck," he said. "She's lost it. Must 'ave gone cold in the night. Funny thing about woods, the scent don't 'old very long. Don't know why." He looked at his watch. "Well, I s'pose we may as well jack it in."

Nobby Creighton said, "'E's sure to turn up sooner or later."

"I hate the thought of giving up so easily after we've come such a long way," said the hospital tart. She was still getting the rough stuff out of her shoes.

I dogged my fag against a tree. "I reckon I know where 'e's got to," I said.

The hospital tart said, "Do you really?"

"Well, I couldn't say for sure."

"If you really think you know where he might be, please take us there," she said.

"Long as you don't drag us a couple of miles for nothing, my lad," said Nobby.

"Look, why don't you stuff it, knuckle'ead?" I was getting dead cheesed with Nobby. "All right," I said, "forget it. Let's go back 'ome. It's all the same to me."

"Don't you start getting saucy with me, my lad."

I leaned back against the tree and started whistling, "Bollocks! And the same to you . . ."

The sergeant said to Nobby, "Just you keep quiet for a minute." He walked across to me. "'Ow far is this place you reckon 'e might 'ave gone?"

"About 'alf a mile as the crow flies."

"About 'ow far as people walk?"

"Three-quarters, maybe."

"All right," he said. "Lead on, Macduff."

From where we were, Thursday woods was on the far side of a bit of a valley. It was quite a bit further than it looked. We had to cross over a couple of ploughed fields and a swamp to get there, by which time the sergeant was cursing out loud, Nobby Creighton was nearly on his benders, and the hospital tart was looking hellish pale. We'd all got mud up to our knees. "It isn't a lot further," I kept saying. When we got to Thursday woods, I led them on to a track which runs straight past the chalkpit.

The entrance to the pit was all overgrown with brambles, and we had to tread very careful. I went in first. Just behind me I heard the dog whimpering, and the sergeant telling it to keep quiet. Only it couldn't have had much effect, because just as I came in sight of the cave, the brute let out a terrific bark and leaped forward. The sergeant hung on to it for a couple of yards, then he tripped over a root, let go the lead, and fell over into a bramble bush. But the first I knew about it was the hound tearing past me and galloping up the side of the chalkpit, with the sergeant effing and blinding and calling it back.

There's a gradual slope from the bottom of the chalkpit which gets steeper and steeper until it rises up sheer for about twenty feet. The cave was in the middle of the sloping part, about half-way to the top. I saw the bloody hound go belting up the side of the pit and straight into the mouth of the cave.

What happened next was that old Ned came hurtling out with the brute on top of him, yelling blue murder. He tried to run down the slope, but his legs were going too fast for him, and he kind of keeled over in a front somersault and rolled all the way to the bottom. He finished up in the middle of a clump of nettles with the dog standing astride of him, snarling and showing its choppers.

The sergeant ran over and shouted, "Leave! Leave!" and the brute got off Ned's chest and walked away. Then the sergeant said, "Sit!" and it sat down and started scratching its earhole. "Goo'bitch," the sergeant said.

The three of them were standing over Ned. He was making little sobbing noises in his throat. Not like proper crying. Then he rolled over and I could see his pan, all covered with spittle and snot and dirt, and his bloody great eyes rolling in all directions.

The sergeant was trying to lift him up and saying, "All right, old mate." Eventually Ned did get up, and the hospital tart was trying to brush some of the chalk off his raggedy old togs. She said, "Come now, we're all your friends, we're going to look after you, there's no need to make such a fuss." But old Ned was still making these queer noises, and he kept on saying, "I ain't done nothin' maister. I ain't done nothin'." The sergeant patted him on the shoulder. "It's all right now, old mate," he said. "We'll fix you up all right." Nobby Creighton was just standing there looking at Ned and shaking his bonce. I heard him say, "You ain't 'alf give us some trouble."

Then the hospital tart said, "You must try to pull yourself together, Mr Hoskin. We're going to take very good care of you." She tipped Nobby the wink to grab one of Ned's arms while she took the other. As soon as they did this he started struggling like a madman, and the three of them had to hang on to him like grim death until he was exhausted. When the brute saw what was happening it ran over and started jumping up at Ned, trying to get in on the act, until the sergeant gave it a belt with the flat of his hand.

When he was quiet again they started to lead him out of the pit.

I just stood there and watched them go. They'd got Ned, and they'd already forgotten about me. They didn't say so much as "kiss my arse". They didn't even look back.

To tell you the honest truth, I was feeling a bit like this character in the Bible, after they'd gone. What's his name? Judas. The original nark. And he'd got thirty pieces of silver out of his day's work, while I hadn't got two brass halfpennies to rub together.

Still, I reckoned I was doing Ned a favour. After all, I thought, he'd be a sight better off in this hospital place along with all the other old codgers. He'd have a decent roof over his napper, a couple of bob a week spending money, and a cup of cocoa regular every morning, even if it didn't have any milk or sugar in it. They might even teach him to play dominoes. In any case, if it hadn't been me, somebody else would have rooted him out before long. You don't get no peace in this world, boy, unless you got the money to pay for it.

However much I tried to convince myself, though, I couldn't help feeling a bit of a pig's orphan. I knew I probably wouldn't have done it if the hospital tart hadn't got a decent set of tits. If she'd been a regular old pirate, I'd have kept my trap shut, and old Ned would still have been squatting in his cave. That's always been my trouble—women. I admit it.

I stayed in the chalkpit for a couple of minutes, then I cut back into the woods. I reckoned that if I was to hang around for a while, they'd probably be gone by the time I got back to the road and picked up the Quickly.

I got to a barbed wire fence and climbed over it, accidentally knocking down this notice which said something about trespassers being prosecuted. On the other side of the fence was a part of the wood which I'd been very keen on when I was a nipper. The trees there were all very thin and tall beech trees with hardly any branches until you got to the top. I'd carved my initials on some of them, along with those of the particular schoolgirl I was busy with at the time. I could even point to one tree where I nearly broke my neck trying to get up to a maggie's nest.

The ground slopes down very sharp and then it levels off a bit. Just at the place where it starts getting flat there's a bird bath sunk into the ground. It's nothing special, just a kind of cement basin about five foot long and a yard wide, with little steps going down to the middle, which is about six inches deep. This bird bath has been there ever since I can remember.

I went down the slope, sat on a fallen tree trunk, and lit a fag. Then I happened to notice the bird bath, and I suddenly started wondering who could have shoved it there in the middle of the woods, miles from anywhere. Previously I'd always taken it for granted.

I wondered if it was the hermit, old Gascoyne, who'd built it. I imagined him sitting, the same as I was, on the trunk of a tree, in his scoutmaster's rigout with his dirty old bony old knees sticking up, just watching the birds. Then maybe he had this idea about building a bird bath where they could frig about and enjoy themselves. He'd probably think about it for a week or two, then he'd make up his mind to start.

He'd have to order a bit of cement and sand from the builders' materials people over at Whitmarsh, and ask for it to be dumped right at the end of the Bottom. Every day he'd have to cart the stuff up there, a bit at a time, and cover it over with leaves. After about a week, maybe, he'd be ready to start work. He'd have to scrounge the tools from somewhere—a trowel and a shovel—and he'd also have to bring a bucket of water from the pond about half a mile down the lane.

So one day he'd go up there—maybe it'd be pissing down rain that day, but it wouldn't worry old Gascoyne—and he'd dig a hole out ready, mix up the mortar, and get cracking on the bird bath.

He wouldn't try to hurry the job; there wouldn't be any bastard breathing down his neck and telling him to get a rift on. When it was finished he'd cover it over with a couple of sacks, and come back the next morning to see if it was dry. If it was, he'd go down to the pond again and bring up a couple of buckets of water and shove them in.

After that he'd sit in the bushes about fifty yards away and watch, hoping to see the birds come down and start skylarking about in his bath, but he'd no doubt have to wait some time, because birds aren't stupid. They'd know you don't usually see a bird bath in the middle of nowhere, and they'd imagine it was some kind of trap. Until one started, then the rest would follow.

Come to think of it, I've never seen any birds in there myself. But I've never actually watched for any length of time.

After old Gascoyne snuffed it, I don't suppose anybody took much notice of the bird bath. Ever since I can remember it's always been choked up with sludge and dead leaves.

It was still choked up when I walked down and had a shufti at it close to. I broke a branch off a tree and started raking out the leaves. When I got down to the second step I fished out a dead thrush.

I didn't stay long after that. It was long past dinner time and my guts were rumbling. On the way back I was feeling a bit more cheerful. After all, it was no odds to me what they did to old Ned. And I'd got plenty of other things on my mind. Carol, for instance. It was only another six days to our next meeting.

I took a short cut back to the road. The others still hadn't

arrived by the time I got there. The dopey-looking hospital
bastard was lying stretched out in the back of the car reading a
Beano. He looked round at me and called out "Did you find 'im?"

"Yep," I said.

He just nodded and turned over the next page.

When I was passing through the Village I stopped at the
telephone box and rang Nobby Creighton's number. His wife
answered. She's even more dense than Nobby, if that's possible.
I put on a deep voice and pretended I was Harry Corfield, the
farmer up at Paling End, which is about four miles from the
Village, and right on the edge of Nobby's beat.

I said there'd just been a burglary up there, and would Nobby
please come up straight away, because the bloke that had done
it was locked in one of the barns, and I didn't reckon I could
keep him in much longer.

You can only get to Corfield's farm up a long winding lane
which all the carts and tractors use. It's always thigh deep in mud
this time of year, and I knew Nobby couldn't check because
they're not on the blower up there.

Nobby's wife said he was out on a job, but she was expecting
him in any moment, and he'd come straight over. Meanwhile
she said to try and keep the bloke shut up in the barn.

CHAPTER THIRTY

EVERY fortnight, after that first time, me and Carol used to hold
our meetings on Wednesday afternoon, while her folk were away
visiting granny in dock.

What we'd do, we'd start off by checking up the figures and
comparing notes about the talent scheme for about twenty
minutes, then one of us would sort of wander over to the settee,
still rabbiting on about the scheme, and about ten minutes after
that we'd be ramming home the bolt on the old door and really
getting down to business.

It wasn't as cushy as that every time, though. Sometimes she'd
just sit at the table looking hellish serious and worried and she'd
say, "Davey, I've been doing a lot of thinking lately."

"About what?" I'd say.

"About us. You know. I've come to the conclusion that what
we're doing is terribly wrong."

"What's so terribly wrong about it?" I'd say. "Nearly everybody
does it all the time. The ones that don't only wish they could."

"Yes I know, but that's different. I mean, when you're married it doesn't matter."

"You mean you just have to sign your monicker on a bit of paper, and that makes it legal. Is that what you mean?"

"No. There's more to it than that."

By this time I'd be round there stroking the back of her neck, and biting her ear.

"No Davey, it's no good. We've got to stop some time . . . I mean, there's no reason why we shouldn't still be good . . ."

"Friends?"

"Yes."

By now I'd have got two or three buttons undone.

"Davey, you mustn't. Honestly, I'm serious."

A bit later we'd be on the old settee and she'd be saying, "All right, darling, but this has definitely *got* to be the last time." And afterwards she'd say, "I'm sure I don't know what Mummy and Daddy would think." And I'd say, "What the eye doesn't see, the heart doesn't grieve over." Somebody wrote that in my autograph book when I was a nipper and I've remembered it ever since.

And the next time—a fortnight later—she'd be all for getting down to it directly I walked in the door. Women are funny like that.

But the best things in this life never last long enough, and eventually it came to the last meeting. The scheme was due to finish a week the following Sunday, and there was going to be a big service to mark the occasion, with the Bishop of Forbury coming down and all.

Her parents had gone off to the hospital as usual. Carol was looking a bit under the weather. She said she'd just got over a nasty cold.

We had our usual little natter about the scheme. The money had just about finished coming in. As I'd expected, everybody had lost interest when they found out that the Bottom was more than a hundred quid in the lead. I'd only taken about a fiver in the last ten days.

Carol totted up the figures. Then she said, "What a shame. It looks as if we're going to be about four hundred pounds short."

"Yeh," I said. "Still, we ain't done too badly. Anyway, we ain't finished yet."

"How d'you mean?"

"I was havin' a bit of a natter with Garfield Chubb a few weeks ago," I said. "He as good as promised five 'undred quid. Only 'e's in the middle of a business deal, an' 'e's not quite sure if 'e can afford it, see?"

"That's wonderful! And you haven't told me a word about it. Davey, you are secretive."

"Mind, 'e didn't guarantee nothing."

"Well, at least we still have a good chance of making it up to three thousand."

She'd perked up a lot when I told her about Garfield Chubb. But a couple of minutes later she started to come over all thoughtful again.

"Davey," she said.

"Allo?" I was thinking, "hi-yi, here it comes."

But she said, "D'you think this talent scheme has made any difference?"

"What kind of difference?"

"D'you think it's brought people closer together?"

"Well, it's definitely brought you an' me closer together."

"Yes I know, but I mean spiritually has it brought people closer together? I'm wondering if it's made any difference at all. I think people will always go on squabbling whatever happens. Like this awful argument about the recreation ground."

Actually, the recreation ground lark was all the rage in the village at the time. Old Paulson had called a public meeting about it a fortnight before, and made a little speech. He reckoned that although he lived up the Village himself, he supported Mr Chubb's generous offer to hand over the field down at the Bottom, because it was a bigger piece of land, and there were far more children down there to enjoy it, etc.

Then a lot of other people spoke up. Naturally, everybody that lived down the Bottom reckoned it was a wonderful idea, and all those that lived up the Village were dead against it. In the end, when it was put to the vote, it was carried by ninety-two votes to sixty-one. There was nearly a free fight after. Mrs Fforde-Hunter had been chasing around ever since then, organizing a petition against it that she was going to send to the Forbury Council. She knew which way the wind was blowing, all right. I knew she wouldn't get very far, though. There's a big bunch of Reds on the Forbury Council, and they're not all that keen on the Mrs Fforde-Hunters of this world.

I said, "Well, people 'ave got to have something to chew over, otherwise life'd get too boring. See, if everybody was to agree with everybody else, there'd be nothing to natter about."

"I suppose you're right," she said.

She didn't make any fuss this time. About the other business I mean. Only just before we started undressing she kind of clutched hold of my shoulder.

"Davey," she said. "Can I ask you a question?"

"Certainly," I said.

Then she said, "Never mind."

I don't think I mentioned that I forgot to bolt the door before we started, like I usually did. At least, I must have forgotten, because right in the middle of the proceedings I saw the door swing open, and then I noticed two pairs of feet, one male and one female. I recognized Carol's mother and father out of the corner of my eye.

Only it was a bit too late just then to make much difference, because we were three-quarters of the way up the mountain, and once you get that far, boy, there's nothing can turn you back.

I could hear Carol moaning and gasping underneath me, like they do, and in the distance I could hear another noise like a woman having hysterics in the next room.

In the finish we were just lying there, looking up at Carol's old man, who hadn't taken his eyes off us for a second.

He opened his mouth and coughed, then he said in his very dry, pernickety little voice, "Carol, I think you ought to know that your grandmother passed away suddenly at seventeen minutes past one this afternoon."

Then he tiptoed out.

CHAPTER THIRTY-ONE

So that's the end of my song. I can sing no more. There's an apple up me jacksie, and the first young gentleman to touch all four walls of the gymnasium can have the bloody core.

Very nearly, anyway. I mean it's very nearly the end of the song, not the apple effort.

Old Garfield Chubb got his planning permission, and coughed up the five hundred nicker a few days before the big church service. Which meant that we finished up with the three thousand, and even had a couple of hundred to spare. Everyone up the Village was highly chuffed, because with Chubby's contribution they'd raised a bit more than the Bottom. But they soon wiped the smirks off their pans when it got round that the old recreation field was going to become a new housing estate.

Particularly Mrs Fforde-Hunter. Her house was slap opposite, and she reckoned that all the new houses just across the road would take a couple of thousand quid off the value of her place. Apart from that she didn't exactly appreciate the prospect of a lot of snotty-nosed nippers shouting rude words up at her bedroom windows. She got up another petition, which she reckoned she was going to send to the Queen.

Still, you've got to make way for progress.

So the old bishop came down from Forbury, gave his blessing and said his piece, and departed whence he came. They reckoned the church was packed, and a lot of them at the back even had to stand. I didn't get to the big service myself. For one thing I'd kind of gone off religion, and for another thing I had a bit of unfinished business to attend to, down the marsh with the Sprat.

After what I'd been used to it was like plucking a Jew's harp, compared with thumping on a theatre organ, but I like to keep in practice.

It wasn't more than a couple of weeks before all the business about the talent scheme was forgotten. Everybody in Garside was either nattering about Johnny Salt deciding to go into a monastery, or yattering about Ma Purkiss deciding to go over and live at Teddy Paulson's place. Apparently Teddy Paulson's missis was getting worse and worse, and Hilda Purkiss told Mavis Tidy that there ought to be someone staying there all the time in case of emergencies, and after what Teddy had done for Joe before he died, she could hardly refuse.

Johnny Salt suddenly became very popular when it went round that he was leaving. The church council held a special meeting to try and get him to stay. Even Ma Pinches reckoned that he was the best vicar Garside had ever had as far back as she remembered, which wasn't all that much of a compliment when you consider that Canon Fosdick was the only other one she'd known. He wouldn't change his mind, though. He said he'd been thinking it over for a long time, and now he'd made the decision he couldn't go back on it.

Anyway, Johnny Salt went off to this monastery somewhere in Wales, and a new vicar arrived to take his place. He was a big slummocky-looking bastard, this new bloke, with a loud booming voice, and frizzy, gingery hair. Very jolly. According to Ma Whichelow he'd once played bridge for Cumberland.

Sometimes I'd see Carol and Sydney Chubb belting by in the Alpine, only she never waved—she'd just look straight to her front. It wasn't very long after this new vicar arrived that they got engaged.

It must have been around that time that I got the big itch, and had this idea about going to New Zealand.

I couldn't say why I picked on New Zealand exactly. It was like a mixture of things, such as it being a bit off the beaten track in case it starts raining thingummybob ninety, and also because I happen to approve of the New Zealanders. They're kind of quiet, not like the Aussies. Not half so loud-mouthed as the old cobbers, sport.

I don't remember ever having actually come across one, but I've seen them on the television. All they do is come over here about every five years and give us a tanking at rugby. They don't make a big song and dance over it, either. You'll see the captain being interviewed just before they go back and he'll say yes, it was a very enjoyable tour, and he hopes to be back in five years' time, if he's not too old by then. Then he'll say he's sorry but he's got to dash off and make a telephone call before the boat sails, and he'll ask the bloke that's interviewing him if he's got three coppers for a threepenny bit. None of this, "first class show", and "absolutely marvellous, old boy" business.

What I thought was, I'd go out there, buy a few sheep and a bit of land, and wait until they multiply. It's nearly all sheep out there. Say I started off with fifty, I'd maybe have a hundred after the first year, two hundred after two years, and so on. After ten years, I'd have quite some sheep.

It wouldn't be just as simple as that, I know. I'd have to eat and sleep during that time. Still, maybe I'd find myself a nice little paper round on the side.

I was twenty-one, and I wasn't beholden to any bastard any more. So I wrote to this place in London, and not long after I went up to see this emigration bloke. Very decent he was. Talked to me like a Dutch uncle. Said that young blokes like me with plenty of ambition and no family ties were just what the country needed. About a month afterwards I got my sailing date.

In the meantime I'd flogged the paper round back to Bert Fisher, the Forbury newsagent, for three hundred quid. He was dead niggled at having to pay for it, after handing it over to me for free, but I told him about the new housing estate, and I said there was a bloke over at Whitmarsh who was very keen to get his fingers on it. In the end he coughed up without a murmur. What with the hundred I'd got from Garfield Chubb for services rendered, plus the fifty from Teddy Paulson, and what I'd saved already, I had more than eight hundred quid in the post office.

A week before I was due to embark I decided to go up to London, have a scout round, and see what was on the loose until it was time for the off. I reckoned I'd take all this stuff I've written with me, and hand it in to one of these publishers. If nothing else, it'd probably give them something to giggle over while they sit under the crystal chandeliers in their jolly old club, jugging up the port and brandy, and asking the flunkey please would he mind drawing the curtains a bit because the sun's in their eyes.

Of course, there's always a chance they might fork over fourteen thousand quid. Jesus, that's a laugh! Think how many poxy ewes you could get for that money.

I said cheerio to Doris, then I picked up my gear and staggered off to the bus stop, just outside the church. I'd flogged the Quickly the previous day and got quite a good price considering the bashing it'd had.

It was a bit early for the bus, so I had a wander through the boneyard. There was a whole lot of scaffolding along one side of the church, and about six workmen were crawling about on the roof. Whatever they were doing, they weren't rushing it. Maybe they'd got a good job up there, and were trying to make it last.

There was a brand-new gravestone on Joe Purkiss's grave which said:

> *To The Treasured Memory*
> *Of A Devoted Husband*
> *And A Good Servant*
> *In The Lord*
> JOSEPH ALBERT PURKISS
> *who passed away*
> *peacefully*
> *3rd August,* 1961
> *aged* 71.

When I got down to the church gate there was this little nipper hanging over it. He'd got one of these leather helmets on that kids wear, with ear flaps hanging loose down the sides. He couldn't have been more than four or five.

This kid pointed up at the church roof.

"My Dad's up there," he said.

"Is 'e?" I said. "''E wants to be careful 'e don't get tired and fall off."

The kid said, "Is that where God lives?"

"Well," I said. "''E don't exactly live there, see? 'E just drops in every now and again when 'e's passing through."

"When will he be passin' through next time?" this kid said. He was still playing up and under on the gate.

"You can never tell," I said. "''E don't keep to no reg'lar time-table. I 'spect 'e'll send us a postcard."

"Oh, 'as 'e gone on 'is 'olidays, then?"

"Yeh, that's right."

"I 'spect 'e's gone to Weston," the kid said. "We always go to Weston for *our* 'olidays."

"Very nice place, Weston," I said.

"Do all the good people go to church, then?" the kid said.

I said, "What's your name, sonny?"

"Ron."

"Well, listen Ronnie, you ask too many awkward questions."

He climbed down off the gate and looked at me a bit surprised. "Why do I ask too many ockard questions?" he said.

I heard the bus coming round the corner, so I had to belt back across the boneyard. Then I picked up my gear, and charged to the top of the stairs.

When the old bus turned the corner of the Green and rattled on down through the Village, I couldn't help feeling a bit peculiar to think I wasn't going to be around in Garside for a hell of a long time. I knew I'd come back eventually, of course, but not until I was a millionaire. Then maybe I'd buy the Hall and settle down there for keeps.

Going through the Village I noticed a couple of wagons unloading bricks at the old recreation ground. It made me start thinking about the talent scheme all over again, and about Carol and Johnny Salt.

There's quite a lot in this religion caper, when you come to weigh it up. I mean, I can see what they're getting at, in a way, although they go the wrong way about it most of the time. Of course, it's all right for them that's cracking on a bit. I don't deny it. But you can't really afford to take much notice when you still got your stack to make.

I was thinking, "Maybe when I've made my second million I'll retire to a monastery and shave my bonce and be a jolly old monk, like Johnny Salt. Might even bump into him."

Mind you, it must be a funny old number being a priest. All these peculiar togs they have to wear. And then, it's not like saying two and two equals four, and chalking it up on a blackboard for everyone to see for themselves. After all, who believes in angels? Show me one person who believes there's four angels standing one at each corner of his pit when he's in kip, and I'll show you a nutter.

All these characters in dog collars, walking around and trying to persuade people not to do this, that and the other. And not even a decent pension attached to it. I was talking to Johnny Salt once, and he reckoned the trouble with the church was, it had become sort of separate from everything else. He said it would be a lot better if vicars and people could just wear ordinary togs, because after all, they weren't any different from anybody else. He also said there was no need for churches, and that services ought to be held in people's houses, with all the neighbours dropping in. He reckoned that that's how they started doing it when old J.C. was alive, and he said all the stage paraphernalia had crept in since.

I don't think I'd mind being a monk, though, like Johnny Salt. I'd be the bloke that looks after the cellar where they keep the mead. Either that, or I'd be the old father that takes all the young nuns' confessions.

I might go into a monastery, at that. Of course, I should have to be cheesed off with the French Riviera, and flying off to the States for business conferences, and giving 'em a caning over at Monte every other week-end. I'd have to be so I couldn't even look a Rolls or a Ford Thunderbird in the radiator grille, and if you stuck half a fresh salmon in front of me, with a sprig of parsley on top, I wouldn't even say thank you for it.

Naturally, if I did decide to take the old vows, I'd shove a bit of gilt in some Swiss bank or other, just so's I wouldn't be stuck for a nicker if I decided it wasn't exactly my cup of poison. About half a million or so. The rest of it I'd present to the United Nations in the cause of world peace.

The only thing I'd insist on is that they had a special chair with my name on it. You'd see all these chairs with the names of countries on them—Portugal, Venezuela, Belgium, United States and the rest, and blokes squatting in them with earphones on, listening to old Kruschev or somebody spouting his head off, all round this big sort of curved table.

There'd be this one chair, right at the end, with nobody sitting on it. It wouldn't have the name of a country on the back, there'd just be a plain printed card which said, *Brother Peach*.

Brother Davey! That'd be a right old snigger. Brother Peach, hi-yi!

Brother Davey bloody Peach! Hi-yi!